Chicago
SCALE
ONE INCH TO
140 MILES

Population

Distribution is based on the
Canadian Census 1961 and
the United States Census 1960

Rate of Growth in the previous decade

| Decreasing | 20-49·9% |
| White squares: black dots | |

| 0-19·9% | 50-99·9% |

| over 100% |

Canadian National Average Growth Rate
1951-1961:   30·1 per cent

United States National Average Growth Rate
1950-1960:   18·5 per cent

☐   250,000 persons
□   25,000 persons
·   2,500 persons

NEW YORK
SCALE ONE INCH TO 140 MILES

Longitude 75° West of Greenwich

85°

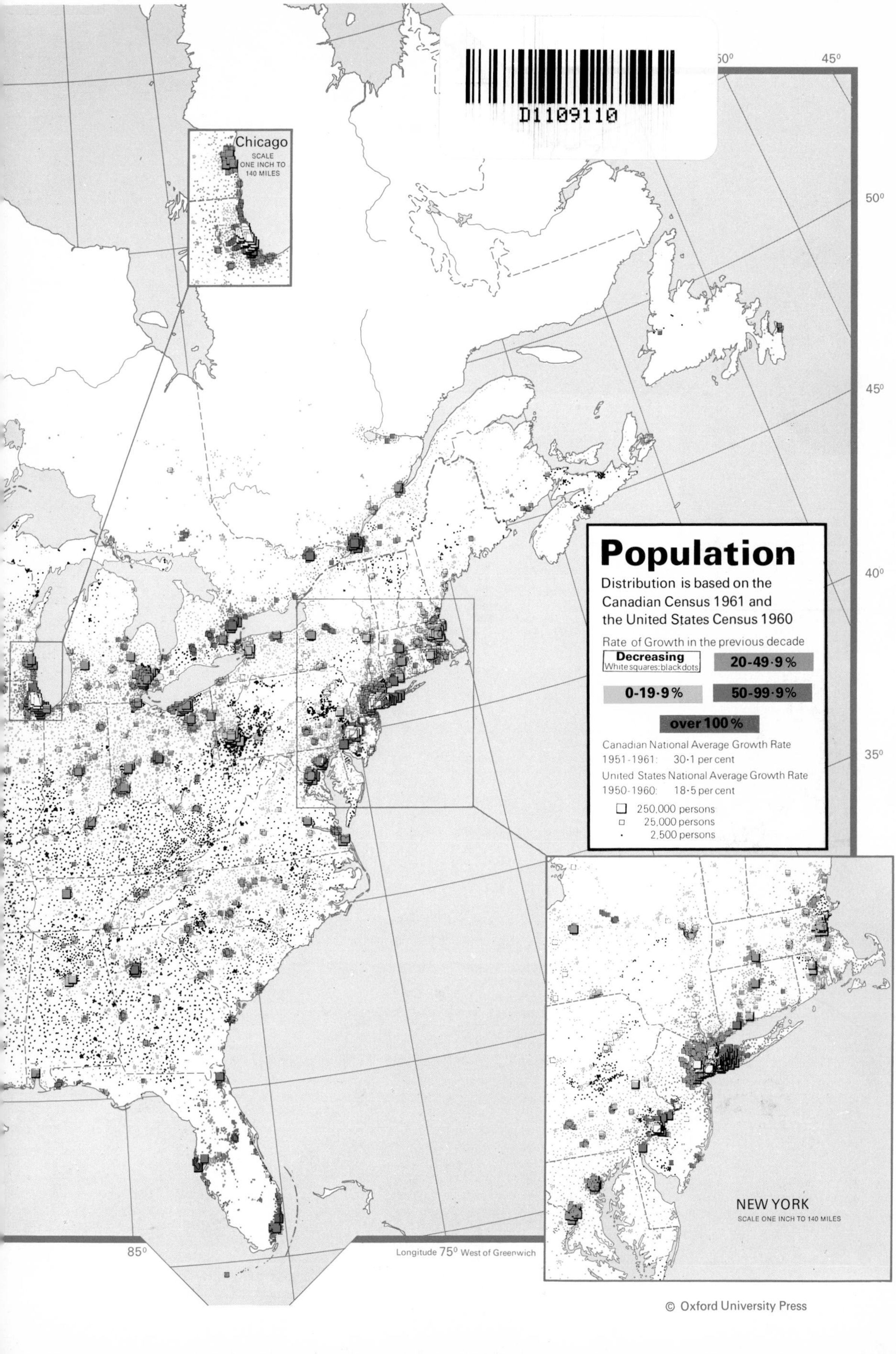

© Oxford University Press

50°

45°

50°

45°

40°

35°

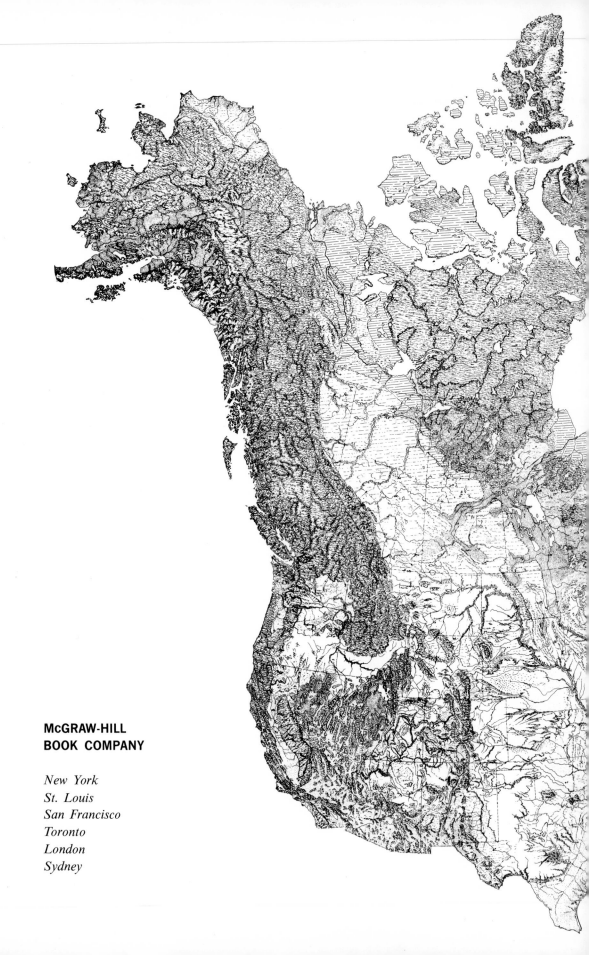

**McGRAW-HILL
BOOK COMPANY**

*New York
St. Louis
San Francisco
Toronto
London
Sydney*

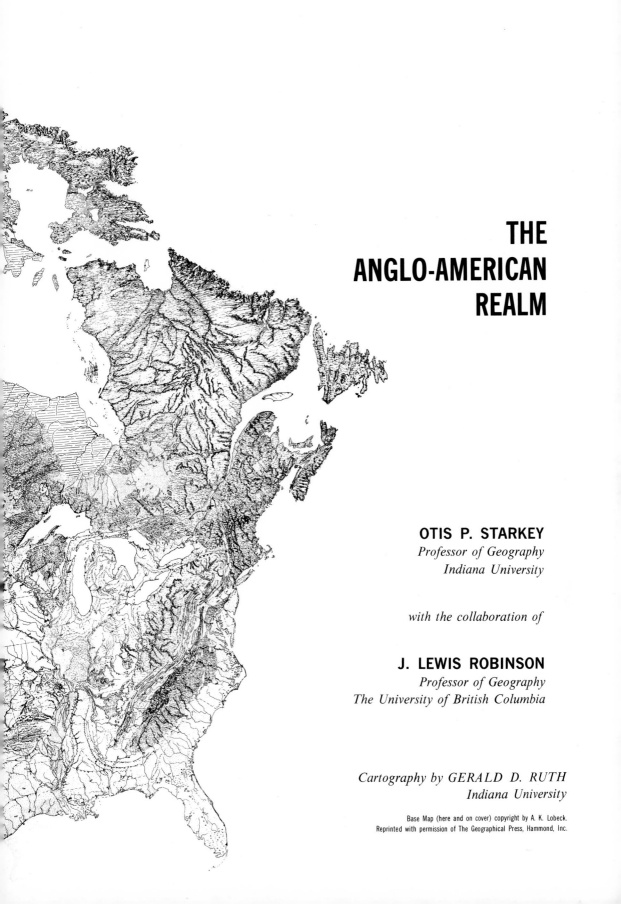

THE
ANGLO-AMERICAN
REALM

OTIS P. STARKEY
Professor of Geography
Indiana University

with the collaboration of

J. LEWIS ROBINSON
Professor of Geography
The University of British Columbia

Cartography by GERALD D. RUTH
Indiana University

McGRAW-HILL SERIES IN GEOGRAPHY
JOHN C. WEAVER, Consulting Editor

VERNOR C. FINCH was Consulting Editor of this series from its inception in 1934 to 1951.

THE ANGLO-AMERICAN REALM

Copyright © 1969 by McGraw-Hill, Inc. All Rights Reserved. Printed in the United States of America. No part of this publication may be reproduced, stored in a retrieval system, or transmitted, in any form or by any means, electronic, mechanical, photocopying, recording, or otherwise, without the prior written permission of the publisher.

Library of Congress Catalog Card Number 68-28421

60851

1 2 3 4 5 6 7 8 9 0 HDBP 7 5 4 3 2 1 0 6 9 8

Modern Anglo-America requires new geographic analysis. The many books on Anglo-American geography based on physiographic regions, agricultural regions, or traditional regions usually describe a rural-oriented economy but lack a balanced treatment of the geography of our industrialized, rapidly urbanizing societies. Their conventional explanations do not paint the whole picture in an era in which bulldozers can fill swamps and level mountains; in which natural gas, petroleum, uranium, and other fuels can be economically transported thousands of miles; in which air conditioners create indoor climates, in which automation is replacing routine labor; and in which raw materials yield only a minor portion of the national income.

This book examines the geographic structure of Anglo-America anew, using conventional treatment when such seems appropriate, but applying new approaches and analyses when such seem to give a more accurate portrayal. No textbook intends to present a complete description of certain characteristics of Anglo-America. Because the real world, and any part of it, is too complex for any one mind to comprehend, geographers make generalizations which seem significant and organize their data around certain themes. In this book the chosen central theme is *man in Anglo-America* with special emphasis on economic and urban aspects. The method used is first to give a general analysis of each region and then to examine particular places as examples.

The geographer paints a portrait of the earth in terms of space, just as the historian tells the story of human development in time sequence. Geographers have difficulty in defining their regions and representative areal patterns, just as historians have difficulty in defining eras and selecting significant trends and influential personalities. Other social sciences have similar problems in classifying and selecting their data. The student new to geography is apt to assume that the subject is a simple matter of *what is where.* True, this is the starting point, but geographic description remains in the elementary stage until supplemented by analysis and synthesis. The geographer selects those aspects of reality which seen together suggest an accurate regional portrait, choosing maps, illustrations, and statistical information with this end in mind. Just as two portrait painters may paint differing pictures of the same man, two geographers may present somewhat different characterizations of a particular area. Each, if well done, should give a clearer regional picture than a mere cataloging of certain facts about the region.

PROBLEMS OF GEOGRAPHIC ANALYSIS

This study of Anglo-America assumes that there are five major factors in regional geography:

1 The land: its extent and quality
2 The historical events that have been significant in influencing later land use
3 The accumulation of structures on the land, including fields, buildings, routes, cities, and monuments
4 The inhabitants of the land: their numbers, character, culture, and rates of increase
5 The income that inhabitants earn and the

economic structure within which they earn it

Description is part of the story. Some facts are necessary to give a common basis for discussion. More fascinating (and more difficult) are the explanations that must be incorporated into the descriptions. Explanation must use data from many other disciplines: history, anthropology, economics, sociology, political science, and most of the physical sciences. Complete knowledge can never be attained by any one person, but the integration of knowledge from the viewpoint of several disciplines makes understanding more attainable.

The problem of geographic interpretation of areal patterns is complicated by the dynamic nature of many of the features, both physical and human. Changes in weather, floods, and earthquakes are obvious examples of the instability of the physical environment. Even more dynamic and complex are the relations of man to physical resources: For example, the available land resources increase both with new discoveries and with the creation of new techniques applied to known resources; natural resources such as soil, forests, and ores become depleted and exhausted. Past uses of the land may be visible in existing land-use patterns; such relict features may be destroyed by urban-renewal projects or strengthened by sentimental ties which may sustain activities long after their economic justification has decreased. Economic changes are reflected on the landscape, positively in booming cities, or negatively in ghost mining towns. Finally, human relations to the land may be modified by changing styles, politics, and personal objectives.

The problem of regionalization   It is not possible to consider all of Anglo-America simultaneously. In this book, as in other geography textbooks, the continent is divided into *regions,* that is, into areas that have similarities in at least one significant respect.

The regional concept has been used in most geography textbooks and in detail recently in Bogue and Beale, *Economic Areas of the United States.* In that work, the basis for regionalization was essentially land use (mainly agricultural), and upon these regions metropolitan areas were superimposed. Other books have used regions based on landforms, land use, census divisions, agricultural crops, manufacturing, or combinations of these. This volume emphasizes economic and especially urban relationships. Unfortunately for the academic "pigeonholer," the data do not fall conveniently into tight compartments. When discussing the New York Gateway, for example, it is necessary to bring in northeastern Pennsylvania which is analyzed more fully in the following chapter. The Pittsburgh area could be as well described with the Great Lakes region as with the Ohio Basin. Regional boundaries are in part matters of convenience, and boundaries are of necessity often drawn arbitrarily and in many cases represent compromises. The region is a tool in geographical analysis, not an end in itself.

The regions used may be dictated by statistical considerations. Some statistics are available by counties, cities, Standard Metropolitan Statistical Areas, and urbanized areas; others are available only for states (provinces in Canada) or groups of states. Some statistics have been grouped by economic areas,[1] some by Federal Reserve districts, and some have been mapped by government agencies, business research organizations, and individual geographers. In this book, which uses

[1] See Donald J. Bogue and Calvin L. Beale, *Economic Areas of the United States,* Free Press, New York, 1961; and U.S. Bureau of the Census, *United States Census of Population: 1960, State Economic Areas,* Final Report PC(3)-1A, Washington, 1963.

statistical bases for regionalization, regions have been necessarily tailored to county and state and provincial boundaries because data have been available for these units.

In many regions, the exact boundary is not significant because the periphery of the region is relatively unsettled and unproductive. When the boundary is in a well-settled area (as between New York and Philadelphia), the interurban zone will have commercial and cultural relations with both centers. If one delineates a "transition zone," one substitutes for the regional boundary problem the equally difficult problem of determining the boundaries of the transition zone.

SPECIAL FEATURES OF THIS BOOK

Emphasis on population The book allots space to each region approximately in proportion to the number of people it supports. Within each region economic activities are discussed in proportion to their contribution to income. This gives more emphasis to urban activities. Obviously one cannot follow too closely such allocations since some activities (such as retail trade) require little explanation. On the other hand, some large but little-developed areas require numerous pages for evaluating their handicaps and their potentialities.

National accounts data The book uses a variety of national income, personal income, and other national accounts data which provide convenient common denominators for evaluating the economic importance of each region and activity. To aid in the use of national accounts and other data, a graph has been devised which facilitates comparison of regional data with national data. The national per capita average is a baseline for each category of data. For any state or province, city or region, local per capita averages

greater than the national base are shown by bars drawn above the baseline; averages less than the national base are shown by bars below the baseline. At the bottom of each graph a percentage figure indicates the percent of the national population included in the unit for which the graph is drawn (see Figures 1-3 to 1-12).

Basic data and other statistical tables Summarized Basic Data, generally comparable from chapter to chapter, appear at the beginning of each regional chapter. More specialized data are presented within the chapter in statistical tables and graphs. The Basic Data are derived from the United States and Canadian census reports (in some cases updated to 1967 or the latest available year on the basis of trends and estimates by government agencies) and from standard government references. The sources of other tables are given in the book. The student should use the Basic Data for convenient comparisons between regions and SMSAs but not for memorization. Analysis of statistical data should provoke questions for further research or discussion. For example, how does the per capita income of a city or region compare with that in other parts of the region? With other regions? Why the differences? Are there any relationships between population growth and per capita income? Between land area and population size? Between area and income? Between income and kinds of economic activity?

Variety of analyses Because regions and cities vary greatly, complete uniformity in treatment is not desirable. The text stresses geographic aspects which are especially characteristic; often regional examples are used to illustrate general principles.

Selected references Bibliographies are brief with relatively few references to older journal articles, some of which, partly out-of-date, may be misleading to the undiscriminating student. Some general references are noted at the end of Chapters 1, 3, 4, 19, and 23. Students should read current government data, current journals (popular as well as professional), and newspapers. The text is not intended to be an encyclopedic reference work; hence there is no attempt to discuss every important city.

Outline   The introductory section gives a broad picture of geographical patterns in the United States and Canada, including settlement and the evolution of modern urbanized economies. *Part Two* analyzes the American Commercial-Manufacturing Core. *Part Three* looks at those regions in midwestern and southeastern United States which are making the transition from agricultural to urban activities. *Part Four* deals with that part of the United States in which water shortage has been a common problem. *Part Five* discusses Canada and Greenland. *Part Six* offers a statement of certain broader Anglo-American relationships and trends, with some forecasts for the year 2000.

Acknowledgments   Although the authors have traveled widely in Anglo-America, the text could not have been written without materials provided by the works of geographers, government and private agencies, and other library sources. The most important of these are acknowledged in the *Selected References* and in credit lines under illustrations and tables.

Among the first reviewers of the preliminary text was Dr. J. Lewis Robinson whose innumerable suggestions and understanding criticisms proved so invaluable in revision that the senior author asked him to collaborate on part of the book. Although Professor Robinson's collaboration is limited mainly to the Canadian chapters, there are few pages in the book that have not been improved because of his suggestions.

The novel approach used in this book made it especially desirable to have the early drafts of the manuscript reviewed by a number of geographers whose criticisms proved most helpful. At a later stage, W. Glenn Cunningham, John J. Hidore, Warren Bland, and William D. Brooks commented on chapters on areas with which they were particularly acquainted. About half the manuscript was tested in mimeographed form on students at Indiana University. Any inaccuracies in the final manuscript are the responsibility of the senior author and, for the Canadian chapters, of J. Lewis Robinson. Corrections and suggestions will be gratefully received by either.

Some of the major ideas presented in the text resulted from decades of contact and collaboration with two distinguished geographers: the late Lester E. Klimm and the late J. Russell Smith. Their contribution is gratefully acknowledged.

OTIS P. STARKEY

CONTENTS

THE ANGLO-AMERICAN REALM

PART I
INTRODUCTION

IN LESS THAN A CENTURY Anglo-America has changed from a raw-material and foodstuff-oriented economy to a manufacturing and service-oriented economy; Anglo-Americans have changed from a mainly rural people to a largely urban and suburban people. The present geography of this continent is focused in cities; nevertheless, a geographic analysis of the continent must take into account past economies, resources past and present, and human history, for much of the present geographic patterns have been developed on a foundation of past geographies. Nor should the present geography be considered fixed; it is highly dynamic also. Within a decade it seems probable that three-fourths of all Anglo-Americans will be living in metropolitan areas; and before the end of the century in the life of these people new industries, new modes of life, and perhaps new objectives, may develop which today seem inconceivable.

WITHIN THE LAST CENTURY, urban land use has been increasingly displacing rural land use. An example is the northern end of the Santa Clara Valley, noted as a producer of fruits and vegetables, which is gradually being converted to industrial, commercial, and residential uses. In the background is San Francisco Bay and the Golden Gate; in the center the growing city of San Jose. In the next decades, the San Francisco Bay Megalopolis will take over almost all the level land in the valley, leaving the relatively barren Coast Ranges for recreational purposes. (Photo copyright by Sunderland Aerial Photographs, Oakland, Calif.)

CHAPTER 1

TWO PROGRESSIVE COUNTRIES

Anglo-America includes two democracies, the United States and Canada, which together occupy an area twice that of Europe or seven-eighths that of the Soviet Union. Throughout this homeland of over 200 million people, English is commonly understood and Anglo-Saxon manners and ideas of freedom and justice are prevalent. Its settlers, although drawn from many ethnic groups, have adopted, except in a few areas, a modified British tradition. Within the lifetime of our older citizens, these countries have filled in their frontiers of settlement, changed from rural to urban economies, and advanced to world leadership. Especially in the last two centuries their citizens have developed cultural, political, technical, and economic ideas which have pervaded and changed most of the world. Whatever judgments critics of Anglo-America may make, the modern world cannot be understood without a comprehension of the wealth, power, techniques, and ideals of this cultural realm.

The high rank of the Anglo-American countries in most fields is so notable that a plain statement of the facts appears to be propaganda. For example, the one-fifteenth of the world's people living in Anglo-America produce about one-third of the world's goods and services. The productive power of the Anglo-American democracies and selected other countries is compared with the world average in Table 1-1.

TWO WEALTHY COUNTRIES

The rise of two prosperous Anglo-American nations has been attributed to their great natural resources: their extensive forests, their offshore fisheries, their fertile farmlands, and their vast deposits of mineral fuels and metallic ores. Undoubtedly these resources attracted early settlers and provided capital for economic growth. But

TABLE 1-1   Indices of Productive Power: Anglo-America and Selected Countries Compared with the World (100 = average for all countries for which data were available in each category)

Category	United States	Canada	Mexico	United Kingdom	U.S.S.R.	India
Gross National Product per Capita	1,170	830	93	500	340	36
Living in Cities (percent)	240	160	110	310	150	55
International Trade per Capita	240	865	70	535	45	10
Mechanical Energy Used per Capita	620	470	55	365	160	27
Cultivated Land per Farmer	1,000	2,190	130	225	120	85
Steel Consumption per Capita	620	320	30	370	225	7
Fertilizer Used per Cultivated Acre	130	30	30	640	200	5
Motor Vehicles per Capita	1,240	580	50	295	40	3
Literacy	175	175	115	175	165	35
Physicians and Dentists per Capita	240	230	60	155	225	20

SOURCE: Calculated from data in tables in Norton Ginsburg, *Atlas of Economic Development*, University of Chicago Press, Chicago, 1961. For most categories data for about 100 countries were available.

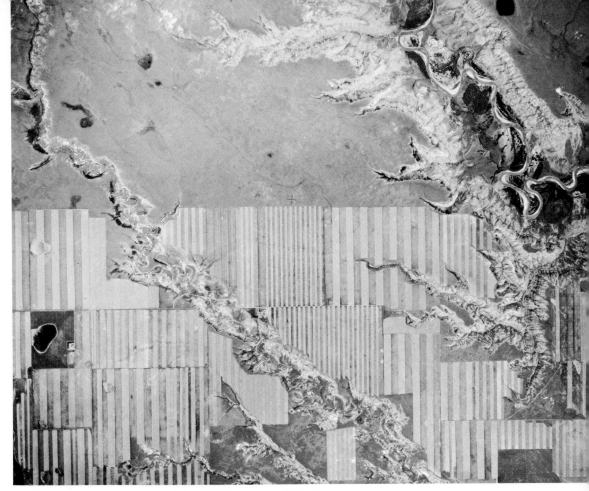

THE MONTANA-ALBERTA BORDER shows how the boundary between two political regions may be reflected in the landscape. The soil, relief, and climate are the same on both sides of the 49th parallel, but United States laws make the Montana land profitable for the dry farming of wheat. (Photo from Air Photo Library, Lands and Forests, Alberta Government.)

resources alone provide an inadequate explanation for rapid development; Indian groups, although settled amid the same natural wealth for centuries, produced only primitive cultures; indeed the area where Indian civilization flowered most—in the pueblos of the Southwest—was poor in natural resources.

In Anglo-America, as in all other countries, the earth offers opportunities; it may present challenges but rarely dictates the human responses to these challenges. To what extent the resource potential of a place will be exploited at a particular time depends on a combination of human knowledge of the resource, technical ability, effective business organization, social incentives to think and work, and a political setting favorable to development. To this lengthy list should be added historical accident since many human activities have been located by whims or other accidental factors.

Thus, although some resources are essential, the true wealth of Anglo-America lies in its people: their knowledge, skills, organization, and their will to develop the raw materials of the earth they control. Human ingenuity converts a few cents worth of Minnesota iron ore into thousands of dollars worth of steel tools, and a few bushels of Iowa corn (worth about 3 cents a pound) into much more valuable pork chops, cornflakes, and margarine. The technology that makes these industrial miracles possible involves an accumulation and integration of skills whose roots go back to Rome, Greece, Egypt, China, and even to our Stone Age ancestors. Nature, techniques, great leaders, and hard work combined to make Anglo-America the wealthy area it is today.

Economists have made estimates of the total wealth of the two Anglo-American neighbors. Although land and land resources may be the foundation upon which their economies are erected, this accumulated wealth tends increasingly to consist of structures, tools, goods, and human modifications of the earth's surface. This is illustrated for the United States in Table 1-2 and for Canada in Table 1-3. Note

the relative magnitude of the items that are probably located largely in cities.

Obviously many of the chronological increases in value in Tables 1-2 and 1-3 result from price inflation. More significant are the differential rates of growth of particular items. Thus land represented 35 percent of the total United States wealth in 1900, but only 17 percent in 1958. Farm land,[1] the leading land item in 1900, was surpassed by non-farmland in 1925. All wealth associated with urban activities shows a rapid increase in Table 1-2; thus from 1900 to 1958, although non-farm structures increased 25 times and government structures 134 times, farm structures increased in value less than 11 times. Likewise the Canadian data (for a much shorter

[1] Farmland does not entirely represent wealth provided by nature because land values include such man-added items as fertilizer, fences, farm roads, drainage and irrigation ditches, as well as the cost of clearing the forest, breaking the sod, and adding fertilizer.

TABLE 1-2   United States National Wealth, 1900, 1925, 1950, 1958 (billions of current dollars)

Category	1900	1925	1950	1958
LAND	30.9	101.6	189.3	290.9
Farmland	14.5	37.1	58.4	87.6
Forests	1.5	3.2	11.9	13.7
Non-farmland	10.9	47.4	83.5	148.8
Public	4.0	13.9	35.5	40.8
STRUCTURES	35.0	161.4	507.3	833.7
Farm	3.3	12.5	26.8	36.0
Residential	15.7	72.6	25.5	392.1
Mining (underground)	0.4	3.9	15.8	31.8
Government	2.0	19.0	95.5	168.2
All Others (including factories)	13.6	53.4	159.8	205.6
EQUIPMENT	12.5	69.6	221.3	378.7
Producers' Durables	6.5	33.8	110.0	199.9
Consumers' Durables	6.0	35.8	111.3	178.8
INVENTORIES AND MISCELLANEOUS	9.2	51.6	136.7	179.5
Farm Inventories	4.6	8.8	24.4	26.1
Non-farm Inventories	5.4	28.1	69.3	95.6
Public including Monetary Metal	1.6	5.0	29.6	33.5
Foreign Assets	−2.3	9.7	13.4	24.3
TOTAL	87.7	384.2	1,054.6	1,682.9

SOURCE: U.S. Bureau of the Census, *Statistical Abstract of the United States*, Washington, 1965, p. 351.

period) show an especially rapid growth in urban wealth.

Most of this $1,682 billion worth of United States national wealth and nearly $120 billion in Canadian capital stock is of value only in relation to people who can use it effectively. If the Anglo-American economies were to become so bankrupt that an attempt was made to sell their wealth, at most only one-tenth could be converted into a form of value detached from its labor force. Of what value would be structures in ghost towns and cities; roads and railroads upon which no freight moved; farms without farmers; and factories and shops without artisans, clerks and, most important, without customers? Anglo-America then must be viewed as a going concern. A naturally wealthy land—yes—but wealthy because well-integrated economies comprising over 200 million people have used their lands and resources as a fulcrum with which to raise their prosperity.

Accounting for National Income

The data for United States national wealth and Canadian capital stock provide a good introduction to national accounting. Many more data are available on current *national income,* the annual earnings received from the use of the national wealth after deducting the amount of wealth consumed during the year by wearing out machinery and structures and by allowing for the depletion of soils, minerals, and other natural resources. By use of such income data and related statistics, the income attributable to each part of the Anglo-American realm and to each source of income within each region may be estimated. Although the use of such income data should not be taken to imply that all Anglo-American geography can be reduced to monetary terms, nevertheless the income approach provides a common denominator, offering a convenient and meaningful skeleton around which other data can be organized.

TABLE 1-3 Canadian Capital Stock, 1949, 1963 (in billions of 1949 dollars)

Category	1949 Construction	1949 Machinery	1963 Construction	1963 Machinery
Agriculture and Fishing	1.08	2.13	1.58	4.50
Forestry	0.13	0.09	0.36	0.26
Mining	0.70	0.38	2.35	1.14
Construction	0.10	0.32	0.19	1.05
Manufacturing	4.36	3.75	7.70	9.30
Utilities	9.70	3.36	15.98	7.52
Commercial	2.70	0.81	5.88	3.45
Government and Institutions	10.71	1.36	23.79	2.89
Consumer	17.84		32.00	
Total	47.30	12.22	89.83	30.09
Grand Total	59.52		119.92	

IMPORTANT NOTE: The data above are only roughly comparable to Structures and Equipment in Table 1-2. The above table is derived from P. Camu, E. L. Weeks, and Z. W. Sametz, *Economic Geography of Canada,* Macmillan, Toronto, 1964, pp. 98–99. A fuller discussion of Canadian national wealth will be found in O. J. Firestone, *Canada's Economic Development: 1867–1953,* Bowes and Bowes, London, 1958, pp. 344–354, where in table 98 the following estimates of Canadian national wealth are given on a basis roughly comparable to the United States totals in Table 1-2: 1900, $5.5 billion; 1925, $25.7 billion; 1933, $25.8 billion.

Income accounting will force many students to revise their ideas of Anglo-America. Few of us realize to what extent urban activities have become the basis of our economy and culture, because most Anglo-American traditions originated in a land of forests, prairies, farms, and ranches. For example, in 1960, although three-tenths of the United States population was rural, only one-sixteenth of the labor force was agricultural. Increasing numbers of farmers work part time off the farms or are semi-retired, with the result that total farm income is only one-twenty-fifth of total United States personal income. In Canada, where farming is relatively more important, farmers' income is one-seventeenth of total personal income, and agriculture occupies one-tenth of the labor force. Whence does the huge Anglo-American production originate? Table 1-4 shows the relative importance of urban activities in Anglo-America as compared with those in selected other countries.

The data given in Table 1-4 are for *gross national product* (GNP), the total annual value of all goods produced and services rendered without any deduction for depreciation of equipment or depletion of resources. For the United States in 1966, the GNP was estimated at $740 billion; after deducting for depreciation and certain tax payments, the national income was estimated at $610 billion. Not all of this

went to individuals, their *personal income* being increased by withdrawals from funds saved (e.g., insurance and annuity payments) but decreased because corporations did not pay out all their income as dividends, the directors preferring to invest the rest in expanding the business. Personal income therefore was only $580 billion, but of this only $505 billion was *disposable* personal income because the government absorbed $75 billion in taxes levied on individuals. Of this disposable personal income, people saved $27 billion, leaving $478 for expenditures on consumption.[2] How this money was spent is shown in Table 1-5 for both the United States and Canada.

The reader will note in Table 1-5 that the percentage of the United States expenditure on food, beverages, and tobacco, all largely derived from farm products, is more than six times as great as the percentage of the product derived from farming (Table 1-4). This paradox results from two characteristics of farm production data. First, the *farm income* reported is *net*[3]

[2] Canadian data would show similar relationships. For details, see *Canada Year Book*, Queen's Printer, Ottawa, 1965, pp. 1002-1013. For a more complete statement of United States national accounts, see U.S. Bureau of the Census, *Statistical Abstract of the United States*, Washington, 1967, sec. 11, especially p. 316.

[3] In national accounting all figures used should be net income figures, for example, *value added by manufacturing* rather than *value of the manufactured product*. This avoids the duplication of values. In many cases it is impossible to obtain accurate value-added data for units smaller than states or for various provinces of Canada.

TABLE 1-4   Industrial Origin of Domestic Product, 1965 (percent of total product)

Country	Agriculture	Manufacturing	Construction	Transport	Trade	All Other
United States	4	31	5	6	15	39
Canada	6	26	6	9	13	40
United Kingdom	3	36	7	9	12	33
Paraguay	36	16	3	4	23	18
India	51	18		13		18

Data are only approximately comparable.
SOURCE: U.S. Bureau of the Census, *Statistical Abstract of the United States*, Washington, 1967, p. 868.

income; that is, from the value of the farmer's product are deducted his expenses for farm machinery, taxes, fertilizer, and other items paid for outside the farm. Second, commodities raised by the farmer are not fully produced when they are loaded on the farm truck. Before they reach the ultimate consumer, they must be shipped, stored, packaged, and distributed through wholesale and retail outlets. Thus, to the farm value of the wheat must be added freight, elevator charges, commissions, the cost of milling into flour, the cost of packaging, more freight, the cost of baking the bread, and finally, the cost of wrapping, trucking, and selling the bread to the consumer. Thus, although the original foods were farm-produced, the value added by preparation and transportation is largely added in the cities. The same is true of almost all goods sold through our *exchange economy;* to take advantage of the huge savings brought about by regional and occupational specialization, large sums must be expended in preparing the goods for the ultimate consumer, but these sums are much smaller than the savings effected through regional and industrial specialization.

GEOGRAPHIC PATTERNS AND REGIONS

Income is but one criterion by which various parts of a country may be examined. To compare the various parts of the United States and Canada, the geographer employs two other analytic devices: geographic *patterns* and geographic *regions*. In addition to facilitating comparisons, these devices help to describe and explain the distinctive local character of a particular place or area (sometimes referred to as its *geographic personality.*)

Patterns

In flying over central Indiana, Illinois, and Iowa, even the unskilled observer will notice that the majority of fields and country roads have a rectangular pattern. In the towns, most street patterns are likewise rectangular, and the map shows mostly rectangular county and township boundaries. This pattern results from the township-range survey upon which titles are

TABLE 1-5   Anglo-American Personal Consumption Expenditures, 1963

	United States		Canada	
Category	Billion dollars	Percent	Billion dollars	Percent
Food, Beverages, Tobacco	95.2	25.4	8.1	29.8
Clothing and Accessories	37.1	9.9	2.6	10.4
Housing	48.9	13.0	4.3	15.8
Household Operations	52.4	13.9	3.3	12.0
Personal Medical and Death Expenses	31.9	8.5	2.4	8.8
Transportation	47.2	12.6	3.3	12.0
Personal Business	24.9			
Recreation	22.7			
Education and Research	5.7	16.7	3.2	11.7
Religious and Welfare Activities	5.4			
Foreign Travel, etc.	3.5			
Total	375.0	100.0	27.2	100.0

SOURCES: U.S. Bureau of the Census, *Statistical Abstract of the United States,* Washington, 1965, p. 328; and *Canada Year Book,* Queen's Printer, Ottawa, 1965, p. 1012.

THE DISTINCTIVE PATTERN of rectangular roads shown here in southern Michigan is characteristic throughout the American Midwest and results from the rectangular survey and the government sale of land by quarter sections. (USDA photograph.)

based in most of the United States northwest of the Ohio and west of the Mississippi and in western Canada. Under this survey system, the original land titles were generally assigned in rectangular units such as 80 acres, 160 acres, or larger; usually it proved easier to lay out roads and fields parallel to the property boundaries, especially in level or gently rolling areas. In more rugged areas and near streams, as in southern Indiana, surface features appear less regular since the early settler adjusted the field and road patterns to the relief rather than to the land survey.

Recognition of such patterns saves effort in geographic study, for the trained pattern observer can learn useful facts about an extensive area by discovering one repeating pattern. Unfortunately, in most areas, the individual patterns are not so simple as in the illustration above, and the patterns for each type of data—for example, for climate, soils, vegetation, and roads—do not match. Rather, these patterns overlay each other and the landscape intertwines so many patterns that the resulting design may

be as complicated as in the most intricate Oriental rug. Yet the trained geographer can disentangle such involved patterns and discover recurring regularities which give character to the area.

Regions

If an area has significant unifying characteristics—including recurring patterns—that differentiate it from surrounding areas, a geographer may describe it as a *region*. A region may be large or small. Thus Anglo-America is a very large cultural region unified by a common language and traditions. The Everglades of Florida form a small region unified by swampiness. The Tennessee Valley is a region bound together by its drainage into the Tennessee River. The regional method of studying a country saves effort since the generalizations learned about each region are likely to be true for the great majority of the many places in that region.

Geographers use two major categories of regions: uniform and nodal (Figure 1-1).

THE IRREGULAR PATTERN shown here in New Brunswick is typical of a glaciated area used primarily for forest industries. (Photo: New Brunswick Travel Bureau.)

The first two regions described above are *uniform regions:* certain significant features are prevalent (although not always to the same degree) throughout the region. Thus, in most of its area Anglo-America has certain cultural features that are lacking or rare in Latin America to the south and in Soviet Eurasia across the pole. Other examples of uniform regions are: the *Corn Belt,* that agricultural region within which the farm economies are centered around the raising of corn; the *Colorado Plateau,* a Western relief region characterized by high plateaus dissected by deep canyons; the *Mojave Desert,* an arid region in southeastern California.

In contrast to the uniform region is the *nodal region,* an area within which the unifying factor is relationship to a common point or node. For example, the *retail trading area of Indianapolis* is that region whose residents normally shop in Indianapolis stores; the *hinterland of Norfolk* is that inland area from which goods are normally shipped or to which goods are imported through the port of Norfolk.

Most regions used by geographers are extremely arbitrary. Although regions reflect actual conditions on the earth's surface, they are created by men to help visualize and solve certain earthbound problems. They are areas that are linked together by common phenomena, common problems, and human organizational features including culture, routes, and governments. If the regions are natural (based on relief features, climate, or vegetation), they may be permanent—at least in terms of a human lifespan. But regions based on cultural features change as man changes; thus there was no Corn Belt until corn was developed into a crop and until American farmers evolved the technique of marketing corn by feeding it to livestock. Should some other crop (or industry) prove more profitable than corn or should Americans become vegetarians, the Corn Belt as such would disappear.

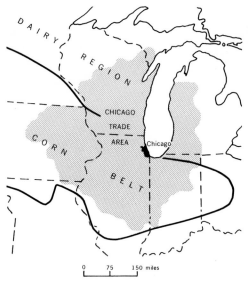

FIGURE 1-1   *The Corn Belt is a uniform region throughout which most farming is centered on corn. Corn is also raised in the Dairy Region, but the farm focus is on dairy production, and corn serves mainly as fodder for dairy cattle. The Chicago Trade Area is a nodal region unified by its commercial focus on Chicago; a more refined classification might differentiate two nodal regions: the Chicago Retail Trade Area and the larger Chicago Wholesale Trade Area.*

Since regions can be based on many sets of criteria, obviously any place can be simultaneously in a number of uniform and nodal regions, each useful for solving a particular problem. Thus Caldwell, New Jersey, might be in the grocery-shopping area of Caldwell, in the clothing-shopping area of Montclair, in the wholesale-distributing area of Newark for some types of goods and in the wholesale-distributing area of New York City for other types of goods. In terms of uniform political regions, West Caldwell is in the United States, in the state of New Jersey, and in the county of Essex. West Caldwell in terms of uniform physical regions lies in the humid continental climatic region within the middle latitudes and in the physiographic region known as the Triassic Lowlands.

It would be convenient if many kinds of regions could be fitted together. Occasionally they can, but rarely exactly. Most re-

gions referred to in textbooks are multipurpose regions based on criteria that fit relatively well together. In this volume, as in all regional textbooks, the author proposes to use arbitrary regions, but before introducing them, he wishes to present a number of types of regions so that the reader will be aware of the ingredients from which more generalized regions have been mixed.

Regions Used for Analyzing National Accounting Data

The regions used in analyzing national accounting data are based on states or provinces since in most areas complete estimates are not available for smaller units. These regions, used by the two Anglo-American governments, provide a good preliminary overall regional survey of Anglo-America.

U.S. Office of Business Economics regions   The United States regional subdivisions used below have been adopted by the Office of Business Economics[4] to present the national income data regularly tabulated in the *Survey of Current Business*. These regions are based primarily on income characteristics, industrial composition of the labor force, and selected statistical series reflecting demographic, ethnic, cultural, and social factors. Boundaries for these regions are shown in Figure 1-2.

New England   This is the most mature of these regions. Long established with its modest natural resources largely exhausted, New England depends primarily on an accumulation of capital and skill. Its leadership is in finance, light industry, and pro-

---

[4] To add to the confusion in official statistics, other United States agencies use groups of states which differ from the O.B.E. grouping. Some government agencies (including the Federal Reserve Bank) divide certain states between two regions. There are almost as many sets of regions as there are agencies using them. The Canadian regions used are less controversial, partly because Canadian provinces are more closely bound to economic realities and partly because the Canadian public thinks in terms of the accepted political regions.

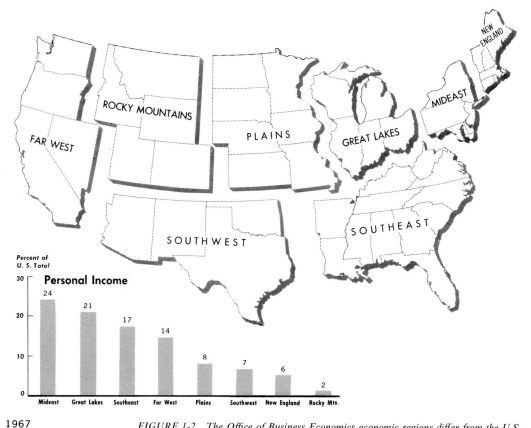

Percent of
U. S. Total

Personal Income

30

24

21

20

17

14

10

8

7

6

2

0

Mideast Great Lakes Southeast Far West Plains Southwest New England Rocky Mts.

1967

FIGURE 1-2   The Office of Business Economics economic regions differ from the U.S. Census regions mainly in adding Delaware, Maryland, and the District of Columbia to the Middle Atlantic states; adding Nevada to the Pacific states; and in recognizing the close relationships of Arizona and New Mexico to Oklahoma and Texas. Alaska and Hawaii are included in the Far West.

fessional services including education and research. In all these activities, New England is now in strenuous competition with other urbanized areas. Fortunately New England is well located at the northern end of the Atlantic Metropolitan Belt (Megalopolis) with rapid connections to Atlantic Coast markets as well as to Great Lakes and European markets.

Figure 1-3 shows how New England compares economically with the United States as a whole. This graph is the first of many graphs of this type to be used throughout this book. Why is it used? The author could, of course, graph the actual figures for income, but these might be misleading since almost every populous Anglo-Ameri-

can region, state, province, or city has at least a little of each kind of activity. For most, such a graph would show merely that trade, services, and manufacturing were the major sources of income. The type of graph presented here shows rather how the income or other data for New England deviate from the same data for the United States as a whole. If the bar points upward, the activity or source of income identified is greater than the United States average. If the bar points downward, that category is below the United States average. If the bar extends to the bottom of the chart, the category is lacking in this area. If no data are available, an estimated bar may be included with the letter D (disclosure). This letter means that the government is not legally able to disclose the data because to do so would divulge information about an individual business.

How are these bars derived? First, the population of the area considered is calculated as a percentage of the United States data. Next, the percentage of the total United States production (or income or other data) located in the area is calculated. If the two percentages are the same, the share of the area in that activity is proportionate to its share in the national population; in other words, the per capita figure is the same for the region and for the country as a whole. In such a case, no bar would be drawn upward or downward. If the per capita figure for the area is twice that for the United States, the bar is drawn upward to show a 100 percent positive deviation; if the per capita figure is half that for the United States, the bar would be drawn downward to show a 50 percent negative deviation.

This type of index is sometimes called a *location quotient*. It shows only one very important fact: how much concentration there is of a particular activity in an area compared with that for the country as a whole. A negative deviation does not necessarily imply backwardness; it may imply that the local businessmen find other activities more rewarding. For instance, a negative deviation in furnace manufacturing might simply result from the fact that the city in question is located in southern Florida far away from the problems of winter house heating. A comparison of the bars of two regions suggests categories in which each locality is specializing.

The Mideast or Middle Atlantic states   The term *Middle Atlantic states* has been commonly applied to New York, New Jersey, and Pennsylvania; hence the Office of Business Economics has adopted the name *Mideast*.[5] Delaware, Maryland, and the District of Columbia have been added to these states. This extension includes almost all the southern end of the Atlantic Metropolitan Belt. The resulting region, like New England, is characterized by a high degree of economic maturity with accumulations of skill and capital. Better equipped than its northeastern neighbor with raw materials and with somewhat better access to materials from outside the region, the Mideast has both heavy and light industries. Manufacturing is important but less important to the region than to New England. On the other hand, the Mideast is more highly specialized in commercial, financial, and political activities. Since it has more than

[5] H. S. Perloff and others in their studies in economic history use the Office of Business Economics regions but use the name *Middle Atlantic states* for the region called *Mideast*.

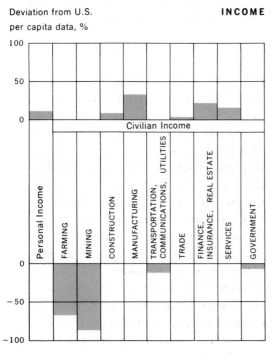

Deviation from U.S. per capita data, %   **INCOME**

FIGURE 1-3   The data used for these charts is 1965; data for other recent years would show similar deviations. Above-average income in manufacturing, finance, and services characterize areas with mature economies.

New England = 5.67% U.S. Pop.

one-fifth of the American population and one-quarter of the buying power, it is not surprising that most large American corporations find it convenient to have their headquarters in the Mideast.

The Great Lakes states (East North Central) This group of states is about twice as large as the Mideast in area, approximately the same in population, and somewhat smaller in buying power. Industry is the dominant economic activity, and with this area's excellent access to fuels, iron ore, limestone, lumber, and a variety of agricultural materials, it is not surprising that the heavier industries dominate here. Farming is more important than in the Mideast and New England but accounts for less than 4 percent of the total income. The largest commercial centers are sited on the Great Lakes; their financial, political, and professional services, although great, do not account for as large a share of economic activity as in the Mideast.

The Plains states (West North Central) The income graph for these states (Figure 1-4) contrasts sharply with that for New England. The eastern edge of these states touches on the American Commercial-Manufacturing Core, an area that includes approximately New England, the Mideast, and the Great Lakes states, but agriculture becomes increasingly important westward. Farming and ranching account for less than one-seventh of the income in these states, but this fraction can be misleading. Many of the factories either process agricultural raw materials or turn out goods for use on the farm. Likewise many of the commercial, financial, and political services are dependent on agricultural activities.

With the increasing mechanization of farming, much of this region is losing population, and an increasing proportion of its economic activity is being concentrated in metropolitan areas. Although it is twice as large as the Great Lakes region, the Plains region has only two-fifths of the buying power of that region. Although centrally located within the continent, rich in soil, and not lacking in minerals, the Plains region has not kept up with the growth of the national economy.

The Southeast This region, generally mild in climate, approximates the Plains region in size and the Great Lakes region in number of people. The purchasing power of the region is about three-quarters that of its equally populous northern neighbor, as is

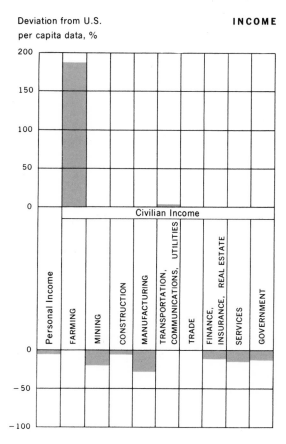

FIGURE 1-4 The Plains states include the Dakotas, two of the few states that in most years have farming as the major source of income.

Plains States = 8.24% U.S. Pop.

suggested by the income graph (Figure 1-5). Once mainly a land of cotton and tobacco, the Southeast today combines some well-farmed and many poor rural areas with growing industrial cities and boom areas such as Florida. Well supplied with fuel and raw materials, populous enough to provide a huge regional market and a large labor force, the region nevertheless has not developed rapidly enough to provide education and economic opportunity for many of its people. But low average figures, although significant, conceal the real progress in many Southeastern areas. For example, per capita incomes of about $2,100 annually in large Southeastern cities such as Atlanta are about the same as incomes in Detroit or industrial New England cities, but Southeastern averages are pulled down by the many poor rural counties with per capita incomes of $700 to $1,000. Uneven distribution of income is the pressing problem.

The Southwest   In contrast to the Southeast, the Southwest, boomed by oil, natural gas, and copper; by industrial development based partly on these materials; and by the westward movement of cotton production, has attained a level of living approximating the national average. The region has almost the same area as the Plains region or the Southeast; however, its population is somewhat greater than that of the Plains region and about half that of the Southeast. The Southwestern pattern of population distribution contrasts with that in the regions discussed previously. In a region where rainfall is commonly inadequate, many areas remain almost unsettled except where minerals or streams provide a local basis for development. Especially conspicuous are the population concentrations centered on oil and natural gas fields in Texas and Oklahoma, near ore fields in Arizona, and by irrigation water along the Rio Grande and the Gila rivers. The income graph for this region (Figure 1-6) reflects the specialization in minerals, agriculture, and government, as does the similar graph for the Rocky Mountain states (Figure 15-3).

The Rocky Mountains   These states, economically similar to the Southwest, have a similarly spotty population pattern. The economy is based largely on irrigation agriculture and mining with some manufacturing. Because of the huge amount of land in national parks, military reservations, and other government-managed property, government is a more important source of income than in any other American region. As in the Southwest, water is a limiting factor, and much land is unused because it

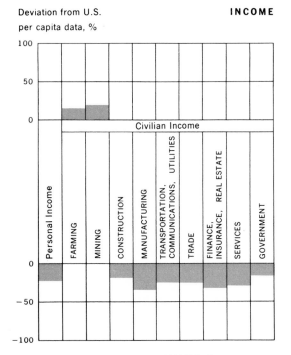

Southeast = 21.50% U.S. Pop.

FIGURE 1-5   The Southeast is often described as having a poor "industrial mix"; that is, its most widespread industries are those which have shown slow growth in the nation, for example, farming and mining.

is too dry, too rugged, or too infertile. The Rocky Mountain states support less population than the single state of Indiana although they are 15 times as large in area.

The Far West This region contains a wide variety of environments and economies, bound together mainly by recency of settlement and location on the Pacific away from the Commercial-Manufacturing Core. Nearly one-eighth of the American people live here, and the proportion has risen each decade. Statistical data for the region are greatly influenced by California which accounts for three-fourths of the population and somewhat more of the regional income (Figure 1-7). The region as a whole has a well-balanced economy including diverse agricultural production, mineral fuels, water power, lumber, and booming manufacturing plants. Rapid growth is exhausting natural resources, and urban land use is cutting seriously into productive farmlands. Mild climates, scenery, and distinctive ways of living have attracted permanent residents and tourists alike to this area. Although heavy and consumer goods industries are not lacking, industrial development emphasizes advanced technology with products such as aircraft, scientific instruments, missiles, and motion pictures—all industries requiring skills that local schools specialize in developing.

Canadian Regions

Many textbooks describe the United States and Canada as though they were similar countries, separated by a rather nominal boundary. Furthermore Canadians and Americans are in most respects no more different from each other than are Missourians and Californians. The two countries are *about* the same size,[6] produce many of the same products, have approximately the same levels of living, and have somewhat similar political organizations. Indeed, without too much distortion some American regions can be studied as continuations of Canadian regions, and vice versa.

[6] Canada is nearly 250,000 square miles larger in area.

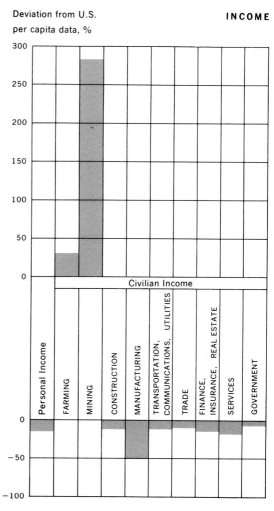

FIGURE 1-6 Petroleum, natural gas, and copper have given the Southwest a high positive deviation in mining. The Southwest, like the Southeast, includes many progressive and productive centers, counterbalanced by extensive unprogressive areas declining in population; hence despite many high-income areas, the average personal income for the region is below the United States average.

However, the differences between them are equally striking. Canada is generally north of the United States, and two-thirds of its huge area can be settled only sparsely, if at all. The 20 million Canadians, about one-tenth the size of the population of the United States, are concentrated largely in four areas close to the southern boundary. Economically, Canada matured somewhat later than the United States, and the Canadian prairie was settled a decade or more later than the prairie south of the border. Today Canada, although it has advanced industrially in certain regions, is more dependent on agricultural and raw-material industries than is the United States. Likewise Canada is more dependent on foreign trade, and its leading exports, although they now include increasing amounts of manufactures, are mainly foodstuffs, ores, and forest products.

Politically and culturally, Canada is more closely tied to the British Commonwealth than to the United States. This has

greatly influenced Canadian history, traditions, and even Canadian settlement; today Commonwealth membership provides important Canadian markets and entails certain political loyalties and commitments which sometimes seem to conflict with its close economic ties with the United States.

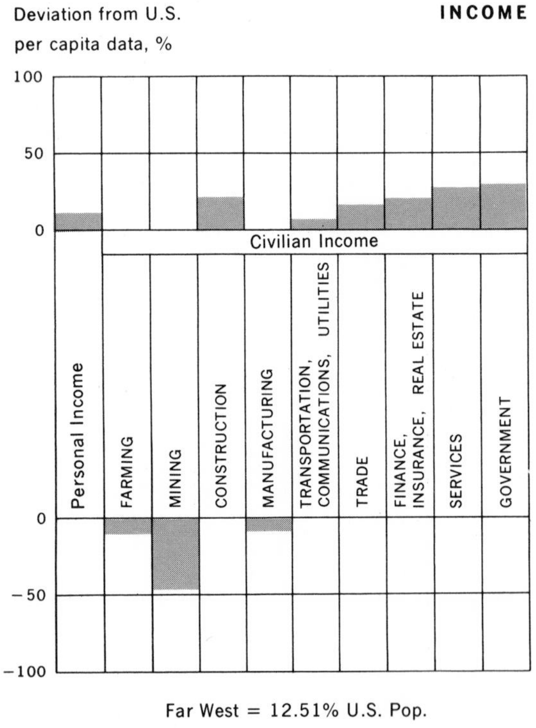

Canadian statistics In Canada national accounting and other statistical data are coordinated by the Dominion Bureau of Statistics (D.B.S.). The regions used consist of one or more provinces. Canadian national accounts on the provincial level are not yet as detailed as those for the states of the United States. The Canadian data based on employment in Figures 1-8 to 1-11 are not comparable with United States income data and should therefore be used mainly for comparisons between Canadian regions.

The Atlantic Provinces of Canada Newfoundland, New Brunswick, Nova Scotia, and Prince Edward Island include a number of scattered population centers separated by water, forest, swamps, and barren areas. About one-tenth of the Canadian population lives there, but they earn much below the average Canadian income, the majority from low-wage occupations such as lumbering, mining, farming, and fishing and from industries and trade based on these primary activities. Semi-isolation from the remainder of the Canadian economy is a major handicap.

Quebec Slightly wealthier are the three-tenths of all Canadians living in Quebec who earn about one-fourth of the national income (Figure 1-8). Farming and lumber-

Deviation from U.S. per capita data, %   **INCOME**

Far West = 12.51% U.S. Pop.

FIGURE 1-7 The Far West represents the future Anglo-American economy with growth and strength in the production of services rather than goods.

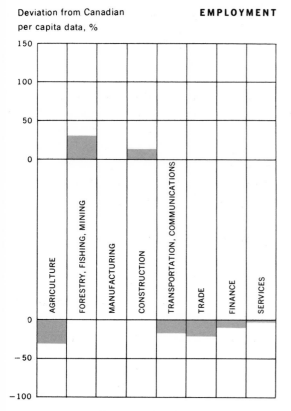

Deviation from Canadian per capita data, %

EMPLOYMENT

Quebec = 29% Can. Pop.

FIGURE 1-8   Note that the Canadian deviation graphs are based on employment rather than income data. Raw materials are still important in the Quebec economy; agriculture would be high if compared with United States data, but compared with a Canadian base it appears relatively low.

around Toronto includes the Canadian counterparts of most industries in the Great Lakes states. Central and northern Ontario, in contrast, are sparsely settled raw-material and vacation areas.

The Prairie Provinces   In contrast to their name, the larger part of the Prairie Provinces is forested; however, the sixth of the Canadian population living there is mainly on the southern grasslands. Grain, livestock, and minerals are the bases for a generally prosperous economy (Figure 1-10).

ing remain important and employ about one-tenth of the labor force. Resources such as waterpower and forests have encouraged development in the processing industries. In addition, Montreal, major seaport and rival of Toronto for the commercial leadership in Canada, manufactures a great variety of consumer goods.

Ontario   Southern Ontario, accounting for two-fifths of the Canadian income, is economically the most advanced area in Canada (Figure 1-9). Although farm and mineral products are not lacking, the economy is definitely urban, and the area

FIGURE 1-9   Agriculture, forestry, and mining are not lacking in Ontario, but they do not provide a share of employment up to the Canadian average.

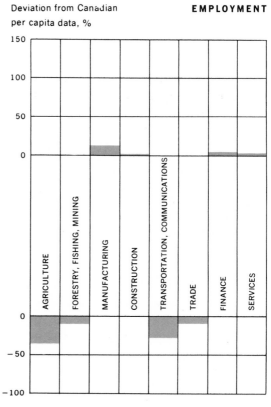

Deviation from Canadian per capita data, %

EMPLOYMENT

Ontario = 34% Can. Pop.

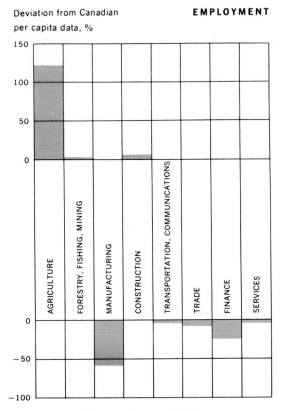

Deviation from Canadian per capita data, % **EMPLOYMENT**

Prairie Provinces = 17% Can. Pop.

FIGURE 1-10   *The Prairie Provinces, like the adjacent Plains states, are farm-oriented, although other
activities have been growing.*

small city. The mineral resources are scattered and are worth mining only if they are valuable in relation to their weight, for example, gold. There seems to be little prospect that this vast area, making up two-thirds of Canada, will ever support even a half million people.

REGIONS AND POPULATION

Because natural phenomena and man are distributed complexly over the earth's surface, to draw a realistic portrait of Anglo-America three sets of regions are used in addition to the national accounting regions above:

British Columbia Like the Atlantic Provinces, British Columbia, with about one-eleventh of the Canadian population, depends largely on forestry, mining, farming, and fishing (Figure 1-11). In contrast to the Atlantic Provinces, this region has an above-average per capita income. Blessed with waterpower, extensive virgin forests, and proximity to the oil and foodstuffs of the Prairie Provinces, this region is booming.

Northern Frontier The northern parts of the provinces just discussed and the Yukon and Northwest Territories poleward contain altogether a population about that of a

FIGURE 1-11   *The British Columbia graph reflects the scarcity of arable lands and the importance of raw-material-based industries.*

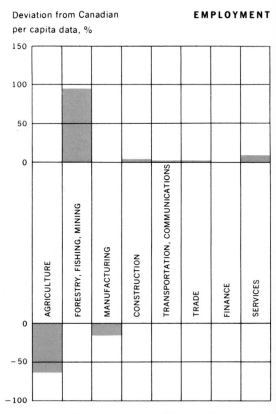

Deviation from Canadian per capita data, % **EMPLOYMENT**

British Columbia = 9% Can. Pop.

1 Vegetation regions, referred to first in Chapter 2 (Figure 2-3)
2 Physiographic regions, described in the regional chapters, 5 to 22
3 Economic regions and subregions, mentioned mainly in Chapters 5 to 22

Each of these sets of regions contributes to our analysis of Anglo-America. Fortunately it is possible to correlate these various regions approximately, as shown in Tables 1-6 and 1-7. It should be noted, however, that these regions rarely coincide exactly.

Vegetation Regions

The next chapters describe the aboriginal Anglo-America which the European settlers found, by dividing the continent into broad vegetation regions. These uniform regions have many advantages. Natural vegetation commonly coincides with certain combinations of climatic and soil conditions. Because explorers spent only a small part of the year in any one area, the natural vegetation suggested to them what the weather was like at other times of the year. Natural vegetation is also closely related to broad soil types, and provides a rough index of soil quality.

Regional Chapters

This textbook is divided into chapters based largely on population and economic unity. Each region contains a group of people who are somewhat allied together historically as well as in present commercial, industrial, and political relationships. Boundaries between these regions

TABLE 1-6   Approximate Comparison of Regions Used: United States

O.B.E. Regions	Vegetation	Physiographic	Regional Chapters
New England		New England Upland	New England
Mideast		Coastal Plain Piedmont Appalachians	New York Gateway Delaware-Chesapeake Gateways
Southeast	Eastern Woodlands	Coastal Plain Piedmont Appalachians Low Interior Plateaus	Southeast Coastal Plain Gulf South Southern Uplands Ohio Basin
Great Lakes		Low Interior Plateaus Central Lowland Canadian Shield	Ohio Basin Great Lakes
Plains	Prairies and Steppes	Central Lowland Great Plains	Midwest
Southwest	Southwest Grass, Shrub, and Woodlands	Great Plains Basins and Ranges	Southwest
Rocky Mountains	Mountain Grass, Shrub, and Woodlands	Rocky Mountains Intermontane Plateaus	High West
Far West	Pacific Forests, Shrub, and Grass Tundra	Sierra Nevada-Cascades Valleys and Coastal Pacific Ranges Alaskan Plateaus, Ranges, and Lowlands	Southern California San Francisco Hinterland Pacific Northwest

are sometimes sharp; more commonly they are transition zones between clusters of people. The use of the regions and their boundaries is not to minimize interregional ties but to aid in describing the distinctive characteristics of the various parts of Anglo-America.

CONCLUSIONS

Three themes run through this book: *people, resources,* and *income.* Although the land in itself is not neglected, the author considers that land becomes an asset only to the degree that people know about its resources, how to use them, and how to organize themselves to use them effectively. The high income of most Anglo-Americans has resulted from such intelligent use of resources and from multiplying such resources by the intensive application of skill to a relatively small value of raw materials. The problem areas of Anglo-America—such as Appalachia—are not areas lacking in resources but rather areas to which insufficient skill has been applied to support a population first settled when relations among man, resources, and income were different.

The relationships among people, resources, and income differ greatly from region to region. The explanations for these regional differences are rarely simple; they involve the legacies of history, the changing value of resources, the skills and energies of man, and success or failure in competition with other regions.

One method of evaluating the national economies is national accounting. These data can also be applied to regional analysis, as was shown by a brief survey of economic regions. Other types of regions—vegetation, soil, climatic, and physiographic—will also prove useful for understanding Anglo-America. The organization of this textbook is based largely on regional groups of people who have much in common and do much of their business with one another.

SELECTED REFERENCES

Government

Canada Year Book (annual), Queen's Printer, Ottawa. The Canadian equivalent of the *Statistical Abstract of the United States.*

"Personal Income by States since 1929," supplement to the *Survey of Current Business,*

TABLE 1-7   Approximate Comparison of Regions Used: Canada

D.B.S. Regions	Vegetation	Physiographic	Regional Chapters
Atlantic Provinces	Eastern and Northern Woodlands	Appalachians Canadian Shield	Atlantic Gateways
Quebec			
Ontario		Canadian Shield Central Lowland	Ontario Heartland
Prairie Provinces	Prairies and Steppes Northern Woodlands	Great Plains Canadian Shield	Canadian West
British Columbia	Pacific Forests, Shrub, and Grass	Rocky Mountains Coastal Ranges and Valleys	
Northern Frontier	Northern Woodlands Tundra Icecap	Canadian Shield Western Cordillera Arctic Islands	Northlands

1956. Includes a full statement of national accounts.

U.S. BUREAU OF THE CENSUS: *County and City Data Book: 1967,* Washington, 1967. New editions or supplements appear every few years.

————: *Statistical Abstract of the United States* (annual), Washington.

Other

BOGUE, D. J.: *The Population of the U.S.A.,* Free Press, New York, 1959.

CAMU, P., E. L. WEEKS, Z. W. SAMETZ: *Economic Geography of Canada,* Macmillan, Toronto, 1964. A largely economic discussion with tables summarizing Canadian regions.

CAVES, R. E., and R. N. HOULTON: *The Canadian Economy: Prospect and Retrospect,* Harvard University Press, Cambridge, 1959.

FIRESTONE, O. J.: *Canada's Economic Development, 1867–1953,* Bowes and Bowes, London, 1958.

JONES, C. F., and P. E. JAMES (eds.): *American Geography: Inventory and Prospect,* Syracuse University Press, Syracuse, 1954. Includes a chapter on regions.

PERLOFF, H. S., E. S. DUNN, JR., E. E. LAMPARD, and R. F. MUTH: *Regions, Resources, and Economic Growth,* published for Resources for the Future, Inc., Johns Hopkins, Baltimore, 1960. A historical and economic analysis by the O.B.E. economic regions described in this chapter.

Atlases

Atlas of Canada, Queen's Printer, Ottawa, 1957.

Goode's World Atlas, 12th ed., Rand McNally, Chicago, 1964.

Prentice-Hall World Atlas, Prentice-Hall, Englewood Cliffs, N.J., 1963.

The United States and Canada (Oxford Regional Economic Atlas), Clarendon Press, Oxford, 1967.

CHAPTER 2

THE LANDS
AND THE
SETTLERS:
NORTH
AND EAST

Modern Anglo-America is constructed on skeletons of features from the past. Its settlers from Europe did not start with virgin territory; the land had already been used, crisscrossed with a network of routes, fields, houses, and villages whose location and arrangement had been determined by the customs and objectives of an earlier era. Even the first European settlers inherited a modest but significant arrangement of trails, water routes, clearings, and village sites from the Indians.

Anglo-American coastlines, plains, mountains, and many streams are about the same today as they were in the sixteenth and seventeenth centuries. On the other hand, the *organic* resources were much richer when soils were unleached, virgin forests and prairies were stocked with game, and streams and offshore banks were crowded with fish. To colonists from the well-settled, thoroughly tilled, not over-rich soils of Western Europe, this almost free land which could be bought, or conquered, cheaply from the Indians, was indeed a land of promise. To understand what happened, the land's potential must be considered in terms of primitive plows, canoes, sailing ships, and pack animals rather than in terms of a society equipped with automobiles, bulldozers, and twentieth-century technology.

The impact of the new land on the prospective conquerors, traders, or settlers was also influenced by their goals and attitudes and by the fact that they became aware of the North American continent in a piecemeal fashion. In contrast, after centuries of exploring and surveying, twentieth-century Anglo-Americans can visualize the continent as a whole and then consider how settlers nibbled into its huge, roughly triangular mass (Figure 2-1). One angle of this hypothetical triangle may be placed at Bering Strait, across which most pre-European settlers entered the continent beginning perhaps 20,000 to 30,000 years ago. Thence successive groups of migrants advanced probably spreading out from the broad level corridor extending southward east of the Rockies. Much later, perhaps 3,000 years ago, Eskimos crossed the strait to the American Arctic tundras, thinly settling a coastal zone 3,000 statute miles eastward to western Greenland where they encountered the Norse Vikings about the tenth century.

Another side of the triangle extended from eastern Greenland to Panama, a distance of about 5,000 miles. Its northern end is only 1,200 statute miles from the Norwegian coast and the voyage from Europe to Newfoundland could be made in several stages, the longest about 500 miles. (The shortest trans-Atlantic air and shipping routes still cross the North Atlantic and the great circle route from Ireland to Newfoundland is about 1,900 miles). This route was often so stormy that the much longer route, about 4,000 miles from Spain to Puerto Rico, was preferred since westbound sailing vessels benefited from the steady northeast trade winds.

FIGURE 2-1   *This is a useful but overgeneralized map of the North American environment and settlement. Compare it with Figures 2-2 and 2-3 to determine the relative accuracy of the discussion of Figure 2-1 in the text.*

The Latin American part of this triangle was significant to Anglo-America because in Mexico originated almost all the crops cultivated by Indian farmers to the north. The 31-mile-wide Panama Isthmus provided a much-used shortcut for the Spaniards to Pacific Latin America and later for Americans to California and the Pacific Northwest. From the Panama angle a 6,000-mile arc northwestward completes the triangle to Bering Strait.

The center of this hypothetical triangle lay west of Lake Superior. In the sector between south and east of this central point, the land was generally wooded, and much was suited for cultivation (the Eastern Woodlands). This sector, so convenient to Europe, attracted almost all settlers in Anglo-America up to nearly 1850; it also con-

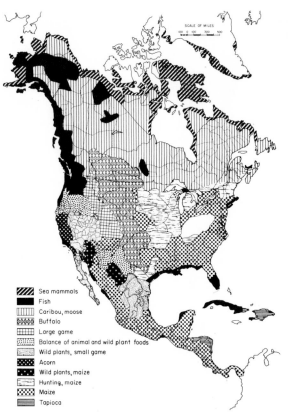

Sea mammals
Fish
Caribou, moose
Buffalo
Large game
Balance of animal and wild plant foods
Wild plants, small game
Acorn
Wild plants, maize
Hunting, maize
Maize
Tapioca

FIGURE 2-2   The food basis of American aboriginal life. Compare this map with Figure 2-3. (Both maps are after Harold E. Driver and William C. Massey, "Comparative Studies of the North American Indians", TRANSACTIONS, The American Philosophical Society, vol. 47, part 2, pp. 177, 184.

tained some relatively dense areas of aboriginal population, although the densest aboriginal settlement was along the Pacific Coast. From east to northwest of the central point, the land was (and remains) largely infertile, glacier-scoured terrain which had a small but scattered aboriginal population. This land (the Northern Woodlands and the tundra), which makes up the largest part of Canada, attracted few settlers. The remaining sector from northwest to south, thought of by most twentieth-century Anglo-Americans as "the West," was a vast game-rich land of grassy and semi-arid plains, punctuated by forested and often snowcapped mountains. This spectacular area was the last to be settled

by Europeans; indeed settlement has not yet filled the land and perhaps in the more rugged and barren areas never will.

The Aborigines

The new land was sparsely inhabited—at most there were 2 million Indians and 50,000 Eskimos north of the Rio Grande. These peoples were divided into hundreds of tribal groups, possessing many distinctive languages and cultures, which anthropologists have analyzed in considerable detail. All had a Stone Age culture less advanced than the indigenous cultures of Mexico and Peru. To European settlers, the Indian provided trails, knowledge of the land and several major techniques for exploiting the land, cheap labor in the fur trade, and allies in fighting other Europeans. Eventually in most areas the settler found the Indian a pest to be pushed westward into unwanted lands, or exterminated. Lacking at first firearms, steel tools, and European scientific knowledge, the Indian, weakened by European-introduced diseases, liquor, and intertribal war, could delay but not stop European advances.

For our purposes, the aborigines will be discussed briefly under each major environment. Although this treatment oversimplifies the picture of Indian society, since the *material* features of most Indian cultures were closely related to the flora and fauna of their physical environment, the resulting portraits are not unrealistic (Figure 2-2).

THE EUROPEAN BACKGROUND OF THE SETTLERS

The colonial civilizations that Europeans developed in America were influenced also by the religious, social, and economic settings in Europe. In the seventeenth century, western Europe was politically and religiously in a turmoil; economically it was expanding and demanding raw materials from overseas, especially precious metals, timber, pitch, fish, furs, and such new luxuries as tobacco and sugar. European society was highly stratified, and opportunities for the lower classes, no matter how skilled, were negligible. For most people, comfort and security were scanty. Land and other means of rising into the favored classes were not easily obtained.

The new lands did not attract the timid. The Atlantic crossing required a hazardous voyage of two to three months. The *Mayflower,* only 90 feet long, carried 25 sailors and 102 passengers, together with domestic animals and stores needed for the voyage and to equip the new settlement. Such conditions attracted mainly the bold and the desperate who, dismayed by prospects in Europe, believed their chances better in the New World. Many were willing to come even as indentured servants. The trans-Atlantic voyage was, of course, much harder on political prisoners and convicts and especially on Negro slaves, all of whom contributed to the burgeoning colonial economies.

The colonists were not so much dissatisfied with European life as with their place in it. They came not to create a new type of society but hoping to reproduce European settlements under conditions more favorable to themselves. Although temporarily subsistence farming was often necessary, the settlers did not intend to become peasants but rather to produce commodities for trade. There were, of course, risks from Indian raids, but war, torture, and looting occurred in Europe during the same period.

European trading companies and wealthy proprietors financed much of the early settlement. The objective was to establish fortified trading posts at which furs, fish, timber, tobacco, and other crops could be collected and shipped to Europe. This system was modified by distance since when four to six months were required to send a message to London, Paris, or Amsterdam, control and support from overseas were

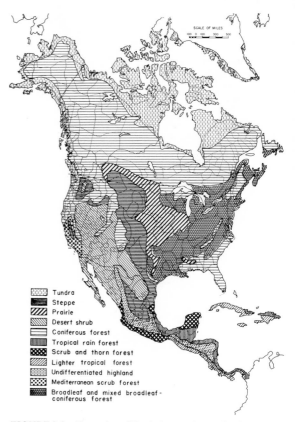

FIGURE 2-3   *Vegetation of North America (generalized).*

tenuous. The colonists were forced to improvise and by so doing they often established new institutions better suited to survival on the edge of the wilderness.

The Frontiersman and the Moving Frontier

Whatever the European background of the colonists, they acquired new characteristics as they advanced into the wilderness. The frontiersmen did not wish to give up their European culture; in fact most of them started towns, churches, and schools soon after their arrival at their new homesites. Yet contact with the Indians, the problems of a new environment, and distance from the European homelands combined to modify the culture of the frontiersmen.

Not all settlers moved to the frontier; some found opportunities as clerks, artisans, or professional men in the established cities.

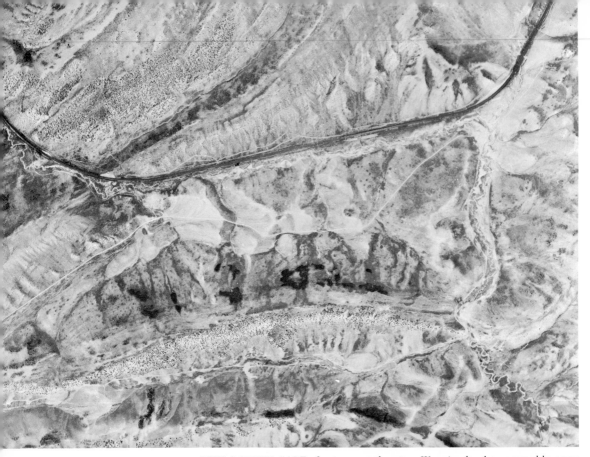

THIS BARREN PART of extreme southwestern Wyoming has been crossed by game trails, Indian trails, trapper routes, and by the Mormons and other settlers. Note the numerous roads faintly visible. After having passed the highest point on its main route the Union Pacific descends here along the headwaters of the Bear River, which drains into Great Salt Lake. The roads visible are of historic importance; the main highway (Interstate 80) is some miles to the north. (USDA photograph.)

But even in areas of earlier settlement, the expansion of the frontier meant increasing business as well as potential opportunity for those dissatisfied with their economic progress.

The stereotype of the frontiersman is the pioneer farmer who built his cabin and cleared land for crops and for pasture for his animals. The advance of settlement is ordinarily thought of as the advance of the agricultural frontier. But there are other kinds of frontiers, each having distinctive characteristics: the rather transient frontier of the fur trader and trapper; the boom frontier of the miner of precious metals; the fast-moving frontier of early cattlemen; the carefully planned advance of the railroad promoter and related real estate promotions. Whichever frontier entered first into a new area paved the way for the advance of other types of frontiers. Each kind of frontier advanced at its own pace: some of them overtook and pushed ahead of others. The agricultural frontiers were most influential in marking the land, but the farmer did not advance alone; at times he was stimulated by miners, cattlemen, transportation promoters, and urban settlers; elsewhere he stimulated their advances.

The frontier[1] did not always advance.

[1] The U.S. Census considered the frontier to be where the population dropped below two per square mile.

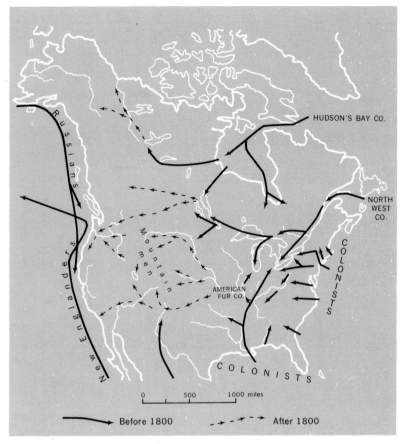

FIGURE 2-4   *The fur traders whose routes are indicated on this map were responsible for much of the early exploration of the Anglo-American interior.*

Sometimes frontiersmen occupied land, found it wanting in resources for permanent settlement, and, after a struggle, retreated. In some instances the land never should have been occupied for agriculture; the soil may not have been rich enough or the climate humid enough for profitable farming. Elsewhere the resource—perhaps an ore vein or a forest—became exhausted, or changing market conditions converted a once suitable land use into an unprofitable venture. Often people clung to a land use after economic justification for such use vanished; it has not proved easy for men to change their manner of life, especially if they were too old, too conservative, or too lazy to readjust to new circumstances.

THE NORTHERN WOODLANDS

The first environment to be exploited by arriving Indians as well as by European fishermen and fur traders was a land of long, dark, cold winters (Figures 2-4 and 2-5). Its snows lie unmelted on the ground almost until the advent of the short, warm summer. Spring arrives suddenly and the long, sunny days convert the frozen marshes into homes for multiplying insects. The length of the summer days in part makes up for the short growing season. Then after a brief autumn, winter reigns again.

The forest (Figure 2-3) is predominantly coniferous—consisting especially of spruce, fir, and pine—although there are some

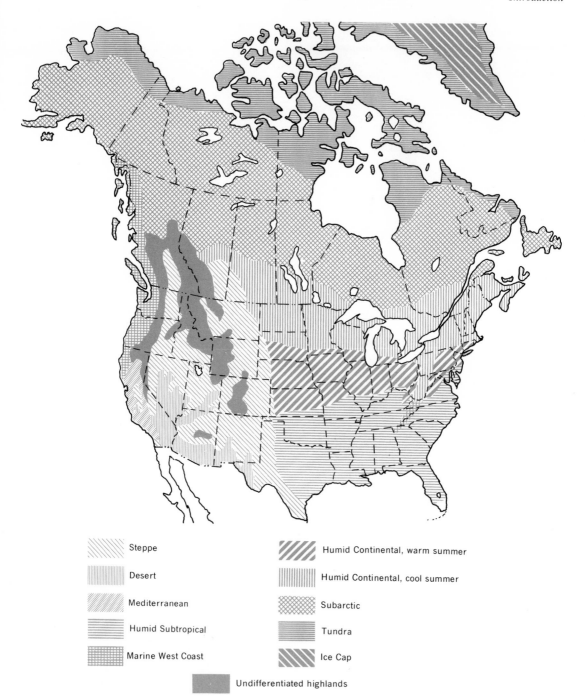

Steppe

Desert

Mediterranean

Humid Subtropical

Marine West Coast

Humid Continental, warm summer

Humid Continental, cool summer

Subarctic

Tundra

Ice Cap

Undifferentiated highlands

FIGURE 2-5   The climatic regions of Anglo-America. Note that all climatic regions are based on averages, so that in exceptional years actual conditions may depart considerably from the conditions represented by each climatic type. (After Köppen, as modified by Trewartha.)

ACID SOILS

- Tundra
- Podzol
- Gray-brown podzolic
- Red-yellow podzolic-latosolic
- Prairie

OTHER SOILS

- Chernozem
- Chestnut-brown
- Desert
- Mountain (varied, often rocky)

FIGURE 2-6   *Generalized soil regions of Anglo-America. There are innumerable local variations in soils based on differences in underlying rock, drainage, slope, and vegetation.*

birches and other deciduous trees. On the southern border, the forest is tall and lumber-rich, but northward the trees are too stunted and too widely spaced to be commercially valuable and a moderately tall tree represents a century of slow growth. The forest is rarely continuous because areas of bare rock, marsh, lake, and shallow soil inhibit its spread.

Soils (Figure 2-6)

The mature soil is a *podzol,* an acid sandy soil whose upper layer contains undecomposed needles and other raw humus. But much of the area, scraped clean by the former continental glacier or covered with glacial rock debris, lacks adequate soil for plant growth. Waterlogged soil, arising from glacially dammed streams, is another common handicap. Furthermore, in the northern part of the area, *permafrost,* a condition in which the subsoil remains frozen all year, blocks underdrainage. Such poor drainage develops *muskegs,* boggy areas filled with peat. There are a few isolated areas of fair soil, for example, the Clay Belt of northern Ontario, but they make up a minute fraction of the whole Northern Woodlands.

Animals

The greatest natural attraction of the North Woods is its fur-bearing animals: beaver, mink, marten, fox, muskrat, and many others. Game, fish, and berries aided the traveler who found the Indian canoe an ideal vehicle on the many natural waterways.

Indians

All the Indians depended on hunting and fishing, and their mainstays were the woodland caribou and moose. The local groups of people were small and scattered because many square miles of hunting ground were needed to nourish a few Indian families. In summer, game was plentiful and was supplemented by berries, seeds, and roots; in winter, famine might result from poor hunting even though every kind of animal was considered potential food. Life was highly nomadic; the Indian followed the game on foot, snowshoe, or by canoe. The conical tepees were easily moved; and hides, fur, bark, wood, and stone were the major raw materials from which the simple household goods were constructed. Especially in the south, recognized intertribal trade routes existed over which a few necessities were traded long before Europeans arrived.

The Tundra and the Eskimo

The Northern Woodlands grade northward into the almost treeless, marshy tundra. Conditions of life there are well known because elementary school geographies invariably describe the Eskimo, a people distinct in language and culture from the Northern Woodland Indians. This vast polar and subarctic area has had only minor significance in the development of Anglo-America. More detailed treatment is therefore deferred to Chapter 22.

The Fur Trader Opened the Routes

Norse visitors to Vinland traded in furs, as did a few European fishermen who visited Newfoundland and eastern Canada about 1500, but such trading had little influence on the course of later settlement. About 1580 French fur traders sailed up the St. Lawrence Estuary, and nearly 30 years later a permanent settlement was established at Quebec. Soon after, French traders, missionaries, and explorers pushed inland through the Great Lakes, reaching the Mississippi River in 1673 and gradually spreading their trade up the Mississippi tributaries. About the same time British colonies on the Atlantic engaged in fur trading although in some areas it soon became secondary to agriculture. In 1670 the Hudson's Bay Company was chartered by the British government, and soon its traders penetrated into Canada through Hudson Bay, competing strenuously with French traders based at Montreal who gradually extended their outposts in the Great Lakes country and down the Mississippi Valley (Figure 2-4).

After the Louisiana Purchase (1803) American traders expanded westward, and several American fur companies penetrated into a southward spur of the Northern Woodlands in the Rockies. The American Fur Company, organized by John Jacob Astor, even expanded its posts to Astoria at the mouth of the Columbia River. After the War of 1812, these posts came under the control of the Hudson's Bay Company. Fur trapping was important in the United States until the middle of the nineteenth century and is still the leading industry in parts of northern Canada (although the total output is only about $1 million annually). The depletion of wild animals and especially the competition of fur ranching have almost destroyed the business. But the contribution of past traders and trappers remained significant because they opened trails and routes across the country, established contacts with the Indians, and served as guides for later settlers. Many of their trading posts have grown into large cities, for example, Chicago, St. Louis, Detroit, and Winnipeg.

A common pattern should be stressed here which applies to each resource used by advancing pioneers, whether the resource was fur, fish, soil, grassland, timber, or minerals. The advance of the frontier westward was motivated by the demand for some product which could be marketed in eastern Anglo-America or across the Atlantic. In each case, groups of people were dissatisfied enough in Europe or in eastern Anglo-America to take great risks and undergo considerable hardships to better their fortune. Had beaver hats never become fashionable in Europe, Canada would have been more slowly explored and settled. Had fish and lumber been in surplus supply in Europe in the seventeenth century, New England might not have developed then.

THE EASTERN WOODLANDS

There is no sharp boundary between the Northern and Eastern woodlands; indeed, areas of Northern Woodlands occur on elevated areas within the Eastern Woodlands. Many of the same fur-bearing and game animals are found in both areas. The distinction between the two is rather that the Eastern Woodlands are suited for agricultural settlement. Even the Indians engaged in farming, although by no means as intensively as their European successors.

All the early visitors to the Atlantic Coast noted the tall timbers so desirable in a society based on wooden ships, wooden houses, and firewood for fuel. This was the eastern edge of almost 1 million square miles of forests, broken only by small Indian clearings, marshes, lakes, and rocky barrens and, on the western margin, by areas of prairie (Figure 2-3). In New England white pine, birch, beech, maple, and hemlock were characteristic; southward oak, chestnut, hickory, and poplar predominated and, in the Southeast, the southern pines, rich in naval stores (turpentine and resin), were common along the coast. Cypress occupied the alluvial areas of the Southeast. These tall Eastern forests were rarely impenetrable: their thick, leafy canopy discouraged undergrowth; and trails suitable for pedestrian or horseman were easily blazed, if indeed they had not been already pounded out by herds of game and by Indians following the animals. The forests were not lacking in food: in season berries, wild plums, crab apples, grapes, and nuts were common; and ducks, turkeys, pigeons, deer, rabbits, bear, raccoons, squirrels, and other animals provided meat from the land, as did fish from the streams and lakes. Offshore the fishing banks, especially north of New York, had attracted fishermen at least a century before the land was settled. For the small ships of the seventeenth century, the much indented Atlantic Coast provided innumerable harbors. Bays and river banks offered sites for fishing villages and small agricultural settlements.

Whereas the coasts and forest vegetation are roughly similar to those of Western Europe, the climate is somewhat more variable. Though the weather is equally humid, and seasonal changes are similar, daily and seasonal changes are more severe since prevailing winds in America blow from the interior toward the coast instead of from the coast inland as in Western Europe. The sunshine is also warmer at each season as the American areas are more southerly in latitude than the European homelands. The Eastern Woodland area varies in climate from north to south, but in all latitudes it is characterized by marked daily and seasonal change. Climatologists today divide this area climatically into two regions, *humid continental*[2] to the north and *humid subtropical* to the south, the dividing line being the 32° January isotherm (Figure 2-5).

Soils

The Indians had little technical knowledge of soils, clearing parts of the forest when they needed new fields and cultivating their hills of corn amid the stumps.[3] In the Eastern Woodlands soils became exhausted

after a decade, if not sooner; the old fields were abandoned, and often the village was relocated. The seventeenth-century pioneer had only slightly more agricultural knowledge than the Indian, but somewhat better tools. After decades of settlement, he learned to use plant indicators to determine the soils' potential. The major soil groups (Figure 2-6) *roughly* coincide with climatic and vegetation regions: thus the humid continental woodland has gray-brown podzolic soils, whereas the humid subtropical area has red and yellow podzolic soils. Both soil groups include many soils which although initially fertile, become leached, acid, and eroded after continuous cultivation. If not eroded, most soils in both groups respond well to fertilization. The gray-brown soils with a virgin profile topped by leaf mold, beneath which lies a thick humus-rich topsoil and a heavier subsoil, are the more fertile. In the Great Lakes area these soils, formed from glacially deposited material, rich in lime, are superior in structure and fertility.

---

[2] The terms used to describe climate, soil, surface features, minerals, etc., being those of modern earth science, were not, of course, used by the Indians or pioneer settlers; most of these features can be identified in early accounts. For example, William Wood, *New Englands Prospect*, London, 1634, p. 9, states that:

The countrey being nearer the Equinoctiall than England, the dayes and nights be more equally divided. In Summer the dayes be two houres shorter, and likewise in Winter two houres longer than in England. In a word, both Summer and Winter is more commended of the English there than the Summer Winters and Winter Summers of England; and who is there that could not wish, that Englands Climate were as it hath beene in quondam times, colder in Winter and hotter in Summer? or who will condemne that which is as England hath beene? Virginia having no Winter to speake of, but extreame hot Summers, hath dried up much English blood, and by pestiferous diseases swept away many lusty bodies, changing their complexion not into swarthinesse, but into Palenesse; so that when as they come for trading into our parts, wee can know many of them by their faces.

[3] The barking or girdling of trees let the full sunlight onto the forest floor in a few months' time and thus made it ready for planting. The ground commonly was burned over before

being planted, to free it of dead branches, dry leaves, and the light herbaceous vegetation that was present. The forest topsoil was dark with leafmold, rich in potash, and congenial to the heavily feeding Indian corn. In a few years wind and weather completed the task of bringing down the dead timber. The deadened hardwood trunks and roots decayed rapidly in the moist, warm summers.

With one or two exceptions the plants cultivated by the Indians had originated far to the south of the United States under tropical or subtropical conditions. The list of native crops includes several kinds of corn, such as dent, flint, and sweet corn, various kidney or navy beans, squashes or pumpkins, the common sunflower, and the Jerusalem-artichoke. . . . Excepting the Jerusalem-artichoke, these are all annual plants which, in contrast to most of the crops of northern Europe, require warm weather for starting. A large part of our humid East is as warm in summer as a tropical region. Summer in the middle Mississippi Valley is as warm by day or night as summer in the Tropics, perhaps warmer. Hence, carrying the warmth-loving domesticated American annuals northward from Mexico and Central America to the eastern woodland areas involved no very serious problems for the aboriginal cultivators. It may be assumed, however, that it took many generations for agriculture to spread from Mexico to Chesapeake Bay. As it spread, a gradual selection of plants that would mature in a shorter and shorter growing season took place. These in turn became the parents of our modern commercial corn, beans, and pumpkins.
Carl Sauer, *Climate and Man*, in YEARBOOK OF AGRICULTURE, U.S. Department of Agriculture, Washington, 1941, p. 161.

The red-yellow soils differ from their northern neighbors in color, in being more acid, and in being more subject to leaching and erosion. They were formed in regions of higher average temperatures with heavier rainfall; since they are rarely frozen in winter, when cleared they are leached and eroded throughout the year.

In the Eastern Woodlands (and other regions) many soil areas do not exactly fit the regional description. Within both soil regions described above, there are areas of alluvial and windblown (loess) soils which are above average in fertility. Underlying rocks also influence the surface soil and add additional variety; limestone, glacial silts, and some crystalline rocks produced superior soils, whereas sandstone, former beaches, and glacial boulders influenced the soil adversely.

Indians

The Eastern Woodland Indians were a great resource to the early settlers because they introduced Europeans to maize (corn), tomatoes, squash, lima and kidney beans, and many other plants, both wild and domesticated.[4] In general, these Indians were dependent on agriculture based on clearings which were abandoned when the soil became exhausted. The Algonkian-speaking tribes of the humid continental climate were poorly organized groups who lived in small semipermanent villages of rectangular, barrel-roofed huts. More effectively organized and more warlike were the Six Nations of the Iroquois who controlled most of the Appalachian corridors. All these peoples traded among themselves, carrying goods long distances on their backs or by canoes; all hunted, often following game trails (for example, the Buffalo Trace of southern Indiana) which later became pioneer roads.

[4]Tobacco is not included because the variety planted in Virginia, Maryland, and elsewhere by Europeans was obtained from Indians in the West Indies. The potato from Peru was introduced to Anglo-America by way of Europe.

South of the Algonkian area the Indian tribes were much more dependent on agriculture and lived in more permanent villages. In contrast to the Indians northward, workers specialized in crafts in the villages, and there is definite evidence that the culture was influenced by the Indian civilizations of Mexico. Large clearings in the woodlands were planted in corn and beans (sometimes two crops a year), and tribes such as the Creeks of Alabama quickly adopted European crops, domestic animals, and tools when these were introduced by white settlers. Hunting was important but southern furs were less in demand in European markets than northern beaver.

The Farmers Alter the Woodlands

As the agricultural frontier advanced, the vegetation and the soil were soon greatly changed. The division of the land into fields and pastures by fences, the trails, roads and eventually railroads, the farmsteads, hamlets, and towns—all clearly marked the advance of the frontier. Crops and domestic animals replaced indigenous plants and wild animals; even new weeds and pests were introduced by the settler.

Cattle, sheep, swine, and poultry were introduced into the Atlantic seaboard colonies by the first settlers. Openings in the forests, natural meadows, and abandoned Indian fields provided some pasture, but grasses suitable for haymaking were rare. The introduction of European grasses solved this problem, and in a few decades livestock industries developed along the coast, for example, on the large estates around Narragansett Bay. Settlers moving inland often started their agricultural activities by raising livestock because animals could be driven eastward to markets more economically than crops could be shipped.

New England and eastern Canada   The fertile lands were pockets separated from one another by areas of rough, stony land. Settled in a day when Indians were a menace, the rural populace clustered around towns sited on such features as the fertile alluviums of the Connecticut Valley. Some of the hills were cleared for grazing, but many rugged or infertile lands remained empty—in fact, many areas then cultivated have since reverted to meadow or forest. The colonial New Englander raised crops, and especially animals, to supply the towns, occasionally with a surplus for export.

Eastern Canada developed agriculturally more slowly than New England; its small population before the American Revolution was interested mainly in fishing along the coast and in the fur trade inland. A few thousand French farmers occupied long, narrow farms along the St. Lawrence River. After the American Revolution, numerous loyalists migrated to the Maritime Provinces and eastern Ontario, developing an agriculture somewhat similar to that in New England; other settlers soon followed.

The Tidewater country   Along the South Atlantic Coast, deep estuaries subdividing a broad coastal plain provided easy access to potential farmlands. Soon planters had laid out sizable plantations, cultivated at first by indentured servants, later by slaves. Crops not readily grown in Britain, notably tobacco, indigo, rice, and, later, cotton, provided valuable exports. Timber and naval stores from the forests provided additional products in world demand. True, the sandy soil soon lost its virgin fertility, but there were extensive new lands to be cleared. In this physical setting developed the Southern planter aristocracy: farmers wealthy enough to own extensive lands and the slaves to work them. In contrast, the penniless Southern pioneer moved inland to the Piedmont or even into the Appalachian Valleys.

The old "West"   Inland from the Tidewater was the more rugged but generally more fertile Piedmont, and westward, beyond the abrupt Blue Ridge, the even more fertile Great Valley. In Pennsylvania these "western" areas were settled by Germans (Pennsylvania Dutch) and Scotch-Irish pioneers, immigrants attracted by almost free land and by the tolerant government of the Penn family. Southward much of the Piedmont was assigned in extensive grants to Southern planters. Some of these grants were subdivided into large estates, others into small farms occupied by small farmers moving westward from the Tidewater. In contrast, the Great Valley and some of the narrower valleys in the southern Appalachians were settled by Germans and Scotch-Irish migrating southwestward along the Great Valley. In such settings developed the traditional pioneer farmer who built a log cabin, killed the forest trees by girdling, and then planted crops amid their stumps. After the American Revolution, some of these peoples advanced rapidly into the southern tributaries of the Ohio Valley, and northward into southern Indiana and Illinois.

Across the Appalachians (Figure 2-7)   In the North the lowlands of the Hudson-Mohawk Valley might appear to offer an ideal land for pioneers, but until after the Revolution most of these lands were unavailable. The best lands in the Hudson Valley were owned in huge estates whose titles went back to Dutch colonial days. Westward the powerful Iroquois occupied the land, and, to complicate matters, some of this land was claimed by both New York and Massachusetts. During the war the power of the Iroquois (allied with the British against American rebels) was destroyed; shortly the titles were assigned to a motley assortment of land companies. Two major groups moved westward there: first, loyalists who settled on lands in eastern Ontario which remained British, and, second, New Englanders. Both of these, in contrast to the Southern pioneers, advanced in groups, clearing the woods and settling in towns, as had been the custom in

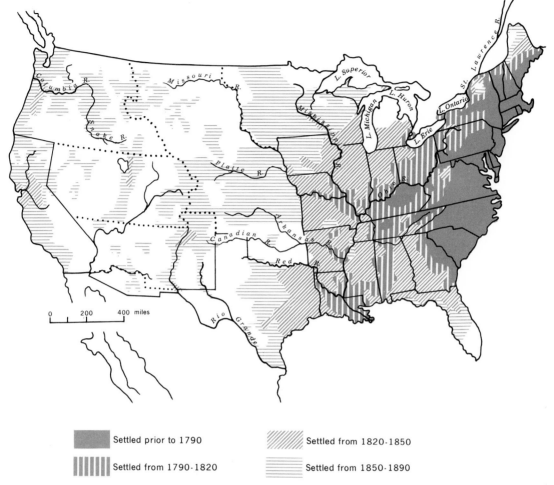

FIGURE 2-7 *A generalized map of the advance of United States settlement. The advance of the frontier shown here reflects mainly agricultural settlement.*

New England. A major road (the Genesee Road) carved out across New York State was used by New Englanders to settle the Western Reserve of northeastern Ohio, an area originally claimed by Connecticut. Several decades later the Erie Canal (completed in 1825) roughly paralleled the Genesee Road and increased the influx of settlers by the northern route.

Meanwhile, Pennsylvanians and Southern groups were pouring into the Ohio Valley by three main routes: (1) over the Cumberland Gap from the Great Valley, (2) over the National Road (now U.S. 40) to the Ohio at Wheeling, and (3) over Forbes Road from Philadelphia to Pittsburgh. Thus by 1800 a great arc of pioneer lands was occupied from eastern Ontario down the Ohio Valley and into central Kentucky and Tennessee.

The Gulf plain Southerners from the Carolinas and Georgia could avoid the Appalachians by following the Coastal Plain southwest and westward. About 1830–1840, as soils in the Atlantic South became leached and infertile, poor farmers and slaveholding planters alike moved into western Georgia, Alabama, and Tennessee, seeking lands to grow more cotton. Navigable rivers, flowing south to the Gulf of Mexico, provided an outlet for the cotton harvest. After first settlement, the wealthier planters bought many of the better farmlands, building impressive homesteads while the "poor white" group raised corn, cattle, hogs, and some cotton on the poorer lands. The large plantations flourished especially on the dark, limey soils of the Black Belt of Alabama and Mississippi and on alluvial strips adjoining the Mississippi and other rivers. The westward movement continued across the Mississippi, and before the Civil War a railroad was extended to the river at Vicksburg. In Louisiana some of the plantations were established a half century before the land was purchased by the United States (1803). In eastern Texas some settlers moved in overland from the Old South; others came by sea via the Gulf Coast.

The rectilinear survey   The pattern of pioneer settlement was greatly influenced by a new survey system. In the Atlantic colonies lands had been sold largely in terms of distance and directions from landmarks such as streams, bays, boulders, and large trees. Property boundaries were irregular; overlapping titles were common. To overcome this difficulty, in 1785 Congress introduced a new system of land surveying which, with some later modifications, determined the broad patterns of most land titles north of the Ohio, west of the Mississippi, and in Alabama and Mississippi. Starting from a parallel of latitude as a base line and from a principal meridian, surveyors divided the land into square townships, each 6 miles on a side. Each township was further divided into 36 sections, each 1 mile square (640 acres). The price of the land was generally small, $1 or $2 an acre, although higher bids were accepted by the land offices for the preferred lands. An understanding of this system will explain the rectangular road and field patterns and the regular town spac-

ings in much of the United States. A similar system was used in western Canada.

Like so many schemes of this kind, this plan did not work perfectly: the surveyors were not always accurate; because of streams, lakes, and hills, the section lines often proved to be awkward property boundaries. But in the more level areas local roads generally followed the section lines, and the survey townships[5] became the initial local units of government, responsible for schools and the upkeep of local roads. Each township had its hamlet; a cluster of nine or more townships made up a county, in the approximate center of which was the county seat. Some county seats, better located than others in relation to through routes, grew into cities of more than local importance.

The wooded Midwest   The gently rolling or flattish lands of the Midwest proved ideal for a checkerboard layout of fields, lots, and roads. Most of the area was settled after the Indians had been moved westward, and farmsteads were evenly spread over the land rather than clustered in towns for defense. In contrast to the irregular roads of the Appalachian Plateau and the Ohio Valley, this land of straight roads and large rectangular fields was ideally suited for the mechanized agriculture that later developed. The soils offered some problems: for example, much of northern Indiana and adjacent Michigan and Ohio was swamp which had to be drained by ditch or tile before cultivation. Transportation to Eastern or Southern markets was another problem since the fertile loam soil areas commonly had boggy mud roads. Streams were used to float much farm produce southward to the Ohio and Mississippi; later canals were built to con-

---

[5] The *survey* or *congressional* townships are easily identified on topographic maps and are still used in describing land titles. The present units of local rural government, which may differ from the survey townships, are called *civil townships*.

nect these rivers with the Great Lakes. During the mid-nineteenth century the railroad net connected the farmer to world markets, the cost of freight diminished, and the prices received by the farmer rose accordingly. Although the farmer had many problems with the fluctuations of farm prices and with the weather, his primitive pioneer existence had ended; soon his manner of living and extensive use of farm machinery dazzled the land-hungry peasants in Europe.

Within a decade after first settlement, the Midwestern farmer required manufactured goods. His economy was not based on crude handmade tools (although he used these until better became available); he preferred to buy tools and other manufactures and specialize in his farming. He sold his produce to merchants instead of rafting his goods to New Orleans, as the first settlers had done. City life developed quickly, and by 1820 Cincinnati, for example, was not only packing pork and milling flour but also manufacturing whiskey, furniture, clothing, pottery, cotton cloth, and steamboats.

CONCLUSIONS AND SELECTED REFERENCES

As Chapter 3 is a continuation of this chapter, concluding materials begin on page 54.

CHAPTER 3

THE LANDS AND THE SETTLERS: THE WEST

The early explorers thought of Anglo-America as a land of boundless forest, except for small Indian clearings (Indian old fields). Within a century reports of extensive grasslands changed the picture, but the significance of these was not realized until much later. Early travelers followed forest-bordered rivers, and the first settlers in the grassland areas sought these well-wooded sites. Small grassy areas were welcomed as natural pastures, but extensive grasslands, requiring new tools and new techniques, were shunned.

The historian Daniel Boorstin[1] points out "the vagueness of the

[1] *The Americans: The National Experience*, Random House, New York, 1965, pp. 221-274.

LAND RELIEF of most of the populous parts of Anglo-America. (USDA photograph.)

land" in the minds of American settlers moving westward. Much of the land, Boorstin asserts, was discovered and explored during the process of settlement. Myths developed which exaggerated its resources, while other myths, such as that of the Great American Desert, stressed its terrors. Certainly the Western lands were different from anything previously experienced by people brought up in the culture and environment of northwestern Europe. Serviced by army units, land surveys, land offices, and government-financed railways, the half century 1840 to 1890 (about a decade or two later in Canada) in which settlers advanced into the West represents a migration rarely matched in human history in numbers, daring, and accomplishment.

THE PRAIRIES AND STEPPES

The vegetation map (Figure 2-3) of Anglo-America suggests an oversimple climatic explanation of the grasslands. Adjoining the forest was the relatively humid prairie, originally a land of lush grasses, about a yard high in summer. Westward the tall grass changed to the short grass (steppe) as the rainfall lessened, and the indigenous vegetation consisted of moderately high grasses mixed with dwarf grass, the latter becoming more important as the soil moisture decreased. An impressive amount of evidence has accumulated that this distribution of plant types was in part a result of human interference. For example, the prairie areas of central Illinois are humid enough to support trees; indeed, some steppe areas seem suited for prairie or even forest vegetation. Among the suggestions advanced to explain the prevalence of grass were the grazing habits of bison and the spread of grass fires, set both by lightning and by Indians. It has been further suggested that windswept fire spread more easily on the flatter plains while the wooded wind-sheltered valleys were relatively protected from it. Whatever the cause, the grasslands were interspersed by long fingers of woodlands in alluvial valleys.

Soil and Vegetation (Figure 2-6)

The grassland soils include three major soil groups: today called the prairie soils, the chernozems (black earths), and the chestnut-brown soils. In contrast to the acid soils of the woodlands, these soils range from slightly acid to strongly alkaline. The dark *prairie soils,* almost neutral and with a fine crumb structure, almost coincide with the moister part of the tall grasslands. Humid enough for a variety of crops and high in fertility, they are excellent farm soils once their tough natural sod has been broken. The *chernozems,* found on the border between the prairie and the steppe, are blackish when freshly plowed, a color attributed to humus from decomposed grass roots. These fertile soils, with their ability to accumulate lime and their excellent structure, are ideal farming soils, provided the rainfall is adequate for a good crop. Westward on the short grassland, the *chestnut-brown soils* are similar to the chernozems but lighter in color because of the lower organic content in rain-deficient areas. These also are good soils, provided enough moisture can be furnished either by irrigation or dry-farming techniques.

Animals

The tall grasses of the prairie and the mixed medium and short grasses to the west (so much more luxuriant than the present pastures there) once supported a huge animal population. Great herds of shaggy-headed bison ranged the entire area and even eastward as far as central Pennsylvania, following ancient trails which led to natural pastures, water holes, and salt licks. Other herbivorous animals were also plentiful: the pronghorn antelope, jackrabbits, squirrels, and prairie dogs. Feeding on these were the coyote and the wolf. Finally there were and are the pests, such as the Rocky Mountain locust, which at intervals erupt well into the prairie area.

Indians

The prairie area was occupied by agricultural Indians, some related in language and other ways to the Eastern Woodland Indians. The Prairie Indians hunted bison but also farmed and traded their tobacco and maize with the Indians of the Plains. These latter were warlike hunters who occupied the short grasslands, the Rockies, and parts of the arid intermountain plateaus and basins. They depended on bison flesh for food, and bison skins to make clothing and covers for their portable tepees. Buffalo chips (dried bison manure) warmed the tepees. In the seventeenth century, Plains Indian life had been revolutionized by the acquisition of

THE SOD HOUSE, shown here in Custer County, central Nebraska, about 1890, was the grassland settler's way of getting shelter with the minimum amount of wood. (USDA photograph.)

the horse, derived from Spanish horses from Mexico. This gave the tribes greater mobility, increasing their ability both to hunt bison and to raid intruding settlers.

New Problems in the Grasslands

The scattered prairies in the forested Midwest were welcomed: They offered good pasture and when plowed provided unusually fertile soil. In Illinois early pioneers sought farmsteads which included both woodland and prairie; fortunately such were available because forested lands commonly bordered the streams. Further west the prairie dominated, and the settler needed new techniques and new tools: The little available timber was inadequate for log cabins, fuel,[2] and rail fences; the virgin deep-rooted sod was not easily broken by a team and cast-

iron plow. Stone to pave the roads or wood to make plank roads was scarce; consequently prairie roads alternated between deep mud and dust. Streams were distant, and machinery to dig deep wells was not available at first. Freight to market was so expensive that it took 4 bushels of Illinois grain to yield cash equal to that received for 1 bushel by eastern Pennsylvania farmers.

About 1840 the prairie soils of Illinois, Iowa, and adjacent states became worth exploiting. Local prices of grain rose when the railroad net arrived. The new steel plows broke the sod with ease; the reaper and other tools facilitated harvesting, enabling the farmer to handle more acres with no additional hours of labor. Experience showed that after the sod had been broken, the rich prairie soils could be cultivated more easily than woodland soils, and the freedom from stones, sticks, and stumps

[2] "Buffalo chips" served as fuel; sod houses reduced the need for lumber among early pioneers on the Western prairie.

facilitated the use of machinery. Finally the trains which collected the grain and animals returned with fuel, lumber, and manufactures from the East; later, cattle from the Western Plains were shipped in by rail for fattening.

The cattlemen   Many early pioneer farmers were cattlemen at first, driving or shipping surplus animals eastward while they were clearing their lands for large-scale tillage. About 1850 a new breed of cattlemen discovered the interior grasslands, especially those of Texas. Several decades of conflict between these cattlemen and pioneer farmers started after the Civil War, the struggle being most severe on the prairies and steppes along the advancing rail lines (Figure 3-1). In 1865 mass cattle drives started northward because the Texan herds had increased rapidly during the Civil War years when Eastern markets were inaccessible. The cattlemen aimed to reach the railroad, and the terminals of the cattle trails changed as the railroads advanced westward. A decade later grazing lands were increased as cattlemen advanced northward east of the Rockies, occupying most of the Plains by 1880. Soon a conflict for the use of the open range arose between the cattlemen and the sheepherders who, starting from California, had expanded eastward to the Plains.

At first the rancher considered the range free while the farmer occupied his quarter section more intensively and struggled to keep out intruding cattle. Wooden fencing was expensive on the grasslands but the invention of the cheaper barbed wire (1874) led to the end of the open range. After a decade or more of struggle, the Western grasslands were fenced. Later farming, by either irrigation or dry-farming techniques, provided some fodder for the livestock. The tough Texas Longhorns were replaced by Herefords. On the margins of cultivation, the fenced ranch (commonly including some cultivated land) replaced the open range.

The problems encountered on the prairies were accentuated on the steppes of the Plains. There is no sharp boundary where the Plains begin. The rolling farmlands of the Midwest slope up westward, and annual rainfall gradually lessens. Kansas, for example, with over 40 inches of rainfall in the southeast, has less than 20 inches at the Colorado border. The long grass of the prairie gave way to short grass; streams suitable for boats or at least canoes were replaced by intermittent streams whose sparse waters (if any) spread over broad gravelly channels. The soils are alkaline soils, and although the little leached, semi-arid soils are fertile, their water supply often proves inadequate for profitable yields.

Innovation and settlement   Several innovations were needed to exploit this semi-arid land; most were introduced in the Plains about 1880, a period of above-average rainfall. Barbed wire enabled the rancher to regulate the grazing and breeding of his herds. Well-drilling machinery made deep wells economically feasible, and the variable-blade windmill used the strong winds to pump water to the surface. Hard wheats, which not only yielded a superior bread flour but withstood shipment and storage better than the soft wheats, were introduced because they flourished well in semi-arid environments. Hard wheats required a new type of flour mill—using rollers instead of grindstones—and such mills were introduced from Hungary. The huge wheat fields required larger machinery to plow the soil, and harvest, thresh, and bail the crop cheaply, and Midwestern factories supplied it. In the drier areas, a new technique, known as *dry farming,* used since the 1880s, operated by using two years' rain to grow one crop and cultivation methods designed to conserve soil moisture.

These new techniques required access to the industrialized Great Lakes area and the East for supplies, machinery, and mar-

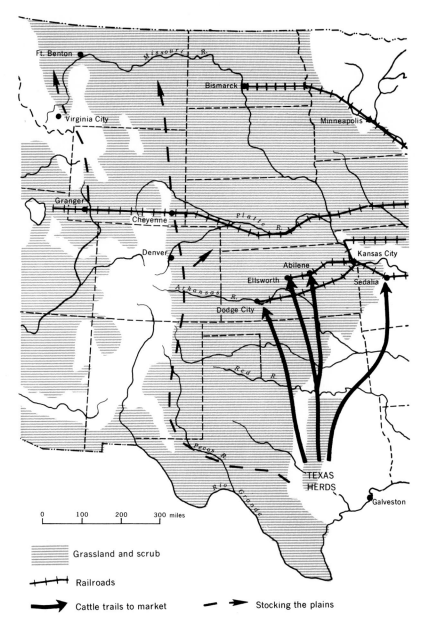

FIGURE 3-1   *The range cattle industry was advancing northward and westward from 1850 to about 1880, as suggested by the arrows. The invention of barbed wire led to the end of the open range, so that today few Western ranches are unfenced.*

kets; such access was facilitated by railroads. The first transcontinental railroad (the Union Pacific) reached the Pacific in 1869. Like many other Western lines, the Union Pacific was heavily subsidized by government loans and land grants (usually free right-of-way and alternate sections of land in a broad zone parallel to the track). Thus the railroads had good reasons to encourage settlement, both to get more freight and to sell land.[3] Even today many Western railroads own lands of little agricultural value

[3] The railroads at first received low prices for their land since adjacent lands were available for $1.25 an acre from the federal government.

THIS WAS A RICH GRASSLAND in west Texas in 1903. Compare it with the same area (opposite page) 40 years later. (USDA photograph.)

which contain valuable minerals—especially petroleum and natural gas.

The Prairie Provinces The Canadian prairies were more favored by nature than the neighboring American Plains. The grass-lands which occupy the southern third of the Prairie Provinces have equally fertile soils and, because of lower evaporation, more humid conditions than the American Plains. They were, however, less accessible to pioneers and farther from adequate markets. The Canadian East did not compare with the American East as a market for flour, and European markets were some-what more distant by the usual routes (though shorter via the relatively undepend-able Hudson Bay route). Most significant, a 500-mile barren stretch of the Canadian Shield separated the Canadian prairies from well-settled eastern Ontario, whereas the American prairies adjoined settled areas to the east and southeast. The first farmers in the Canadian area arrived via Hudson Bay; others came via the Red River Valley through the United States. Finally in the 1880s the Canadian Pacific Railroad pro-vided direct connections to St. Lawrence ports. The resulting settlement, more or-derly than in the United States, provided larger farms, many devoted to mixed farm-ing in the moister area, others devoted primarily to grain. In semi-arid southern Saskatchewan and Alberta, ranches were established; later irrigation farming was added. But markets and transport costs re-mained a problem; it is twice as far from Peace River wheat fields to Winnipeg as from Denver to Kansas City and nearly twice as far from Edmonton to Montreal as from Minneapolis to New York. The west-ern edge of the Canadian spring wheat belt is further west than Los Angeles!

DESERT SHRUBLANDS

The grass does not end suddenly at the Rockies—indeed there are scattered grass-lands west of the Rockies and large areas of desert shrub east of the Rockies, notably in central and southern Texas—but roughly the Rockies represent the boundary between extensive grassy turf and woody vegetation consisting of stunted bushes and trees ad-justed to semi-arid or arid climates. In these Western areas and especially in the South-west, the vegetation patterns are patchy; often lightly wooded uplands, desert shrub

OVERGRAZING CONVERTED THE RICH TURF into bunch grass and the mesquite tree, almost valueless for grazing, spread like an orchard over the land. (USDA photograph.)

lowlands, and almost barren areas appear within the range of the eye. The plants are xerophytic (adjusted to drought) and able to take full advantage of rare rains.

North of about 37°, except in California, the growing season is less than 160 days, and winter is severe enough to keep a snow cover for at least a month. In the Southwest from Texas almost to the Pacific, mild winters are followed by scorching summers with strong winds possible at all seasons. Variations in altitude, exposure to the sun and wind, and distance inland from the Pacific create a great variety of local climates. Thus coolness and moisture characterize the mountaintops and high plateaus; scorching winds the open basins, coolness the shady canyon, and exceptionally mild weather the narrow strip along the Pacific Coast.

Water scarcity is the overriding consideration. Early travelers went from water hole to water hole. Much of the water originated outside this arid area, the surplus from the wooded mountains filling the Colorado, Gila, Rio Grande, and Pecos before it flowed into areas where evaporation greatly exceeded precipitation. The prevailing vegetation—be it mesquite, cactus, greasewood, creosote bush, sagebrush, or evergreens—reflected the humidity of the subsoil.

Soils

Soil acidity is no problem for settlers in this region of alkali soils. Many of the soils are valueless for other reasons: they may be too coarse, the wind blows away the fine sands and silt; they may be too shallow—winds, with a lack of plant roots to hold the soil in place, denude the bedrock; finally soils lack adequate humus because there is not enough plant debris to create it. This proved to be no land for the farm settler who could not adjust his moist-land tillage to new conditions.

Animals

Compared with the Plains, this area is poor in animals; rabbits, deer, antelope, mountain sheep, snakes, and lizards were widespread and still remain in smaller numbers.

Indians

Two contrasting types of Indians lived in the arid West. Most advanced were the sedentary Pueblo Indians who built permanent villages of adobe, wood, and rock—usually

THE INDIAN DEVELOPED an impressive culture in a poor grassland, as Pueblo Bonito, the largest of United States prehistoric ruins, shows. When Europe was emerging from the Dark Ages, this 800-room town, now 100 miles northwest of Albuquerque, housed 1,200 people. (New Mexico Department of Development.)

on defensible hilltops, or in the mouths of caves, as in Mesa Verde. These peoples cultivated corn, beans, and other foods and in the extreme southwest, cotton. They were skilled weavers, potters, and masons. In addition to the dog, the domestic animal common to all Indian tribes, these farmers had domesticated turkeys. They hunted for rabbits and antelopes, and collected wild nuts, but primarily they were peaceful farmers. They traded and sometimes fought with nomadic hunters (for example, the Navajos), whose tribes lived in the same general areas. The life of the Navajos was greatly altered when they obtained horses and sheep from the Spanish.

In the northern part of the desert shrub lands and in the generally wooded Rockies, the Indians, culturally related to the Plains tribes, were resourceful hunters who often cooperated with the beaver trappers (called Mountain Men). The latter followed the Rocky Mountain trails and, after the beaver were exhausted, served as guides for pioneers en route to Oregon or California.

Many of the Indians of Nevada, Utah, and Southern California were primitive hunters and seed gatherers. In contrast to later white settlers, the Indians of Southern California did little to improve the arid and semi-arid lands which since have become among the most valuable pieces of real estate in the world. Indeed these Indians were among the most primitive people in North America, being ignorant of agriculture and depending mainly on acorns and seeds supplemented by whatever small game they could trap. Along the Coast, rafts (they were ignorant of boats and canoes) were used to catch seafood.

The Miner's Place in Western Settlement

Until 1849 the arid and semi-arid West was a wasteland to be crossed en route to Oregon, the furs of the Rockies, and the Pacific Coast, or coastal California. The scattered settlement of most of this shrubland can be attributed to the prospectors who in two decades scanned most of the area (Figure 3-2). Elsewhere in Anglo-America mining had provided only minor and spasmodic impulses to settlement.

True, the first settlers kept their eyes open for gold but found little in the East. Iron

THE GHOST TOWN, *symbol of a mining settlement whose ores became exhausted or unprofitable to exploit, is widespread in the West. This is Cabezon, New Mexico, about 65 miles west of Santa Fe.* (New Mexico Department of Development.)

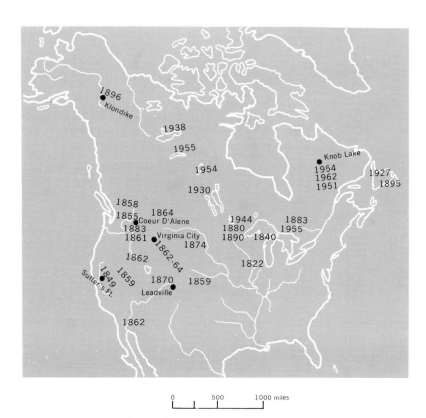

FIGURE 3-2   *Selected dates of important ore discoveries in Anglo-America. In contrast to the advance of the agricultural frontier, mining development jumped around in time and space. The map shows only a fraction of the mining strikes and a mere sampling of the names of important mining camps.*

ore in quantities sufficing for small colonial furnaces was widely available, and because cheap wood was everywhere available for fuel, coal had little attraction. Lead, widely used for bullets and brass, was in demand, and lead deposits provided some stimulus to settlement in the middle Mississippi Valley. Lake Superior iron and copper ores were not used until industrial development was well advanced. The mining frontier did not advance steadily as did the farm frontier; it leapfrogged from place to place.

The initial impulse resulted from the discovery of gold in 1848 in central California, near Sacramento. In western Canada the corresponding discovery of gold occurred in 1858 in the Fraser Valley. The metal was found in gravel beds from which it could be separated with a few dollars worth of equipment and very little technical skill. In the following decades prospectors explored the Western states and provinces in search of further mineral wealth; although few prospectors won great wealth, enough did so to encourage continued prospecting.

For a decade or two, mining was carried on by small groups; thereafter it became an activity requiring capital, technology, and elaborate machinery. To continue in operation, mines required sufficient deposits of ore to justify expensive mining equipment, concentrating plants, smelters, and the construction of rail connections. Such elaborate organizations created demands for other activities: the raising of food for the miners, and the manufacture of mining tools and machinery. But mining towns tended to be so ephemeral that ghost towns became common throughout the West. Some founded by miners have remained after nearby mines have closed or become insignificant, for example, Denver and Sacramento.

PACIFIC FORESTS

North of Monterey Bay, California, to Anchorage, Alaska, a lush forest of tall conifers covered the coastal zone, extending inland

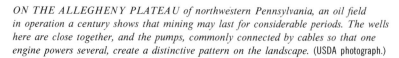

ON THE ALLEGHENY PLATEAU of northwestern Pennsylvania, an oil field in operation a century shows that mining may last for considerable periods. The wells here are close together, and the pumps, commonly connected by cables so that one engine powers several, create a distinctive pattern on the landscape. (USDA photograph.)

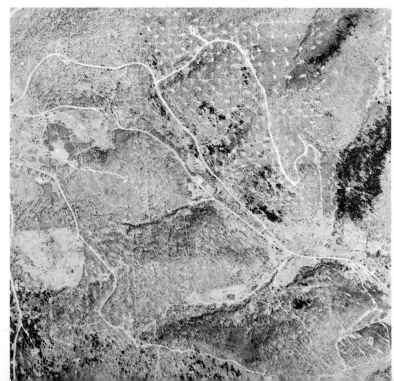

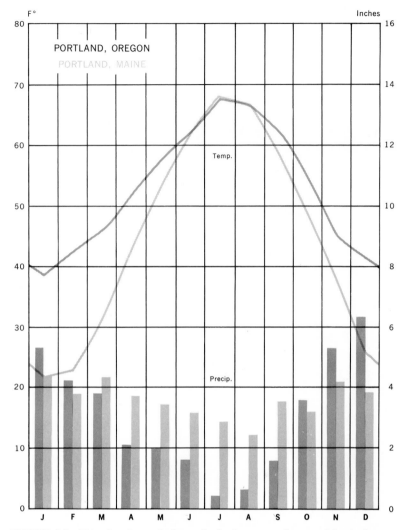

FIGURE 3-3   This climatic graph shows clearly the contrast between Atlantic Coast climates, influenced largely by offshore winds, and Pacific Coast climates, influenced by onshore air masses.

5 to 200 miles. A fraction of the original forests remains to show the varied species: the giant redwoods are dominant in the summer-drought area of central California; Douglas fir, hemlock, and cedar in Oregon, Washington, and southwestern British Columbia; and Sitka spruce farther north. All yield excellent timber. These tall trees benefit from the humid climate, the lack of extreme daily and seasonal weather changes, and the fogs and cloudiness characteristic of the coastal area.

The most amazing thing about this North Pacific coastal region is the mildness of its climate, attributable in part to the prevailing air masses from the Pacific and in part to cool offshore currents (Figure 3-3). Summers range from cool to pleasantly warm: in July Portland averages 67, Seattle 66, Victoria 60, and Juneau 55°F. Winters are mild for the latitude; note these January averages: Portland 39, Seattle 41, Victoria 39, and Juneau 25°F. Rainfall is moderate (30 to 50 inches annually) except in the

THE PACIFIC CONIFEROUS FOREST was used for woodworking long before European settlement, as the totem pole at Ketchikan, Alaska, indicates. (Travel Division, Alaskan Department of Economic Development.)

mountains, but much of it comes in the cool season when evaporation is slow.

Soil

Tillable soils occupied a very small part of the area, mainly in alluvial valleys, and belong mostly to the gray-brown podzolic group characteristic of the Eastern Woodlands.

Indians

The Indian tribes of the North Pacific Coast included many linguistic groups, but almost all were culturally advanced people who made good use of the seafood and timber resources. Their homes were substantial rectangular wooden houses, decorated with totem poles and other wood carvings. The land provided some game and berries, but their major dependence was on the sea. Large dugout canoes, some equipped with sails, searched the estuaries, channels, and open sea for fish, which were eaten either fresh or dried. Farming was not practiced.

The Lumberman and Permanent Settlement

The Pacific forests seem to provide the only clear example of lumbering leading to permanent settlement. Elsewhere lumbering has been transient in its influence or has been a by-product of the clearing of the land for the farmer. In the Pacific area the forest was first cut to supply lumber for California and other points on the Pacific. The industry has continued for more than a century and with the advent of tree farming seems likely to continue indefinitely.

Until less than a century ago, trees were in surplus supply in the Anglo-American woodlands (Figure 3-4). The settler found them useful for housing, fencing, fuel, and even plank roads, but his primary objective was the good soil. The Southern farmer girdled the trees and let them rot; in the North, groups of settlers cut the trees, rolled them together, and destroyed them in huge

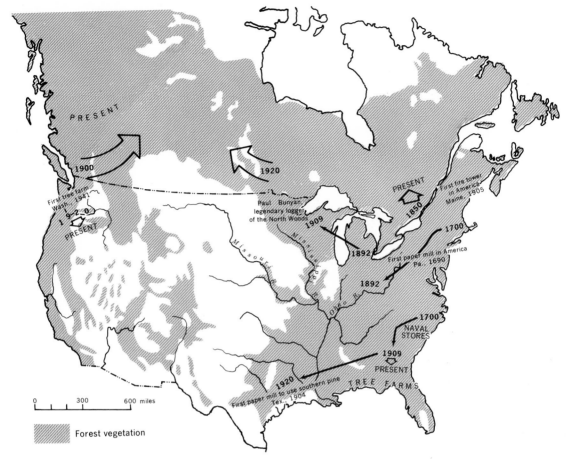

FIGURE 3-4 This map suggests the transient nature of Anglo-American lumbering. It may be stabilized by the widespread adoption of tree farms and by the selective harvesting of government-owned forests.

bonfires. Wood was the major Anglo-American fuel until 1880.

In Canada, lumbermen were advancing north of the agricultural St. Lawrence Lowland in the third quarter of the nineteenth century. In the United States, lumbermen were clearing the Eastern lands too rugged or infertile for farming. In 1875 leading American lumbering centers included Williamsport (Pennsylvania), Indianapolis (Indiana), and Grand Rapids (Michigan). All these cities had become minor lumber handlers by the end of the century as the lumbermen moved north into lands too poor for the corn-hog-beef-cattle type of farming prevalent in the Midwest.

In the Southeastern Coastal Plain, forestry was a colonial industry, providing especially naval stores. Southern pine was considered an inferior timber as long as northern white pine was available. Early in the twentieth century, the Southeast became a leading lumber supplier—a permanent supplier because its forest matures more rapidly since the growing season is longer. Extensive lands worthless for other purposes became available for softwoods on the Coastal Plains and for hardwoods in the Appalachians. But all these lumbering activities (including related manufacturing) employed only a few hundred thousand persons, for, as elsewhere,

THIS SHOWS THE SCARS created by forestry in Skagit County, western Washington. The virgin forest remains in the upper left corner of the photo. Note the lumbering roads and converging skid tracks created by dragging the logs to central loading points. (USDA photograph.)

lumbering alone did little to establish significant permanent settlement.

In the West, lumbering on the wooded mountains early supplied timber for local building, mine props, and fuel. Large-scale lumbering for Eastern markets began after the exhaustion of better-grade softwoods in the Great Lakes states, in other words, within the present century. Near the drier western areas much forest land has been placed in national forests and parks, partly to provide recreation lands and partly to protect essential water supplies. In the Pacific Northwest (producing over half of all United States lumber since 1949) the forest lands, too rugged or infertile for other uses, are being replanted with trees.

In Canada, forests have been a major national asset. Pulp and paper manufacturing have continued to be the largest single manufacturing industry, and forest products have provided several leading exports. Lumbering has opened up extensive areas; relatively few workers, however, harvest the timber and most lumber towns (or camps) remain small. There has been greater employment in the re-lated industries concentrated mainly in cities founded to serve other purposes. The lumber frontier, still advancing northward in interior Canada, has proved important in opening up new lands in Newfoundland, New Brunswick, and especially British Columbia.

CONCLUSIONS

It has been argued by Frederick Jackson Turner and others that the best free land had been occupied by 1890 and that with this closing of the frontier the course of American development changed. Since 1890 much more land has been homesteaded than before that date. Much of the land occupied after 1890 was semi-arid land, usable only because dry-farming and irrigation techniques had been developed (Figure 3-5). Perhaps more significant than the actual filling up of the land has been the change in the nature of pioneering. As the frontier moved westward out of the Eastern Woodlands, the pioneer equipped only with an axe, a rifle, some crude agricultural implements, a wagon, and some

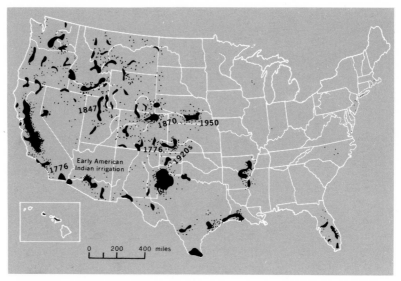

FIGURE 3-5 *Although a few irrigation settlements developed earlier, as suggested by the dates on the map, the bulk of the irrigated lands have been made productive since 1890.*

cattle had little chance of success. In the twentieth century more capital, better tools, and more agricultural know-how have been available. Pioneering has become more experimentation in new techniques and less an advance into little-known areas. This new type of pioneering is still going on—in the deserts, on the slopes, on lands which proved unprofitable as previously used. Thus those who have converted abandoned Southern croplands into managed forests, who have drained the Everglades marshes and made vegetable gardens, who have built artificial lakes in hill country and sold lakeshore sites for summer homes, are all modern pioneers.

Much of the land in the interior West is still in the public domain; the shortage is not of land but of usable land. There is even more unused land in central and northern Canada and Alaska. Many competent observers believe these subarctic and arctic areas of long, bitter winters, infertile soils, stunted trees, or marshy arctic pastures will remain unused except where minerals are discovered. Perhaps new techniques, yet unforeseen, may advance the frontier northward as well as lead to new advances, for example, into Appalachian areas which are now on the economic toboggan. New techniques may create needed lands for our growing populations or intensify production on the long settled lands. The frontiers of increased production are far from closed!

SELECTED REFERENCES

BAKELESS, JOHN: *The Eyes of Discovery, The Pageant of North America as Seen by the First Explorers* (paperback), Dover, New York, 1961.

BILLINGTON, R. A.: *Westward Expansion*, Macmillan, New York, 1949, 1960, 1967. An interesting account of settlement by a historian who is well aware of the environmental background of American history. For another point of view, see Thomas D. Clark, *Frontiers in America*, Scribner, New York, 1959. Both volumes have detailed bibliographies.

BREBNER, J. D.: *Canada*, University of Michigan Press, Ann Arbor, 1960.

BROWN, R. H.: *Historical Geography of the United States*, Harcourt, Brace & World, New York,

1948. A useful book weakened by the author's practice of discussing each area for only a limited period.

CHAMBERS, J. W. et al. (eds.): *Philips Historical Atlas of Canada,* Moyer Division, Vilas Industries, Toronto, 1966.

DRIVER, HAROLD E.: *Indians of North America,* University of Chicago Press, Chicago, 1961. A good summary by topics with excellent maps. For a discussion of typical tribes in each region, see Robert F. Spencer, and Jesse D. Jennings et al., *The Native Americans,* Harper & Row, New York, 1965. Pamphlets published by the Bureau of Indian Affairs (U.S. Government Printing Office, 1965 and 1966) give an excellent nontechnical summary of Indian life. They are entitled, for example, *Indians of the Dakotas.* Other pamphlets deal with the Central Plains, the Great Lakes area, North Carolina, the Gulf Coast states, Oklahoma, New Mexico, Arizona, the Lower Plateau, California, the Northwest, and Alaska.

KERR, D. G. G.: *An Historical Atlas of Canada,* Nelson, Toronto, 1960.

PAULLIN, C. O.: *Atlas of the Historical Geography of the United States,* American Geographical Society, New York, 1932. *American History*

Atlas, Hammond, Maplewood, N.J., a low-priced paperback atlas, has much valuable material partly from the Paullin atlas (available only in libraries).

SAUER, CARL ORTWIN: *Land and Life,* University of California Press, Berkeley, 1967. A collection of articles, many relevant to this chapter, written by a leader in American geographic thought.

U.S. BUREAU OF THE CENSUS: *Historical Statistics of the United States: Colonial Times to 1957,* Washington, 1960. Sections A, C, J, K, L, M, and T are especially relevant to this chapter. Equivalent Canadian data are in M. C. Urquhart and K. A. H. Buckley (eds.), *Historical Statistics of Canada,* Macmillan, Toronto, 1965.

U.S. DEPARTMENT OF AGRICULTURE: *Atlas of American Agriculture: Physical Basis,* Washington, 1936. This large atlas is especially detailed on climate and soil. The numerous soil surveys on individual counties are much more detailed and broader in scope. See also the various volumes of Yearbook of Agriculture (annual), Washington. The volumes on *Climate and Man:* 1941, especially pp. 157–235; on *Soil:* 1957; and on *Land:* 1958 are particularly relevant.

CHAPTER 4

CHANGING WAYS OF LIVING; 1860-1965

FIGURE 4-1 *The century 1860–1960 was dominated by the rise of cities. Today United States population and production are concentrated in and close to the Standard Metropolitan Statistical Areas (SMSAs). Each SMSA includes a central city of at least 50,000, the county in which the community is included, and the surrounding counties (if any) which are largely urbanized and closely connected with the core community. The boundaries of the SMSAs are changed (usually enlarged) every few years by the census.*

The preceding chapter stressed how several kinds of resource users entered Indian Anglo-America, advanced westward from Atlantic ports, each group exploring the continent in terms of furs, pastures, soils, timbers, or minerals. To make these resources accessible, routes were constructed, suitable lands were developed, and towns performed numerous functions which aided resource users in marketing their products. During the first 250 years after the Atlantic settlement, the economy stressed food and raw materials, and the prosperity of towns and cities seemed to be based on their ability to serve rural hinterlands.

Our ancestors required food, clothing, shelter, government, amusement, professional services, and intellectual, artistic, and religious stimulation as do modern Anglo-Americans. But the satisfaction of each of these needs required different proportions of their total time and income than today, and many of their needs were satisfied in different ways. In the colonial period, for example, many of the tasks now per-

STANDARD METROPOLITAN STATISTICAL AREAS

AREAS DEFINED BY U.S. BUREAU OF THE BUDGET TO MARCH 1967

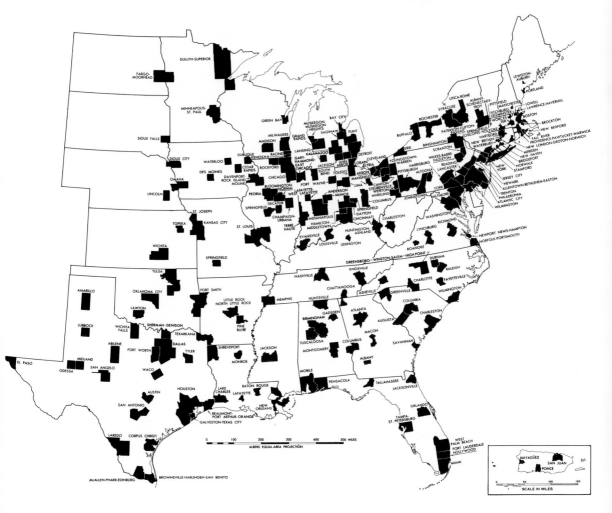

formed by city workers were performed by the farmer. He raised much of his own food and manufactured many of his implements; his wife spun thread from locally raised wool, wove the cloth, and tailored it into clothing. The farmer hauled his produce to market and sold or bartered it in the marketplace. Services rendered today by physicians, lawyers, architects, entertainers, and other specialists were performed —perhaps rather amateurishly—by the farmer and his neighbors.

Later in the colonial period, rural inhabitants in long-settled areas took advantage of specialized services available in the seaport towns, but on the frontier the almost self-sufficient economy continued into the nineteenth century. Manufacturing had already been started in many towns, large and small, but the products were mostly simple and turned out on a small scale. Large cities were few so that in 1820 only seven Anglo-American cities had populations exceeding 20,000. Mostly these were commercial cities, exporting the produce of their

W. S. and C. H. Thompson's Skirt Manufactory

AN AMERICAN SKIRT FACTORY about 1860. The operation is obviously mass production, but the sewing machines used are simple and the power is foot-generated. Clothing was fifth among American manufactures in 1860, being exceeded by flour and meal, cotton goods, lumber, and boots and shoes in the value of its product. In terms of labor employed, clothing was first, employing 42,749 male and 77,875 female workers. (This and the drawing on the next page are from U.S. Centennial Commission, THE UNITED STATES ON THE EVE OF THE CIVIL WAR AS DESCRIBED IN THE 1860 CENSUS, U.S. Government Printing Office, 1963.)

hinterlands and importing goods not locally produced.

The rapid progress of industry in the nineteenth century led to better agricultural implements with which the farmer produced more both per acre and per hour of labor. Likewise better tools improved the productivity of the trapper, the rancher, the lumberman, and the miner. For example, city-developed technologies made it possible to exploit ores too poor in quality to be worked by primitive methods. City-made vehicles carried raw materials more cheaply to markets, and this enabled the raw-material producer to compete in more distant markets. Thus raw materials became available to the world's cities and at the same time raw-material producers demanded and could afford to pay for more urban goods and services.

Increased productivity per person enabled each citizen to multiply his consumption. This increased demand occurred mainly in tools, luxury goods, a wide range of consumer goods (telephones, automobiles, refrigerators, radios), and a long list of professional services (medical, educational, recreational, cosmetic, scientific, commercial); all goods and services produced in cities.

THE RISE OF THE CITY

This historical discussion is pertinent to the regional geography of Anglo-America because its basic settlement patterns were laid out when raw materials were the mainstay of the economy. Since then Anglo-Americans have been remaking their economy along more urban lines but almost always building on settlement patterns established to meet the needs of the earlier economies. Some early settlements have stagnated or declined, but each settlement group has fought hard to maintain the value of its property, to find new activities to replace

Wheeler's Patent Reaper at Work

AGRICULTURAL IMPLEMENTS *was twenty-third among American manufacturing* *industries in 1860. Its 14,814 workers supplied 2,423,895 farmers with simple* *machinery such as Wheeler's patent reaper shown here.* By this time steel implements had largely replaced the wooden and iron-tipped implements common around 1800.

declining activities, and many of them have succeeded in doing so. Indeed cities, which are generating mammoth land values per acre, have been expanding into and displacing productive orange groves in California, Corn Belt farms in the Midwest, and cotton fields in Texas. The city, once the servant of the food and raw-material producer, has become the master. In 1931 Mark Jefferson, an outstanding American geographer, wrote "Cities do not grow up of themselves. Countrysides set them up to do tasks that must be performed in central places." This is still true but the "countrysides" stimulating the growth of most Anglo-American cities are no longer rural; today the great majority of city customers live within the same city, in its suburbs, or in other cities. The business of large metropolitan areas such as New York, Chicago, Toronto, or Los Angeles consists largely of performing services for other residents of the metropolitan area. This urban dominance is relatively new: in the United States the urban population first exceeded the rural population in 1920, in Canada in 1931.

Anglo-Americans rarely appreciate how dominant the city has become in the economy today. Traveling from coast to coast, one traverses woodlands, cornfields, pastures, grasslands, shrublands, and deserts; yet less than one-twelfth of the people in the United States (less than one-ninth in Canada) live on farms and ranches; and in the United States less than one-quarter (one-quarter in Canada) live outside of cities and towns. Indeed many of these rural inhabitants are classified as *rural non-farm;* that is, they work in nearby cities, are retired, or perform other tasks not classified as farming or ranching.

The Anglo-American shift to a largely urban economy started slowly with the rise of American industry in the early nineteenth century. The pace accelerated during and after the Civil War. Agricultural and raw-material industries were outstripped by United States manufacturing in the 1880s, and today play a basic but nevertheless statistically small part in the production of the 1960 gross national product.

The following sections discuss this rural-urban transition for the United States. Since the statistics and dates for particular stages of development are different for Canada and the United States, Canada will be discussed separately.

The United States Economy in 1860

Just before the Civil War, about half the population lived west of the Appalachians. The frontier line extended approximately from San Antonio, Texas, to western Minnesota, with major outlying population centers in California, and smaller settled areas near the north Pacific Coast, in eastern Utah, along the Rio Grande, and at the foot of the Colorado Rockies. Most large-scale industry was concentrated in the northeastern quarter of the country, and the major centers, including Boston, Buffalo, Chicago, St. Louis, Cincinnati, Baltimore, Philadelphia, and New York, enclosed an area which continues today to be central in the *American Commercial-Manufacturing Core*. An open railroad net served this partly industrialized area, but connections westward reached only central Missouri and Iowa; southward connections were limited to a few through lines whose control became major military objectives in 1863–1864. Canals, the Great Lakes, and the Mississippi River system supplemented the railroads. Most of the roads were unpaved and unsuitable for long-distance transport.

As historians stress, the country was divided into regionally conscious areas, a fact that contributed to the Civil War. The Middle Atlantic states and New England emphasized industry, commerce, and the production of perishable or bulky foodstuffs and raw materials for nearby markets. The Midwest was not lacking in industry, but its specialty was the production of food for shipment east and south. The Southeast specialized in cotton and tobacco, while Texas was expanding as a cattle producer. Small towns were widespread in the Northeast, South, Southeast, and Midwest; most

performed political and commercial functions with some resource-based industries, for example, cotton ginning, grist milling, saw milling, tanning, and distilling. The West was relatively isolated but stressed mining, range livestock, food crops, and a few other products for local markets.

For the country as a whole, more than three times as many people were employed on the farm as in manufacturing. The Northeast accounted for 72 percent of industrial employment, the Midwest for only 12 percent, and the South for less than 10 percent. The leading United States industries were cotton goods, lumber, shoes, men's clothing, and iron. Most of these were closely tied to raw materials and were produced for sale to the consumer. The manufacture of tools and machinery was not unknown, but elaborate machines for industrial production were either imported or manufactured, using crude methods by local craftsmen. The system of subcontracting and subassemblies, so characteristic of modern industry, was almost unknown.

The United States: 1860–1920

The Civil War and the further westward expansion of settlement produced great changes in the decades 1860–1880. The military needs of the Civil War and postwar reconstruction encouraged the growth of heavier industry; expansion of the rail net to the Pacific multiplied the demand for iron and steel. As the grasslands were occupied, agricultural machinery became heavier and more complicated. The growth of gold mining supplied new capital, and the mining of other ores produced more industrial raw materials. Immigration, after slackening during the Civil War, brought in over 5 million people in the next two decades, increasing both the labor force and the market for its products.

The 1880s might be termed a pivotal period in American economic history. Indian wars, the bison, and untamed Western

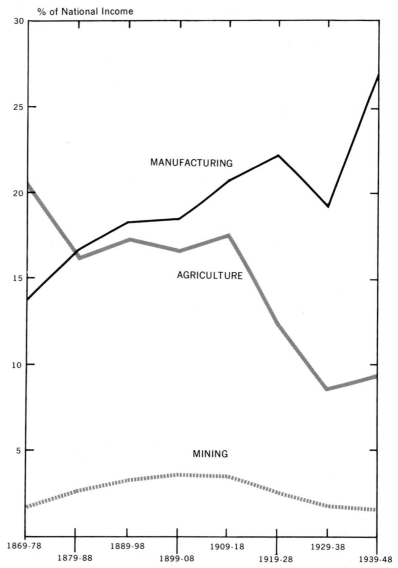

% of National Income

MANUFACTURING

AGRICULTURE

MINING

1869-78   1889-98   1909-18   1929-38
        1879-88   1899-08   1919-28   1939-48

FIGURE 4-2   Changes in selected sources of national income: 1869–1948. Notice that these items never accounted for as much as one-half the national income; services (personal, professional, business, and governmental) have always been a major part of the national income. In recent decades services (except for domestic) have become relatively more important.

herds of semiwild cattle were gone; some sedentary settlers had at least sampled most of the nation's lands. Although some of these changes were more conspicuous than important, four developments which were the culmination of post-Civil War growth deserve emphasis.

First, after 1880, the contribution of man-

ufacturing to the national income every year exceeded that of agriculture. Note on Figure 4-2 that from 1879–1888 to 1909–1918 the proportion of the income derived from manufacturing and agriculture remained about the same. Actually both fields of activity were becoming much more productive, and each stimulated the other. Thus, the intro-

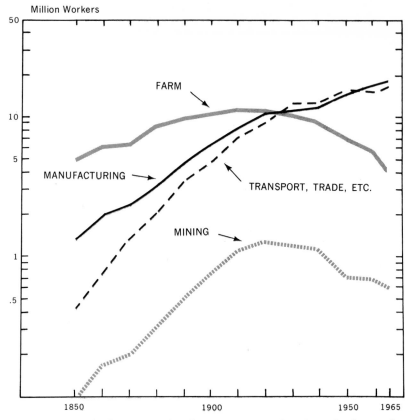

Million Workers

FARM

MANUFACTURING

TRANSPORT, TRADE, ETC.

MINING

1850   1900   1950   1965

FIGURE 4-3 Employment in selected major activities: 1850–1965. The data on this graph and on Figures 4-4 to 4-6 have been plotted on a semi-logarithmic scale so that, despite differences in magnitude, equal slopes on any curve represent equal rates of change.

duction of steam-powered farm machinery in the 1880s and of farm tractors and automobiles two decades later, cut both farm costs and labor requirements and at the same time created automotive industries which demanded more steel. More city workers demanded more food and raw materials; in turn this expanded market enabled the farmer to buy more manufactures. These changes were reflected in the number of workers employed in each category (Figure 4-3).

Second, after 1880, mineral fuels (coal, oil, and natural gas) surpassed wood as sources of power and fuel—in other words, fossil fuels were replacing forest fuels. This change resulted in part from the exhaustion of forests near the market, perhaps even

more from the invention of new engines and furnaces to use fossil fuels.

Third, in the 1880s (and later) the increase in the production of industrial raw materials continued rapidly while agricultural production was increasing at a slower rate. Figures 4-4 and 4-5 show increased production of selected agricultural and non-agricultural commodities. In contrast to many such graphs in which wheat is plotted in bushels, cotton in bales, and pig iron in tons, all the data here have been reduced to long tons. Thus we can note that the tonnage of pig iron nearly caught up with the tonnage of wheat in 1890 and 1900 and exceeded the wheat tonnage after 1900. If we compare each agricultural commodity curve with each nonagricultural commodity curve,

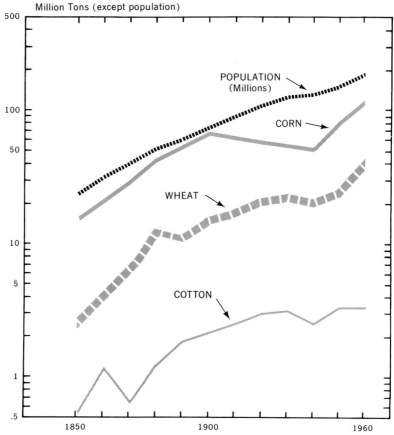

FIGURE 4-4 United States production of three major crops is compared with the growth of the American population. Data are plotted for census years only.

it becomes apparent that nonagricultural production was generally increasing more rapidly.

Fourth, because of these changes urban growth was stimulated more than rural growth, as indicated in Table 4-1.

Why this greater growth in urban production and population? Increases in rural production reflect in part increases in the United States population; more people require more food. To make this comparison easy, the curve of United States population growth has been plotted alongside the curve of potato production in Figure 4-6. Other factors also influence the demand for agricultural commodities. These will be mentioned briefly, but the reader may enjoy investigating each point further: (1) decrease

in the demand for fodder (especially after 1920) as draft animals were replaced by internal-combustion engines; (2) in-

TABLE 4-1 United States Population Growth: Rural, Urban, and Selected Cities (millions)

Year	1880	1900	1920
Rural	36	46	52
Urban	14	30	54
SELECTED CITIES			
New York	1.192	3.347	5.620
Detroit	0.116	0.286	0.994
Chicago	0.503	1.699	2.702
Los Angeles	0.011	0.102	0.576

SOURCE: U.S. Bureau of the Census, *Historical Statistics of the United States: Colonial Times to 1957*, Washington, 1960.

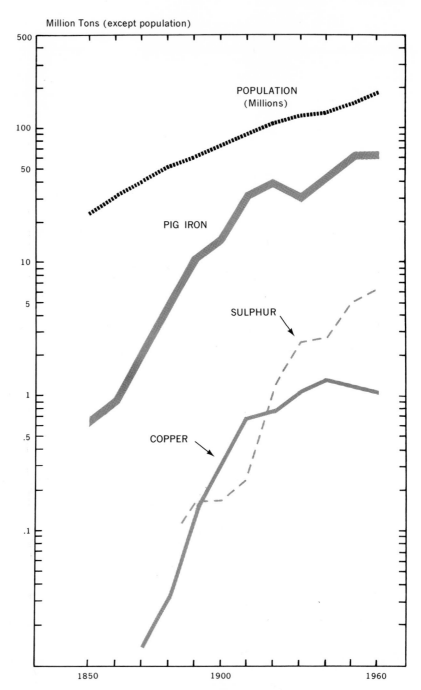

Million Tons (except population)

FIGURE 4-5 *In contrast to the growth of agricultural production shown on Figure 4-4, the growth of industrial raw-material production rises much more rapidly than
the population. The curves of raw-material production are, of course, affected by the
competition of imports.*

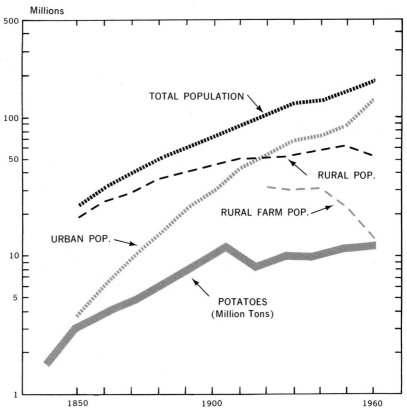

Millions

FIGURE 4-6   *These curves show the relative increase in the urban and rural non-farm population in recent decades. Potatoes are so widely used that it might be assumed that the potato curve would rise with the population since few potatoes are imported or exported. Perhaps the failure of potatoes to keep up with the population reflects the popularity of low-calorie diets, the lower-calorie requirements because of the smaller amount of muscular labor, or the use of substitutes such as sweet potatoes and rice.*

creases and decreases in the exports of meat, wheat, and cotton; (3) adoption of lower-calorie diets with a consequent lower per capita demand for food. Per capita rural production tends to be relatively steady, but the demands for urban-produced manufactures and services increase with rising living standards and with each new product and service offered on the market.

The United States about 1920

The 1920 census reported that, for the first time, over half of the United States population was urban. This census also used a new category, *rural non-farm* which showed that many rural people were not engaged in what were ordinarily thought of as rural activities (see Table 4-2).

Farm population equaled about half the population living in cities and small towns. Even more significant, 1929 national income estimates showed that agriculture contributed only about one-eighth of the national income, a fraction that decreased each decade thereafter.

The urban population occupied surprisingly little land—only about one-tenth of one percent of the acreage in 1920. Population density for the United States averaged 35.6 per square mile for the entire country but in cities ranged from 1,000 to 25,000 per square mile. Transportation facilities occupied twice as much land as cities and rural lands used by city dwellers for recreation probably totaled more. Thus the 1920 urbanized economy concentrated on a very small part of the nation's land.

The American city of 1920, although it was the parent of the city of the 1960s, had some distinctive characteristics. It was much more compact, and its people were more dependent on public transportation, especially the streetcar, and, in the larger cities, the subway, elevated railroad, and commuter railroad services. The major shopping and business section was "downtown" (the Central Business District or CBD), but for food and small purchases there were many local stores, mostly small. Factories were located close to the city along the railroads. Public transportation brought the majority of the workers to their jobs. Whether on pleasure or business, people commonly walked as much as a mile or two to their destinations. Especially in metropolitan areas, executives and professional people lived in small nearby towns and commuted by train to work. Most Americans traveled more than 20 miles from home only on annual vacations. Automobiles had become fairly common in farm areas and among the wealthier city people (in 1920 there was one passenger automobile for every 13 people, whereas in 1915 there had

been only one for every 40). Although the city dominated America, its full suburban expansion awaited the common ownership of the automobile.

Adjustments were also taking place in the rural areas. In 1920 for the first time, fewer farm workers had been counted than in the previous census. This resulted not from a decline in farm production but rather from an increase in output per worker, resulting in part from mechanization and improved farm techniques. Consequently a considerable out-migration of younger workers was occurring in even the prosperous farm districts: some migrating to nearby cities, others moving to newer parts of the country. For example, an out-migration started in most of the Southeastern and Plains states in or before the decade 1910–1920. At the same time many migrated to the more urbanized areas of the Midwest and Northeast, as well as to Florida, Texas, and the Pacific states. With higher per capita farm production, farm living standards improved. Better roads and vehicles meant less rural isolation, higher output per worker meant more luxuries such as running water, electricity, and telephones. In addition, the automobile made it possible for some farmers (or members of their families) to work at least part of the time in nearby cities.

Rapid growth in the 1920s brought about a host of problems. Most American cities, especially in the East, had been designed to serve modest populations, employing slow-moving vehicles. Urban water supplies and arrangements for the disposal of sewage and industrial wastes were inadequate for towns growing at rates of 25 to 50 percent per decade; in addition, an increasing per capita residential use of water resulted from more plumbing, and increasing industrial use of water aggravated the situation, forcing many cities to tap distant water supplies. Traffic was by far the most universal problem because in many cities (excepting the Northeastern metropolitan areas) the pri-

TABLE 4-2 Distribution of United States Population by Type of Settlement, 1920 (millions)

Places over 500,000	16.4	
Places of 100,000–499,999	10.9	
Places of 2,500–99,999	26.9	
URBAN POPULATION		54.2
Places with less than 2,499	9.0	
Other Rural Non-farm Population	10.5	
Farm Population	32.0	
RURAL POPULATION		51.5
TOTAL		105.7

SOURCE: U.S. Bureau of the Census, *Statistical Abstract of the United States,* Washington, 1965, pp. 15, 614.

vate automobile gradually replaced public transportation. Trucks added further to the congestion of streets designed for carriages and horsecars.

THE ECONOMIC EVOLUTION
OF CANADA: 1867–1960

In contrast with the United States, Canadian manufacturing did not equal agriculture as a source of income until the decade of World War I. Even in 1953 the percentage contribution of the primary industries remained high—about three times as high as in the United States. As in the United States, the tertiary industries (trade, transportation, utilities, government, and services) have grown rapidly. To explain the trends shown in Table 4-3 an outline of Canadian history is desirable.

Federation

In 1867 the Dominion of Canada was established by act of the British Parliament. The new federal government consisted of Nova Scotia, New Brunswick, Quebec, and Ontario. Interior and northern Canada belonged to the Hudson's Bay Company; and British Columbia, Prince Edward Island, and Newfoundland were separate British colonies. Even the initial federation was not economically unified. New Brunswick de-

pended mainly on lumber exports; Nova Scotia mainly on fishing. These Atlantic colonies had agreed to federate only on the promise that a railroad would connect them with Montreal,[1] thus making Halifax and Saint John ice-free outlets for the St. Lawrence trade. Quebec and Ontario had important lumber industries; but livestock, dairy products, and wheat provided their major exports, and some consumer goods manufacturing had developed. The growing railroad net soon bound these diverse units together and brought in others.

British Columbia joined Canada in 1871 after being promised that a transcontinental railroad would be started in 2 years and completed in 10 years. (The Canadian Pacific opened transcontinental service 14 years later.) The Hudson's Bay Company lands were absorbed into Canada in 1870, and Prince Edward Island joined the federation in 1873. These rail connections did not lead to the immediate settlement of the Canadian West because world wheat prices fell from 1873 to 1893 and freight rates to world markets were almost prohibitive. During the nineteenth century, the growth of the Canadian provinces was slow compared with that in the neighboring American states (Table 4-4).

[1] The promised railroad was not completed until 1876.

TABLE 4-3   Canadian National Income by Industry, 1870–1953 (millions of Canadian dollars)

Primary Industries

Year	Farming	Fishing and Trapping	Mining	Forestry	Manufacturing	Tertiary Industry	Part of Income from Primary Industries, %
1870	153	5	4	44	87	96	44.9
1890	217	13	11	53	180	214	36.6
1910	509	21	59	86	508	752	30.2
1930	581	19	151	61	968	2,649	16.6
1945	1,161	61	274	162	2,707	5,306	16.8
1953	1,881	60	617	327	5,667	9,561	15.1

SOURCE: O. J. Firestone, *Canada's Economic Development; 1867–1953*, Bowes and Bowes, London, 1958.

Prairie Settlement

The settlement of the Prairie Provinces in the early twentieth century was stimulated by a combination of political, economic, and technical factors (Figure 4-7). The Canadian government paid the Canadian Pacific Railroad a subsidy of $11,000 a mile on new line in exchange for a freight rate reduction. More efficient grain-handling methods were devised, and this further reduced marketing costs. Demands for the hard wheat of semi-arid lands increased with the development of new types of bread flour. Most important was the introduction of Marquis wheat which ripened a week earlier than other spring wheat varieties, thus reducing the risks of a killing frost before harvest. Consequently the first decade of the twentieth century showed a tripling of Prairie Provinces' population (Table 4-4). The local market was soon sufficiently large to justify the establishment of industries there—at first, mostly those related to the processing or shipping of farm and forest products: flour milling, sawmilling, butter, and cheese processing, railroad-car repairs, meat packing, and farm clothing.

Eastern Expansion

Prairie settlement also increased the demand for Eastern manufactures, and United States demands for Canadian raw materials further stimulated some Canadian industries. Railroad expansion required rail ties, steel rails, cars, and locomotives; greater wheat production required grain elevators, freight cars, lake ships, and milling machinery; wood-pulp and newsprint exports required lumbering tools, railroads, and paper-mill machinery.

Along the railroads across the Canadian Shield, nickel, copper, and iron ores were discovered north of Lake Huron and Lake Superior. At the same time wheat exports from Ontario and Quebec ceased because their growing urban populations absorbed all that their soils could produce. In both Quebec and Ontario, farm employment declined from 1911 to 1951 while manufacturing employment tripled.

Western Expansion

While industry and other urban services were expanding in the St. Lawrence Valley, changes were occurring in the Canadian

TABLE 4-4   Population Growth: Canada and American Border States, 1880–1931 (thousands)

Region	1881	1891	1901	1911	1921	1931
Maritime Provinces	871	881	894	938	1,000	1,008
Quebec and Ontario	3,286	3,603	3,832	4,533	5,315	6,306
Prairie Provinces	113	245	439	1,335	1,964	2,353
British Columbia	49	98	179	392	525	694
CANADA	4,325	4,833	5,371	7,206	8,788	10,377
	1880	*1890*	*1900*	*1910*	*1920*	*1930*
Maine, New Hampshire, Vermont	1,328	1,370	1,449	1,529	1,563	1,621
Michigan and Minnesota	2,417	3,403	4,171	4,885	6,055	7,405
The Dakotas and Montana	174	682	964	1,537	1,833	1,911
Washington	75	357	518	1,142	1,357	1,563
UNITED STATES	50,189	62,980	84,372	102,370	118,108	122,775

SOURCES: M. C. Urquhart and K. A. H. Buckley (eds.), *Historical Statistics of Canada*, Macmillan, Toronto, 1965; and U.S. Bureau of the Census, *Historical Statistics of the United States: Colonial Times to 1957*, Washington, 1960.

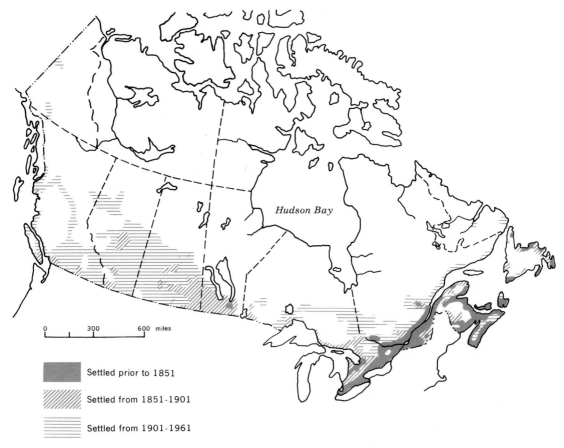

Hudson Bay

0   300   600 miles

Settled prior to 1851

Settled from 1851-1901

Settled from 1901-1961

FIGURE 4-7   The expansion of Canadian settlement. Compare with Figure 2-7, and note how little of Canada was settled in 1901 when most habitable parts of the United States had been settled at least thinly.

West in the interwar period. Coal, oil, and natural gas were discovered in the Prairie Provinces, especially in Alberta, and new industries were added to use local fuels to supply local demands. British Columbia also benefited from mineral discoveries, from increasing demands for lumber and newsprint, and from the use of its waterpower in processing raw materials.

Population Growth

The Canadian population almost doubled from 1911 to 1951, but the increase was not uniformly distributed. A small part of the increase resulted from the addition of Newfoundland (1949) as the tenth province. Although all provinces showed some growth, most did not keep up with the natural rate of increase. Three showed a net growth from immigration; their order is easily explained in terms of the metropolitan growth and new resource exploitation described above. The largest growth was in Ontario, the industrial core of Canada; British Columbia and Alberta also gained by net migration. Expansion northward was small and spotty; most population growth occurred in the well-settled southern areas suited to urban development.

Thus Canada somewhat later underwent an economic transformation essentially similar to that in the United States. The vast areas of Canada include wide farm- and ranchlands, extensive forests, rich mines, and extensive wastelands. Although rural activities occupy the bulk of the productive acreage, the cities produce the bulk of the income (Table 1-4).

EVOLVING PATTERNS IN TWO PREDOMINANTLY URBAN ECONOMIES

At the end of the Civil War the United States was still a partially developed nation on the fringe of the European-dominated world economy. By 1957 it had become a major force in international economics, holding a first-rank position among the nations of the world in the production both of raw materials and of manufactured goods. Meanwhile, in spite of war and recession, its greatly enlarged population had come to enjoy the highest average level of living of any people in all history.[2]

Except for differences resulting from size of population, a similar comment could be made about Canadian development. Both Anglo-American economies have been changing from activities largely based on raw materials and muscle-powered craftsmanship to those based on power, machines, technically designed goods, and many highly specialized urban services. The change is by no means completed and possibly never will be.

This combined industrialization and urbanization has done much to erase the differences among at least the well-settled parts of Anglo-America. From southeastern Canada to Florida to California to British Columbia, the supermarket, the gas station, the highway, the motel, and many other man-made features are remarkably ubiquitous. Ideas that originate in one part of Anglo-America are soon diffused by mail, tele-

phone, television, and travel to all but the most isolated places. The regional differences, so sharp in Indian societies and conspicuous even earlier in this century, have been smoothed and in places overlaid by the sameness of an industrial society. The freeways and the smog of Los Angeles are being duplicated in other metropolitan areas. Climatic differences remain, but even these have less differentiating effect on a predominantly urban society housed increasingly in air-conditioned quarters. There is more variety in rural settings—the orange groves of Florida differ markedly from the cotton fields of Mississippi and the dairy farms of Wisconsin—but farming and other raw-material industries now support only a small and decreasing fraction of all Anglo-Americans.

The increasing urban emphasis, while it has created some widespread uniformities, has at the same time created new sets of patterns on the land. The Anglo-American populace, blessed with an amazing supply of vehicles, has become remarkably mobile and intricate networks of routes have spread over the land. These routes have made possible cheap and rapid shipment of goods and many specialized activities have developed to serve regional and even continental markets. Among the commodities shipped are fuel and power, and these have released many industries from being tied to local supplies of power and muscle.

One of the characteristics of networks is the development of *nodes* where routes come together. These are the obvious sites for commercial and industrial cities whose ability to compete in specialized services depends on access to a wide market. These cities develop into hierarchies, a cluster of small cities being served in more specialized functions by a medium-sized city, and a cluster of medium-sized cities being served by a large city whose citizens offer a greater variety of specialized services.

[2] Harvey S. Perloff et al., *Regions, Resources, and Economic Growth*, published for Resources for the Future, Inc., Johns Hopkins, Baltimore, 1960, p. 9.

ORIGINALLY FONTANA, CALIFORNIA, was an agricultural settlement in Southern California, laid out in rectangular farms irrigated by the melting snows of the nearby mountains. During World War II, the Kaiser steel mill was constructed to service Pacific Coast shipyards and other war industries; after the war, it supplied steel for new industries developing in the Los Angeles area. (Photo: Kaiser Steel Company.)

City Patterns on the Land

Almost all cities started as small towns, and most plans for expansion were inadequate because they anticipated a growth much less than has since occurred. (Thousands of these small towns have stagnated, and at least as many have disappeared altogether.) Most cities started as political, commercial, and social centers, but some were based primarily on a specific environmental feature, e.g., local minerals, waterpower, head of navigation on a river, a good harbor. Others received their initial impetus from man-made enterprise; for example: central location in a county or state was convenient for a political city; location at a division point or junction on a railroad was suitable for a commercial city. Cities grew as they took on functions other than their initial function; in fact, the larger cities have added almost all kinds of urban activities.

Basic activities   Most cities developed certain functions which they performed so well that they could serve areas outside the city in successful competition with other cities. These activities have been called the *basic activities.* For example, if the bakers in a city baked bread so well that people for 50 miles around purchased this bread, this brought income into the city in exchange for its bread-making services. The bread might be thought of as an *export* of that city.

Other businesses developed in the city whose products and services were sold mainly within the city. Thus the bakers patronized local doctors, lawyers, school teachers, and shoe repairmen who provided services classified as *nonbasic* because the demand for them would disappear if all engaged in basic activities moved elsewhere. The nonbasic activities may employ as many or more workers than the basic activities.

Urban hierarchies   Urban functions commonly varied with city size. A small town might have only a post office, schools, churches, retail stores, and a factory. Amid every cluster of small towns there developed a somewhat larger city which had more specialized functions, for example, wholesale businesses, specialized medical and governmental services. Still larger cities became financial centers and offered still greater variety of specialized services. One classification of cities has suggested that cities of over 200,000 develop, in addition to the functions of smaller cities, specialties in wholesaling, numerous political and public services, and the publication of regional newspapers, and that cities of over 1 million have added still further specialized financial and business services, publishing, scientific and artistic activities, and specialized entertainment.

Urban Agglomerations and Dispersion

Transportation provides cities not only with the goods and services their citizens require but also with a market for the goods and services they have to sell. The larger cities occur in clusters or along major transportation routes. With the increasing urbanization of the Anglo-American economy it seems likely that more giant metropolitan areas will develop. One such giant is the string of cities from Boston to Washington, D.C. Among other similar agglomerations that seem predictable within the next few decades are Detroit–Chicago–Milwaukee, Buffalo–Cleveland, Dallas–Fort Worth, San Diego–Los Angeles–San Francisco–Sacramento, and Toronto–Hamilton.

A recent noticeable trend is the tendency of certain industries to move to small cities. The objective is to avoid congestion and expensive land and labor costs.

Classification of Cities

Because most large cities perform more than one function, numerous attempts have been made to devise a compound classification.[3] City data may be delimited on a variety of bases. For example, are the data to be measured on the basis of the *political* boundary

of the *metropolitan area* or of the *urbanized area* (the solidly built-up area attached to the city)? Should the large metropolis be considered as a unit or subdivided into industrial, commercial, financial, and residential districts? Should the analysis be on the basis of products made or sold, value added by manufacturing, or on the number of workers employed? If based on the number of workers or wages, should the amount be credited to the place of employment or to the place of residence?

A valuable basis for urban analysis is to note the proportion of the labor force employed in a given activity compared with the proportion employed for the country as a whole.[4] For example, the New York City SMSA (Standard Metropolitan Statistical Area) if compared with United States data has about twice the proportion of employees in consumer goods manufacturing and is significantly above average in the supply of professional, commercial, financial, and transportation services. In contrast, Philadelphia has relatively high employment in all groups of industry but is only average in services employment. Birmingham, Alabama, has high employment in industries processing raw materials but is below average in most other activities. Washington, D.C., is above average in providing governmental and other services but far below average in all kinds of industry.

Further investigation (e.g., in the *Census of Manufactures*) would pinpoint particular activities. For example, Boston had over 11 times its share of employment necessary to supply its people in the leather industry, St. Louis 4 times its share in beverage industries, Buffalo over 5 times its share in meat products, and Seattle more than 12 times its share in the aircraft industry.

Superficially many Anglo-American cities seem to resemble one another. Classi-

---

[3] Among these are classifications by Chauncy Harris, Howard Nelson, Otis Duncan, and others.

[4] This and the next paragraph are based on O.D. Duncan et al., *Metropolis and Region*, published for Resources for the Future, Inc., Johns Hopkins, Baltimore, 1960, pp. 206–219.

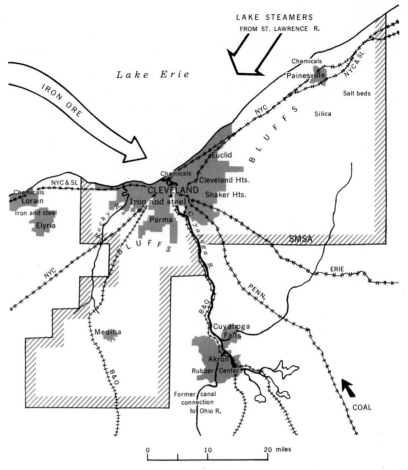

FIGURE 4-8 *The Cleveland area and some factors which account for its economic development.*

fication often proves difficult because each develops its individuality based on unique physical setting, character of trading areas, historical accident, access to specific raw materials, and accumulations of skills and industrial combinations. For example, how would one classify Cleveland, Ohio, located on bluffs overlooking the shores of Lake Erie, where the Cuyahoga River, cutting through the bluffs along the lake, divides the city into two sections (Figure 4-8)? The river, having been dredged to float ore boats from the lake, is important in the steel industries which account for about one-sixth of Cleveland's employment. Helpful to these heavy industries are the railroads that connect with the coal fields 120 to 150 miles to

the southeast and fan out to a variety of markets. Cleveland is also located near salt deposits and is the center of a chemical-producing area. With over 2 million customers who patronize its retail markets, Cleveland needs and has a variety of consumer goods industries including clothing and food processing. Many of its workers have been technically trained, a necessity for its machine-tool, electrical-machinery, and vehicle industries. Commercially, Cleveland is the major wholesale center for northern Ohio, the headquarters for Great Lakes steamship companies, a major lake port, and the headquarters of the Fourth Federal Reserve Bank. Historically, Cleveland was part of the Western Reserve of Connecticut

CLEVELAND, IN COMMON WITH many cities fronting on the Great Lakes, has constructed an artificial harbor with docks on filled land. The Cuyahoga River, the localizing factor in the establishment of Cleveland, contributes its water and its refuse to Lake Erie. The location of the railroad terminal is identified by Terminal Tower, the skyscraper to the right. (Photo: Cleveland Chamber of Commerce.)

(hence the name of Western Reserve University) and was founded by New Englanders; its present population, however, includes many of Eastern European descent with a considerable Negro group. Its SMSA in 1966 contained 1.05 percent of the United States population who earned 1.28 percent of the nation's income. Obviously more could be said about Cleveland, but the data given indicate the distinctive features of this major urban center. The question remains: How is it to be classified?

CONCLUSIONS

Within a century Anglo-America has changed from an economy largely based on rural occupations to an economy based on an adequate amount of rural resources multiplied in value many times by urban skills. Most Anglo-Americans live and work on a small urban fraction of the land area. This concentration on urban land has brought higher living standards, but it has caused so much congestion, noise, dust, and smog that those who could afford it have moved to the suburbs. Human skills, especially technological, have concentrated a huge productive machine in a few dozen metropolises; its parts are held together and coordinated by an amazing network of communications and transportation.

The emphasis on raw materials and power as locating factors for industrial and urban growth is lessening. Raw materials by value make up an increasingly smaller part of the national product. In most cases, they, as well as fuel and power, can be shipped by boat, rail, truck, or pipeline. Specialized labor is very important, but it too can be moved or trained. Accumulations of capital and capital goods can likewise be moved. The question is not whether these locating factors can be moved, but is it worth the cost? Is it worthwhile to tear out an industry from its roots to move it to a supposedly better location? The kind of industry also enters the problem for some industries have strong roots while others are footloose, being able to move almost anywhere within range of the market. Then there are the growing superstructures of service industries, the accumulations of vested interests in communities, and the influences of political planning and power. The resulting patterns and agglomerations on the land are not scientifically ordained; instead they are an equilibrium between what has been and the directions in which the regional economies are trending.

SELECTED REFERENCES

BORCHERT, JOHN R.: "American Metropolitan Evolution," *Geographical Review,* vol. 57 (1967), pp. 301–332.

BROWN, RALPH H.: *Historical Geography of the United States,* Harcourt, Brace & World, New York, 1948, especially chaps. 19 and 29.

CURRIE, A. W.: *Canadian Economic Development,* Nelson, Toronto, 1942.

DEGLER, CARL N.: *Out of Our Past,* Harper & Row, New York, 1959, especially chaps. 9, 11, and 13.

DUNCAN, OTIS D., et al.: *Metropolis and Region,* published for Resources for the Future, Inc., Johns Hopkins, Baltimore, 1960, chaps. 1–4, 7–11.

EASTERBROOK, W. T., and H. G. J. AITKEN.: *Canadian Economic History,* Macmillan, Toronto, 1956.

HOOVER, EDGAR M.: *The Location of Economic Activity,* McGraw-Hill, New York, 1948. A clear theoretical analysis of the economic forces that influence the location of production.

INNIS, H. A.: *Settlement and the Mining Frontier,* University of Toronto Press, Toronto, 1936.

PERLOFF, H. S., E. S. DUNN, JR., E. E. LAMPARD, and R. F. MUTH: *Regions, Resources, and Economic Growth,* published for Resources for the Future, Inc., Johns Hopkins, Baltimore, 1960. A statistical analysis of the changing economic geography of the United States, 1870–1954.

PRED, ALLAN R.: *The Spatial Dynamics of U.S. Urban-Industrial Growth: 1800–1914,* MIT Press, Cambridge, 1966.

U.S. BUREAU OF THE CENSUS: *Historical Statistics of the United States: Colonial Times to 1957,* Washington, 1960.

U.S. CIVIL WAR CENTENNIAL COMMISSION: *The United States on the Eve of the Civil War as Described in the 1860 Census,* Washington, 1963.

General references for United States regions

FEDERAL RESERVE BANKS: Each bank publishes a journal or review as well as special studies. The reports issued by the Boston, Philadelphia, Richmond, Cleveland, St. Louis, Kansas City, Atlanta, Dallas, Minneapolis, and San Francisco banks are especially valuable to geographers.

U.S. BUREAU OF THE CENSUS: *Statistical Abstract of the United States* (annual); *County and City Data Book: 1967.* These books summarize the data in detailed census reports and other government statistical reports. Census reports are often prefaced by or accompanied by monographs or statistical summaries on special subjects.

U.S. BUREAU OF MINES: *Minerals Yearbook* (annual), vol. 3, *Area Reports,* is especially pertinent.

U.S. DEPARTMENT OF AGRICULTURE: Yearbook of Agriculture and *Agricultural Statistics* (both annual) are generally of interest to geographers. For the innumerable special studies and pamphlets published by this department, see current price lists.

U.S. DEPARTMENT OF THE INTERIOR: Popular reports are being issued on, for example, *The Natural Resources of Wyoming,* and other states. Also a variety of special reports on land utilization problems.

U.S. GOVERNMENT: Yearbooks or handbooks obtainable from U.S. Government Printing Office, Washington, D.C., 20402. (Free price lists are available on such subjects as maps, commerce, soils, agriculture, and weather.)

U.S. OFFICE OF BUSINESS ECONOMICS: *Growth Patterns in Employment by County: 1940–1950 and 1950–1960,* 8 vols., Washington, 1965 (one volume on each O.B.E. region); *Survey of Current Business* (monthly).

Nongovernmental sources

BOGUE, DONALD J., and CALVIN L. BEALE: *Economic Areas of the United States,* Free Press, New York, 1961. Rather encyclopedic, but a convenient, quick reference and regional analysis.

DUNCAN, OTIS D., et al.: *Metropolis and Region,* published for Resources for the Future, Inc., Johns Hopkins, Baltimore, 1960.

EDITOR AND PUBLISHER: *Market Guide* (annual), 850 Third Avenue, New York, 10022. Gives data on all counties and SMSAs, and especially detailed industrial data on cities that have daily newspapers.

JENSEN, MERRILL (ed.): *Regionalism in America,* University of Wisconsin Press, Madison, paperback edition, 1965.

MOUZON, OLIN T.: *Resources and Industries of the United States,* Appleton-Century-Crofts, New York, 1966.

RAND MCNALLY: *Commercial Atlas and Marketing Guide* (annual). Available only by subscription. See libraries.

SALES MANAGEMENT: *Survey of Buying Power* (annual), 630 Third Avenue, New York, 10017. Population, income, and sales data by states, provinces, counties, and cities, both in dollars and in percentages of national totals.

Yearbooks of encyclopedias, also almanacs: see articles on states and products.

PART II

THE AMERICAN COMMERCIAL– MANUFACTURING CORE

IN THE NORTHEASTERN QUARTER of the United States the rural culture has almost been submerged under growing metropolitan developments. The farmer's frontier is retreating, and much mediocre land has been emptied or converted into recreational use. Even the best soils go out of farm production when real estate subdivisions, factory sites, or expressway construction outbid the farmer. The uniform regions—whether based on landforms, soil regions, or agricultural regions—remain partly visible, but superimposed on them are nodal regions; indeed functional organization of the modern economy stresses a web of routes centered on focal metropolises.

This is a relatively old area of settlement in Anglo-America; its industries are mature—indeed some are decadent and being replaced by new industries based on technology, specialization, and skilled labor. Even faster is the growth of the service industries. Such rapid urban growth, often urban sprawl, brings problems of landscape design, both urban and rural, to provide better settings for twenty-first century living.

NEW YORK, ECONOMIC CAPITAL of the American Commercial-Manufacturing Core, attained its rank partly because of the focus of routes around the southern end of Manhattan Island. Many business decisions controlling the American economy are made on Wall Street, near the southern tip. Artistic and fashion decisions are made in the Midtown District, upper right. (The Port of New York Authority.)

CHAPTER 5

THE ATLANTIC MEGALOPOLIS AND NEW ENGLAND

FIGURE 5-1 Landforms of New England. Very little of New England is plain,
the uplands in most areas sloping down gradually to a rockbound coast.
(Base map copyright by A. K. Lobeck. Reprinted with permission of The Geographical Press,
Hammond, Inc.)

MEGALOPOLIS

About half of the American population and somewhat more than half
of all personal income are concentrated in the northeastern part of
the country. Almost all these people and income are within a somewhat smaller region called the American Commercial-Manufacturing
Core, extending approximately from the Atlantic at Portland, Maine,

BASIC DATA:

AREA INCLUDES	Land Area (thousand sq. mi.)	Population Change 1950–1960	1960 (thousands)	1967 (thousands)	Personal Income 1967 (billions)
ATLANTIC MEGALOPOLIS	52.6	17.5%	37,200	44,000	$145.0
NEW ENGLAND	66.0	12.5%	9,881	10,710	$ 35.9
Massachusetts	8.2	9.8	5,158	5,500	$ 19.1
Rhode Island	1.2	8.5	860	910	2.9
Connecticut (less Fairfield County)	4.4	25.3	1,990	2,270	8.3
Maine	33.2	6.1	974	1,015	2.6
Vermont	9.6	3.2	390	400	1.1
New Hampshire	9.3	13.8	609	675	1.9
MAJOR SMSAS					
Boston-Lawrence Area	1.8	8.1%	3,109	3,600	$ 13.4
Providence	0.6	7.4	816	900	2.7
Springfield-Holyoke	1.1	16.9	492	535	1.6
Hartford (County Area)	0.7	27.8	689	830	3.3

CLIMATE   Humid continental: near coast modified by marine influences.

	Temperature (°F) Jan.	July	Precipitation (inches) Annual	Season
Portland, Maine	23	68	42	All year
Hartford, Connecticut	28	73	43	All year
Burlington, Vermont	19	69	32	Summer maximum
Hyannis, Massachussets	31	70	42	All year

VEGETATION   Second-growth forest; oak in southeast; mixed in center; spruce and fir in northern Maine.

SOIL   Much rough land; gray-brown podzolic with podzols in north.

MINERALS   Sand, gravel, building stone; for Maine, also cement and clay.

west to Milwaukee, thence south to St. Louis, and east to the Atlantic at Baltimore (Figure 5-2). In Part II the major subdivisions and structure of the ore will be analyzed, with each chapter including certain adjacent less-developed areas whose development is based mainly on proximity to the highly urbanized core.

The longest settled, most economically mature, and most intensively developed part of the United States is the eastern edge of the core, variously called *Megalopolis* or the *Atlantic Metropolitan*

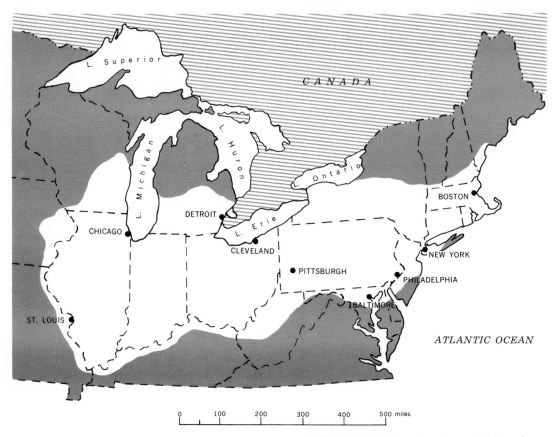

FIGURE 5-2   *The American Commercial-Manufacturing Core, for a century the unchallenged economic heartland of the country, is expanding westward and now penetrates the eastern edge of the Midwest, including an area erroneously but commonly considered predominantly agricultural.*

Belt (Figure 5-3). Extending nearly 600 miles from southern Maine to eastern Virginia, this agglomeration of cities, villages, and suburbs, with its incongruous assortment of street plans, is gradually being merged into a single economic unit, incorporating such historic centers as Boston, New York, Philadelphia, Baltimore, Washington, and the Hampton Roads ports. Each year the open spaces between these cities become smaller; in the core of the region almost the only open space consists of cemeteries, parks, and airfields. The Atlantic Megalopolis houses one-fifth of the nation's people who produce one-quarter of its value added by manufacturing and handle one-third of its wholesale trade. Truly this urban strip joins a multitude of major gateways into the continent.

The Atlantic Megalopolis[1] has other characteristics besides statistical leadership:

1 Like the huge London metropolitan area, although it produces all kinds of manufactured goods, the Atlantic Megalopolis is relatively lacking in raw materials. Most of the raw-material resources commonly attributed to the region are of historical rather than current importance.

2 Compared with the large local demand

[1] The term *Megalopolis* was used by Gottmann to apply to the Boston-Washington area. It has now become apparent that other megalopolises are developing in Anglo-America; hence the term Atlantic Megalopolis is used to identify the first megalopolis.

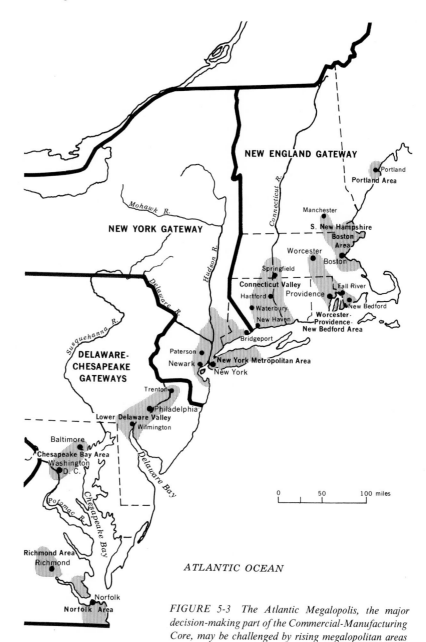

NEW ENGLAND GATEWAY

Portland
Portland Area

Mohawk R.

Connecticut R.

NEW YORK GATEWAY

Manchester

S. New Hampshire

Boston Area

Worcester

Hudson R.

Boston

Springfield

Connecticut Valley

Hartford

Providence

Fall River

Waterbury

New Bedford

Worcester-
Providence-
New Bedford Area

New Haven

Bridgeport

Delaware R.

Susquehanna R.

Paterson

Newark

New York Metropolitan Area

DELAWARE-
CHESAPEAKE
GATEWAYS

New York

Trenton

Philadelphia

Lower Delaware Valley

Wilmington

Baltimore

Chesapeake Bay Area

Washington
D. C.

Delaware Bay

Potomac R.

Chesapeake Bay

| 0 | 50 | 100 miles |

Richmond Area
Richmond

ATLANTIC OCEAN

Norfolk

Norfolk Area

FIGURE 5-3 The Atlantic Megalopolis, the major decision-making part of the Commercial-Manufacturing Core, may be challenged by rising megalopolitan areas around the lower Great Lakes.

for fuel and power, it is almost lacking in local fuel resources.

3 Although nearby farms have been made highly productive, they supply only a fraction of the huge food demands of nearly 40 million people.

4 The Atlantic Megalopolis is highly dependent on a network of ocean, inland waterway, rail, highway, pipeline, and air routes to bring in the huge amounts of raw materials, fuels, and foods the region requires. Indeed it is one of the world's major focal points of Anglo-American and overseas routes.

5 New York and many smaller cities within the region have been centers of national

and even world leadership in specific activities. There is a great concentration of professional people in almost every field: scientific, artistic, political, and economic, together with the offices, libraries, museums, meeting halls, and laboratories needed as equipment for developing and testing ideas and operative plans.

6 Although the Atlantic Megalopolis is congested, its unrivaled opportunities for jobs, business deals, entertainment, society, political intrigue, and even crime, attract people from throughout the United States and many foreign countries.

7 The Atlantic Megalopolis includes a tremendous diversity of local specialization: thus Boston leads in education, Hartford in insurance, the Delaware Valley in heavy industry, the Chesapeake area in seafood and vegetables, and Washington in government. The region has the advantages of both division of labor and large-scale operations within a compact area easily accessible by train, freeway, or plane to leading American markets.

Although the Atlantic Megalopolis is densely settled *on the average,* it and especially the adjoining areas include many uninhabited or sparsely settled areas (Figure 5-4). Some of these areas have never been settled; others were abandoned after forests had been cut over and where local agriculture proved unable to withstand the competition of more fertile lands in the Midwest. These sparsely developed hinterlands are a great advantage to megalopolitan communities to which they supply domestic water and recreational areas.

NEW ENGLAND

The northern end of the Atlantic Megalopolis terminates in New England, an area economically and culturally focused on Boston. Historically and conventionally, New England comprises six states, but Fairfield County, Connecticut, has been excluded because it is part of the New York Metropolitan Area. During the first two centuries of Anglo-American history, New England surpassed or equaled other areas in leadership. Today its income totals less than half that of the New York Metropolitan region, but New England capital, skill, and intellectual leadership still exert major influences on national development.

The continued leadership of New England can hardly be attributed to great natural resources. True, early settlers found there six natural resources of which they took full advantage: (1) fish from adjacent banks; (2) natural harbors; (3) oak and white pine suitable for ships and other construction; (4) small areas of fertile soil; (5) waterpower easily harnessed; (6) small deposits of lead, copper, and bog-iron ores. But compared with those of other Anglo-American regions, New England natural resources have been niggardly. The minerals today are unworked or of minor importance. The soils are generally stony and infertile, and the rough terrain is hardly ideal for modern mechanized farming. Its forests have been cut over, and pasture or inferior stands of timber occupy the former areas of tall virgin forest. Its climate is cold and raw in winter and too cool in summer for the profitable growth of many crops. Most New England development arises not from natural resources but from the skill and energy with which the settlers used the little that the land offered.

Physical Structure and Settlement

Most of New England is a rugged upland of hard crystalline rocks: largely granite, gneiss, and marble (Figure 5-1). The upland surface is commonly from 100 to 1,000 feet high except for steep north-south ranges

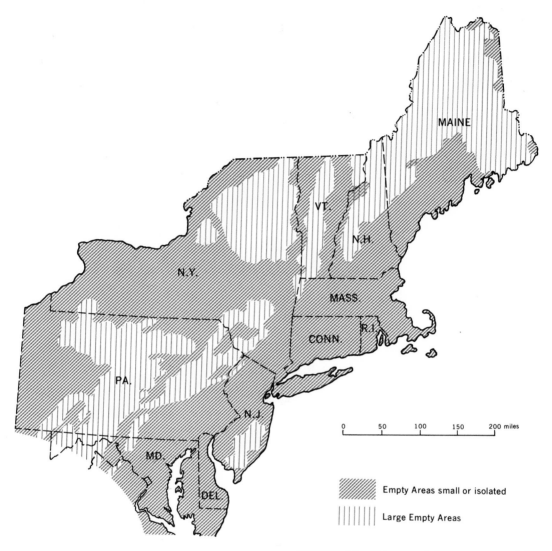

Empty Areas small or isolated

Large Empty Areas

FIGURE 5-4   This map of the empty areas of the Northeastern states is based on the field research of Lester E. Klimm after World War II. It shows that many areas within Megalopolis were unsettled and used mainly, if at all, for recreational activities. Such breathing spaces are desirable for an urban society, but how many will there be by 1980?

which rise above the general level. Most conspicuous among these ranges are the steep White Mountains of New Hampshire and adjacent Maine, the rounded Green Mountains of Vermont, and the plateaulike Berkshire Hills of western Massachusetts. The upland surface has been scoured by continental glaciers which planed off the hilltops and filled in the valleys; deposited boulders, clay, and sand over the surface; blocked stream channels to form innumerable lakes and swamps; and helped to form a variety of coastal features such as Cape Cod, Nantucket, and the estuaries of Maine. Projecting into the upland are fertile basins covered with glacial soil such as the Boston and Narragansett basins. Less influenced by the glacier were the central Connecticut Valley, the Berkshire Valley, and the valley of western Vermont. The areas of fertile

A NEW ENGLAND HARDWOOD FOREST in southern Maine with the boulders so common in New England. This woodlot is being thinned so that the remaining trees may grow to equal the tall trees cut for masts in colonial days. (American Forest Products Industries, Inc.)

soil concentrated village settlement just as the millsites, where streams descended from the upland, located early industry.

Agriculture

Climatically New England has some advantages as well as limitations for agriculture. Its annual rainfall is adequate and well distributed; droughts are rare. The length of the growing season varies from 200 days in the extreme southeast to 100 days in the extreme north; equally important the growing season is shortened considerably by altitude on the uplands but lengthened in a few sheltered valleys. Temperatures in winter average 30° in southern New England and 20° in the north. Summer temperatures, averaging 65 to 70° (with some very hot

spells in the coastal basins), are always pleasant in the north and on the uplands. Climatically, most of New England is suited for potatoes, hay, and forests.

Much of the upland is submarginal for modern agriculture; much of the lowland is poorly drained or infertile. In the north, the soils are podzols: sour, ash-colored sandy soils associated mainly with coniferous trees, especially spruce, fir, and pine. In the south, the *gray-brown* or *brown podzolic soils,* similar but less acid and less leached, are clothed with hardwoods. In both areas stones and boulders, formerly widespread, have been piled up to build stone walls. The better and more accessible soils have been improved by adding lime, nitrates, and manures. The present fields are relatively free from erosion so that the intensively culti-

THIS SAMPLE OF A central Massachusetts landscape, some 20 miles northeast of Worcester, shows how much wooded land occurs on the edge of and even within the Atlantic Megalopolis. The small farms shown are declining, being unable to compete with urban industry for labor. (USDA photograph.)

vated areas are probably more fertile today than a century ago.

Until about 1830, wheat, wool, and beef were produced for nearby markets and even for export. But with the growing exploitation of the better soils in the Midwest where the plains were better suited to large-scale, mechanized agriculture, New England farms could not compete; consequently half of the cropland went out of production. Today New England obtains nearly all its flour, beef, pork, butter, and cheese, and the bulk of its fresh, canned, and frozen fruits and vegetables from outside its borders. Many of the descendants of early New England farmers moved westward; others moved into the cities to work in the factories; some live on the farm but work mostly in the city.

Less than 50,000 operating farms remain; most of these are tilled so intensively that Massachusetts and Rhode Island are among the leading states in value of crops produced per cultivated acre. Farmers near the megalopolitan sections benefit by high prices for their dairy products, poultry, and vegeta-

bles. In a few regions there are local specialties: potatoes from Aroostook County, Maine; blueberries from coastal Maine; cranberries from Cape Cod; and wrapper tobacco from the central Connecticut Valley. Nevertheless farming occupies a minute proportion of the area: wooded hills and mountains, lakes and marshes, and extensive pastures predominate over cultivated fields. Even rural areas adjoining the huge Boston market are largely wooded.

Extractive Industries

The visitor to New England is so impressed by the extensive forests and the numerous fishing ports that it seems incredible to him that natural resources contribute so modestly to the present regional economy. Fishing, for example, yields a catch of $60 million annually. Although this is one-sixth of the annual fishing catch of the United States, it is only equal to the personal income of a single New England city of 30,000 people. Mining (quarrying) yields about the same annual product, much of which consists of sand and gravel used for concrete. New England forests produce less than 2 percent of the American lumber output, which is valued (as raw lumber) about the same as the fish catch. Waterpower, so important in the initial location of New England industry, totaling 1,369,000 kilowatts has been developed, but this supplies less than one-quarter of the electricity demanded in the area. The greatest acreage of land is used for agriculture which yields farm incomes totaling about $575 million annually, or about the total personal income of New Haven, Connecticut.

Manufacturing

Manufacturing still accounts for about one-third of New England's earned civilian income although many of its former industries have moved southward or to the Midwest. New England must import most of its industrial raw materials; its waterpower must be supplemented by huge receipts of coal and petroleum. Many of its factories are old, and most of its streets and roads were designed for the horse-and-buggy days. Yet with all these handicaps New England continues to produce industrial goods—especially those goods that benefit from skilled labor, advanced engineering techniques, and emphasis on quality. Other industries exist in New England to process local raw materials such as Maine lumber, Vermont marble and maple syrup, and Atlantic fish; to process imports such as crude oil and raw sugar for New England consumption, and to prepare perishable products such as bread for nearby markets; but the foundation of the New England economy is manufacturing based on skill, technology, and originality.

Manufacturing in New England in the early nineteenth century could be easily categorized. First, there were the mills, paper factories, leather tanneries, and factories processing fish and whale products. Closely allied to these were industries processing and packing imported raw materials, the rum distilleries, and brass factories. Second, there were industries which put together local raw materials: shipbuilding, wagon and carriage building. These in turn encouraged other industries, especially the hardware industry. Third, there were textile and clothing industries (including shoes) which were most concentrated in eastern New England. Fourth, especially in southwestern New England there were mechanical industries producing clocks, firearms, and a variety of notions sold by Yankee peddlers throughout the frontier lands to the west. Finally, within the next half century out of the mechanical industries developed machinery industries which serviced not only New England industry but other American industrial regions.

A century later many of these industries were declining. The industries based on local raw materials declined as the materials became scarce. Industries based on semiskilled labor and automatic machinery moved to other areas where labor and power were cheaper and markets somewhat nearer. The cotton textile industry was the prime example of this migration; in 1925 New England had 80 percent of this industry, in 1963 only 7 percent. Factories which produced high-quality textiles and clothing requiring skilled labor migrated more slowly, but New England has lost out in woolens and shoes also. On the other hand, eastern New England is one of five dominant centers for research and development projects (the others are New York, Washington-Baltimore, Los Angeles, and San Francisco) and Massachusetts has more than twice its per capita share of the nation's research and development projects (Table 5-1).

Transportation

The industrialized portions of New England occupy compact areas in which high-speed highways and railroads have largely displaced the once dominant water transporta-

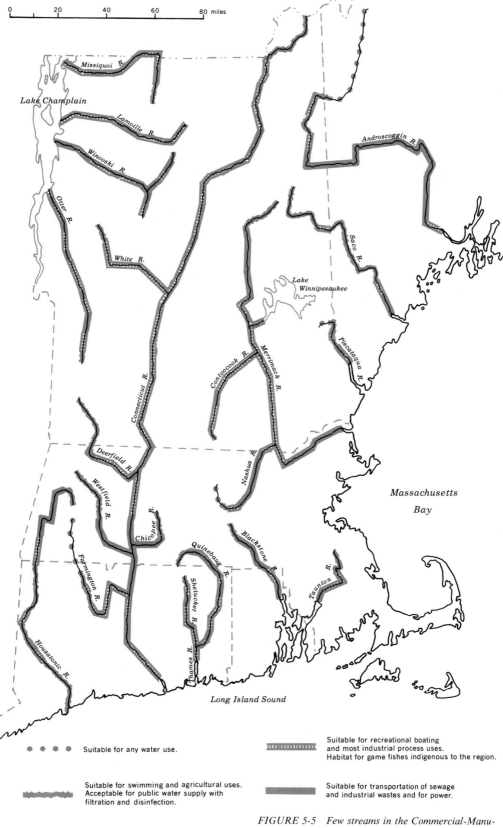

0   20   40   60   80 miles

Missiquoi R.

Lake Champlain

Lamoille R.

Winooski R.

Androscoggin R.

Otter R.

Saco R.

White R.

Lake Winnipesaukee

Connecticut R.

Contoocook R.

Merrimack R.

Piscataqua R.

Deerfield R.

Westfield R.

Nashua R.

Chicopee R.

Massachusetts Bay

Blackstone R.

Quinebaug R.

Farmington R.

Taunton R.

Shetucket R.

Housatonic R.

Thames R.

Long Island Sound

• • • •   Suitable for any water use.

Suitable for recreational boating and most industrial process uses. Habitat for game fishes indigenous to the region.

Suitable for swimming and agricultural uses. Acceptable for public water supply with filtration and disinfection.

Suitable for transportation of sewage and industrial wastes and for power.

FIGURE 5-5   Few streams in the Commercial-Manufacturing Core are free from pollution. Industrial waste, sewage, and soil erosion contaminate these once clear streams.

tion. Small mileages are involved in driving between representative centers: for example, Boston to either Providence or Worcester is 44 miles; Portland to Providence, 149 miles; Providence to Springfield, 80 miles.

Although the older roads, passing as they do through town centers, are congested, freeways serve much of southern New England. Railways also offer good service among the industrialized areas with convenient connections to the Port of New York and interior United States. Overseas trade is predominantly through the Port of New York except for fuels and a few other bulky commodities such as scrap iron. Air services, local, transcontinental, and trans-Atlantic, afford adequate connections with extraregional centers.

Other Tertiary Sources of Income

Transportation is but one of the tertiary activities which provide services for the economy. Table 5-2 demonstrates that for New England as a whole, primary production (farming, mining, forestry, and fishing) accounts for about 1 percent of the total personal income; manufacturing and construction account for nearly one-third of the total; thus two-thirds of the income is derived from services and from payments unrelated to current civilian production. In a mature economy such as New England, it is to be expected that one-quarter of the

TABLE 5-1   Fifteen Leading "Export" Employment Industries in Massachusetts, 1951 and 1962

Industry	Rank in Employment 1951	Rank in Employment 1962	Export[1] Employment as a Percent of Industry Employment, 1962
Footwear, except Rubber	1	1	82
Electronic Components and Accessories	8	2	76
Private Colleges and Universities	7	3	65
Communications Equipment		4	59
Research, Development, and Business Services		5	53
Special Industrial Machinery	2	6	78
Private Hospitals		7	33
Women's, Misses' and Juniors' Outerwear	10	8	52
Electrical Transmission and Distribution Equipment	3	9	68
Life Insurance	13	10	47
Metalworking Machinery and Equipment	6	11	55
Miscellaneous Plastic Products		12	68
Ammunition, except for Small Arms		13	62
Paper Products except Containers and Boxes	15	14	68
Rubber Footwear	12	15	91
Broad-woven Fabric Mills (wool)	4		
Broad-woven Fabric Mills (cotton)	5		
Fabricated Rubber Products	9		
Leather Tanning and Finishing	11		
Paperboard Containers and Boxes	14		

[1] An "export" industry is defined here as one producing goods or services for out-of-state consumers.

SOURCE: *New England Business Review*, April, 1965.

Courtesy Massachusetts Department of Commerce and Development

FIGURE 5-6   The Worcester Chamber of Commerce has used this map to stress its central relations to markets. Most other cities in the Atlantic Megalopolis could show that a 500-mile radius around their cities would include equally large markets. (Worcester Chamber of Commerce.)

TABLE 5-2   Industrial Sources of Civilian Income Received by Persons for Participation in Current Production and Total Personal Income: New England, 1966 (in millions of dollars)

Source	Mass.	R.I.	Conn.[1]	Maine	N.H.	Vt.	New England
Farms	77	8	73	117	18	57	350
Mining	10	2	8	2	3	7	30
Construction	820	131	521	117	103	57	1,750
Manufacturing	4,777	797	3,806	631	587	268	10,866
Trade	2,390	343	1,212	299	237	123	4,603
Financial	835	104	502	67	69	35	1,613
Transportation and Utilities	848	114	410	110	76	51	1,609
Services	2,346	271	1,144	218	204	134	4,319
Government	1,684	282	764	260	190	106	3,285
Other	59	10	28	14	14	2	117
Civilian Income	13,846	2,062	8,469	1,835	1,492	839	28,543
Personal Income	17,675	2,730	10,621	2,422	1,901	1,066	36,415

NOTE: Personal income includes receipts from military expenditures, pensions, annuity payments, and other sources of income not derived from participation in current civilian production. These data are published annually in the July or August issue of *Survey of Current Business.* The data above are from vol. 47 (1967), no. 8, tables 63 and 70, p. 37.

[1] Includes Fairfield County, Connecticut.

personal income will be derived from property in such forms as interest, dividends, insurance annuities and payments, pensions, and withdrawals of capital. The remaining five-twelfths of the total personal income is derived from an elaborate network (infrastructure) of services and service agencies: transportation, communications, utilities, financial organizations, schools and research laboratories, hospitals, and governmental agencies. Such a service structure is characteristic of any mature economy; many of the services rendered make possible the efficiency of New England industries; others are themselves basic ("export" industries) serving major markets outside New England as well as the region itself.

Income Patterns

The Basic Data and Table 5-2 provide further indications of income patterns within New England. Note how much larger the personal income is in the three southern states. An examination of atlas maps of population and transportation will soon demonstrate that the northern states have most of their modest activity concentrated close to the megalopolitan area. The people (and the economic activity) are largely concentrated in or on the edge of a relatively few valleys and basins. Three of these are outstanding: the Boston Basin which economically has merged with the Merrimack Valley to the north; the Narragansett Basin (Providence) into which drains the Blackstone River on which Worcester is located; and the Connecticut Lowland which includes New Haven, Hartford, and Springfield. Economically closely associated with the Connecticut Lowland is the Naugatuck Valley (Waterbury). Industrially less important valleys include the Thames Valley of eastern Connecticut; the Berkshire Valley of western Massachusetts; the Vermont, Champlain, and upper Connecticut valleys of Vermont; and the lower Fore, Androscog-

gin, Kennebec, and Penobscot valleys of Maine. The larger cities are in these lowlands, either on navigable waterways or near falls where waterpower could be developed. Today many of these streams are of minor importance for power or navigation; nevertheless their place in economic history is marked by the continuing location of important cities.

Commercial Orientation

Although Boston is still the commercial hub of New England (the Boston Federal Reserve District includes all of New England except Fairfield County), New York is increasingly handling overseas trade with New England. A study by Howard L. Green[2] shows that most of Connecticut is served as much or more by New York than by Boston (Figure 5-7). Indeed the pull of the larger New York market is reflected in the rapid growth of industrial cities extending from Long Island Sound to Holyoke, Massachusetts. In the same way in eastern New England, metropolitan Boston tends to control some of the business of a ring of outlying centers such as Providence, Worcester, Manchester, and Portland. Thus, although cities such as Providence, Springfield, and Hartford have excellent newspapers, their sales are limited to the local cities; the outlying areas which normally would be in their newspaper hinterlands tend to read Boston or New York papers.

THREE MAJOR FOCAL AREAS

About two-thirds of the population and business of New England is concentrated in three major areas. These highly urbanized areas occupy only one-twelfth of the area of New England or one-third that of southern New England in which all the areas are located. These areas are joined

[2] Howard L. Green, "Hinterland Boundaries of New York City and Boston in Southern New England," *Economic Geography*, vol. 31 (1955), pp. 283-300.

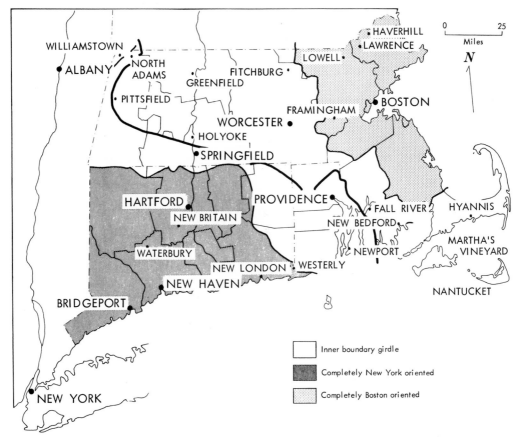

FIGURE 5-7   How New York has taken away much of the hinterland claimed by Boston is shown by this map based on a median boundary line derived from seven hinterland criteria. [Map from Raymond Murphy, THE AMERICAN CITY, McGraw-Hill, 1966, after Howard L. Green, "Hinterland Boundaries of New York City and Boston in Southern New England," ECONOMIC GEOGRAPHY, vol. 31 (1955), fig. 9.]

together by strips of well-settled land, and it seems certain that in another decade they will form one urban complex.

The Boston Area

About 3.5 million people reside in nearly 100 towns and cities which focus on the central city of Boston (population 650,000). Boston Harbor, on the Charles Estuary at the head of Massachusetts Bay, was in the days of New England maritime supremacy the leading American port, sharing its trade with nearby Gloucester, Marblehead, Salem, Lynn, and Quincy. Today the urbanized area spreads across the low-lying Boston Basin, up on the low rimming hills formed of crystalline rock, and northward into the Merrimack Valley. The intricate network of street and road patterns cannot

be understood unless it is realized that this urban crazy quilt started as a multitude of towns[3] and villages whose design fitted local topographic conditions, some since much altered by engineering projects.

The Boston Basin was first altered by glaciation and later by man. When first settled in 1630, it consisted of plains inter-

[3] Political organization in New England differs from that common elsewhere. Although each state is divided into counties, the subdivisions of the county, the towns, are the major local governments. These like townships elsewhere may include both rural and urban areas; some towns have grown into cities. See Raymond E. Murphy, *The American City*, McGraw-Hill, New York, 1966, pp. 20–21, 434–66.

FIGURE 5-8 Much of the land shown in the photograph of the Prudential Project had not been filled in by 1722. (The Bostonian Society.)

rupted by numerous swamps and ponds, above which rose low glacier-deposited hills, some of which formed small islands in Massachusetts Bay. The city of Boston occupied the bulging end of a narrow peninsula on which rose Beacon, Copps, and Fort hills. The well-sheltered shores of the city provided adequate spaces for wharves only 6½ miles from the open sea. With Massachusetts Bay and the Charles permitting local waterborne traffic, Boston proved an ideal political and commercial center for Massachusetts. Soon land became so crowded there that other towns were established on nearby areas of well-drained land: Cambridge, Roxbury, Charlestown, Somerville, Newton, and Quincy. Later marshy areas were drained or filled so that the present shoreline extends well beyond the original coast: thus the Back Bay project, commenced in 1856, filled in the flats adjacent to the neck of the Boston peninsula and added an area of rectangular blocks to the meandering street pattern of old Boston.

The original commercial nucleus (Central Business District, or CBD) was on a cove east of Beacon Hill. When railroads entered the city between 1835 and 1855, lines from the north crossed the Charles to build stations north of the CBD, both groups building their terminals on filled land. The CBD gradually expanded to fill most of the areas between the railroad terminals and between Beacon Hill and the docks to the east. Boston thus developed a business center focused on about a square mile of area; in the present century this became so crowded that many business activities moved to suburban and satellite city locations (Figure 5-9).

Although many historic sites remain in the Boston area, they are becoming submerged by modern developments. A freeway cuts through downtown Boston and an inner belt and an outer expressway intersect the innumerable roads and railways fanning out from the harbor. While sky-scrapers are rising in old Boston, new science-oriented industries line the encircling roadway now nicknamed "Electronics Row."

Industry in the Boston area Although Boston is primarily a commercial and service center, manufacturing accounts for one-third of all employment. Figure 5-10 shows how Boston compares with the United States in the per capita value added by manufacturing in each industrial group. Boston claims to have the largest single metropolitan group of engineers and scientists in the world; hence it is not surprising that the electronics industry is the leading branch of industrial employment and that transportation equipment and machinery are in second and third place. Employment in the durable goods industries surpasses that in nondurable goods. However, among the leading industries are food products, apparel, leather products, and printing and publishing.

Boston industries are found throughout the area, but the newer industries are especially concentrated in some 43 industrial parks. The city of Boston has most of the regional specialties, whereas suburban cities are likely to have only a few each; thus Gloucester specializes in fish packing, Beverly in shoes and shoe machinery, and Lynn in electrical goods and shoes. With a few exceptions, the industries are those in which resources play a small part compared with skilled labor and technology.

Other employment A third of all Bostonians perform commercial and financial work; in addition large numbers are employed in government and services. The remainder work on construction, transportation, public utilities, and a great variety of miscellaneous projects. Essentially these workers are producing not goods but services. Some of these activities, for example, university education, scientific research, insurance, publishing, and investment banking, serve

Manufacturing and wholesale

Retail-services and Multi-family residences

Single-family residences

Major highways

FIGURE 5-9 The Boston metropolis has sprawled out beyond the limits of the Boston Basin but the focus on the Boston Harbor is still evident.

THE FREEWAYS AND THE Prudential Project seem to add a discordant note to the charm of old but overcrowded downtown Boston. (Aerial Photos of New England from Boston Chamber of Commerce.)

the entire country; others, such as wholesaling, newspaper publishing, government, transportation, and baking, serve primarily New England; the remainder, including retail trade, nonspecialized medical services, and entertainment, serve mainly the Boston area.

Routes and trade At one time Boston was a focus of ocean and inland waterway routes (in 1804 the Middlesex Canal completed a

FIGURE 5-10 This deviation graph, based on data from the U.S. CENSUS OF MANUFACTURES, 1963, *should be compared with similar charts throughout the regional chapters. As most large SMSAs have industries in almost all categories, the striking positive and negative deviations from the national per capita average are more significant than the mere listing of industries. Census regulations prohibit the disclosure of value-added and other data which would divulge the operations of individual businesses; for this reason where one or two firms account for most of the production in a category, it is necessary to estimate the height of the bars from non-census data. In such cases, the graph indicates this by using the letter D (disclosure). Apparent inconsistencies between the employment data in the text and the graph result from the value-added data used in the graph as well as from the per capita deviations used in calculating the length of the bars.*

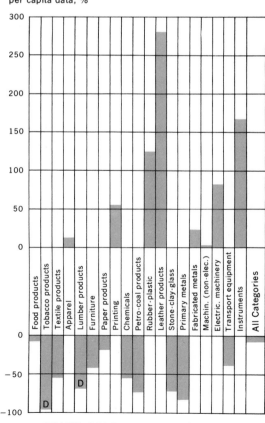

Deviation from U.S. per capita data, %

VALUE ADDED BY MANUFACTURING
Boston SMSA = 1.66% U.S. Pop.

water link with the Merrimack River above Lowell); later it became a railroad center and a great ocean port. More recently it has become primarily a focal point for freeways and airlines, although its rail and ocean routes are still important. The bulk of the tonnage handled in the port is petroleum, with smaller amounts of sugar, lumber, fibers, and other raw materials. Its exports are mainly steel scrap, foodstuffs, and a small tonnage (but high in value) of varied manufactures. The tonnage handled is somewhat more than one-tenth that of New York and is less than that handled by Philadelphia, Baltimore, or Norfolk.

Boston satellites The history of two Merrimack Valley satellites of Boston will serve to illustrate the changing adjustments of New England towns to their environmental setting. In 1823 a company located at Waltham on the Charles River, finding the waterpower there inadequate, established a cotton textile mill to use the greater waterpower at Lowell. By the middle of the century steam power was introduced to supplement waterpower, and woolen textiles became important. Industry expanded, and immigrants (Polish, Greek, and French Canadian) came in to supplement a labor force originally recruited from New England farms. The peak years of the textile industries were during World War I, thereafter many mills (especially cotton textiles) moved south, and Lowell sought for new industries including electronics. Lawrence, 10 miles downstream, has a similar industrial history.

To the south and southeast of Boston is an area not included in the Boston metropolitan area but commercially closely tied to it. The largest city is Brockton (83,000), the outstanding American manufacturer of men's shoes. Southward, a sandy area consisting of islands (Nantucket, Martha's Vineyard), Cape Cod, and the shores of Buzzard's Bay was until a century ago the head-

quarters of a prosperous whaling industry. Today most of the area is a vacationland for urban New Englanders. Its principal whaling port,[4] New Bedford, although still specializing in the scallop catch, earns much more by manufacturing clothing, textiles, metal tools and parts, rubber, and plastics.

The Narragansett Basin

Somewhat larger than the Boston Basin but with only one fourth the population, Narragansett Basin seems better endowed by nature. Its bay, much divided by islands and peninsulas, provides marvelous harbors and local water transportation. Its soils are more fertile and its climate milder than in the Boston area, and its streams have several excellent waterpower sites, one of which powered one of the first textile mills in America. But Boston, founded a few years earlier, remains the regional hub, while Providence serves as capital and commercial center of Rhode Island. Its excellent natural harbor attracts mainly oil tankers, private yachts, and fishing vessels.

Industrially the Narragansett Basin repeats the Merrimack Valley story with a few variations. Cotton textiles powered by the Blackstone River and later by the Fall River (which dropped 130 feet in a quarter mile) was the major industry. When in mid-century waterpower proved inadequate, Fall River, with its tidewater location better suited for coal imports, pulled ahead of Lowell as a cotton textile producer. Fall River, in the early 1920s the leading cotton textile city in the country, had only one mill left in 1965. Textiles have not disappeared from the basin, but they are limited to highly specialized products.

[4] *Nowhere in all America will you find more patricianlike houses; parks and gardens more opulent than in New Bedford. Whence came they?—All these brave houses and flowery gardens came from the Atlantic, Pacific, and Indian Oceans. One and all they were harpooned and dragged up hither from the bottom of the sea.*

In New Bedford, fathers, they say, give whales for dowers to their daughters, and portion off their nieces with a few porpoises apiece. . . .

Herman Melville's MOBY DICK

Fortunately the area attracted other industries. Providence and nearby Attleboro produce half the costume jewelry in the nation, an industry established in 1794. Silverware is a closely related industry, and altogether over 700 firms work in precious metals. Among the heavier industries are machinery, electronics, fabricated metals, and chemicals.

The Narragansett Basin illustrates how the people of once-Puritan New England have changed. Newport and other waterfront resorts attract vacationists, high society, and an annual jazz festival. Woonsocket, a diversified manufacturing center to the north of Providence, is sometimes known as *La Ville du Nord* because of its large French Canadian population. Five-sixths of all Rhode Island church members are Roman Catholics and the senior senator is of Italian extraction. But remnants of Puritan New England can still be found in museums and in old houses carefully preserved.

Although Worcester is 40 miles up the Blackstone River from Providence, it is tributary to Boston, the same distance to the east. Lacking local resources, its continued industrial prosperity and modest growth seem attributable, as in so much of industrial New England, to the advantages of an early start and the traditional skill of its workers. Although the outstanding products are primary metals, metal products, and machinery, nearly half of its industrial workers are engaged in a wide variety of other industries.

The Connecticut Lowland and New Haven

The upland west of Worcester is lightly settled, containing much woodland and the large Quabbin Reservoir which supplies water to Boston. One hour (by freeway) west of Worcester is the fertile trough of the central Connecticut Valley, first settled 15 years after the Pilgrims landed at Plymouth. On alluvial soil above average for New England, the frontier farmers raised crops and fattened cattle to be driven to the Boston market. An early industry critical to a pioneer community was the manufacture of muskets; from this developed the Springfield Armory. Later other mechanical industries were developed; for example, the first successful automobile in the United States was constructed in Springfield in 1892–1893. Today, complicated machinery, electrical goods, games and toys, and parts for transportation equipment are major Springfield products. Nearby centers, using at first local waterpower, developed other specialties, for example: Holyoke, paper and machinery; Northampton, brushes and artillery.

New Haven   Three years after settlement in central Massachusetts, another group approached the Connecticut Lowland from the south, founding New Haven in 1638. The rocky Connecticut coast is the edge of a low, glacier-scoured plateau trenched by numerous streams which have eroded roughly parallel valleys. These provided millsites and waterpower for early industry. Within the upland is a north-south trough, created by faulting and overlooked by abrupt hills of igneous rock. The river flows in the trough as far south as Middletown (where it cuts southeast across the crystalline rock) while the trough is occupied by the Quinnepiac Valley to New Haven. This city of 150,000, with a metropolitan population of a half million, is located on a natural harbor, recently improved by a new wharf with an attached industrial district.

Metal manufactures   The industrial emphasis in Connecticut is largely on metal manufactures designed by artists or engineers and produced by master craftsmen. This industry, at least as old as the republic, is characterized by two methods developed there and now widely used in all modern industry. Chauncy Jerome devised a technique of stamping out brass parts from sheets instead of laboriously cutting each part by hand; this made possible the cheap production of clocks and watches. Also about the end of the eighteenth century, Eli Whitney (also known for his invention of the cotton gin) began making muskets with interchangeable parts and machine-bored barrels. These techniques and the development of machine tools by Elisha Root and others made possible assembly-line methods of production and both improved the quality and lowered the cost of the finished products. Connecticut (especially western Connecticut) has no monopoly on machine tools and assembly-line production; hence it has lost many distant markets to competitors while retaining nearby markets. Yankee craftsmen and engineers, however, are still noted for developing new machines and new techniques.

Toys, firearms, locks, clocks, and machinery, representative New Haven products, are also typical western Connecticut

products (Figure 5-12). Nearby is Naugatuck Valley, "Brass Valley," famed for its clocks, watches, plumbing supplies, and brass parts for electronic apparatus. The principal city is Waterbury (107,000) which claims to have started the brass industry in 1750 by making brass buckles. In 1802 brass buttons were manufactured from sheet brass obtained from scrap metal (ships sheathing, etc.) hand-fused, then rolled by homemade machinery driven by horsepower. A half century later Waterbury was the world's largest producer of brass kettles, pins, and clocks. The brass industry has not been altogether prosperous, partly because aluminum is replacing brass for some uses and partly because ordinary brass goods can be manufactured for distant markets as cheaply elsewhere as in Naugatuck Valley. Fortunately industry in Waterbury is more diversified today; nearly as many workers are employed in chemical, rubber, and miscellaneous industries as in brasswork.

Hartford, New Britain, Meriden, Wallingford, and many smaller Connecticut cities also produce metal goods and related products. Hartford is the major metropolitan center of Connecticut. Once reached by ocean shipping, it is now only a minor river port unloading coal and fuel oil, New Haven handling whatever other modest ocean traffic seeks Connecticut ports. In addition to its industry and political importance as a state capital, Hartford is a leading insurance center, having the home offices of some 40 insurance companies. The reasons for this are largely historical: New England has long had a surplus of capital, and financial busi-

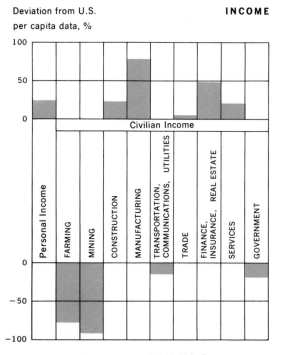

Deviation from U.S. per capita data, %

INCOME

Connecticut = 1.46% U.S. Pop.

FIGURE 5-11 This deviation graph suggests a progressive economy emphasizing industry, financial activities, and services. The statistics upon which this and Figure 5-13 are based are given in Table 5-2. The relatively low ratings of Connecticut in trade, transportation, and government may be accounted for in part by the performance of some of these functions within New York City.

nesses including insurance are outstanding in many large New England cities. Hartford happened to be the home of long-established, well-managed insurance companies and other companies have found it desirable to take advantage of Hartford's reputation.

The Connecticut economy   The industrialized Connecticut economy (see Basic Data and Figure 5-11) has grown more rapidly than that of any other long-established state. Its above-average personal income and above-average income in construction, manufacturing, trade, finance, and services suggest a booming economy. Why? Proximity to New York is part of the explanation; as to the rest, certainly it is brains rather than brawn —a good infrastructure has permitted the efficient use of Connecticut skills. Thus flexibility from easy contacts with a diversity of skills, ideas, and business organizations also enters the picture. From New York to Hartford is barely 100 miles, traversable largely by freeway. Telephones, railroads, and a network of good highways permit convenient conferences among planners, subcontracting, and rapid shipment to nearby distributing centers. Finally the shrewdness and skills long attributed to the Connecticut Yankee help to keep his descendants, as well as later arrivals, prosperous.

LESS PRODUCTIVE REGIONS

Western New England

This hilly upland area, above which rise the rounded Berkshire Hills, the somewhat higher Green Mountains, and the extremely rugged White Mountains, has narrow valleys carved into a rolling upland. Two wider limestone valleys centered on Pittsfield and Burlington offer limited areas of good farmland. This extensive, largely forested area has less population than much-smaller Rhode Island. Population growth has been negligible; for nearly a century many of its

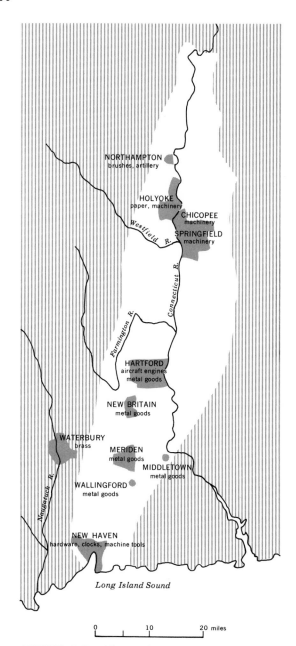

FIGURE 5-12 Adjacent farming areas, navigable waterways, and local waterpower located most of these cities in or near the Connecticut Valley; but their continued prosperity depends on the skill of their workers, their relations to allied industries, and their access to markets in Megalopolis, the nation, and overseas.

sons have migrated, and in parts of the area French Canadians have bought up abandoned farms. Cold in winter, pleasant in summer—it attracts modest numbers of winter sports fans and crowds of summer vacationists from the cities to the south. Much of the area yields dairy products, lumber, and maple sugar, but most of the income comes from a few modest-sized cities: especially Pittsfield (with a huge General Electric plant), Burlington (metalworking), and such small quarrying centers as Rutland (marble) and Barre (granite). Primarily this region is a charming outpost of Megalopolis, supplying it with recreation, tombstones, milk, and a number of specialized manufactures (Figure 5-13).

Southern Maine and New Hampshire

This region is transitional between the sparsely settled region just discussed and highly industrialized southern New England. Once its trade was divided between Portland and Manchester but today well-paved roads and expressways are pulling it toward Megalopolis, into which it will eventually be absorbed. Many of the industries are related to locally available raw materials—for example, vegetables, fish, lumber, and paper processing along the Maine coast; apparel and small manufactures are also common. Such is the attraction of town industry for rural labor that its poultry and dairy farms are reported to be more poorly cared for than in western New England.

Manchester   Manchester, New Hampshire, on the Merrimack River with its many falls, recapitulates the history of many older New England cities. Founded in 1722, it remained a minor rural village on the muddy "Mast Road" over which tall timber was hauled to coastal shipbuilding yards. Samuel Blodget started a canal around Amoskeag Falls so that boats could ship out produce from central New Hampshire. The canal was completed in 1807, and the new and much used river route connected with the Lowell-Boston Canal. Several small industries were started in Manchester (hopefully so renamed in 1810 after the leading English textile city), but little industrial development occurred until in 1831 the Amoskeag Manufacturing Company bought up land and water rights near the 50-foot falls. Gradually a huge textile mill was built which (during the next 75 years) attracted labor from the declining New Hampshire farms; one huge mill employed two-thirds of the city's labor. In 1922 a nine month's strike at the mill started a decline which ended in bankruptcy in 1935. Shortly after, a group of local businessmen bid for the mill and succeeded in leasing space in

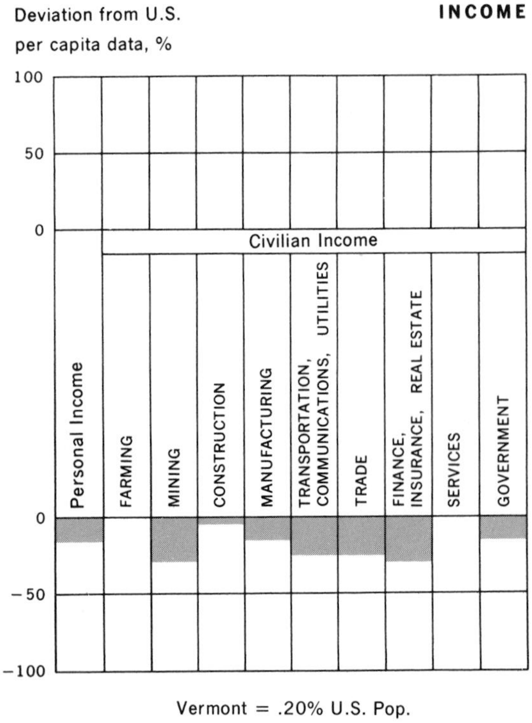

Deviation from U.S. per capita data, %

INCOME

Vermont = .20% U.S. Pop.

FIGURE 5-13   *In spite of its charming cities and countrysides, Vermont, like most of northern New England, is below the national average in most income categories. This would not be true for cities such as Burlington, but high urban indices there are counterbalanced by data from rural areas. Note the relatively high ratings in farming and services (tourism).*

LIKE MANY NEW ENGLAND CITIES, Manchester was based on waterpower, and its once-productive textile mills were crowded along the river and adjacent millraces. The textile industries have moved south and the mills now house a variety of small industries. (Eric M. Sanford.)

it to 120 small industries, attracted by local and state financing, skilled labor, and location less than one hour by rail or expressway from Boston. The Manchester SMSA with over 100,000 people, long the wholesale center for southern New Hampshire, now has added technological industry attracted by locally trained skilled labor.

Portland This metropolitan area of 145,000 is the wholesale and financial center for about half of the million people living in Maine plus the tens of thousands of summer residents. Its well-sheltered harbor, a major fishing port, handles nearly as much tonnage as Boston and like other New England ports handles mainly imports, especially fuel. An oil pipeline connects Portland Harbor with Montreal. Exports are mainly local products, wood pulp and fish, although some wheat is received from a Canadian National rail line built to handle Canadian traffic when the St. Lawrence is closed by ice. In addition, Portland benefits from tourism which brings in about one-seventh of all Maine income.

Northern Maine

The northern three-quarters of Maine contains much empty land—but forests that have been cut over are now yielding a modest harvest of lumber and wood pulp. Its half million people are largely concentrated in a few places, namely in the Penobscot Valley, along the coast, and in the potato area of Aroostook County. The major commercial center is Bangor, which with its suburbs has only 60,000 people. This river port serves a vast region of woods and lakes and provides an outlet for its newsprint, pulp, and lumber. Its industries are largely concentrated on wood and paper products, leather products, textiles, and small-metals manufactures.

Along the coast are fishing and lumbering towns which have developed a considerable resort business. The adjacent countryside, where used at all, produces poultry, dairy products, blueberries, firewood, and Christmas trees. More prosperous is eastern Aroostook County in extreme northeastern Maine, a pocket of glacial soils almost ideal for potatoes which are grown for megalopolitan markets.

CONCLUSIONS

The once Anglo-Saxon population of New England has changed and the populous areas are now largely inhabited by Irish, southern European, and French Canadian stock. Whether these people have the inventive and organizational qualities of the earlier Yankees is of major importance to the region, which has few resources other than capital, ingenuity, and skills. Almost every New England city can give a list of major inventions or other "firsts" which can be attributed to its citizens. Will the future bring forth as much accomplishment? There is no evidence that the new racial stocks cannot learn the skills and traditions of the past. Can New England overcome the emigration of many of its best peoples, the migration of its industries southward and westward, and the growth of rival universities and research laboratories nurtured in Yankee traditions?

New England's population continues to grow except in a few areas in the north, but the rate is below that for the nation as a whole, and there is a net outward migration. The only Yankee state in which population growth has been above the national average is Connecticut.

Our changing economy may improve the competitive positions of New England. As our people demand modern goods, scarcity of power and raw materials may be more and more overshadowed by the possession of skill. Interstate highways are overcoming the barriers of the Berkshires, and planes en route from Europe can stop more easily in Boston than in crowded New York on their way to interior terminals. With the further growth of Megalopolis, an expansion in Massachusetts and Rhode Island comparable to the recent growth of Connecticut seems not unlikely.

SELECTED REFERENCES

ALEXANDER, LEWIS M.: *The Northeastern United States,* Van Nostrand, New York, 1967. One of a series of regional paperbacks.

FEDERAL RESERVE BANK OF BOSTON: *New England Business Review* (monthly). At least half the numbers of the *Review* have material of value to the geographer.

GOTTMAN, JEAN: *Megalopolis: The Urbanized Northeastern Seaboard of the United States,* Twentieth Century Fund, New York, 1961.

GREEN, HOWARD L.: "Hinterland Boundaries of New York City and Boston in Southern New England," *Economic Geography,* vol. 31 (1955), pp. 283–300.

KENNEDY, JOHN F.: "New England and the South," *Atlantic Monthly,* January, 1954, pp. 32–36.

KLIMM, L. E.: "The Empty Areas of Northeastern United States," *Geographical Review,* vol. 44 (1954), pp. 315–45.

MURPHY, RAYMOND E.: *The American City: An Urban Geography,* McGraw-Hill, New York, 1966. Many of the examples are taken from the New England area.

U.S. DEPARTMENT OF AGRICULTURE: *The Changing Fertility of New England Soils,* Agricultural Bulletin no. 133, Washington, 1954.

WARD, DAVID: "The Industrial Revolution and the Emergence of Boston's Central Business District," *Economic Geography,* vol. 42 (1966), pp. 152–171.

WILSON, H. F.: *The Hill Country of New England: 1790–1930,* Columbia University Press, New York, 1936. An interesting study of changing occupations in Vermont and New Hampshire.

WRIGHT, JOHN K. (ed.): *New England's Prospect,* American Geographical Society, New York, 1933. Old but excellent background material.

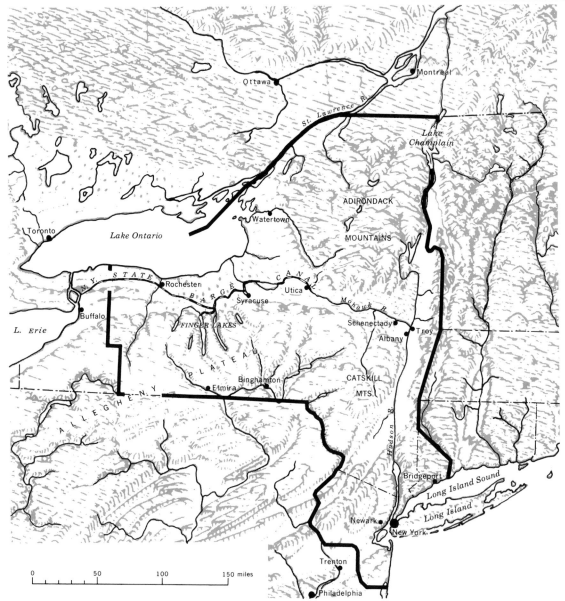

FIGURE 6-1   Landforms of the New York Gateway Region. (Base map copyright by A. K. Lobeck. Reprinted with permission of The Geographical Press, Hammond, Inc.)

CHAPTER 6

NEW YORK: GATEWAY AND MEGALO-POLITAN CAPITAL

New York epitomizes the booming metropolitan civilizations developing in Anglo-America as well as in other continents. Like all such nodal areas, New York is a gateway for diverse ideas, goods, skills, and funds which its enterprisers receive, process, and then deliver to the world markets. Here is a testing ground for new ideas, styles, books, art, businesses, and security issues. On the highest level, New York is an international capital, the scene of the debates and behind-the-scenes maneuvers in the United Nations. Above all, New York is a focus of controls—financial, technical, commercial, political, and artistic. Decisions are made which may alter the way of life throughout the world.

BASIC DATA:

AREA INCLUDES	Land Area (thousand sq. mi.)	Population Change 1950-1960	1960 (thousands)	1967 (thousands)	Personal Income 1967 (billions)
NEW YORK					
GATEWAY	48.3	16.6%	19,426	22,680	$84.4
Most of New York State	44.5	13.0	14,206	16,900	60.6
Fairfield County, Connecticut	0.6	29.6	654	780	3.4
Northern New Jersey	3.2	22.0	4,566	5,100	20.4
NEW YORK METROPOLITAN AREA	4.5	15.1%	15,612	17,530	$64.5
New York City	0.3	−1.4	7,782	8,100	30.2
Other Long Island	1.2	129.2	1,967	2,600	9.7
Westchester and Rockland Counties	0.6	33.9	946	1,150	4.2
Northeastern New Jersey SMSAs	1.8	24.3	4,263	4,900	18.0
Fairfield County	0.6	29.6	654	780	3.4

CLIMATE — Humid continental, influenced by the sea in the New York Metropolitan Region.

	Temperature (°F) Jan.	July	Precipitation (inches) Annual	Season
New York City (Manhattan)	32	74	42	All year
Albany	23	73	33	All year
Rochester	26	72	31	All year

VEGETATION — Second-growth deciduous or mixed forest.

SOIL — Gray-brown podzolic with some podzols; considerable local variations.

MINERALS — Sand, gravel, stone; for New York also iron, lead, zinc, cement rock; for New Jersey also iron and zinc.

Part of New York's power results from its wide-flung contacts. Since the Erie Canal was opened in 1825, its port has been a major entrepôt for goods and men moving between trans-Atlantic routes and the Anglo-American interior. Located halfway between Washington and Boston, New York provides a convenient interchange between the merchants and manufacturers of the Atlantic Megalopolis and the raw-material and industrial producers of the interior. It is blessed with a deep, commodious harbor into which projects the rocky length of Manhattan Island. There New Yorkers have built skyscrapers that have become worldwide symbols of modern urban economies.

UPPER NEW YORK BAY, *one of the world's best natural harbors, is formed by the submerged Lower Hudson Valley. It is sheltered by low, glacially formed hills which cross Staten Island (bottom left) and continue in Brooklyn after an interruption by the Hudson at the narrows, crossed since 1965 by a bridge.* (The Port of New York Authority.)

THE NEW YORK GATEWAY

Physical Setting

The Appalachians, separating the Atlantic Coastal Plain from the interior, are not particularly high among the world's mountain ranges, but before the days of earthmoving machinery their long, parallel ridges constituted an appreciable barrier. These ridges, 2,000 to 6,000 feet high, could be avoided by using three natural routes: to the south the interior can be reached up the tortuous Mississippi after a long bypass around Florida. To the north is the more direct St. Lawrence route, formerly handicapped by the rapids of the upper St. Lawrence River, by

falls over the Niagara Escarpment, and by ice which closes the route one-third of each year. Between these gateways numerous parallel river valleys penetrate inland, cutting across most of the parallel ranges of the Appalachians. Of these, only one, the Hudson-Mohawk route, rises gradually and almost imperceptibly to the 570-foot altitude of Lake Erie. From this natural corridor, other easy routes branch off northward to Montreal, northwestward to Lake Ontario, and south into rolling western New York State (Figure 6-1).

The land around New York Harbor is better suited for trade than for farming.

Ice Age glaciers scraped off New England, piling a mass of sand and boulders to form Long Island, a natural breakwater sheltering Long Island Sound. Protecting Upper New York Bay on the south is Staten Island, a continuation of the same glacier-deposited sand and boulder ridges that formed Long Island. The Narrows, a mile-wide channel carved by the Hudson River, separates the two islands. A rocky, ice-scoured prong of the New England Upland extended south to form the Bronx, separated by the Harlem River from Manhattan Island. Another prong of the New England Upland extended southwestward across northern New Jersey to Reading, Pennsylvania; fortunately for the Hudson-Mohawk route, the Hudson River carved a gorge through this crystalline ridge to form the scenic Hudson Highlands.

Long before men arrived in this area, the coast had been submerged, and ocean waters flooded the valley mouths. The former stream courses formed deep channels in Lower and Upper New York bays and 150 miles up the Hudson. Other channels extended northward through Hell Gate into Long Island Sound and westward toward Newark and Perth Amboy. Although this ramifying harbor has impeded overland transport, necessitating many ferries, bridges, and tunnels, its long waterfront with deepwater connections offered an unrivaled site for docks and slips which could handle anything from launches and canal barges up to the largest ocean liners and aircraft carriers. Its approaches are almost free of fog and ice and require little dredging. It requires no tidal basins, and there is adequate anchorage: its channels, 26 to over 40 feet deep, handle mammoth tonnages with surprisingly little congestion.

The Rise of the New York Gateway

In the early seventeenth century the Dutch established fur-trading posts on southern Manhattan Island and upstream near the site of Albany. Settlement was somewhat speeded up after British annexation (1664), so that by the outbreak of the American Revolution most of the land draining into the Hudson had been at least sparsely settled. Although New York was a major colonial port, it was neither as populous as Philadelphia nor as influential as Boston. But after the Revolution, the skill of its merchants, the regularity of its shipping services, and the rise of a transshipment service to smaller Atlantic ports aided its growth (Table 6-1). The foreign trade of New York quadrupled from 1800 to 1830 when New York became the most populous American city, handling about three-eighths of all United States foreign trade. About the same time the settlement of western New York and Ohio and the opening of the Erie Canal stimulated further development. Railways, canals, and turnpikes rivaled one another for traffic to and from the interior. Which-

TABLE 6-1   Population of Northeastern Port Cities, 1770-1960 (in thousands)

City	1770	1800	1850	1900	1960 (city)	1960 (metropolitan area)
Montreal	5	15	175	326	1,150	2,000
Boston	16	25	137	561	697	2,589
New York	21	64	696	3,437	7,782	14,289
Philadelphia	28	81	408	1,294	2,002	4,342
Baltimore	5	27	168	509	939	1,727

SOURCES: R. R. Palmer (ed.), *Atlas of World History*, Rand McNally, Chicago, 1947, p. 195; and U.S. Bureau of the Census, *Statistical Abstract of the United States*, Washington, 1961, pp. 14-20, 24-25.

ever vehicle was used, New York possessed the best natural route so that by 1860 five-eighths of all American foreign trade was channeled through New York.

New York was also the major port through which immigrants entered the country. After quarantine inspection at Ellis Island, they sought foreign neighborhoods where they could seek employment in their own language groups. Although many moved inland, others replenished their meager wallets by working at such industries as clothing, packing, and construction. Immigrant labor was a major factor in New York industrial development.

The Recent Growth of New York

Until 1930 the New York Area grew more rapidly than the country as a whole, for the maturing nation demanded more and more of the services offered there. Ambitious young Americans, as well as immigrants, were attracted by the opportunities of the growing metropolis. Since 1940 this growth has slowed down because its congested area has not attracted people as much as Florida and California. Yet in the decade 1950–1960, the New York Metropolitan region was not stagnant; its population increased 15 percent, about four-fifths the growth rate for the nation. The continued importance of New York seems assured, since its own people—earning over one-tenth of the nation's income—provide in themselves a huge market for goods and services.

THE METROPOLIS AND ITS HINTERLAND

It is no easy matter to map the hinterland of the Port of New York; indeed hinterland boundaries are among the least certain of regional boundaries.[1] Specific types of businesses and individual firms may depart from

the general hinterland pattern which itself is bounded by transition zones rather than sharp lines.

The New York Hinterland

The New York hinterland today is much larger in area but much less productive than the Metropolitan area. Upstate New York, for example, has 1.2 million more people than New York City but the total personal income of these people is one-eighth less than that earned in New York City. Decades ago when farming was relatively more important in the economy, the upstate hinterland played a larger part in the prosperity of the metropolis; now it provides such necessities as water supply, dairy products, and recreational areas; in addition its medium-sized and small cities add to industrial diversity within the New York Gateway.

The Hudson-Mohawk route   By far the most developed sector of the New York hinterland is parallel to the Hudson-Mohawk route. North from New York City the wide, brackish Hudson estuary is adjoined by well-settled suburbs which soon give way to the wooded recreational lands and wooded estates of the Hudson Highlands. Beyond the highlands the Hudson occupies a northern part of the Great Appalachian Valley; clearly visible to the west from the river are the so-called "Catskill Mountains," actually the eastern edge of the Appalachian Plateau, a resort area which also is the major source of New York City water supply. The 32-foot Hudson channel terminates at Albany, state capital and port for ocean vessels. A few miles north the New York State Barge Canal (and major rail–highway routes) turn westward up the Mohawk Valley, finally connecting with the Great Lakes at Buffalo. Most of this route is adjoined by pastoral rolling countryside, largely used for dairy farming but with specialized orchard and vineyard areas. The northern part of New York State, however, includes

---

[1] For a discussion of these problems, see Donald J. Patton, "General Cargo Hinterlands of New York, Philadelphia, Baltimore, and New Orleans," *Annals A.A.G.*, vol. 48 (1958), pp. 436–455; also Howard L. Green, "Hinterland Boundaries of New York City and Boston in Southern New England," *Economic Geography*, vol. 31 (1955), pp. 283–300.

THE MOHAWK VALLEY ascends gradually from the Hudson River toward the level of the Great Lakes. This "water-level route" carries two railways, the canalized Mohawk River, an expressway, and two other highways. (New York State Department of Commerce.)

the rugged Adirondacks, lake-strewn mountains ideal for vacationlands.

The New York State Department of Commerce divides the state into 12 economic areas (Figure 6-2). The areas along the Hudson-Mohawk route are summarized in Table 6-2 which shows the predominance of New York City and the considerable diversity along the Hudson-Mohawk routes. Specific industries in each area and town are attributable to local resources, historical accident such as the founding of a factory by a local businessman, or to the fact that the industry could have been located anywhere on a through route provided the city had labor, buildings, and other attractions. Of the many cities along the Hudson-Mohawk route, two of the largest will serve as samples.

Syracuse SMSA, in 1967 populated by over 650,000, includes the site of an Indian village which served as the capital of the Iroquois Confederacy. Indian trails, the ancestors of modern routes, converged there. The site became more attractive to white men when salt springs were discovered just south of Lake Onondaga; about the beginning of the nineteenth century, Salina and nearby towns supplied salt to the northeast including the upper Ohio Valley. With the construction of the Erie Canal to Syracuse in 1820, that village to the east of the salt springs overshadowed and eventually absorbed the salt towns. Salt shipments continued important until after the Civil War when the declining springs were abandoned for brine wells used by a growing chemical industry. About the same time, Syracuse

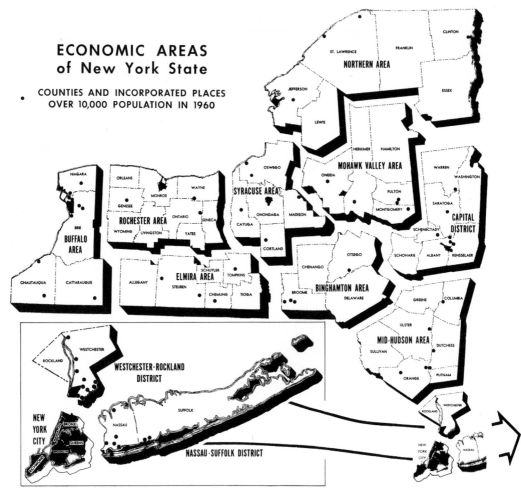

ECONOMIC AREAS of New York State

COUNTIES AND INCORPORATED PLACES OVER 10,000 POPULATION IN 1960

FIGURE 6-2   Twelve economic areas of New York State, according to the State of New York Department of Commerce (Table 6-2).

turned to the manufacture of metal products. Today durable goods (electrical equipment, air-conditioning equipment, alloy steel products, and pottery) are the leading industries. In recent decades the Erie Canal has been replaced by the New York State Barge Canal, located north of Syracuse as is the New York State Thruway. The city's industries are consequently locating northward, while the city center is a growing commercial center with trade and services now accounting for more than half of all SMSA jobs.

Rochester, a somewhat more populous SMSA, has a setting in many ways similar to that of Syracuse, yet differences in both environment and leadership have given it a different character. The settlement was founded about 1790 to use the waterpower of the Genesee River for sawmilling and flour milling, especially the latter. As grain production shifted westward, the economic base shifted to seeds, orchards, and plants and to the use of immigrant labor to manufacture ready-made clothing. Industrial emphasis changed again because of the leadership of a handful of science-oriented men. Outstanding was George Eastman, a local

TABLE 6-2   Economic Data for Areas on the Hudson-Mohawk Route (in millions except per capita income)

| | | | | Income, 1964 | | |
Area	Population 1966	Per Capita	Farm	Trade Wages	Services Wages	Manufacturing Wages
NEW YORK STATE	17.903	$3,162	$340	$8,146	$5,762	$10,920
New York City	7.960	3,251	1	5,220	3,987	5,123
Nassau–Suffolk	2.386	3,497	23	736	416	881
Westchester–Rockland	1.050	4,516	3	366	249	526
Mid-Hudson	0.730	2,594	37	170	119	374
Capital District	0.807	2,520	16	281	183	444
Northern Area	0.388	1,810	33	72	53	124
Mohawk Valley	0.466	2,275	21	100	57	273
Syracuse Area	0.739	2,408	35	237	135	452
Rochester Area	1.027	2,862	88	304	182	932

Area	Major Industries, 1964
New York City	Clothing, food, printing, etc.
Nassau–Suffolk	Aircraft, machinery, instruments
Westchester–Rockland	Food, electronic, chemicals, clothing
Mid-Hudson	Machinery, clothing, resorts
Capital District	Electrical, paper, chemicals
Northern Area	Paper, aluminum, resorts
Mohawk Valley	Metals, machinery
Syracuse Area	Machinery, food, chemicals
Rochester Area	Photographic, food, machinery, men's clothing

SOURCES: New York State Department of Commerce, *Business Fact Book*, 1966 Supplement, Albany, 1967, and Business Fact Books on each area. Per capita and farm incomes are given by place of residence; wages where earned.

clerk who in 1880 turned his hobby into a business by inventing the dry photographic plate. Others were John Bausch and Henry Lomb, William Gleason, and George Taylor. Consequently photographic equipment and instruments now dominate industrial Rochester, with machinery second, food products third, and apparel a poor fourth.

The southern route   South of the Hudson-Mohawk route in the southern tier of New York counties the rolling lands of the northern Allegheny Plateau have also been occupied. Thence routes to the coastal cities were extremely indirect, extending either northward via the Erie Canal or southward along

the winding Susquehanna Valley whose stream was interrupted at low water by shallows and rapids. Agitation developed for a railroad, and in 1851 the Erie Railroad was completed from the Jersey shore of the Hudson to Lake Erie.

The terrain northwest of New York City is extremely rugged although its ridges rise generally to only 2,000 feet. Its valleys open to the north and south, not toward New York Harbor, and its ridges trend northeast-southwest. Considerable areas 30 miles from the city remain almost uninhabited, and even in recent decades some areas have declined in population. Nevertheless this area could be traversed if there was sufficient incentive. The headwaters of the Delaware, the Susquehanna, and minor streams were close together, and gaps in the ridges could be found if winding routes were followed.

The incentives were the needs for anthracite coal from the Appalachian ridges and valleys of Pennsylvania, and lumber, found there and in the Allegheny Plateau to the west. Soon a group of railroads, often referred to as the Anthracite Roads, entered into competition with the Erie. The Delaware, Lackawanna and Western and the Lehigh Valley railroads extended their lines to Buffalo. Anthracite spurs were also constructed by the Reading, the Pennsylvania, and the Central Railroad of New Jersey. One coal line even extended to central New England, using the famed Poughkeepsie Bridge across the Hudson to bypass New York City.

In New York State the southern route serves the low northern end of the Allegheny Plateau where agriculture is generally declining except in favored areas along the Finger Lakes where wine grapes are a specialty. More than half the income is earned in manufacturing, concentrated in the Binghamton SMSA and a number of smaller cities, each with a few specialties based on a skilled labor supply developed by a progressive business organization. Thus the Binghamton SMSA has Endicott-Johnson shoes, International Business Machines (IBM), and Ansco (photographic equipment), all concerns which require accessibility to northeastern markets but whose costs are not based on orientation to specific raw materials.

The Coastal Plain Eastern Long Island and central New Jersey form a generally infertile, sandy area, mostly classified as *pine barrens,* sparse scrubby woodland not good enough for lumbering. It has one major advantage: space near New York City. With the expansion of the rail net, its beaches became vacationlands for New Yorkers. With the arrival of the Air Age, its interior provided space for commercial and military airfields. With metropolitan expansion, its more accessible areas are being occupied by residential suburbs.

Three main highways, a freeway, eight railroad tracks, numerous pipelines, and a little-used waterway cross the Plain between New York and Philadelphia. The rural area between the New York and Philadelphia suburbs is barely a dozen miles, and even these green strips may disappear within the next decade. Fortunately for lovers of fresh air, a relatively uncrowded area stretches east of the Philadelphia–New York–Boston axis. In eastern New Jersey wide beaches, some intensively used in summer but others relatively untenanted, offer swimming for the urban millions who live only an hour or two away. Sea breezes keep midday temperatures down, and numerous lagoons and inlets offer fishing and boating for those so inclined. So heavy is the beach traffic in summer that New Jersey has found it worthwhile to build a north-south toll road all the way to its southeastern tip.

THE LOCAL GEOGRAPHY OF THE NEW YORK METROPOLIS

The New York Metropolitan Area is so large and so complicated that doing business there would be chaotic if it were not geographically organized. Few New Yorkers know all the Metropolitan area or understand its organization; almost all, however, have visited its Central Business District and understand that part of its complicated organization relevant to their particular tasks.

An analysis of the New York metropolitan organization is available in a 10-volume survey of the New York Metropolitan Re-

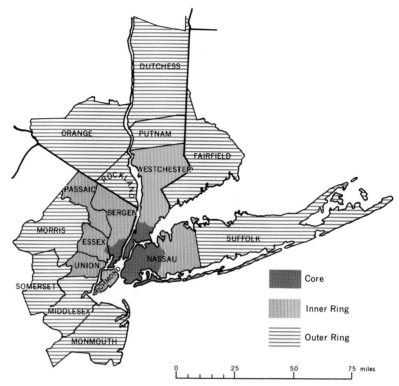

FIGURE 6-3   Three zones used in planning for the extended New York Metropolitan Region. (After Hoover and Vernon.)

gion.[2] The area used for planning, divided into three zones (Figure 6-3), is somewhat more extensive than the Bureau of the Census New York–Northeastern New Jersey Standard Consolidated Area. The 17 million population of the New York area and its significance as the largest central place in the Anglo-American economy have justified its description in more detail than will be possible for other American metropolises.

The Central Business Districts

As the New York Metropolitan Area includes a considerable number of cities, there are many CBDs, each identifiable by its tall buildings and by its financial and commercial employment. Most of these

CBDs have local functions only; a few, such as downtown Brooklyn, Jersey City, and Newark, have some national functions. The major CBD with international, national, and local functions occupies Manhattan Island south of 60th Street, an area about 2 miles wide and 4 miles long, whose skyscrapers form a high, jagged skyline when seen from adjacent waters.

History and the Manhattan pattern   Many of the New York City patterns described below are also found in other Anglo-American metropolitan areas but are especially characteristic near New York. Most of the older cities have a section of irregularly laid-out streets such as those of lower Manhattan. Most too have had their topography modified by construction projects. For example, the coastline of Manhattan has been filled

[2] Of these, the volumes by Hoover and Vernon and by Vernon listed in the Selected References have been used largely to supplement the author's knowledge of the area in which he was brought up.

in to create additional land so that Greenwich Street, which bordered the Hudson shore in 1830, is now two blocks inland.

In 1812 the City Hall was completed one mile north of the southern tip of Manhattan; the city was not expected to grow much further north. However it did grow and developed street patterns which although generally rectangular, consisted of diverse sections; the section on the west being parallel to the Hudson shore, that on the southeast parallel to the East River, while the central streets paralleled the axis of the island.

Soon a more systematic street pattern became desirable (Figure 6-4), and, beginning in the suburb of Greenwich Village, the city was laid out northward in rectangular blocks. The approximately north-south avenues were numbered from east to west and designed as wide parkways parallel to the axis of the island. The approximately east-west numbered streets were narrow except for certain parkway streets. The wide avenues have proved a tremendous advantage to north-south traffic and the broader east-west streets have become principal shopping and business streets. When the first subway was constructed in 1904, the subway stations were located at each of the broader east-west streets.

By 1855 the city had grown north of 42nd Street (about 4 miles from the southern tip of the island). In 1871 the railroad terminal was moved from Broadway west of City Hall to a more northern location at East 42nd Street and Fourth Avenue, the site of the present Grand Central Terminal, and through trains to Boston and Chicago became available. Other railroads terminated on the New Jersey shore and brought their passengers and freight to Manhattan entirely by ferry until 1908–1910 when railway tunnels under the Hudson and East rivers were completed. The wholesale grocery and produce markets still remain on the New Jersey side of the Hudson shore, and much freight is still handled by ferry.

The present Manhattan pattern   Figure 6-5 reflects the historical development of Manhattan. The old nucleus centered on Wall Street and lower Broadway has become the Financial District. The older ferry terminals and wharves adjoin this area; later on shipping terminals expanded northward along the North (Hudson) River to 70th Street. The wholesale districts were on the western side of the CBD because the bulk of business was along the Hudson-Mohawk routes or westward across New Jersey. As the railroad terminals moved north, a midtown business section developed especially between 34th Street (Pennsylvania Station) and the theatrical district (east and west of Broadway, 38th Street to Central Park) and eastward around Grand Central Terminal. Between the downtown and midtown business sections many apartments and rooming houses were constructed, especially in Greenwich Village and northward in the narrower streets. The eastern bulge of the Manhattan CBD, somewhat away from the main course of business, consists of slum tenements which are gradually being replaced by modern apartment sections, financed either by the city or by insurance companies. Manufacturing consists largely of loft industries, that is, industries which occupy single floors (or less) of large buildings and whose main requirement is nearness to market and labor. The largest of the loft industries is the garment industry (located roughly in the center of the CBD) whose many contractors and subcontractors must keep in close touch with one another, with the wholesalers of cloth, dresses, suits, and trimmings, and with the creators of changing styles. In and north of the garment district is the major retail shopping area, located mainly on Fifth Avenue and such broad transverse streets as 34th, 42nd, and 57th. Within and around

FIGURE 6-4   *Street map for downtown Manhattan and adjacent New Jersey and Long Island. Notice the irregularities in the street plan of lower Manhattan, the regular street plan of most of Manhattan, and the convergence of the original street plans of the separate towns. The passenger ferries shown have been recently discontinued, but freight ferries (especially car ferries) are still significant.* (Map after New Jersey Geological Survey.)

the retail shopping and midtown office districts are the major hotels.

Each morning converging subways, railways, ferries, and buses bring over a million workers into the CBD and take them home at night. At least half come from the core area, but 600,000 are commuters from the Inner or Outer Ring. In strong contrast to most American metropolitan areas, few workers travel to the CBD by private automobile since parking space is expensive and rush-hour expressway driving is much slower than the frequent rail services.

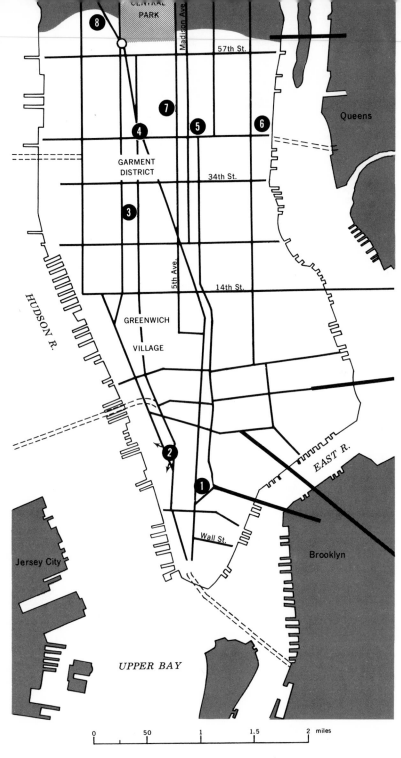

FIGURE 6-5 *A sketch map showing the Manhattan CBD and the location of places in the text. The older part of the city includes City Hall (1) and the produce markets (2). The midtown business district developed between Pennsylvania Station (3) and Grand Central Terminal (5). Times Square (4) is the center of the theatrical district. Recent developments are Rockefeller Center (7), the United Nations (6), and Lincoln Center (8).*

Less apparent to the visitor is the network of communications which makes innumerable business contacts possible. First of all are the skyscrapers which are anchored to the hard metamorphic rocks underlying Manhattan. High-speed elevators connect the various floors of each skyscraper, making it possible for businessmen to confer with many others in a few minutes' journey; a convenient arrangement because offices in related businesses are commonly found in the same building or nearby. For example, Rockefeller Center, with 15 buildings housing 34,000 workers, specializes in various aspects of communication. An efficient subway system makes it possible to go from the midtown office district to Wall Street in 20 minutes. Much business between these districts is, of course, conducted by telephone.

Space in the Manhattan CBD is valuable, and many businesses divide their work. For example, some publishers have their offices in the midtown office district, but the books and magazines they edit are printed and shipped from suburban towns. Insurance companies have their main offices in the CBD, but much of their clerical work may be performed in outlying areas. Five-sixths of the city's wholesalers have their showrooms in Manhattan, but their warehouses may be in the suburbs. More than half of all value added by manufacturing in New York City is produced in Manhattan, but this is concentrated in industries where style and design are more important than bulk, for example, apparel, jewelry, and costume jewelry. The concentration in the CBD is most apparent in the service industries.

The Core beyond the Manhattan CBD

The core is divided into segments by waterways (especially the Hudson and so-called "Harlem" and "East" rivers), by cemeteries and parks, and by present or former political boundaries. Each segment has a CBD and, in addition, a number of neighborhood shopping centers and apartment house areas which have developed around subway and railroad stations. The periphery of the core contains more private homes, often with whole blocks built in a uniform pattern. Most single houses near the CBDs have been converted into small apartments.

The older residential sections if located in an unusually attractive setting have been refurbished or rebuilt into stylish apartments. Examples of these areas are: adjacent to Central Park, along Riverside Drive overlooking the Hudson, and in Brooklyn Heights directly across the East River from the Wall Street Financial District. Less attractive older sections have become slums or at least homes for less privileged groups; for example, Manhattan north of Central Park is a Puerto Rican section which merges into Harlem, the Negro section centered on 125th Street. In central Brooklyn the once stylish Bedford-Stuyvesant section has become a Negro section.

The Bronx This borough, separated from Manhattan by a strait called the Harlem River, is largely a lower and middle-class residential area with more than half of its workers employed elsewhere. Compared with the other large boroughs, its industry is small, employing less than one-tenth of its labor force.

Queens This borough is also largely residential, and more than half of its workers are employed elsewhere. More recently settled than the Bronx, its population is still growing and includes many workers in the upper salary brackets. Originally the borough consisted of many small towns, each with distinctive street patterns and considerable community consciousness. In addition to many fine residential towns, Queens also includes Kennedy and La Guardia airports and scattered industrial areas.

Brooklyn   Before it merged with New York City, the most populous borough was an independent city, and its correct post office address remains Brooklyn, New York. Like Queens, it started as a number of separate towns, many founded by early Dutch settlers. Although two-fifths of its workers are employed elsewhere, Brooklyn has an active business of its own including a CBD across the East River from lower Manhattan. Yet Manhattan dominates each type of activity in the core (Table 6-3). Brooklyn leads Manhattan in industries involving weight or bulk: food products, chemicals, fabricated metal products, machinery, toys, and sporting goods. Although some factories are scattered along the railroads, most are located on or near docks of the East River or Upper New York Bay.

Hudson County, New Jersey   Although most passenger liners dock in Manhattan, freighters are likely to unload in either Brooklyn or Hudson County. The New Jersey area illustrates how physical difficulties may be overcome if a site is strategically located. The Jersey shore of the Hudson is overlooked by a mile-wide upland of volcanic rock, 400 feet high in the north and less than 100 feet high in the Bayonne peninsula. The well-settled summit of the upland is fairly flat or rolling; the narrow lowland to the east has been built out in places a mile or more to make filled land for terminals and docks. Six railroads cross Hudson County and terminate at its docks; two of these cross Newark Bay by trestle and avoid the high area; the northern lines pass by cuts or tunnels through the volcanic rock.

Hudson County's wholesalers share with Newark the northern New Jersey market, fourth largest in the United States. The bulkier industries (petroleum, chemicals, fabricated metals) are concentrated to the south in Bayonne, while cities to the north have extremely diversified industries including machinery, clothing, and packaging. As in the other core counties, three-tenths of the labor force works outside the county, probably in lower Manhattan.

The Inner Ring (Figure 6-6)

There is no sharp line except political boundaries between the Core and the Inner Ring. The Inner Ring includes towns and cities which had (and in many cases still have) independent economies of their own before they were integrated into the metropolitan area. Cities such as Newark (405,000) have sizable CBDs as well as specialized industries. The Inner Ring has more manufacturing than the outer Core and is especially suitable for industries requiring space. Its residential towns have on the whole larger houses on larger plots than are to be found in the Core. Most of the workers in the Inner Ring work in their home counties; many of the commuters travel to local centers such as Newark.

TABLE 6-3   New York Core Business Activity by County or Borough, 1963 (in millions of dollars)

	Wholesale Sales	Retail Sales	Selected Services	Value Added by Manufacturing
Manhattan	46,366	4,339	5,923	4,713
Brooklyn	2,553	2,651	434	2,127
Queens	2,851	2,053	465	1,417
Bronx	1,078	1,201	189	473
Hudson County, N.J.	1,121	705	134	1,385

SOURCE: U.S. Bureau of the Census, *Census of Manufactures: 1963;* and *Census of Business: 1963,* Washington, 1966.

FIGURE 6-6   *The Inner Ring of the New York Metropolis.*

Each part of the Inner Ring has distinctive characteristics; a few examples will suffice. Thus, Newark metropolitan area has durable-goods manufacturing as the principal source of employment (Figure 6-7) in contrast to the Core area where nondurable goods are far ahead. With a deepwater port, uncongested connections by four railroads and numerous highways, the Newark area is well suited to produce chemicals, fabricated metal goods, machinery, electrical goods, and packed foodstuffs. More than two-fifths of the labor force works in factories; in addition, Newark is the commercial and banking center of northern New Jersey.

Westchester County, just north of New York City, is well known as a residential county for upper-class commuters. Thirteen percent of its wage earners earn over $10,000 per year, and 55 percent are white-collar workers. However, this picture is changing since industry has discovered Westchester County. With a seaport at Yonkers and many of the same rail and highway connections at New York City through the Hudson-Mohawk route, this uncongested area with a well-educated labor force seems ideal for many industries. In addition to automobile assembly, elevators, cable, chemical, and publishing industries which have long been established, food packing, pharmaceutical, electronics, ordnance, and machinery industries have been set up. Nassau County, just east of Queensborough on Long Island, in many respects duplicates Westchester County as a commuting, residential, and light industrial county.

Most of the Inner Ring areas have many of the advantages of the Core without its congestion and high land prices. In fact, some of the typical CBD industries (apparel, and printing and publishing) have begun to move to the Inner Ring. So prosperous are many of the Inner Ring communities that luxurious suburban shopping centers, including branches of Fifth Avenue shops, have been established there.

The Outer Ring

Available land in the Inner Ring is being rapidly occupied; thus the once marshy areas such as the Hackensack Meadows between Newark and Jersey City are being developed for industries such as chemicals. In contrast, the Outer Ring includes much land yet unused for urban purposes: farmland, wooded hills, sandspits, and tidal marshes. The Outer Ring provides water supplies for New Jersey cities and parts of New York City.

The Outer Ring also provides a small but significant part of the food of the metropolis: Suffolk County on eastern Long Island supplies poultry and vegetables; rural northern New Jersey also has intensive farming with eggs, milk, potatoes, vegetables, and apples as specialties. The Hudson Valley and northern Fairfield County, Connecticut, supply milk, poultry, fruits, and perishable vegetables.

Bridgeport, Connecticut, is an example of an Outer Ring city. Although it is a city of over 150,000, one-tenth of its workers commute to the New York Metropolitan Area 56 miles away. Its local industries specialize in metals and turn out such diverse goods as machinery, sewing machines, helicopters, firearms, and cable. The location of these industries could be explained in part by the once important port and by the traditional skill of Connecticut metalworkers; today, however, location near the New York market is the major advantage.

FUNCTIONS OF THE METROPOLITAN REGION

Manufacturing (Figure 6-8)

Manufacturing for national and international markets is the largest single source of employment in the New York Metropolitan

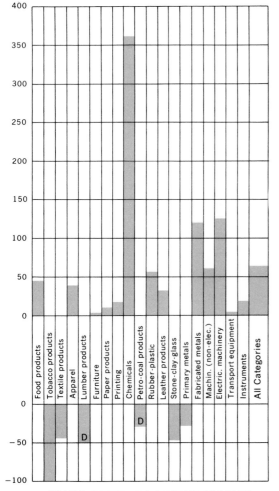

Deviation from U.S. per capita data, %

VALUE ADDED BY MANUFACTURING

Newark SMSA = .95% U.S. Pop.

FIGURE 6-7   *A comparison of this graph with Figure 6-8 shows that Newark has an industrial pattern that is in part similar to and in part distinctive from the pattern for the entire New York area.*

Area. The value added by manufacturing—nearly $20 billion annually—is about one-seventh of the industrial production of the United States and includes some of almost every type of industry. Statistical analysis shows that the bulk of this industry is concentrated in certain specialties and that within the New York area there is a definite distributional pattern (Table 6-4).

Table 6-4 shows that only two categories, apparel and printing and publishing, are highly concentrated in Manhattan. Heavy industries such as primary metals (largely copper), chemicals, and machinery are concentrated in less crowded northeastern New Jersey. Food-products industries, in part port industries but more largely industries supplying the local markets, are found near the residential sections.

Shipping

New York was a commercial center and a seaport long before it became an industrial center, and it remains the predominant American port. It handles more overseas passengers than all other American ports combined and is by far the leading United States air terminal. The heaviest port traffic consists of imports and coastwise receipts—in other words, fuels and raw materials. Many of the coastwise receipts originate in Gulf of Mexico ports and supplement oil shipped by pipeline from Texas and Louisiana. Large quantities of fuel oil and some bituminous coal are delivered directly to power plants, most of which are located on the shoreline, some even occupying valuable land on the edge of the Manhattan CBD.

General cargo which includes a wide variety of manufactured goods is relatively low in tonnage but high in value. Such cargo accounts for the fact that New York has in some years handled nearly half of the United States seaborne trade by value. This type of trade also adds to New York's wholesale business which distributes most general cargo imports.

Where is New York's general cargo hinterland? Railroad carload figures showed that New York surpassed other ports in imports destined to and exports from Connecticut, New York, New Jersey, and the

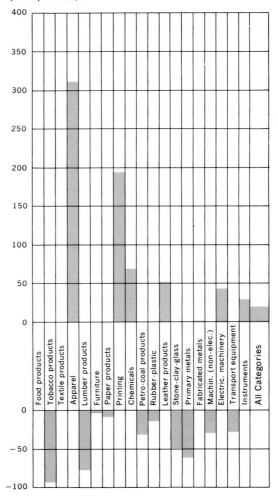

FIGURE 6-8   This graph and Figure 6-7 should be compared with the data in Table 6-4. The table enables the student to compare various industries within the New York area; the graph compares each category with the same category for the United States.

VALUE ADDED BY MANUFACTURING

Greater N.Y.C. – N.E. New Jersey

Standard Consolidated Area = 8.12% U.S. Pop.

THE JOHN F. KENNEDY International Airport, about 10 miles east of Upper New York Bay, was constructed on marshy land adjoining Jamaica Bay. Three other commercial airports aid Kennedy in handling the busy international and national traffic, and others are being planned. (The Port of New York Authority.)

eastern Great Lakes states. New York also handled an appreciable import and export business for Quebec and Ontario and for all but a few states in the western interior.

To what extent this trade has been changed by the St. Lawrence Seaway is yet to be determined; for general cargo the change will probably be minor since service via New

TABLE 6-4   Value Added by Manufacturing in Leading Industrial Categories: New York–Northeastern New Jersey Consolidated Area, 1963 (in millions of dollars)

Industrial Categories	N.Y.–NE N.J. Consolidated Area	Manhattan	Brooklyn	NE N.J.
Machinery	2,737	141	236	1,387
Apparel	2,674	1,739	318	350
Printing and Publishing	2,579	1,807	90	295
Chemicals	2,484	100	271	1,261
Food Products	1,797	102	389	738
Transportation Equipment	1,301	11	58	254
Fabricated Metals	1,000	38	162	455
Instruments	581	51	19	100
Textiles	508	115	107	186
Primary Metals	498	37	41	211
Subtotal	16,159	4,141	1,691	5,237
Total, all categories	19,133	4,713	2,128	6,403

SOURCE: U.S. Bureau of the Census, *Census of Manufactures: 1963*, Washington, 1966.

York by rail or truck is so much faster than by water.

What equipment does New York have to handle this mammoth trade? At one time its piers, wharves, and bulkheads can berth 400 ocean ships, in addition to small ships and barges destined for inland waterways. About 500 tugs help maneuver ocean ships and also about 5,000 other harbor craft, including barges, lighters, car floats, and floating grain elevators. Car floats transport over 1 million freight cars annually and can deliver the 70 percent of the freight handled by rail from any rail terminal to any ship in the harbor. In addition, 25,000 or more trucks enter the city each weekday.

Nearly half a million people are employed in transportation and related activities connected with the business of the port. Many of the goods handled simply pass across the docks en route to or from the interior. Since mechanical conveyors are largely used in loading, much of this business provides little employment within the metropolis. Other goods, for example, oil, sugar, and copper, are processed by local port industries, conspicuous especially in the Inner and Outer Rings. But again these industries are so highly automated that they use comparatively little labor. For example, the value added by the petroleum refining industry is less than $134 million. Other raw materials enter into more complicated industries, for example, the primary nonferrous metals industry (1963 value added, $47 million) supplies raw materials to nonferrous rolling and drawing industries (value added, $228 million) which in turn supplies raw materials to the electrical machinery industry (value added, $1,757 million). Thus raw materials shipped in through the port pyramid into considerable employment (in the electrical machinery industry, 179,000).

The Port of New York, mammoth as it is, has in recent decades lost in relative position to competing ports. Transocean freight rates to other ports are lower or the same as to New York; yet the rail and truck rates to some interior points are lower and the congestion less. New York holds its own on goods with a high value per ton supplied to merchants and manufacturers emphasizing quality. Bulky industries are either leaving the New York area or moving toward its Outer Ring.

New York as a Shopping Center

Many goods can be purchased equally well through the nearest convenient outlet, be it a Podunk general store or a New York supermarket. But consider an evening dress, a fancy necktie, jewelry, or a dining room table; such articles are available in a wide range of price, taste, and quality. These are goods for which people enjoy shopping and for which, in general, the broadest choice is in the largest market—in other words, in New York City. Shoppers can choose to visit moderate-price stores on 34th Street or Sixth Avenue, the higher-quality department stores on Fifth Avenue, or the numerous specialty shops on Fifth Avenue and 57th Street.

Shopping is not limited to the retail buyer. Each year thousands of buyers for medium-sized and large stores throughout the United States arrive in New York to shop for their stores. Dress buyers note the new styles available and place their orders through New York wholesalers. These buyers are not only customers—they are also arbiters of new styles, each selecting what he thinks will appeal to his store's customers. The more popular models will then be produced quickly in quantities by the midtown Manhattan clothing industry.

Maintaining National Markets

Many goods are bought and sold in Manhattan which never appear physically within the New York area. The financial pages of New York papers provide daily quotations for a wide range of commodities as well as for thousands of securities, and brokers can provide up-to-the-minute quotations. The maintenance of such markets facilitates business decisions everywhere and provides a nationwide price basis for a variety of financial transactions.

Banking Services

Not only are New Yorkers well supplied with capital, but also banks and corporations elsewhere may earn interest by depositing large parts of their financial reserves in New York banks. These banks are in an unusually strong position to make loans to businesses which may not be able to procure large enough loans in smaller cities. For this reason, banks in the New York Federal Reserve District make over one-third of all commercial loans in the nation, and nearly two-fifths of these loans are to firms outside the New York Federal Reserve District. In addition, most long-term investment transactions are arranged by syndi-

cates of investment bankers in New York City. Each banking house in the syndicate, with its branch offices and correspondents throughout the country, sells the securities to clients with funds awaiting investment.

Professional Services

The performance of the various manufacturing, shipping, selling, marketing, and financing services described above requires the occasional services of a host of experts. Engineers and scientists are needed to design and test new products and to design the machinery to make them. Designers make the new goods attractive to the public, and advertisers persuade the consumers that the goods are desirable. Financial experts may advise whether the new operation should be financed by the sale of stock or bonds or by bank loans. Legal experts will check procedures to ensure that the new business is operating within the law. Finally many personal services are required by workers in the business, for example, services of doctors, dentists, beauticians, morticians, and entertainers. Thus each new business creates demands for other employment, and the metropolitan economy expands.

Managerial Services

Every aspect of business, whether in small towns or cities, involves management, but the top-management decisions are most likely to be made in New York. There responsible businessmen can get technical and professional advice and the feel of national markets, and can learn of the availability of financing before making decisions that may affect the jobs and well-being of millions throughout the country.

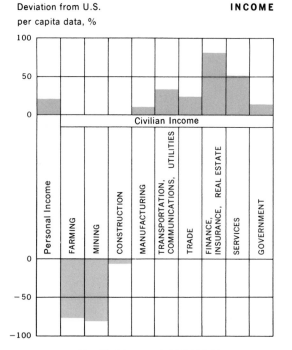

New York State = 9.21% U.S. Pop.

FIGURE 6-9   Compare this deviation graph with that for neighboring Connecticut (Figure 5-11). How are the two similar? How and why are they different?

CONCLUSIONS

In most European cities political, business, and cultural leadership is provided in such capitals as London, Paris, and Vienna. In the United States, political powers are focused in Washington, but business and cultural decisions are made largely in New York. This does not necessarily mean that New York dominates the country although no doubt it has considerable leadership. Rather New York institutions attempt to discover what policies will meet the wishes of potential customers throughout the country. As a funnel through which European styles and other influences enter the United States, New York introduces new ideas and new products into the country as well as encouraging the export of American ideas and products. On the assumption that the best information and skill are to be found in the largest center, most large American businesses and many cultural organizations consider it worthwhile to maintain quarters and make major policy decisions in the Manhattan CBD.

Will New York's leadership continue? Certainly Californians are trying to move the cultural, business, and industrial leadership to the Pacific Coast. Another rival is Chicago where the Great Lakes–St. Lawrence Seaway meets the world's greatest focus of railways near the center of Anglo-American population. However, the New York Area with its early start, with its year-round port to service the American end of the great trans-Atlantic trade route, seems likely to maintain first place. New York City like many metropolitan cores is slowly losing population, but its Inner and Outer Rings are growing vigorously and contributing to its growing metropolitan economy.

SELECTED REFERENCES

CITY OF NEW YORK DEPARTMENT OF COMMERCE AND PUBLIC EVENTS: *New York: The City That Belongs to the World,* 1964.

GOTTMANN, JEAN: *Megaolopolis: The Urbanized Northeastern Seaboard of the United States,* Twentieth Century Fund, New York, 1961.

HOOVER, E. M., and RAYMOND VERNON: *Anatomy of a Metropolis,* Doubleday, Garden City, 1962.

PATTON, D. J.: "General Cargo Hinterlands of New York, Philadelphia, Baltimore, and New Orleans," *Annals A.A.G.,* vol. 48 (1958), pp. 436–55.

THOMPSON, JOHN H. (ed.): *Geography of New York State,* Syracuse University Press, Syracuse, 1966.

VERNON, RAYMOND: *Metropolis: 1985,* Doubleday, Garden City, 1961.

CHAPTER 7

THE DELAWARE-CHESAPEAKE GATEWAYS

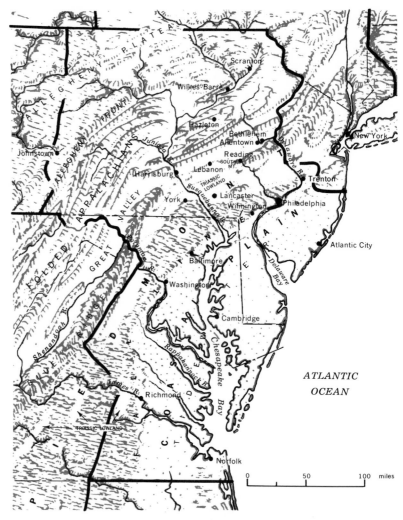

FIGURE 7-1 *Landforms in the Delaware-Chesapeake Gateways Region. Conspicuous features are the topographic features which parallel the coast and the major streams which cut across the grain of the relief features.* (Base map copyright by A. K. Lobeck. Reprinted with permission of The Geographical Press, Hammond, Inc.)

In contrast to the New England and New York gateways, the deeply indented Delaware and Chesapeake gateways had considerable soil, forest, and mineral resources. The lowland extended further inland, and the soils were initially fertile. Agricultural exports assumed early importance, especially near Chesapeake Bay where in the Tidewater country plantations slavery became the basis of the colonial economy. In Pennsylvania, settled somewhat later, agriculture was not neglected, but as many colonists had industrial skills, small-scale manufacturing started a few years after the founding of Philadelphia (1682); in fact, a large-scale iron industry, begun in 1720, exported 33 tons of pig iron to England in 1726.

BASIC DATA:

AREA INCLUDES	Land Area (thousand sq. mi.)	Population Change 1950–1960	Population 1960 (thousands)	Population 1967 (thousands)	Personal Income 1967 (billions)
ENTIRE REGION	67.0	13.2%	15,948	17,910	$58.7
Southern New Jersey	3.9	33.8	1,501	1,850	5.6
Delaware	1.9	40.3	446	540	2.2
Eastern and Central Pennsylvania	31.1	8.9	7,589	7,990	24.9
Most of Maryland	8.8	33.0	3,898	3,550	12.3
District of Columbia	0.06	−4.8	764	820	3.6
Virginia (north and east)	20.0	23.7	2,689	3,100	10.0
West Virginia (part)	0.7	9.0	60	60	0.2
MAJOR SMSAS					
Philadelphia	3.6	19.3%	4,342	4,820	$16.4
Baltimore	1.8	22.9	1,727	1,875	6.6
Washington	1.5	36.7	2,002	2,550	10.5
Richmond	0.7	24.5	436	520	1.7
Hampton Roads SMSAs	0.9	36.1	803	1,000	2.6

CLIMATE   Humid continental to humid subtropical.

	Temperature (°F)		Precipitation (inches)	
	Jan.	July	Annual	Season
Philadelphia	34	77	42	All year
Baltimore	37	79	42	All year
Norfolk	42	78	40	Summer maximum
Richmond	39	78	42	Slight summer maximum

VEGETATION   Largely second-growth forest: birch, hemlock, beech, maple in north; oak and pine to south; marshes along coast.

SOIL   Varies greatly with parent material; easily leached and eroded; gray-brown podzolic grading into red-yellow podzolic in Virginia.

MINERALS   Sand, gravel, cement rock, inferior building stone; coal in the Appalachians.

Throughout the last two centuries this region has developed into an area characterized by balanced agricultural, commercial, and industrial activities. In addition governmental activity in the Washington–Hampton Roads area has in recent decades stimulated the southern Atlantic Megalopolis.

In this essentially urban area, most income is derived from the ability of city populations to serve other areas, near and far. Although local resources are now subordinate to imported fuels and raw materials in the regional economy, historically the broad settlement pattern was evolved in relation to the distribution of local resources which in turn are related to the physiographic regions. Our analysis starts therefore with these regions and their resource-based industry. These activities, although they occupy much of the land today, yield only a minute proportion of the regional income, certainly not more than 2 percent.

In this chapter both uniform and nodal regions are used to present the regional patterns. The physical regions are uniform regions, each of which is associated with one or more resources. In the days of first settlement, the economy was largely re-source-oriented; thus somewhat similar settlement patterns tended to develop throughout each physical region. These patterns did not completely disappear when the economy was organized more along nodal lines based on transportation, markets, and concentrations of craft, technical, and organizational skill. The resource-significant uniform regions paralleled the Atlantic Coast; the urban-based nodal regions were related to routes either transverse to the uniform regions or parallel to easily traversable physical regions such as the Great Valley. The major transverse nodal developments (the Delaware Valley, Chesapeake Bay, and the James Valley) will be discussed along with urban activities in the second part of this chapter.

LANDFORMS AND ASSOCIATED ACTIVITIES

Six physiographic regions extend from the Hudson River to Alabama. Not all of these have exactly the same character everywhere, but they are sufficiently uniform that knowledge of them is a key to physical geography from New Jersey to Alabama. The following description, of course, applies most specifically to the Delaware–Chesapeake Gateways (Figure 7-1).

The Coastal Plain

This low-lying, flattish region consists of unconsolidated sediments deposited underwater, since raised above sea level, and then later partly resubmerged to form an indented coast. Most of the deep bays are blocked by barrier beaches formed by coastal currents; behind the beaches lagoons and extensive tidal marshes are common and, unless sprayed, provide ideal breeding places for mosquitoes. The numerous small harbors are suited only for fishing vessels and small yachts; ports for larger vessels are concentrated along the upper Delaware estuary, on Chesapeake Bay, and around Hampton Roads.

The Inner Coastal Plain includes extensive sandy loams which warm up rapidly in the spring. Its easily worked Sassafras soils are not very fertile but respond well to fertilization, yielding a great variety of farm produce including potatoes, garden vegetables, berries, and eggs for nearby urban markets; seasonal surpluses are canned or frozen. Corn is also a major crop, much being used to feed chickens for the urban broiler market.

The southern portion of the plain is drained mainly into Chesapeake Bay by such well-known streams as the Patuxent, Potomac, Rappahannock, York, and James. In colonial days, these and minor streams such as the Choptank and the Severn were navigable much farther upstream because ships were smaller and channels had not been filled with mud from eroded soils. As there were 8,500 miles of Tidewater shoreline, contact with the sea was easy. The virgin soils of the Coastal Plain, although not rich in the seventeenth and eighteenth centuries, were good enough for five or more crops of tobacco, after which the planters cleared new land. In Virginia, the bulk of tobacco cultivation has shifted to the Piedmont, but southern Maryland

THE EASTERN SHORE of Virginia is part of a sandy peninsula, generally flat, with elevations below 50 feet. The influences of Chesapeake Bay (visible left) and of the Atlantic (five miles to the east) extend the frost-free season to 210 or 220 days. This mild climate, heavy fertilization, and sprinkler irrigation permit the production of huge crops of vegetables, Irish potatoes, and sweet potatoes for megalopolitan markets. (USDA photograph.)

farmers, by applying mammoth quantities of fertilizer, still continue tobacco production.

Socially the southern Coastal Plain was, and in some of the region still is, a part of the traditional South with its planter aristocracy and emphasis on family connections, traditions, and patterns of racial relations. The characteristic economy is best illustrated by Chesapeake Bay, especially by its eastern shore on the Delmarva peninsula. This is an ideal headquarters for the yachtsman and amateur fisherman, and many of the wealthier citizens of Baltimore have built houses overlooking the Chesapeake. Southward are Chesapeake commercial fisheries whose annual catch is valued only at about $30 million. Cambridge, the major fishing port, processes seafood as well as vegetables, thus adding considerable value to the raw foodstuffs.

South of Cambridge the Delmarva peninsula is extremely flat. Soil water conditions vary so that some fields must be drained by tile, while others are watered by overhead pipes to offset brief droughts at critical growth periods. Many farmers contract in advance for the sale of their crops to canners or to shippers who get them to northern markets before local northern crops are ready.

A number of national developments have aided parts of the plain. Some decades ago the more widespread use of tobacco products, seafood, and early vegetables increased local rural incomes. Booming automobile travel has brought many tourists both to visit historic sites in the region and to travel through it en route to Florida, taking advantage of the new Cape Charles–Norfolk bridge and tunnel and the coastal highway.

SINGE BEFORE THE AMERICAN REVOLUTION, Lancaster County, Pennsylvania, an especially fertile, limy part of the Piedmont, has been well tilled by Pennsylvania Dutch farmers. The use of contour strip farming to reduce erosion is a modern innovation. Agriculture is highly diversified with a scientific system of crop rotation, but dairying and poultry are the principal sources of farm income. (USDA photograph.)

The Piedmont

The worn-down crystalline rocks of the Piedmont have heavy loams, well suited for orchards, dairying, and poultry farming when supplied with chemical fertilizers. In Virginia and Pennsylvania the Piedmont includes productive reddish soils on the Triassic Lowlands. Within this Pennsylvania lowland a much smaller limestone area, the Lancaster Plain, yields cigar tobacco, grain, and fine livestock. The carefully manicured farms with huge barns and the well-cared-for appearance of many red-brick towns have been attributed to the thrifty immigrants from the Rhineland who settled here in the early eighteenth century. These so-called "Pennsylvania Dutch" (who speak an anglicized German) devised a system of Corn Belt farming—by buying lean mountain-bred cattle and hogs and fattening them on grain before selling them in the Philadelphia market.

The Appalachians

South Mountain (Blue Ridge) A discontinuous crystalline ridge of sparsely settled, wooded hills, most commonly called South Mountain, connects the New England Uplands with the higher Blue Ridge of Virginia and the Carolinas. Its modest barrier, separating the Piedmont from the Great Valley, can be easily traversed by highway engineers such as those who built the Pennsylvania Turnpike. Historically the "mountain" funneled transverse traffic through its gaps and thus determined the original location of cities such as Reading, Lebanon, and Harrisburg. Its resources are negligible except for iron deposits still used by the Bethlehem steel industry.

The Great Valley This 15-mile-wide lowland with fertile soils derived from underlying limestone and slate supports prosperous Pennsylvania Dutch farms. The valley is drained by major streams which cut across

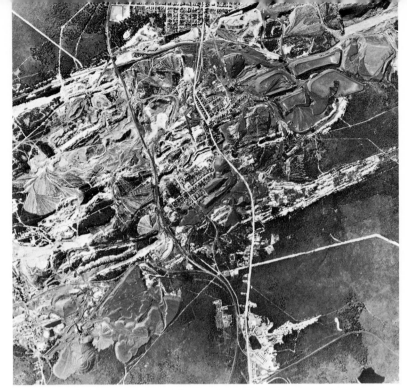

THE PART OF LUZERNE COUNTY, *Pennsylvania, south of Hazleton shows remnants of both the shaft mining (culm piles) and strip mining (spoil banks) of anthracite coal. The unmined land is too infertile for farming.* (USDA photograph.)

the region transversely, providing routes southeastward toward the coast and westward through the Appalachian ridges. Its minerals, including cement rock, slate, and iron ore, attracted a number of long-established industries.

The Ridge and Valley Province (Folded Appalachians)

The Great Valley is the widest and most continuous of a large number of Appalachian valleys, some broad but mostly narrow, which have formed on soft limestones and shales. In the valleys dairy farming and poultry farming are characteristic, but only a small fraction of the land is tillable. The wooded narrow ridges, formed from hard sandstones or conglomerates, rise to an even skyline.

The main resource, anthracite coal, attracted miners during the last century from Britain and elsewhere. Mining, once the main source of employment, now provides only a modest number of jobs, and deserted tipples and huge piles of culm are memorials to a declining industry.

The day of anthracite coal is over. It cannot compete with bituminous coke in the steel industry, or with fuel oil and natural gas in domestic heating. The forests which made this area a major lumber center a century ago have long been cut over; dairying and orchards occupy the few areas of fair soil. The major coal cities—Scranton, Wilkes-Barre, Hazleton, and others—are depressed areas, kept alive mainly by a modest success with textiles, clothing, and other industries whose main requirements are cheap labor and nearness to the megalopolitan market. Scranton, for example, with 13 percent of its labor force in mining and 29 percent in manufacturing in 1950, had by 1960 3.5 percent in mining and 36.6 percent in manufacturing. By building factories for new industries, Scranton has succeeded in replacing the jobs lost in declining industries. However, the population in 1965 was still declining, in both the city and the SMSA.

The impact of anthracite decline can be exemplified by Northumberland County which in the 1950s declined 11 percent in population, with a loss through out-migration of 21,090. The general pattern in the anthracite areas had been that men worked at mining or heavy industries based on coal, while women worked at textiles, clothing, and other light industries. Employment decrease has been especially substantial in the younger groups: altogether the labor force declined from 26,000 to 18,000 while unemployment rose from 11 to 18 percent. Small footloose industries (garments, kitchen cabinets, plastics) have come into the towns, attracted by labor willing to work for two-thirds of a Philadelphia wage. Farms, although they occupy 56 percent of land, contribute relatively little to local income, farm products consisting of $2.6 million in livestock products, compare with a total county income of about $200 million.

The Allegheny Front and Plateau   Similar problems have developed on the Allegheny Plateau whose eastern edge (front) rises abruptly a thousand feet or more. Although dissected by the canyonlike valleys of Susquehanna tributaries, the front represented a considerable barrier to early travelers. After 1840 lumbermen tapped its vast forests, clearing out most of the marketable lumber before the end of the century.

The plateau is sparsely settled because the winters on the plateau are severe. In the more rugged counties less than 10 percent of the land is in farms, and for the whole subregion, only about 30 percent of the land is in farms. Dairy farming is the major rural activity. Bituminous coal, found especially on the western margin of the region, provides the basis for Johnstown's steel industry which accounts for three-fifths of that city's industrial employment. The plateau is a northern portion of Appalachia with counties suffering from severe out-migration, in some cases actual population decline. Table 7-1 indicates the severity of the problem in Appalachian cities less than 100 miles from the Atlantic Megalopolis.

URBAN PATTERNS: THE DELAWARE GATEWAY

When overland transportation was difficult, water transportation was important in locating settlement. Along the Atlantic seaboard, many early towns were located at the fall line which not only was the head of ocean navigation but also provided waterpower sites. From New Jersey to Alabama this fall line occurred at the boundary between the Piedmont and the Coastal Plain, the falls or rapids in each stream being caused by the water's descent from the hard rocks to

TABLE 7-1   Employment, Median Age, and Income in Appalachian SMSAs in Pennsylvania, 1960

	Percent of Labor Force			Median Age	Median Family Income
	Unemployed	*Mining*	*Manufacturing*	*Age*	*Income*
Scranton	8.2	3.5	36.6	35.8	$4,896
Wilkes-Barre–					
Hazleton	10.4	4.9	35.8	36.0	4,772
Johnstown	10.4	7.9	33.0	30.9	4,574
Pennsylvania	4.6	1.6	36.4	32.0	5,719
United States	5.1	1.0	27.1	29.5	5,660

SOURCES: U.S. Bureau of the Census, *County and City Data Book: 1962,* Washington, 1962; and Third Federal Reserve District, *Economic Handbook,* Philadelphia, no date.

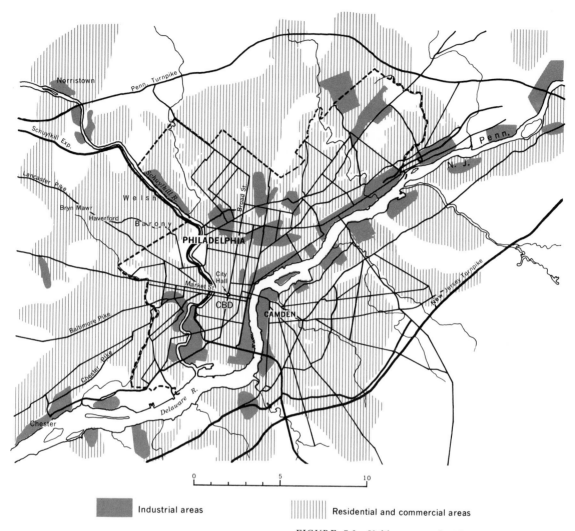

Industrial areas

Residential and commercial areas

FIGURE 7-2 Unlike most colonial cities, colonial Philadelphia had a street plan almost oriented to the cardinal points of the compass; the plan of the outlying areas was greatly influenced by the converging roads and by street plans established in once-independent towns.

the Piedmont to the lower and softer formations of the plain. Trenton, Philadelphia, Wilmington, Baltimore, and Richmond are the major fall-line cities in this region.

Philadelphia

In 1682 William Penn selected the site for Philadelphia on high, dry land 4 miles above the marshy land at the confluence of the Delaware with the Schuylkill River. Where the two winding rivers were only 2 miles apart, a wide street (Market Street) was laid out. In contrast to colonial New York and Boston, a rectangular grid was designed with space for parks and spacious house lots. By 1776, Philadelphia had become the largest city in Anglo-America. Industrially the city rivaled New England but specialized more in goods involving raw materials; thus in 1785 a completely mechanized flour mill was perfected and Philadelphia remained the leading United States milling center until after the Civil War.

Around old Philadelphia a number of

towns including Germantown and Frankford were founded soon after the central city. In these the main streets were oriented to the through roads and not to the rectangular street grid of Philadelphia. Camden and West Philadelphia were ferry towns located across from the east and west ends of Market Street. From the western end of the ferry, the Lancaster Pike (now Lancaster Avenue), West Chester Pike (West Market Street), Baltimore Pike (now Baltimore Avenue), and Chester Pike (Chester Avenue) radiated. Similar radial roads connected Camden with southern New Jersey.

When the railroads were built, their tracks were laid as much as possible in unsettled areas. Two through lines from New York to Washington passed between Philadelphia and Germantown, thence over the rocky or marshy lands on each side of the Schuylkill just beyond what was then the southern edge of the city. These lines, especially near the rivers, provided convenient sites for nineteenth-century factories. Canals, together with the railroads along the Schuylkill, brought coal from the anthracite fields to the north and the northwest.

A route westward   After 1800, Philadelphia merchants became aware of rising competition of New York City, but no easy natural corridor comparable to the Hudson-Mohawk route was available. A possible westward route had been started to Lancaster, an area settled early in the eighteenth century. This dirt road was traversed at first by pack trains, later by Conestoga wagons.[1] As the old road was too slow and overcrowded, in 1796 the state government completed the wide Lancaster Turnpike, with a paved center of crushed stone. In 1834 the turnpike was supplemented by a railroad from Philadelphia to Columbia on the Susquehanna River. The route was continued by canal barge up the Susquehanna and its

tributary, the Juniata, to the Allegheny Front where the barges were pulled by stationary engines over the summit to an Ohio tributary on which they were refloated. This awkward route, somewhat altered, later became the main line of the Pennsylvania Railroad. Although in recent years this railroad has competed successfully with New York's water-level route, in the middle of the nineteenth century it was so slow that Philadelphia lost out to New York in its bid for Midwestern trade.

Modern Philadelphia   William Penn's careful planning proved far from ideal for twentieth-century Philadelphia. The spacious house lots and blocks disappeared. Demands for central city housing led to the construction of thousands of blocks of brick houses, with marble sills and steps, each attached to its neighbor and erected on probably the narrowest house lots in the United States. Streetcars on the narrow streets started the congestion, and the automobile age brought traffic almost to a standstill. Fortunately most Philadelphians used public transportation, at least in the CBD; fortunately, too, subway lines had been built under Broad and Market streets.

Government and private renewal activities have opened crowded Philadelphia in part. A parkway was cut diagonally from the Schuylkill across the blocks of brick houses to City Hall Square. Later the Pennsylvania Railroad moved its main terminal to 30th Street, west of the Schuylkill, and placed its downtown tracks underground, thus opening up new building sites in the CBD. Three modern bridges across the Delaware replaced the cumbersome ferries. Finally a large mall has been opened around Independence Hall, and urban renewal projects are renovating many older portions of the city.

The business of the Philadelphia SMSA   "Apart from farming, the economy of metropolitan

---

[1] Named for the Conestoga, a tributary of the Susquehanna River, these wagons later played a major role in Western settlement.

THE SKYSCRAPERS IDENTIFY *the western half of the CBD of Philadelphia. A line of new buildings is developing between the 30th Street station of the Pennsylvania Railroad and City Hall, occupying land formerly used by a railroad spur (now underground). Benjamin Franklin Parkway (diagonal right) and a submerged expressway (right) permit traffic to bypass the narrow streets of the old city.* (Aero Service Division, Litton Industries.)

Philadelphia is remarkably similar to that of the United States. Both are diversified, both are based largely on manufacturing industries, and every major classification of manufacturing is represented."[2] The industrial specialization in Philadelphia's industry is shown in Figure 7-3.

The geographical pattern of the city is clearly visible from the air. The tall buildings of the Central Business District stand out clearly on the site first planned by William Penn. North and south of it the old brick houses still stand except in scattered areas cleared for port, industrial, or apartment developments. The most spectacular renewal has occurred along the waterfront where efficient port terminals handle about

[2] Federal Reserve Bank of Philadelphia, *Business Review*, September, 1964, p. 12.

half the tonnage of the Delaware Valley ports. Although the central city has declined slightly in population (1950–1960), it still accounts for 51 percent of manufacturing employment in the SMSA, leading in every industrial category except stone, clay and glass products, and primary metals. The heavier industries, petroleum refining and chemicals, are located on the lower Schuylkill; other industries are generally along the railroads. More widely distributed are the clothing, food products, printing and publishing, and textile industries which together account for nearly half the city's industrial employment.

As in most large cities, residences and industry are moving to Philadelphia suburbs and satellite cities. Across the Delaware industrial Camden, specializing in shipbuilding, food processing, and electronics, is also adjoined by an arc of residential suburbs. Downstream both banks of the Delaware are occupied by industries using bulky materials: for example, shipbuilding, locomotives, and paper on the Pennsylvania shore, and petrochemicals on both shores. A mile or so to the west rises the rolling Piedmont with its numerous middle-class commuting towns.

West and northwest of the Philadelphia CBD heavy industries are concentrated near the Schuylkill, once the artery for anthracite coal shipments. Directly west of the city is the so-called "Welsh Barony" with Welsh town names such as Merion, Bryn Mawr, Bala Cynwyd, and St. Davids, a group of upper-class commuting towns along the main line of the Pennsylvania Railroad. Nearby are famous liberal arts colleges, huge estates carved out of the rolling Piedmont, and historic Valley Forge, King of

Prussia, and Hopewell Furnace. Industry has penetrated in a genteel way with contemporary factories housing electrical and computer industries so elegantly that some have been mistaken for college campuses. King of Prussia, Valley Forge, and Fort Washington, all close to the Pennsylvania Turnpike and its extensions northward and southward, now have spacious industrial parks.

Two satellite cities   Trenton, 20 miles upstream from Philadelphia, and Wilmington, the same distance downstream, are independent metropolitan areas which seem destined to be absorbed into the Philadelphia Metropolis. Both cities are located on navigable water on the Coastal Plain; both have expanded up onto the Piedmont. The Trenton SMSA includes the state capital and the educational and scientific activities around Princeton University, but the bulk of its employment is industrial with specialties in consumer goods: for example, pottery, bath accessories, and linoleum. Development across the river from Trenton has been stimulated by the opening of the United States Steel's integrated Fairless plant, designed to serve the megalopolitan market by converting imported ores into industrial steel.

The Wilmington SMSA straddles upper Delaware Bay, the two segments being connected by a bridge carrying a New York–Washington expressway. The central city was founded by Swedes in 1638 on Christina River at the southernmost place where the shore was not marshy. After a modest growth as a flour-milling town (using fall-line power), its industrial emphasis was changed by the Du Pont family in 1802.

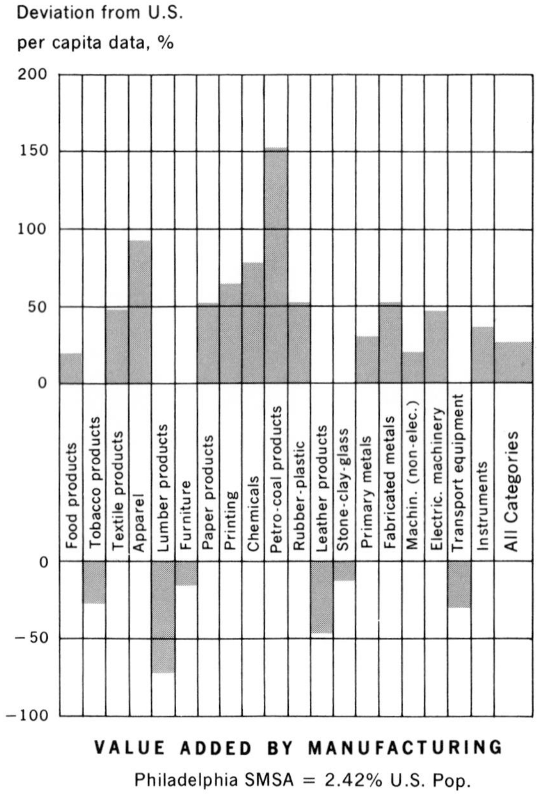

Deviation from U.S. per capita data, %

VALUE ADDED BY MANUFACTURING
Philadelphia SMSA = 2.42% U.S. Pop.

FIGURE 7-3   The Philadelphia SMSA in most industrial categories is remarkably close to the national average. If outlying areas in the Delaware Valley were included, the heavy industries would show more pronounced upward deviations.

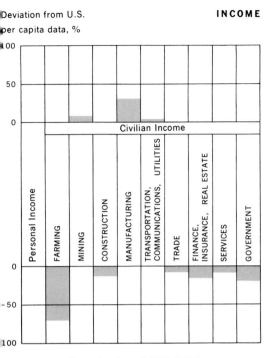

Pennsylvania = 6.00% U.S. Pop.

FIGURE 7-4   The personal income of Pennsylvanians is so close to the national average that no bar appears in the first column. Aside from farming (which is obviously inadequate to supply the needs of Pennsylvanians), the economy of Pennsylvania is close to the national average.

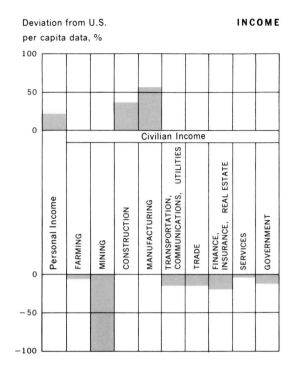

Delaware = .26% U.S. Pop.

FIGURE 7-5   Delaware is a prosperous state central to megalopolitan markets both for its manufactures from the Wilmington SMSA and for its farm produce from its southern counties. Most of the income is earned in the northern county.

Starting as a producer of black powder, the Du Pont industrial empire has expanded, producing in the Wilmington area alone: explosives, ammonia, dyes, cellophane, nylon, rayon, Lucite paints, and synthetic rubber.[3] Du Pont is not the only industry:

others include leather, vulcanized fibers, transportation equipment, and petroleum products.

The Delaware River Port Authority   The port facilities from Wilmington to Trenton are coordinated under an interstate port authority which maintains a 40-foot channel from the open sea almost to Trenton, a distance of 135 miles. The Chesapeake and Delaware Canal, 27 feet deep, provides direct connections with Chesapeake Bay. Specialized facilities provide for the unloading and loading of bulky materials: crude oil, ores, gypsum, coal, and grain. All docks and terminals being connected directly to expressways and railways, lighters and car ferries are unnecessary.

[3] *The mere mention of Wilmington suggests Du Pont, headquartered in the city's two most imposing office buildings, linked together like a massive molecule in masonry. The buildings house the brain trust that supervises the operations of 80 plants in 69 communities in 28 states, not to mention numerous foreign subsidiaries and affiliates. From the upper floors of the central office building may be seen some of the company's plants on both sides of the river. Just a few miles west of the head office in suburban Wilmington are the company's head laboratories—eight neatly tailored buildings geometrically placed within 160 acres of green and quiet countryside. One is an administration building, and research in seven different directions is pursued in the remaining seven.* Federal Reserve Bank of Philadelphia, *Business Review*, August, 1964, pp. 10–11.

The combined ports handle over 7,000 ships connected with 270 ports in 75 countries. By weight petroleum is the single largest item; iron ore, the second import, is used half locally, and about half is shipped by rail to the upper Ohio Valley. The cargo is seven-eighths import tonnage. Over $300 million worth of Philadelphia manufactures are exported annually, but many of these are handled through the Port of New York because of its more frequent shipping connections. It is somewhat ironic that this valley, whose industries once developed on a base of plentiful raw materials, is now growing in part because of its ability to import these raw materials.

Population growth in the Delaware Port Area   As in most metropolitan areas, the population has either decreased or barely held its own in the central cities and gained rapidly in the suburbs (Table 7-2) and outlying towns. Suburban life has become fashionable, and many of the older areas have been occupied by lower-income groups: in Philadelphia, for example, by Negro groups coming from the South. Stylish apartments have held some people in central city areas, but apartment living is also available in the suburbs.

Again industries, especially those desiring space, are growing in the suburbs, and perhaps with more local opportunities, the proportion of workers commuting to neighboring counties (now over 35 percent in four of the seven suburban Philadelphia counties) may decline.

Outlying Philadelphia satellites   Table 7-2 shows that the southern New Jersey and Delaware suburban and rural areas are growing rapidly. In part this represents the growth of beach resorts, in part the growth of commuting settlements, and in part the development of small satellite industrial towns. A similar growth has occurred on the Piedmont and in the Pennsylvania Great Valley. For example, the Allentown-Bethlehem-Easton SMSA combines the steel industries of Bethlehem and Easton, the cement industries of the countryside, and the varied light industries and commercial activities of Allentown. The concentration of the Bethlehem steel industry, one half larger in capacity than the new Tidewater Fairless plant at Morrisville, deserves discussion. Its location must be explained in terms of the past because, once established, steel industries are not easily or cheaply

TABLE 7-2   Central Cities and Other Population: Delaware Port Area, 1950, 1960, 1965 (in thousands)

Area	1950	1960	1965
Philadelphia (*city*)	2,071	2,003	1,964
Other Philadelphia SMSA (*Pa.*)	1,071	1,589	1,929
Camden (*city*)	125	117	116
Other Philadelphia SMSA (*N.J.*)	403	634	734
Trenton (*city*)	128	114	111
Other Trenton SMSA	102	152	175
Atlantic City	62	60	59
Other Atlantic City SMSA	70	101	118
Wilmington (*city*)	110	96	91
Other Wilmington SMSA	98	269	328
Other Delaware Counties	99	139	157

SOURCE: U.S. Bureau of the Census, *Census of Population: 1960*, Washington, 1963; and census estimates.

moved. Anthracite coal is available by canal or rail, 10 to 25 miles northward, and coking coal by rail from central and western Pennsylvania; limestone is available locally; magnetite iron ore from nearby Lebanon, Morgantown, and northern New Jersey. New York City and Philadelphia markets are 75 miles away or less. Heavy goods could be shipped over the Anthracite Railroads to market or to Bethlehem Steel plants at Pottstown, Steelton, or in northeastern New Jersey for further fabrication.

URBAN PATTERNS: CHESAPEAKE GATEWAYS

Centered to the west of 200-mile-long Chesapeake Bay, the southern third of the Atlantic Megalopolis is developing in an area of early colonial growth. The first U.S. Census (1790) showed that the most populous state was Virginia with half again as many people as second-place Pennsylvania. Much smaller Maryland, sixth in population among the 16 states, was not far behind Massachusetts, New York, and North Carolina. With the American people distributed along the Atlantic seaboard as they were in 1790, Washington was more centrally located to be the federal capital than it is today.

The Chesapeake Gateways (Figure 7-6) receive the largest part of their income from the federal government, which accounts for one-third of the total income received directly and, in addition, much income earned serving government workers. Manufacturing accounts for one-fifth of total income, while mining, agriculture, and farming account for only one-fortieth. Somewhat less than one-half remains attributable to trade, transportation, finance, and services.

Much of the industrial and governmental income arises from port functions. Chesapeake Bay and the tributary Hampton Roads and Potomac Estuary make up the world's most spacious harbor, large enough to anchor all the world's shipping. Tides are negligible, fog and storms are rare, and channels are easily maintained. The ports are not as near Europe as ports to the Northeast, but for cargo this makes little practical difference since in recent decades ocean freight rates have been the same from all ports from Hampton Roads to Portland, Maine.

The principal handicaps of these ports had been two: *first,* the routes inland over the mountains were high and winding, and, *second,* the immediate hinterland was relatively undeveloped. As to the first, the com-

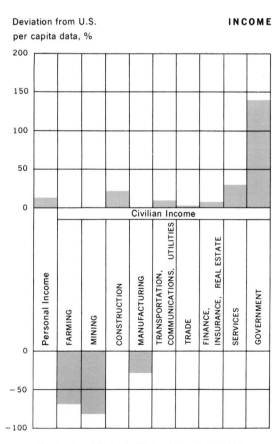

FIGURE 7-6 The expansion of the federal government accounts for the above-average personal income and for the emphasis on services and government.

TABLE 7-3   Mileages by Most Direct Routes: Atlantic Ports and Cincinnati, Chicago, St. Louis, and Minneapolis

From/To	Cincinnati	Chicago	St. Louis	Minneapolis
Boston	876	975	1,178	1,385
New York	659	843	966	1,253
Philadelphia	578	762	885	1,172
Baltimore	494	687	817	1,097
Norfolk	593	885	929	1,295
New Orleans	820	929	695	1,241
Houston	1,040	1,085	794	1,198

pletion of three coal-shipping railroads across the mountains and into the Great Lakes states provides good freight connections by rail, and improved highways carry adequate truck services. As to the second point, heavy industries developing at Baltimore have increased trade of all kinds, and the growth of federal activity has increased industrialization and military needs. Especially important to port development, the Interstate Commerce Commission has recognized that the shorter distances (Table 7-3) from Chesapeake ports to interior points should be reflected in rates on general cargo as much as one to three cents lower per hundred pounds. Consequently on general cargo Baltimore has a rate advantage over Philadelphia in western Pennsylvania, eastern Ohio, much of West Virginia and northern Virginia, while Hampton Roads has a rate advantage in a broad zone immediately

southward. Both ports have an advantage over New York in much of the western Great Lakes states where, however, they must compete with the low cost but slow route via New Orleans.

Table 7-4 shows that tonnage competition among New York, Delaware River, and Chesapeake Bay ports for foreign trade is very close. In value of foreign commerce New York remains far ahead because the fastest routes and best distribution agencies for high-value-per-ton imports are in the New York area.

Baltimore

This city was founded in 1729 nearly a century after the first settlement in southwestern Maryland. Extensive growth of wheat on the Piedmont of Maryland and adjacent Pennsylvania justified the construction there of a waterpowered flour mill. Baltimore,

TABLE 7-4   Commerce of Major Atlantic and Gulf Ports, 1965 (in thousands of short tons of cargo)

Port	Foreign		Coastwise	
	Imports	*Exports*	*Receipts*	*Shipments*
Port of New York	47,528	6,802	32,839	16,397
Delaware River	50,839	3,343	25,209	6,807
Baltimore	19,720	5,888	5,316	1,621
Hampton Roads	4,307	35,072	2,241	3,876
New Orleans	4,786	18,625	1,421	19,963
Houston	4,108	9,711	1,860	20,155
Total, all United States ports	244,874	142,121	201,508	201,508

SOURCE: U.S. Army Corps of Engineers, *Waterborne Commerce of the United States: 1965*, Washington, 1966.

being on the most direct overland route from Philadelphia to Virginia took over commercial leadership from Annapolis, the capital, located 22 miles to the south. After the American Revolution, Baltimore became the new nation's fourth port. The transfer of the federal Capital to Washington greatly increased Baltimore's importance and it became a wholesale center not only for Maryland but for adjacent states to the south and east. Baltimore attempted to compete with New York's water-level route to the Midwest, first by the Cumberland Road (National Road, now U.S. 40), then by the Chesapeake and Ohio Canal, and finally by the Baltimore and Ohio Railroad which, however, was not completed to the Ohio River until 1852.

Baltimore, like most American cities, at first a commercial center, developed early industries either to process local perishable produce or to prepare consumer goods, e.g., packaged foods, clothing, textiles and building supplies, for its trading area. In recent decades, these industries have not grown with the population; rather some, such as textiles, have declined. The recent industrial growth has been in the durable goods industries for which Baltimore, with a fine harbor and proximity to West Virginia coal, has many advantages. Figure 7-7 shows how Baltimore industries compare with the United States average.

Port facilities, reached by a 42-foot channel and occupying 30 miles of Baltimore's 46-mile sheltered waterfront, include specialized docks handling ores, raw materials, and fuels for waterfront industry; for example, ore can be unloaded at the rate of 7,000 tons per hour. Export business has equally efficient facilities which can load 9,800 tons of coal per hour or simultaneously load

grain into nine vessels from elevators with a 13.5-million-bushel capacity. The port also has such service facilities as 11 shipbuilding and repair plants. In contrast to New York which handles much general cargo, Baltimore is largely a bulk cargo port.

The Washington SMSA

Although Washington and Baltimore are growing together and Baltimore serves many industrial functions for Washington, the federal Capital had an independent and somewhat artificial origin, being selected because of its central location in the settled part of the new country. The site was on the fall line (although the Great Falls of the Potomac are some miles upstream). Origi-

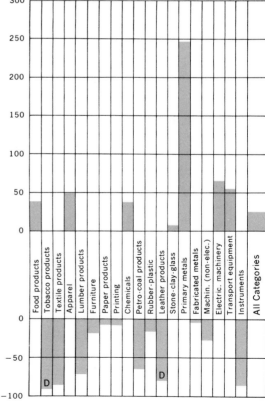

FIGURE 7-7   In recent decades, Baltimore, once noted for its diversified industries, has turned more to heavier industries, especially primary metals and chemicals.

THIS PHOTOGRAPH SHOWS CLEARLY the street grid of central Washington, consisting of repeating rectangular patterns of letter-named east-west streets (parallel to a line connecting the Capitol with the Washington Monument) and numbered north-south streets. The grid, divided into four sectors: NW, SW, SE and NE, is crossed diagonally by a network of avenues named for states. In spite of the careful plan worked out initially for Washington, extensive urban renewal projects and new routes, both highway and public transit, have become necessary for the city. (Aero Service Division, Litton Industries.)

nally the district was to have been square, but in 1846 Congress, not forseeing the future growth of federal business, returned the Virginia portion (now Arlington County) to that state. Unfortunately the site selected for the main government buildings was a low-lying and somewhat marshy Coastal Plain area between the Potomac and its tributary, the Anacostia. The better residential sections are found on the Piedmont.

Washington was well planned. The center of the city is a hillock upon which the Capitol was built. The northwest quadrant includes the major buildings and the CBD, and on the higher land, the embassy section and several fashionable residential sec-

tions. Located along the railroads (or in the suburbs) are the few city industries, either government or related enterprises or processors of consumer goods (flour mills, bakeries, breweries, printing).

The District of Columbia is a peculiar combination of monumental buildings, old residential sections with red brick row houses, and some modern residential and apartment houses sections. One-third of the labor force works for the government and many of the others serve government employees and tourists. Half the population works at white-collar jobs and per household income is considerably above that for the entire SMSA. Washington, in 1960, be-

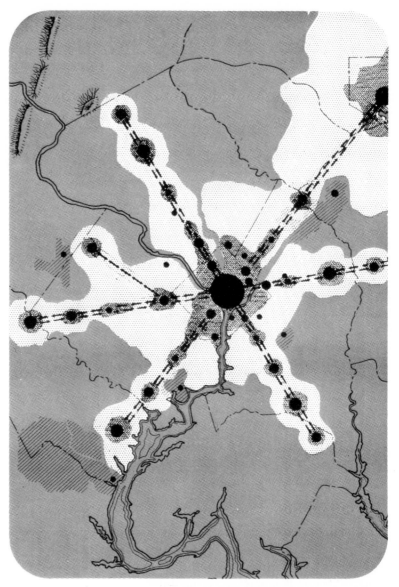

FIGURE 7-8   *Few metropolitan areas have done as elaborate planning as Washington for urban renewal and expansion. This map shows how the National Planning Commission hopes that Washington will expand as radiating urban arms, each rimmed by areas of less intensive development and separated from each other by parkland or open countryside.*

came the first large American city with more than half nonwhite residents. This has been accounted for by federal rule in local government (which enforces civil rights legislation), by the absence of racial discrimination in government employment, and by the nearness to Southern areas where discrimination has led to outward migration. In contrast, Maryland and Virginia suburban areas have a nonwhite population ranging only between 1.8 and 11.7 percent.

The well-settled suburban area has a radius of about 10 miles from the Capitol within which there is much nonresidential activity. Many government agencies are avoiding congestion by building in the suburbs: for example, the Defense Department has the Pentagon Building on the Virginia side of the Potomac and the Army Map Service in Maryland. The Agricultural Center is in Beltsville, Maryland, and National Institutes of Health and the Naval Medical Center are in Bethesda, Maryland. The Dulles International Airport and the Central Intelligence Agency are westward in suburban Virginia. Private research centers, shopping centers, and factories which benefit by government research are also being located in the suburbs. The University of Maryland is less than 5 miles from the district line.

Hampton Roads and the James Valley

The first permanent English colonists in Anglo-America landed at Cape Henry near the entrance to Chesapeake Bay, and then finding much of the land marshy, sailed about 40 miles through Hampton Roads up the four-mile-wide James estuary to found Jamestown. Tobacco farming, the economic base of colonial Tidewater Virginia, is now unusual there. Much of the farmland north of the James has reverted to forest or been converted to urban use, including fishing villages, military installations, and retirement residences. Toward Richmond the better-drained, slightly higher land is devoted to general farming, including some dairying, poultry, and truck. South of the James, a section that grew cotton until the incursion of the boll weevil, now specializes in peanuts and peanut-fed hogs (Smithfield hams).

Hampton Roads　In physical character Hampton Roads (Figure 7-9) is not too different from New York Harbor; in economic development the Virginia area, although growing more rapidly, is far behind. Both harbors have extensive indented shorelines, deep natural channels which can be easily dredged to 40-foot depths up to the piers, low tidal ranges, and relative freedom from fog and storms. Both have access to extensive hinterlands. The immediate hinterland of Hampton Roads is more productive of raw materials. The immediate hinterland of New York is much richer in industry and purchasing power, and its interior hinterland is more easily reached and more productive.

The Hampton Roads area has no outstanding CBD such as the Manhattan CBD which draws both local and more distant business. Indeed many urban functions for the area such as central banking, insurance, government, and tourism are more centered at Richmond. Outstanding functions of the Hampton Roads cities are connected with shipbuilding and repairing, port facilities, and especially with military and civilian employment. On the Norfolk-Portsmouth side of Hampton Roads about two-fifths of the basic military and civilian employment is directly connected with the port. Truly few metropolitan economies are so clearly based on a superb harbor strategically located to guard and to service commercially and militarily the Atlantic Coast of the United States.

Physically the Norfolk-Portsmouth SMSA is a roughly circular area of sandy and marshy land (radius 12 miles) jutting northward from the Dismal Swamp along the Virginia–North Carolina border. The southern part of the circle is still rural, producing early vegetables for northern markets as well as dairy and other produce for the Norfolk market. The much indented northern circle includes a variety of towns and street plans that have grown together except where they are separated by estuaries, military installations, railroad marine terminals, or air bases. Eight railroads deliver and take cargo, military and civilian, to the docks; 40 truck lines also provide land connections; and a peripheral highway, swinging south and east around the city, named *Military Highway,* reminds the visitor of the historic functions of the region.

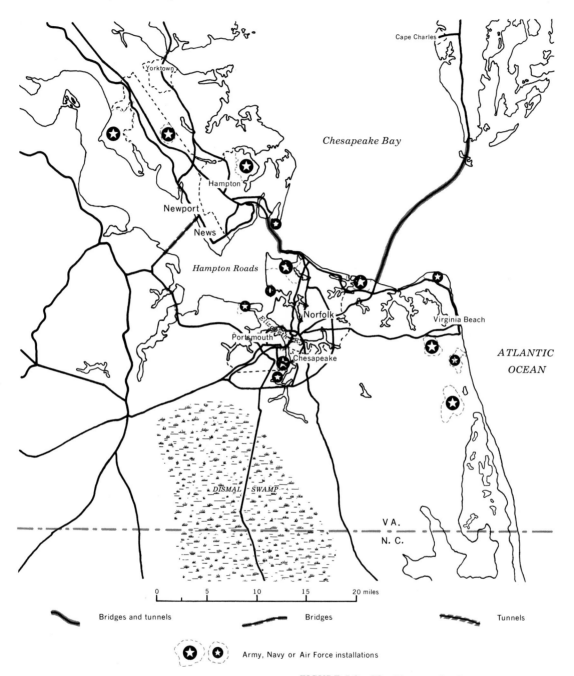

Bridges and tunnels   Bridges   Tunnels

★ ★ Army, Navy or Air Force installations

FIGURE 7-9   The Hampton Roads area consists of scattered military, naval, and commercial harbor installations backed by urban service areas.

Manufacturing employment is modest and is equally divided between durable and nondurable goods. Transportation equipment (automobile assembly and shipbuilding) rivals chemical and food products for first place, and these three categories account for the majority of industrial employment. Those employed in industry number only one-third as many as those in civilian government jobs.

The Newport News–Hampton SMSA is even more dependent on shipping. Its only large manufacturing industry is the New-port News Shipbuilding and Drydock Company which builds ocean liners and makes huge castings and turbines. Adjoining the shipyards is the coal-exporting terminal of the Chesapeake and Ohio Railroad. Langley Air Force Base, Fort Eustis, and Fort Monroe have a payroll of $150 million, or one-fourth of the SMSA income. The other major businesses are fishing, seafood packing, an oil refinery, and tourism (Yorktown, Williamsburg, and Jamestown). The SMSA has comparatively little business with Norfolk, having its own retail centers and CBD. Norfolk, however, has a disproportionate share of Hampton Roads wholesale and service business.

The business of the Hampton Roads ports Coal accounts for over nine-tenths of the export tonnage as well as most of the coastwise shipments. Grain is another important export item. But these items alone do not account for half of nearly $500 million exports by value each year—a variety of general cargo, that is, cotton products, chemicals, and other manufactures, makes up the balance.

The coastwise shipments, a fraction of the export tonnage, are largely coal and some lumber. The coastwise receipts are likewise modest, mainly petroleum. Some interior traffic is also handled on the Intracoastal Waterway which here connects the Chesapeake and Delaware Canal–Chesapeake Bay route with the canal to the Carolina sounds and southward to east Florida.

Import tonnage is commonly only one-tenth as much as export tonnage; in contrast, import value is about half as much as export value, suggesting a considerable value of general cargo imports. Most goods pass through the port without contributing much to its local business, the tonnage used in local factories being but a small part of the whole.

Richmond By far the smallest of the 12 Federal Reserve cities, Richmond is fifty-ninth among United States cities in population, sixty-second among United States SMSAs in population, and sixty-sixth in SMSA personal income. Richmond has fewer people and less income than Norfolk-Portsmouth, its rival in the state, or than Atlanta, its business rival in the Southeast. On the other hand, Richmond is steeped in prestige and tradition as capital of the Confederacy, and storehouse of Southern memories and culture (Figure 7-10). It is primarily a commercial and financial center in which a few specialized industries have developed. Its fall-line location is at the head of navigation on the James, a stream whose lower reaches still handle 5 to 6 million tons of cargo annually, mostly petroleum. At Richmond the fast Megalopolis-to-Florida routes cross the routes from the Midwest and the bituminous coal fields to Hampton Roads. Banks, insurance company home offices, regional sales offices, consumer goods warehouses, and packing plants serve an area from the Potomac Valley well into the Carolinas.

In 1860 Richmond was one of the few Southern cities with a variety of manufactures including iron and steel. After the Civil War it became more specialized, emphasizing industries related to regional raw materials, especially tobacco products which provide nearly one-quarter and food products which provide one-eighth of the industrial employment. Related packaging products industries include aluminum foil, paper, and cellophane. Other major industries are chemicals (and related synthetic fibers—rayon and nylon) and such consumer goods as textiles, clothing, and furniture. Printing and publishing are as important as one would expect in a state and regional cultural capital.

Richmond is not yet a part of Megalopolis (although its business to the north and east is within that region). Its northern suburbs are less than 75 miles from suburban Washington with which it is connected by an interstate highway and a high-speed railroad. The Richmond SMSA is growing faster than the national average. All this suggests the probability that by 1980 the Atlantic Megalopolis will extend at least to the lower James River.

CONCLUSIONS

Although New York is the financial and commercial capital of Megalopolis, the Philadelphia-Baltimore axis stresses industry more; yet it should be noted that the value added by manufacturing in the New York Gateway is more than double that in the entire Delaware-Chesapeake Gateways. The Washington–Richmond–Hampton Roads area is largely oriented to governmental activities.

The availability of extensive level and rolling lands for urban development plus strategic location near the national Capital suggests continued growth for this region. With the increasing dependence of American industry on imported raw materials, the region with its potentialities for port growth, access to coal, relative proximity to Southwestern oil and gas seems well located amid a growing market. The barrier effect of the Appalachians, which once separated the region from easy direct contact with the interior, is being overcome by airlines, expressways, and transmontane railroads. With the expected economic advance of the populous South to the national average of per capita income, this segment of Megalopolis seems destined to grow and grow southward.

FIGURE 7-10   Richmond SMSA's industrialization seems overwhelmed by tobacco products and related industries (paper, cellophane).

SELECTED REFERENCES

BROWN, RALPH, H.: *Historical Geography of the United States,* Harcourt, Brace & World, New York, 1948, especially pp. 58–61, 133–40.

FEDERAL RESERVE BANK OF RICHMOND: *Virginia Profile,* Richmond, 1964.

———: *Maryland Profile,* Richmond, 1964.

GOTTMAN, JEAN: *Virginia at Mid-century,* Holt, New York, 1955.

GREEN, CONSTANCE M.: *American Cities in the Growth of the Nation,* Harper & Row, New York, 1965.

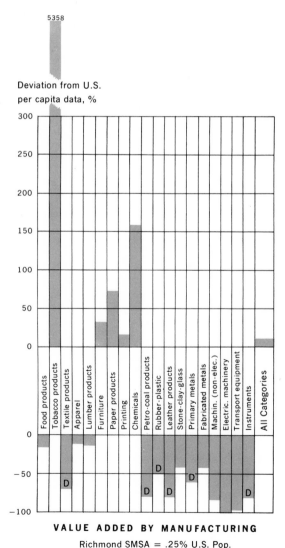

HIGBEE, EDWARD: *The American Oasis,* Knopf, New York, 1957, especially chaps. 8 and 9.

KULSKI, JULIAN EUGENE: *Land of Urban Promise,* University of Notre Dame Press, South Bend, 1967.

NATIONAL CAPITAL PLANNING COMMISSION: *The Proposed Comprehensive Plan for the National Capital,* Washington, 1967.

NATIONAL CAPITAL REGIONAL PLANNING COMMISSION: *The Regional Development Guide 1966–2000,* Washington, 1966.

PRICE, EDWARD T.: "The Central Courthouse Square in the American County Seat," *Geographical Review,* vol. 58 (1968), pp. 29–60.

Virginia Economic Review (periodical), Governor's Office, Richmond.

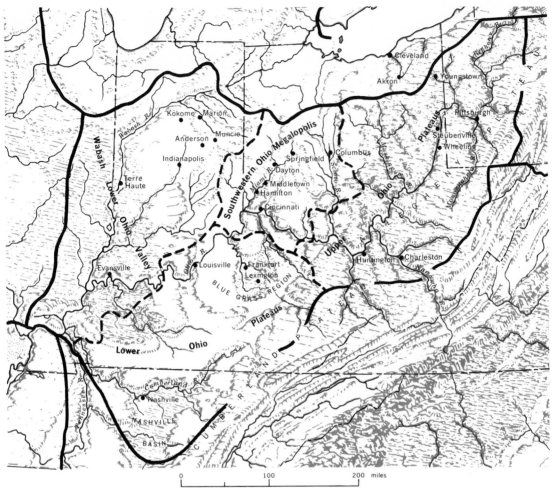

FIGURE 8-1 Landforms and subregions of the Ohio Basin.
The relief of the Ohio plateaus is not great but includes many abrupt escarpments
and bluffs. (Base map copyright by A. K. Lobeck.
Reprinted with permission of The Geographical Press, Hammond, Inc.)

CHAPTER 8
THE
OHIO
BASIN

After the American Revolution, the agricultural frontier was quickly pushed across the Appalachians. Most pioneers did not settle in the mountains but advanced into the Central Lowland, occupying first the low plateaus of the Ohio Basin. The soils of this plateau area, not generally considered fertile today, were in virgin state equal to those on the Atlantic seaboard. But the Ohio Basin was the gateway to more fertile plains areas, drained by the upper Mississippi and its major tributaries, the Ohio and the Missouri, now the home of one-third of the United States population. Rich in soil, forest, fuel, and mineral resources, moderate in relief, and connected by an excellent system of natural waterways, the interior was indeed a land of agricultural promise. Yet even its riches had limits. The bulk of its forests have been

BASIC DATA:

AREA INCLUDES	Population		Urban		Personal Income
	1960	Est. 2010	1960	Est. 2010	1967
	(thousands)		(percent)		(billions)
ENTIRE REGION	18,335	31,000	60	75	$53.6
Upper Ohio Plateaus	6,864	10,000	57	75	19.0
Southwest Ohio Megalopolis	4,981	9,000	68	85	13.7
Lower Ohio Plateaus	2,786	5,000	53	65	8.6
Wabash–Lower Ohio Valley	3,704	7,000	56	70	12.3

AREA INCLUDES	Change, 1950–1960	Population 1960	1967	Personal Income 1967
		(thousands)		(billions)
MAJOR SMSAS:				
Pittsburgh	8.7%	2,405	2,410	$7.7
Cincinnati	24.2	1,268	1,370	4.4
Dayton	33.9	727	785	2.7
Columbus	34.1	755	870	3.1
Louisville	25.7	725	810	2.6
Nashville	21.5	463	535	1.5
Indianapolis	30.4	917	1,040	3.4
Evansville	4.8	223	230	0.7

CLIMATE — Humid continental in transition to humid subtropical; conspicuous changes from day to day.

	Temperature (°F)		Precipitation (inches)	
	Jan.	July	Annual	Season
Pittsburgh	32	74	35	All year
Indianapolis	30	76	38	All year
Nashville	40	80	45	All year

VEGETATION — Second-growth hardwood: oak, ash, maple, beech, tulip tree, basswood; conifers in reforested areas.

SOIL — Eroded gray-brown podzolic with local areas of fertile limestone and alluvial soils; along the northern part of the region; rich glacial soils.

MINERALS — Coal, petroleum, natural gas, cement, sand and gravel, stone, gypsum.

stripped; some fuels and minerals must now be shipped in; and the eastern part of the lowland has become mainly a food-deficit area. Soil leaching and erosion, stream pollution and local overcrowding have played considerable havoc with this land, once supposed to have limitless space and resources.

This Central Lowland, too large and too populous to be analyzed as a unit, is difficult to subdivide. The boundaries of the following subdivisions (Figure 8-2) are rarely sharp; the characteristics of each spill

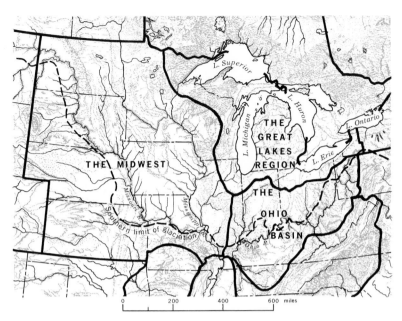

FIGURE 8-2   The subdivisions of the Central Lowland are neither topographically nor economically sharply delimited; each is bounded by a transition zone. (Base map copyright by A. K. Lobeck. Reprinted with permission of The Geographical Press, Hammond, Inc.)

over into the others. This chapter begins the analysis by considering the Ohio Basin, a large region with major problems of declining agriculture and mining, increasing water scarcity and pollution, and many areas of slow or no economic growth. These problems are not lacking in the other two subregions which, however, will be analyzed from a somewhat different approach. The next chapter treats the Great Lakes region, in which access to a wealth of raw materials and fuels at nodal points where lake and overland routes meet has led to a mammoth industrial-commercial development. There is, however, no sharp economic boundary between the Great Lakes and the Ohio Basin; indeed the trade between the two areas, between Pittsburgh and Cleveland, for example, is mammoth. The chapter on the Midwest deals with the more agricultural area approximately west of the Chicago SMSA; in that chapter the stress is on the drastic economic adjustments necessitated by declining agricultural employment. The agricultural subregions considered in that chapter extend into the Great Lakes and the Ohio Basin regions, in both of which

there is a problem of declining agricultural employment. In those regions, however, the problem plays a more modest part in the regional economies because of the greater development of urban activities.

THE OHIO BASIN

This region, based mainly on the area that drains into the Ohio (excluding the Tennessee Valley), topographically consists of two zones, each elongated approximately southwest-northeast. The northern rim is a glaciated plain, an undulating area of fertile soils well suited for farming. To the south is a broader plateau zone, low in the west and higher to the east and southeast, into which are incised the Ohio and its tributaries. The two zones of the Ohio Basin are different, but their problems connect them; the floods and pollution of the Ohio Valley cannot be controlled without regulating both zones. The lowland zone depends on the plateau for coal, recreational areas, and some specialized products, for example, tobacco, hardwoods, glass, steel, and chemicals. The plateau depends on the lowland for governmental assistance and a wide variety of manufactures and services. Economically, the division is not as sharp as the preceding statements imply because certain cities within the plateau, such as Pittsburgh, Cincinnati, and Louisville, are as advanced industrially as the lowland cities.

Problems of the Ohio System

The Army Corps of Engineers has undertaken a study of the Ohio Basin including a projection of potential development by decades to the year 2010.[1] This study is obviously centered around stream problems which are particularly the responsibility of the Corps of Engineers. In the study 19 subregions are mainly based on either parts of the Ohio or tributary watersheds. To simplify the presentation, these 19 subregions have been combined so as to make a total of 4 units (Figure 8-1). Underlying the Engineers' study is the basic problem: To what extent is it worthwhile to control the river? That this can be done is certain, but the cost may be high in terms of money, interference with existing business, and extension of government functions. The problem is especially complicated because the river cannot be controlled for a single purpose; each improvement for one purpose creates advantages and handicaps for other uses, making it awkward to allocate costs to the beneficiaries.

Floods   Severe floods, caused in part by deforestation and in part by heavy spring rains and rapid melting of snow, have created severe damage along the heavily industrial and commercial waterfront areas in all cities including Pittsburgh, Cincinnati, and Louis-

ville. The 1937 flood, for example, put half of Evansville under water. The defense against floods has been twofold: levees to protect the shore against encroaching waters, and dams and forests to impound the floodwaters upstream. Flood-control reservoirs are gradually being built with funds provided jointly by federal and state authorities. Many of these provide by-products in the form of lakes for recreation and domestic water supply. The most thoroughgoing attempt to control floods has been the Tennessee Valley Authority (see Chapter 11) whose watershed affects only a 40-mile section of the lower Ohio Valley.

Navigation   The Ohio and several major tributaries are controlled by a series of dams and locks on which a minimum 9-foot channel is maintained. Several minor tributaries have 6-foot channels. Maintenance of navigation involves some dredging as the Ohio carries a heavy burden of mud. The cargo consists of a few relatively bulky commodities: coal from the plateau, petroleum and other raw materials shipped upriver from the Gulf Coast, some heavy manufactures, but almost no lighter cargo. Some distant shipments of raw materials are included; for example, the coking coal found in the East is needed for metallurgy in areas where inferior nearby coal is being used to generate power. The Ohio tonnage is huge (Table 8-1), exceeding that of either the Panama or

TABLE 8-1   Commerce on the Ohio and Its Principal Tributaries (in thousands of short tons of cargo)

River	1940	1950	1960
Allegheny	3,929	3,594	3,833
Monongahela	29,560	28,510	29,533
Ohio (Pittsburgh to Cairo)	29,549	48,598	79,478
Kanawha	4,499	6,388	10,080
Cumberland	852	1,647	2,815
Tennessee	2,207	3,051	12,441

SOURCE: U.S. Army Corps of Engineers, *Annual Report of the Chief of Engineers: 1950;* later data, *Waterborne Commerce of the United States* (annual), Washington.

[1] U.S. Army Corps of Engineers, "Projective Economic Study of the Ohio River Basin," *Ohio River Basin Comprehensive Survey*, vol. 3, appendix B, Washington, 1965. This part of the study was prepared by Arthur D. Little, Inc.

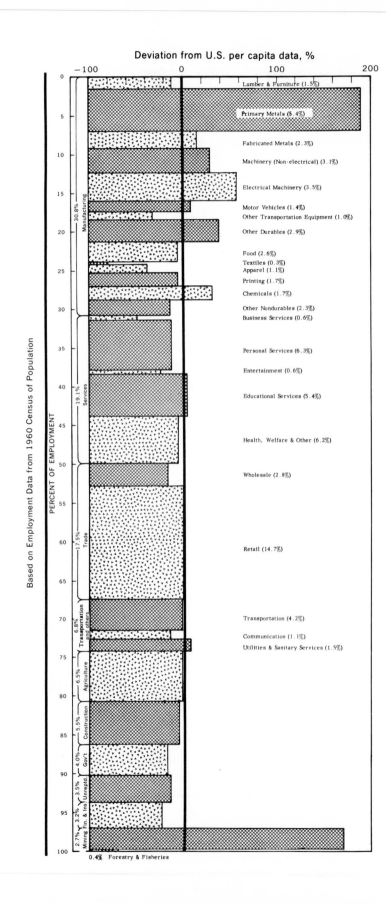

Deviation from U.S. per capita data, %

Based on Employment Data from 1960 Census of Population

PERCENT OF EMPLOYMENT

FIGURE 8-3 *A location quotient graph for all sources of earned income for the entire Ohio Basin. Note that the width of the bars is proportionate to the percent of employment in each industry; the area covered by any bar is not necessarily proportionate to the employment. The scale on the top is comparable to that used in the deviation charts, but negative deviations are shown by bars which do not extend up to the heavy line. Note that these location quotients are only a rough estimate of the relative importance of industries: They assume, for example, that all labor is equally efficient and equally paid.* (Bars from OHIO RIVER BASIN COMPREHENSIVE SURVEY, vol. 3, appendix B, fig. 6.)

Soo canal. The traffic is expected to increase further both because of greater demand and because of improvements now being undertaken in channels and locks.

Power The Ohio system aids power generation in two ways: its tributaries supply waterpower, and its waters are used in generating carboelectric and nuclear power. Most of the hydroelectric power that can be developed economically has been harnessed; in each state the capacity of carbo-electric power plants greatly exceeds the hydroelectric capacity. Even if all the potential hydroelectric power were developed in the basin, it could supply only one-quarter of the power used in 1965.

Water supply Many towns use the rivers for domestic water supply; others dump their sewage into the rivers. Industrial and coal

mine wastes add considerably to the rivers' load so that much of the Ohio resembles an open sewer. Much water is drawn from the river for industrial use;[2] most is used for cooling and then returned hot, in a few places hot enough to injure fish which have survived other forms of contamination.

Recreation Much of the Ohio is no longer satisfactory for fishing or swimming; the best recreational facilities are on the tributaries. Boating, both on small craft and on the few passenger steamers still in service, remains pleasant.

Employment and Income

The basin as described here includes 152,000 square miles inhabited by over 18 million people.[3] Figure 8-3 shows the location quotients for the principal types of economic activity and the percent of employment in each industry. Only in manufacturing and mining does the basin exceed the average for the nation; these provided respectively about 31 and 3 percent of total employment

[2] The Federal Reserve Bank of Cleveland gives the information on water use presented in Table 8-2 in its *Annual Report*, 1964, p. 16.

[3] The area of the Ohio Basin as analyzed by the Corps of Engineers study covers about 163,000 square miles inhabited by over 19 million people (1960). Two Pennsylvania counties and those parts of western Virginia and North Carolina that drain into the Ohio have been treated elsewhere because of their very strong commercial ties outside the basin. Southeastern West Virginia and some of eastern Kentucky are considered under the discussion of Appalachia in Chap. 11.

TABLE 8-2 Water Use: Cleveland Federal Reserve District and United States, 1960 (in millions of gallons per day)

Use for	Fourth District States		United States	
	Withdrawn	Consumed	Withdrawn	Consumed
Industry	31,000	455	144,000	3,200
Electric Power Generation (fuel)	20,483	37	102,200	224
Public Supplies	2,650	270	20,600	3,470
Rural Use	562	236	3,600	2,800
Irrigation	11	10	84,000	52,000[1]
Waterpower	123,780		2,000,000	

[1] An additional 23,000 million gal per day is lost in conveyance.

SOURCE: U.S. Geological Survey.

for the basin in 1960. Mining employment is largely coal mining. Nearly two-thirds of all manufacturing employment is in durable goods, and of the industrial classifications having above the national average in employment, all but one (chemicals) is classified as durable goods. Metals and fuel were the principal foundations upon which basin industry has been constructed.

Population and Migration

One-tenth of the American people live in the basin, and together they are a fair cross section of the nation, including the descendants of Scotch-Irish settlers in the Appalachian Plateau, the Germans settled around Cincinnati, the eastern and southern Europeans and Southern Negroes attracted by mining and industrial employment, and Southern aristocrats in the Bluegrass and Nashville Basin. The Ohio Basin, except in a few SMSAs, has been a region of slow growth with net out-migration characterizing the bulk of the area. The plateaus are mostly areas of poor soil which have seen much farm abandonment and consequent migration to local cities as well as to northward industrial centers. In many counties the decline in farm population began in the last century. The decline of coal mining has caused additional out-migration from smaller cities and towns and increased unemployment among those who remained (to over 10 percent in 20 out of 55 West Virginia counties). Table 8-3 shows the stag-

nation or reduction in coal production for states in this region. The number of hours worked (now only about one-third of the 1940 figure) has declined much more than the tonnage because of the introduction of strip mining and of coal-mining machinery. The economic problems of the rural parts of this region are less severe but closely related to those of the neighboring mountains; indeed large parts of this region have been included within the federal Appalachia program.

THE UPPER OHIO PLATEAUS

The plateau (Allegheny Plateau) in western Pennsylvania (and parts of adjacent states) consists of almost horizontal sedimentary rocks, including numerous beds of high-quality bituminous coal, limestone, clay, glass sand, salt, and some iron ore. Toward the east especially, the rocks have been slightly folded parallel to the Appalachian ridges; this folding has concentrated the oil and natural gas and imparted an approximately north-south trend to the streams which focus mostly on the Ohio at or west of Pittsburgh. The streams are incised 500 to 1,000 feet in the uplands; gentle slopes are limited to uplands and narrow flats along the streams.

The Pittsburgh Area

In 1754, the French descended the Allegheny River to its junction with the Monon-

TABLE 8-3   Bituminous Coal Production; Ohio Basin States, 1946–1965 (in millions of short tons)

State	Average 1946–1950	Average 1956–1960	1962	1964	1965
Pennsylvania	120.4	74.8	65.3	76.0	80.3
West Virginia	151.2	134.2	118.5	141.4	149.2
Ohio	35.5	35.4	34.0	37.3	39.4
Kentucky	74.8	69.0	69.2	82.7	85.7
Indiana	21.5	15.7	15.7	15.1	15.6
Illinois	60.1	46.1	48.9	55.0	58.5

SOURCE: U.S. Bureau of Mines, *Minerals Yearbook: 1965*, Washington, 1966; and earlier numbers.

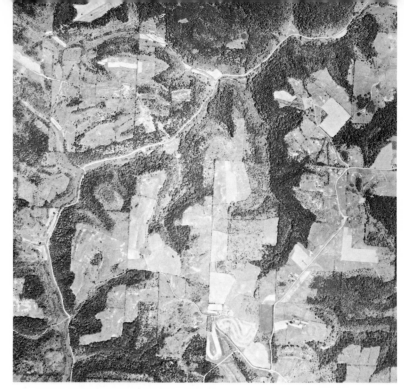

THE UPPER OHIO PLATEAUS include much intricately dissected land, mostly farmed in the last century, but gradually reverting to woodland and pasture. Other areas have been urbanized or at least temporarily made useless by strip coal mining. The area shown in Athens County, southeastern Ohio, is mainly used for dairying and other livestock activities. Only one-eighth of the land is in cultivated crops. (USDA photograph.)

gahela, establishing Fort Duquesne on what is now known as Pittsburgh's *Golden Triangle.* Following British victories, first over the French and later over the Indians, Fort Pitt was established at the site of Fort Duquesne and British settlers entered the area. After the American Revolution settlement was accelerated, and Pittsburgh, at the junction of Forbes Road from Harrisburg, the Cumberland Road from Baltimore, and two navigable streams, proved an ideal spot to start boats and rafts going downstream to Kentucky or even New Orleans.

About 1800 small iron industries, widely distributed throughout the settled United States, were based on small local deposits of iron ore and limestone; charcoal was used for fuel. In Pittsburgh such an iron foundry, built in 1805, supplied cannon to Perry's fleet on Lake Erie and to Jackson's army at New Orleans. Although Allegheny County (in which Pittsburgh is located) had eight

rolling mills in 1829, iron production was only 6,217 tons. In 1859, a blast furnace first used coke for fuel in the Pittsburgh steel industry; further stimulation came from the demands of the Civil War, the expanding railroad network, and the industrial genius of Carnegie, Frick, and others. About the same time, the oil industry developed 100 miles northward up the Allegheny Valley, providing another important fuel and raw material for western Pennsylvania.

For some decades, the Pittsburgh area led the country in steel. Most of the principal corporations were centered there, and the "Pittsburgh Plus" pricing policy helped maintain the local industry although Great Lakes centers were nearer to both Lake Superior iron ore and Midwestern markets. Pittsburgh received (and in part deserved) its reputation of being a dirty, smoky city crowded in congested valleys.

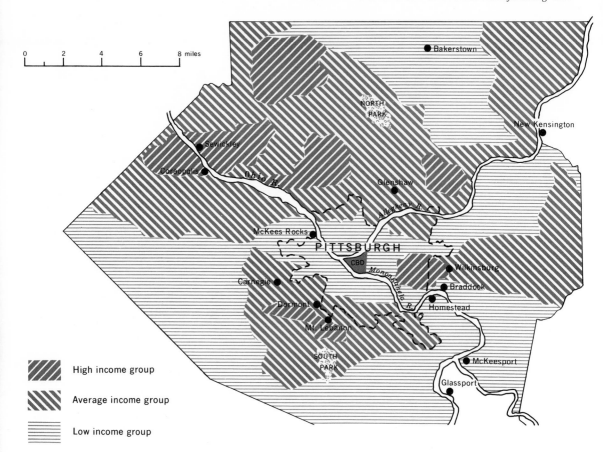

0   2   4   6   8 miles

High income group

Average income group

Low income group

FIGURE 8-4   This map of Allegheny County, the heart of the Pittsburgh SMSA, shows that the high-income areas are on the uplands away from the rivers, railroad tracks, and heavy industries. (Data from Greater Pittsburgh Chamber of Commerce.)

The modern Pittsburgh SMSA The uncertain economic prospect of the Pittsburgh area is based on the fact that 40 to 45 percent of its manufacturing employment is in primary metals. The Federal Reserve Bank of Cleveland has summed up the situation:

Pittsburgh's estimated 32 million tons of annual steel capacity in 1962, over one-fifth of the nation's total, made it the country's largest steelmaking center. The area's relative share of total national capacity, however, has been declining. Geographical shifts in the steel-consuming industries partially account for the western migration of the iron and steel industry; since World War II most new steel plants have located outside Pennsylvania. Pittsburgh's steel industry has encountered declining demand for some of its products, as a result of heightened competition from foreign and domestic steel producers and from substitute materials such as aluminum, concrete, glass, plastics, and wood. High labor costs are widely believed to be a key factor in this situation . . . . Since 1958, Pittsburgh's unemployment rate has been substantially above that for the U.S. as a whole.[4]

Pittsburgh has taken drastic steps to improve both the city and its business. Smoke-control measures have been very effective. Equally spectacular has been the creation of a park where the Monongahela and the

[4] Federal Reserve Bank of Cleveland, *Cross Section of the Fourth Federal Reserve District,* September, 1963, p. 29.

THE GOLDEN TRIANGLE of Pittsburgh, once a congested area, is being renovated by urban renewal. The landscaping, well-planned buildings, and an air-purification program have made the original site of Fort Duquesne an attractive urban feature. (Chamber of Commerce of Pittsburgh.)

Allegheny join to form the Ohio (Figure 8-4). East of this point, the CBD (the Golden Triangle) has been largely renovated, and handsome highway bridges at the Point State Park funnel traffic into expressways along both river waterfronts. On the hills east of the Golden Triangle slums have been replaced by modern apartments and a new civic auditorium. A mile east on the upland are centered the University of Pittsburgh, Carnegie Institute of Technology, the U.S. Bureau of Mines, Mellon Institute, and other research agencies. The better residential areas are mostly on the uplands; the railroads and heavy industries are along the rivers. Separated by deep valleys, the street grids, often contorted to fit the steep slopes, reflect both the topography and the inheritance from former towns.

As the Basic Data show, further population growth is predicted. Employment growth will be in the service industries, not in manufacturing.[5] Many of the present leading industries (for example, primary metals and food processing) are expected to

[5] All predictions are based on the Corps of Engineers Survey which is predicated largely on the assumption that present trends will continue.

employ fewer people than they did in 1960. As in most large cities, the 2010 economy will involve more clerical and planning activity and less handling of raw materials by labor. Pittsburgh will become even more of a commercial-financial center than it is today.

Outlying Areas

The northern part of the plateau produces high-grade oil; the southern part bituminous coal well suited for coking. These mining activities are expected to continue in production, but manufacturing will engage increasing parts of the labor supply. SMSAs such as Youngstown, Steubenville-Weirton,

and Wheeling are little Pittsburghs with somewhat fewer commercial and financial functions. In addition to steel, manufactures include pottery, glass, and chemicals, industries originally based on local raw materials. As the good industrial sites are crowded, water for industrial expansion is scarce, and adjacent uplands are much dissected, only slow growth is predicted for these cities and the surrounding countryside.

Southeastern Ohio–West Virginia Plateau

This plateau is classified as hilly to very hilly except for narrow strips along the rivers. Its main advantages are river transportation, cheap local coal, natural gas, brine, and clay deposits. Farming, mainly livestock and often on a part-time basis, is poor and declining. Mining may increase in production but because of rapid mechanization will provide decreased employment. The hope for future development is based mainly on material-oriented industry.

The Charleston SMSA   Bison seeking salt first trampled out a trail used in turn by Indians, fur traders, and settlers, and now followed by U.S. 60 and the Chesapeake and Ohio Railroad from the upper James River to Charleston and on to Huntington. The brines the bison sought combined with nearby coal and limestone initially localized the Charleston chemical industry. Scientific and engineering skills undoubtedly had much to do with the growth of more complicated chemical industries, such as nylon, synthetic rubber, plastics, and antifreeze production. Rayon, based on local wood pulp and chemicals, is also important. Charleston is the capital of one of two states which lost population in the 1950–1960

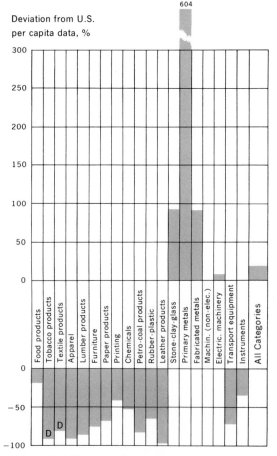

VALUE ADDED BY MANUFACTURING
Pittsburgh SMSA = 1.24% U.S. Pop.

FIGURE 8-5   Although the Pittsburgh SMSA has some activity in each industrial category, the emphasis on heavy industries is obvious.

decade (Table 8-4), and of the 18 counties which Charleston claims as its marketing area, only four gained any population. The industries that flourish in Charleston are so highly automated that the SMSA produces one-third of the West Virginia's value added by manufacturing by employing only one-fifth of its industrial workers. The great resource is coal-generated electricity which requires few workers. Unemployment in 1960 in the state and in most nearby counties was well above the national average, largely because of the decline of coal mining.

Other cities   Three cities in three states form the Huntington-Ashland SMSA. This is primarily a transportation center, Huntington having the major Chesapeake and Ohio shops and being a major river port for coal shipments and petroleum receipts. Industry has developed largely on the basis of cheap fuel; the products include nickel alloys, iron and steel, and glass. Nearby on the Ohio, cheap power from several large power plants spaced along the Ohio, has brought in new industries: aluminum refining and processing (based on bauxite hauled from Louisiana by barge) at Ravenswood (West Virginia).

THE POTENTIAL SOUTHWESTERN OHIO MEGALOPOLIS

Two approaches led early settlers to the middle Ohio area. They descended the Ohio from Pittsburgh or Wheeling, having first crossed the mountains either by the Cumberland Road from Maryland or by the Forbes Road from Pennsylvania. The other approach was from Lake Erie, crossing either to the upper Ohio or to its Muskingum, Scioto, or Miami tributaries and thence to the middle Ohio; about 1830 to 1850 canals traversed parts of these valleys to carry trade from Cleveland to Pittsburgh, Columbus, and Portsmouth, and from Toledo to Dayton and Cincinnati.

Southwestern Ohio is largely open country with much fertile land; in this area begins the axis of Ohio industrial development fanning out from Cincinnati north to Toledo and northeast to Youngstown. In addition to its SMSAs, it contains a variety of small cities, each with industrial specialties. Altogether this subregion seems to have the economic potential to form a Cincinnati-Dayton-Columbus megalopolis.

The Cincinnati-Dayton SMSAs

In contrast to the upstream Ohio areas, these SMSAs have grown in population

TABLE 8-4   West Virginia Population Trends, 1900-1966

Year	Population	Change from Preceding Period		Components of Change from Preceding Period	
		Number	Percent	Net Migration	Natural Increase
1900	958,800	196,006	25.7%	17,200	178,806
1910	1,221,119	262,319	27.4	46,100	216,219
1920	1,463,701	242,582	19.9	−1,700	244,282
1930	1,729,205	265,504	18.1	−53,800	319,304
1940	1,901,974	172,769	10.0	−73,600	246,369
1950	2,005,552	103,578	5.4	−210,800	314,378
1960	1,860,421	−145,131	−7.2	−447,000	301,869
1963	1,813,000	−47,421	−2.6	−113,000	65,579
1966	1,794,000	−19,000	−1.0	−73,000	54,000

SOURCE: U.S. Bureau of the Census.

more rapidly than the United States average. Cincinnati has had the good fortune of being well situated in relation to business-generating areas in each period of economic history. Founded about 1790 as part of a plan to settle the rolling land in the Miami and Little Miami valleys, it soon became a major Ohio port and commercial center where three natural routes crossed. Westward 15 miles the Ohio River turned sharply south, making Cincinnati the logical center for pioneers bound for central Indiana to change to overland transport. The older part of the city was located in a former river valley,[6] later urban growth spread to the encircling upland. Manufacturing developed to supply the newly settled areas to the west, and meat packing and flour milling developed to help market farm produce. In the

[6]The Licking River, now only in Kentucky, became tributary to the Ohio after that river was created by the rearrangement of drainage patterns by glaciation. Its former valley provides flatland for downtown Cincinnati.

1830s, a canal connected the city with Toledo on Lake Erie and soon after railroads converged on the city. Cincinnati was a natural outlet for the rich agriculture of central Indiana, adjacent Ohio, and the Kentucky Bluegrass; later the city financed a railroad southward to Chattanooga to tap Southern trade.

Modern Cincinnati   This city still benefits from its nodal location. Although in the Ohio Valley and not distant from areas of declining agriculture, it is close to the prosperous eastern Corn Belt. A network of railway and highway routes fans out from the northwest to northeast, connecting it especially with the axis of Ohio industry extending northeast through Hamilton, Dayton, Springfield, Columbus, to Akron, Youngstown, and Cleveland. Well situated on the Ohio, it receives fuel and raw materials by barge. Across the Ohio its trade still remains important with good rail, highway, and air connections southward.

Industrially Cincinnati specializes in several types of goods (Figure 8-6). First are manufactures which convert raw or partly processed materials into finished products: soap and toilet articles, detergents and other chemicals, food products, paints, and varnishes. Of about equal importance are the transportation equipment industries: automobile parts, aircraft engines, and truck trailers. Nonelectrical machinery (especially machine tools) and fabricated metals represent a third major group. These industries make up about 55 percent of the value added; the remainder consists of consumer goods industries producing such diverse articles as pianos, mattresses, and playing cards.

Dayton and neighboring SMSAs   Urban development between Cincinnati and Dayton will

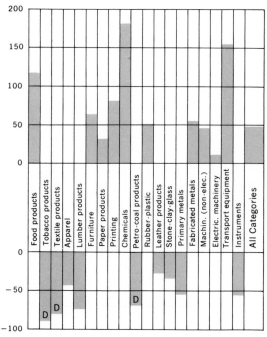

Deviation from U.S. per capita data, %

VALUE ADDED BY MANUFACTURING
Cincinnati SMSA = .71% U.S. Pop.

FIGURE 8-6   Compare this graph with Figure 8-5; why the differences?

THE EVOLVING REGIONAL PATTERN

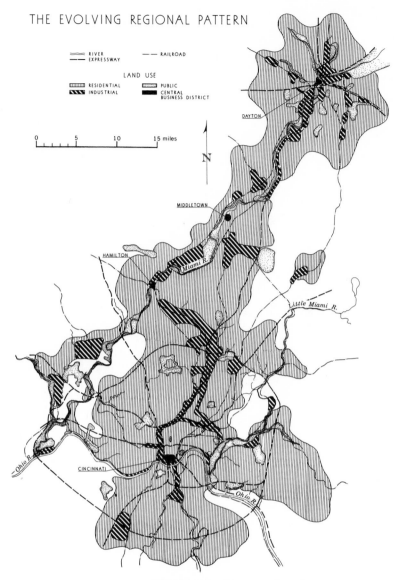

FIGURE 8-7   There is still much open area between Cincinnati and Dayton, but it is filling up so rapidly that planners have already laid out future land use. (Cincinnati Planning Commission from Cincinnati Chamber of Commerce.)

soon be almost continuous (Figure 8-7). Dayton started as an agricultural center for the upper Miami Valley. In 1849 it added railroad cars to a list of diversified manufactures for valley consumption. Although it would be an oversimplification to attribute Dayton's later growth to a number of inventions, these certainly were turning points in its history. Shortly after the Civil War Dayton cash registers introduced a new era in merchandising records. Motor generators, invented in Dayton, provided farms with electricity before rural power lines became commonplace. The Wright Brothers built the first successful airplane at Dayton and, after initial flights on North Carolina beaches, flew regularly at a field now part of the huge Wright-Patterson Air Base. The Miami flood of 1913 wiped out much of Dayton and led to the construction of up-

THREE TRIBUTARIES CONVERGE on the Miami River, which curves around the Dayton CBD. In 1913 the city was flooded so severely that upstream controls including empty reservoirs were instituted soon after. (Mayfield Photos from Dayton Chamber of Commerce.)

stream flood-control reservoirs paid for through regional taxes levied by a new type of government agency, the *Miami Conservancy District.*

Charles F. Kettering of Dayton developed the electric starter for automobiles and improved ignition systems, antiknock gasoline, and other automotive products which led to General Motors expansion in Dayton. Other Dayton firsts include electrical refrigeration, punch-card accounting, multileaved and carboned business forms, and several new chemical products and processes. These are some of the human accomplishments back of the following Dayton industrial employment statistics: nonelectrical machinery, 27 percent; electrical machinery, 24 percent; printing and publishing, 10 percent; rubber and plastics, 8 percent;

transportation equipment, 7 percent; all others, 25 percent.

Smaller cities Springfield, 25 miles northeast of the Dayton CBD, produces predominately durable goods: trucks, diesel engines, pumps. South of Dayton both Middletown and Hamilton produce paper products, originally based on nearby forests long since exhausted; both cities have added heavy industries. Around the cities in the Cincinnati-Dayton-Columbus area are many small cities and towns and extensive farmlands producing corn, soybeans, dairy products, hogs, poultry, and cattle. This Ohio part of the Corn Belt is a prosperous agricultural area; nevertheless the county most productive agriculturally (Darke) has a *gross value* of all farm products slightly less than the *value added* by manufacturing in that county.

The Columbus area The advantages of the Miami valleys also are found in the Scioto-Muskingum watershed, whose commercial capital is Columbus. Centrally located in the state at the junction of the unnavigable Scioto and Olentangy rivers, Columbus was selected in 1812 as state capital, partly because land for the statehouse was contributed by four citizens. In the canal era, Columbus was connected with the Ohio and Erie Canal which passed some miles south of the city. Although initial growth was as a capital city and farm marketing center, its other activities now provide more employment. Industry (two-thirds in durable goods) leads with machinery, vehicles, fabricated metals, and food processing, accounting for three-fifths of the industrial labor. Trade employment slightly exceeds durable goods employment. In third place is government employment (including educational services) which has been increasing more rapidly than total employment. At present, Columbus with no water connections and few local raw materials, competes successfully on the basis of central location; excellent road, rail, and air connections; and political leadership.

Smaller centers The rectangular system of rural land settlement in this region as elsewhere in the lowlands developed a multitude of rather evenly spaced county seats, each performing commercial and service functions for the surrounding farmlands. With the displacement of much farm labor by machinery, these cities sought and found industries that could use advantageously former farmhands and cheap uncongested factory sites. Some of these cities invented their own industries to serve the surrounding area; for example, Marion developed the steam shovel. Many of the industries used mechanical skills characteristic of workers accustomed to repairing farm machinery and automobiles. Table 8-5 lists a random group of these cities and their products.

THE LOWER OHIO PLATEAUS

The Ohio Basin in southern Indiana, central Kentucky, and adjacent Tennessee consists of low plateaus within which areas of level or rolling land alternate with low but rugged lands. The latter are sandstone and shale areas suited mostly for forest; in places they are underlain by coal deposits. The more fertile, less rugged lands are formed over limestone and other relatively soft rocks;

TABLE 8-5 Population (1960) and Industrial Products of Random Small Cities in Central Ohio

City	Population	Representative Products
Ashland	17,419	Rubber goods, printing, pipe fittings
Cambridge	14,562	Plastics, ceramics, spark plugs
Chillicothe	24,869	Papermaking, atomic, aluminum
Lancaster	29,916	Glass, electrical machinery
Mansfield	47,323	Tires, auto parts, electronics
Marion	37,079	Power shovels, refrigerators, axles
Mount Vernon	13,284	Glass, diesel engines, soybean products
Newark	41,790	Transportation equipment, glass
Wooster	17,046	Rubber, ladders, paint brushes, pumps, potato chips
Zanesville	39,077	Glass, tile, electric equipment

SOURCE: Editor and Publisher, *Market Guide*, 1966 edition, New York.

they are generally more populous and more prosperous. Their business is related to four sizable cities: Cincinnati (already discussed), Louisville, Lexington, and Nashville, each having its own characteristics.

Louisville

The river at the falls of the Ohio drops a mere 26 feet in 2 miles. Although these rapids were not impassable—at least at high water—they encouraged the transshipment of goods overland from Louisville just above the falls to Portland or Shippingport below the falls. A canal around the falls was completed in 1830 but did not stop the growth of Louisville which, in addition to its river trade, had become a distributing center for growing southern Indiana, part of the Bluegrass, and central Kentucky.

The traditional industries of Louisville, related to either the produce or needs of the surrounding countryside are food processing, whiskey and beer, tobacco products, lumber products, furniture, and farm machinery. Most of these were nondurables. Recently the introduction of new industries has given the durable goods employment predominance. Machinery including electric household appliances, fabricated metals including plumbing supplies, automobile assembly, and more complicated chemical industries are now among the leading industries.

No doubt Louisville's location on eight trunk railroads and five barge lines, at the intersection of five interstate highways, and on the southwestern edge of the American Commercial-Manufacturing Core has aided its industrial growth, but many other cities have similar advantages. Louisville has also been able to draw on surplus rural labor in the agriculturally declining nearby counties. For example, 6 of the 11 counties within commuting range of Louisville factories showed a net out-migration in 1950–1960. In addition, Louisville has been unusually successful in planning to coordinate industrial land use with residential and commercial use. The city has also been fortunate in its new industries; thus General Electric with its huge, campuslike Appliance Park has shown how to make industrial sites attractive.

The Bluegrass and Lexington

The Kentucky Bluegrass Region with its gently undulating surface, originally covered with grass 2 to 3 feet tall with scattered groves of trees, proved ideal for raising beef cattle, horses, tobacco, corn, and

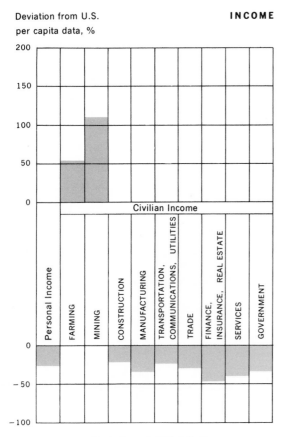

Deviation from U.S. per capita data, %

INCOME

Kentucky = 1.60% U.S. Pop.

FIGURE 8-8   Economically Kentucky is a divided state. The high incomes and diverse urban activities of the cities along the Ohio and in the Bluegrass are overbalanced statistically by the rural and small-town areas.

WEST OF DOWNTOWN LOUISVILLE the falls of the Ohio are now largely
blocked by a dam beyond the bridge shown; the Ohio water is diverted through a canal
and locks to the left, thus forming a navigable waterway much used by tows of barges.
(Louisville Chamber of Commerce.)

FIGURE 8-9   The division pointed out in Figure 8-8 is
apparent on this map. Northern Kentucky specializes in
the production of bourbon whiskey, which is illegal in
most counties of the state. (Kentucky Department of Commerce.)

CONTROL OF ALCOHOLIC BEVERAGES IN KENTUCKY

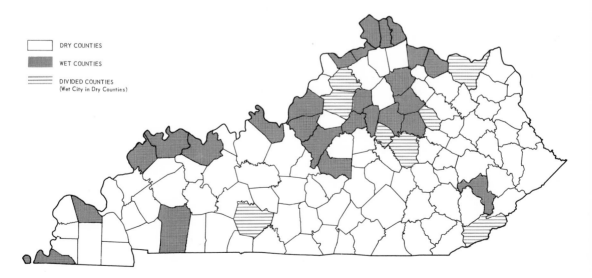

DRY COUNTIES

WET COUNTIES

DIVIDED COUNTIES
(Wet City in Dry Counties)

wheat. Accessible both from the Ohio and via Cumberland Gap, its lands were settled by farmers before 1800. On its phosphate-rich limestone soils, they developed a horse-racing aristocracy with "gracious homes, fences of white board or stone, and lovely green pastures and hayfields."[7]

Lexington, first settled in 1779, recorded its first horse race a decade later. Nearby is Bourbon County after which the distinctive beverage distilled from corn is named. Burley tobacco, for which Lexington is the world's largest market, is another Bluegrass product. Except for tobacco processing, industry is relatively recent. At present the largest factory produces electric typewriters; other electrical industries are becoming important.

The Bluegrass and the Louisville SMSA are the only parts of Kentucky showing a considerable population increase. The hill country to the south and east experienced an out-migration of 77,000 people in the 1950s, causing a 9 percent decline in population.

The Nashville Basin

In contrast to the sandstone-shale farms in central Tennessee is a typical estate in the Nashville Basin. Its 355 acres are mainly pasture, some in bluegrass and others in clover and other hay crops. The soil is shallow but fertile, rich in lime and phosphate; none of the land is in corn, wheat, or other row crops conducive to erosion. The farm produces mainly livestock—100 beef cattle, 140 lambs, some wool, and perhaps a few pedigreed horses. Similar estates are found in the Kentucky Bluegrass but with more emphasis on horses and tobacco. In Fayette County, the heart of the aristocratic Bluegrass estates, the average farm is worth $76,000 with 28 farms of over 1,000 acres. Hardly "hillbilly" farming!

Nashville, capital of Tennessee, brings together the trade of diverse areas: the cotton and hardwoods of the Mississippi Plain, the poor farming areas of the Tennessee Highland rim both east and west of the Nashville Basin, and the developing industries of the Tennessee Valley. It is also a major junction on the Louisville and Nashville Railroad, a company whose trunk lines connect St. Louis with Atlanta, Atlanta with Memphis, and Cincinnati and Louisville with Birmingham, Mobile, and New Orleans. Although considered a Southern city, its business ties are more to the north. Its industries include aircraft parts and synthetic fibers, and a great variety of consumer goods for more local markets.

THE WABASH AND LOWER OHIO VALLEYS

The northern two-thirds of this area is rich glaciated Corn Belt land, in most respects a continuation of west central Ohio. Blessed with hardwoods, proximity to coal, local gas fields, and plentiful farm produce and farm markets, its towns turned early to manufacturing. Its industries, long established to process farm products and supply farm needs, have expanded, taking advantage of labor migrating from the southern hills or displaced by machinery on the farms. Indianapolis, the state capital, still has large stockyards, food-packing plants, milling facilities, and fertilizer plants. Its present specialties (aircraft engines, automobile parts and assembly, electric machinery, and pharmaceuticals) result from its convenient location in relation to major manufacturing regions rather than from local resources. To the north and east of Indianapolis, a cluster of county seats (Muncie, Marion, Anderson, Kokomo) boomed in the 1880s when natural gas discoveries were used to manufacture glass, especially glass jars then widely used for preserving fruits and vegetables. These cities and others are now outposts of the Detroit automobile industry, producing

[7] U.S. Department of Agriculture, *Soil,* Yearbook of Agriculture, Washington, 1957, p. 368.

such parts as batteries, transmissions, cable, lamps, starters, generators, and gears. These industrial developments explain why in Indiana, a state noted for its corn, beefsteaks, and pork chops, the 1965 civilian income obtained from farms was $612 million; from manufacturing, $4,985 million; from other urban activities, nearly another $5,000 million.

Evansville

The lower Wabash Valley has had a more uneven history. Evansville had an out-migration of 21,364 in the 1950s. In the 1940s Evansville had been known as the "Refrigerator Capital of the World"; in 1954 Servel, Inc., discontinued making gas refrigerators, and International Harvester decided to discontinue its refrigerator line. Unemployment was high until new industries were obtained, mostly of the durable goods type. Whirlpool Corporation started manufacturing refrigerators; several plastic plants entered the picture; a huge aluminum plant has been erected east of Evansville to take advantage of cheap coal, Ohio water, and Ohio barge transportation. The Evansville SMSA population now is growing at close to the national rate. Meanwhile the commercial outlook has been mediocre because its trading area included many low-grade coal-mining and mediocre farm areas, both with declining employment. Evansville has attracted mostly durable goods industries which are cyclical in nature; Terre Haute, 110 miles to the north, has had a similar history.

The lower Wabash Valley and some alluvial strips along the lower Ohio contain good farmland, some in need of drainage, on which the long growing season permits a diversity of crops. With the westward ex-

pansion of the Commercial-Manufacturing Core, this area would seem to have many of the advantages for growth now exploited by Louisville and Cincinnati.

CONCLUSIONS

The southern Ohio Basin consists largely of narrow valleys incised into a rolling, commonly infertile upland. In contrast, the area subjected to Wisconsin glaciation and limited areas with limestone or alluvial soils are agriculturally productive, but even these areas are losing farm population as a result of farm mechanization and consolidation. The upland areas have difficulty in supporting their population; their problem is part of the Appalachia situation to be discussed

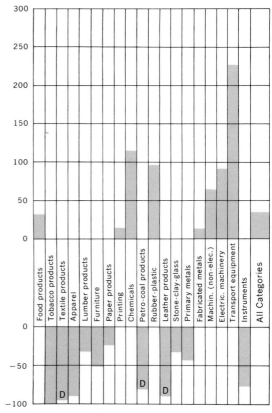

VALUE ADDED BY MANUFACTURING
Indianapolis SMSA = .51% U.S. Pop.

FIGURE 8-10 Industrially Indianapolis has considerable resemblance to Cincinnati (Figure 8-6). How might you account for the differences between the two graphs?

THE ALCOA WORKS, aluminum smelter, and rolling mill, are on the north bank of the Ohio east of Evansville. Coal, shipped cheaply by barge down the Ohio or from southern Indiana mines, powers the plant. (William Cornelia from Evansville Chamber of Commerce.)

more fully in Chapter 11. Population growth has been most rapid in the metropolitan areas of which only Dayton, Columbus, and Indianapolis had rates of growth equaling or exceeding the average rate for all SMSAs, 1950–1960.

The forecasting of the future development of a region is necessarily hazardous. Incorporated in this chapter have been many of the forecasts prepared by Arthur D. Little, Inc., for the Corps of Engineers study. The forecasts are based largely on the assumption that present trends will continue; yet if our recent history shows anything, it demonstrates that revolutionary technological changes may alter recognized trends rather abruptly. Thus any long-range forecasts must be checked and corrected at intervals. The forecasts do provide some tentative basis for planning; they do give some idea of the size of the capital expense which might be justifiably made in managing the water resources of the Ohio Basin. The forecasts do not (and probably cannot be expected to) allow for such conceivable changes as, for example, the replacement of coal-generated power by nuclear power or the development of heavy industry less dependent on huge quantities of cool water. On the other hand, even if partly wrong, such forecasts may have a great influence on business and political decisions and may be a partial cause of what they predict.

Assuming then that technology will not displace water as a major economic factor (and few have ventured to predict otherwise), the basic problem of this region is to use its water efficiently. This presents major problems: (1) water storage for flood and navigation control and efficient use, (2) the avoidance of pollution. Air pollution is a further problem in an area so heavily endowed with smoky industries and with motor vehicles; perhaps nuclear power or electric power generated at the mines may solve this problem.

Many of the cities in the southern half of this region have been peripheral to the main stream of American development. With the further development of the Southeast, with the lessening importance of good agricultural land, with the problems of moderate relief conquered by bulldozers, this region may become more central to markets. This might attract more industry to this land of charming hills and mild winters.

SELECTED REFERENCES

BARTON, THOMAS F.: "The Sewer or Waste Disposal Use of the Ohio River," *Journal of Geography,* vol. 59 (1960), pp. 326–336.

BOWMAN, MARY J., and W. WARREN HAYNES: *Resources and People in East Kentucky,* published for Resources for the Future, Inc., Johns Hopkins, Baltimore, 1963.

FEDERAL RESERVE BANK OF CLEVELAND: *Cross Section of the Fourth Federal Reserve District,* Cleveland, 1963.

GARLAND, J. H. (ed.): *The North American Midwest,* Wiley, New York, 1955.

LANDSBERG, HANS H., LEONARD L. FISCHMAN, and JOSEPH L. FISHER: *Resources in America's Future,* published for Resources for the Future, Inc., Johns Hopkins, Baltimore, 1963.

MILLER, E. W.: "The Industrial Development of the Allegheny Valley," *Economic Geography,* vol. 29 (1953), pp. 388–404.

U.S. ARMY CORPS OF ENGINEERS: "Projective Economic Study of the Ohio River Basin," *Ohio River Basin Comprehensive Study,* vol. 3, appendix B, Washington, 1965.

WEST VIRGINIA DEPARTMENT OF COMMERCE: *West Virginia Economic Atlas,* economical statistical series nos. 1 and 2, Charleston, 1961.

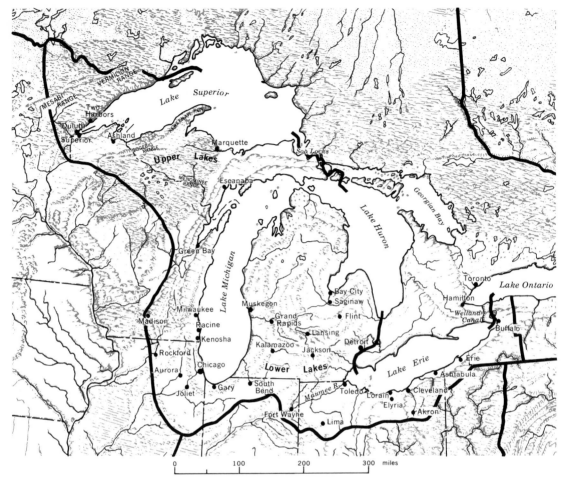

FIGURE 9-1   Landforms of the Great Lakes region. (Base map by A. K. Lobeck. Reprinted with permission of The Geographical Press, Hammond, Inc.)

CHAPTER 9
THE GREAT LAKES REGION: GATEWAY AND MAJOR FOCUS

The Great Lakes region demonstrates the changing relationships of an area to natural resources (Figure 9-1). Until the end of the eighteenth century, this area was of interest mainly to the fur trader and the trapper. A half century later its southern half had been occupied by the farmer while its northern half was being opened to obtain raw materials to manufacture farm implements and build wagons, railroads, and boats to haul farm produce eastward. Before the end of the nineteenth century, the lakes were a major route linking Northern ores, lumber, and limestone with Appalachian coal, and bringing Midwestern grain and meat to Eastern markets. Recently the Great Lakes–St. Lawrence Seaway has opened the lakes to ocean freighters, and Labrador and other ores are starting to replace the increasingly scarce Minnesota hematites at eastern lake ports. At the same time that other natural resources are being exhausted, demand is growing for fresh water, of which the lakes have the greatest supply.

BASIC DATA:

AREA INCLUDES	Land Area (thousand sq. mi.)	Population Change 1950–1960	Population 1960 (thousands)	Population 1967 (thousands)	Personal Income 1967 (billions)
ENTIRE REGION	144.9	21.1%	25,363	27,835	$96.5
Part of New York State	2.7	18.8	1,452	1,565	4.9
Erie SMSA, Pennsylvania	0.8	14.3	251	270	0.8
Northern Ohio	11.3	24.1	4,037	4,150	15.1
Michigan	57.0	22.8	7,823	8,400	29.0
Northeast Minnesota	27.1	8.7	441	460	1.1
North and east Wisconsin	31.1	21.2	3,062	3,680	11.5
Northeastern Illinois	8.5	20.2	6,835	7,650	29.5
Northern Indiana	6.4	23.1	1,462	1,660	4.6
MAJOR SMSAS:					
Buffalo	1.6	20.0%	1,307	1,330	$ 4.5
Cleveland	1.5	25.7	1,909	1,990	7.1
Detroit	2.0	24.7	3,762	4,000	15.5
Chicago–Northwest Indiana	4.7	21.6	6,794	7,450	29.6
Milwaukee	1.0	25.0	1,233	1,310	5.1

CLIMATE   Humid continental, temperatures moderated near lakes.

	Temperature (°F) Jan.	Temperature (°F) July	Precipitation (inches) Annual	Precipitation (inches) Season
Cleveland	28	71	35	Slight summer maximum
Detroit	27	74	31	Slight summer maximum
Chicago	26	74	33	Summer maximum
Duluth	9	66	29	Summer maximum

VEGETATION   Second-growth hardwoods along streams and on farm woodlots; mixed woodland in the south; in the north, birch, beech, maple, and hemlock and pine (largely cutover with considerable regrowth in aspen).

SOIL   Gray-brown podzolic soils and podzols north of about 44°N. Parent materials in southern two-thirds are enriched by calcareous glacial deposits and lacustrine deposits.

MINERALS   Iron ore around Lake Superior (also copper in Michigan); some lime-stone, petroleum, coal, and salt in lower Michigan; sand, gravel, and crushed stone.

The business of the Great Lakes region is mammoth, second only to that of the Atlantic Megalopolis. Its population, two-thirds as large as that of the Atlantic Megalopolis, is concentrated near the lower lakes, and despite the importance of raw materials, its production is largely urban—indeed nearly three-fifths of its people and two-thirds of its personal income are concentrated in the five SMSAs listed in the Basic Data. Its industries, generally heavy, are becoming increasingly diversified; the region is the outstanding industrial area in the country, but its rank in all other activities—farming, mining, trade, and services—is fairly high. After funneling its trade for many decades by canal, rail, and highway to Atlantic ports, the region is now connected by the Great Lakes–St. Lawrence Seaway directly with ocean ports two-thirds of the year.

This region and the rest of the Central Lowland have been customarily discussed as a group of agricultural regions (Figure 10-2) upon which certain industrial and commercial centers have been superimposed. Historically this descriptive device has much justification, although the beginnings of commerce and industry commonly date, in most areas, only a decade or two after pioneer agricultural settlement. From the start the Midwestern settler was commercially minded, and his log cabin was a first step toward the hoped-for manor house. Although the pioneer farmer, the lumberjack, and the miner cannot be neglected in a dis-

cussion of the Great Lakes region and their successors still occupy much of its land, for some decades most of its regional income has been produced in the city. Local resources are far from negligible, but more important is the economic structure that has grown far beyond the original resource base. The agricultural regions, many of which extend far into the Great Lakes region, will be discussed more fully in Chapter 10.

Landforms, the Land Survey, and Settlement

The Great Lakes region is generally an area of low relief, its principal topographic features being low hills and water bodies: lakes, ponds, rivers, marshes, and swamps. The northern border of the region, underlain by locally ore-rich metamorphic rocks, was in part covered with generally infertile glacial materials. In the southern portion of

FIGURE 9-2   The rectangular patterns so characteristic in most of the trans-Appalachian United States can be traced to the rectangular survey which divides each state into 36-square-mile townships measured from selected initial points. Each can be identified (as shown on the diagram to the left) by an abbreviation, for example: T2S R4W. Within each township sections of one square mile are identified by numbers (diagram to the right). (USDA.)

RECTANGULAR COORDINATED LAND DIVISION SYSTEM

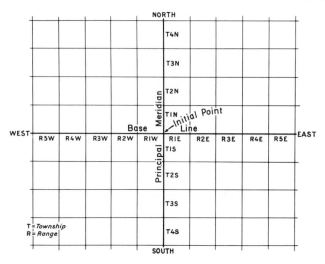

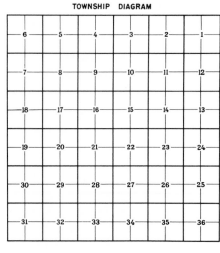

the region almost horizontal layers of sedimentary rock are covered with a thick layer of calcareous glacial drift and the outstanding relief features commonly result from glacial deposition. The divide separating the Ohio and the Mississippi drainage from that to the Great Lakes is so low that cutting canals between the two drainage systems was a minor engineering feat.

The Rectangular Survey

This system of land surveying, already discussed in Chapter 2, encouraged an even spacing of farmsteads, roads, and towns (Figure 9-2). Departures from the general plan were necessitated by water bodies: swampy areas being avoided and stream and lake sites sought for domestic water supply, navigation, and control of route crossings. In the less settled northern areas, the rectangular road system is less conspicuous, but the survey is marked by the rectangular grid of county and township boundaries. As the region developed, towns sited either on lake harbors or where major roads and railroads cross rivers, grew more rapidly than other towns, thus becoming major commercial centers. Other cities, smaller and performing less varied services, grew up to serve less extensive trading areas.

In the better settled lower lakes area, the towns developed a hierarchy of commercial functions. The smallest towns (second-order places on Figure 9-4) with local retail functions are served by a smaller number of third-order places which also offer wholesaling and other specialized services. Even more specialized services are offered by the still smaller number of fourth-order places which are commercial capitals for subregions, for example, Grand Rapids, commercial center of western Michigan. Even larger places are regional business capitals for extensive areas: Detroit for the area with automobile and affiliated industries; Cleveland for most of north and central Ohio; Buffalo for the eastern end of the

MOST OF THE EASTERN SHORE of Lake Michigan is referred to as the "Michigan Fruit Belt." With temperatures stabilized by winds from the lake, the coastal zone is profitable for intensive farming: orchards on the sandy moraines (upper part of the photo), and truck crops on the drained muck soils elsewhere. (USDA photograph.)

Lake Erie. Chicago serves also as a subnational business capital for the entire Central Lowland.

Sources of Income

The Great Lakes region obtains about two-fifths of its income from industry. Trade is the second largest source of income. Farming, contributing much more to the region than in the Northeast, yields less than one-twentieth of the income provided by industry. Mining income is still smaller, many ores now being shipped in—even the fuel coming from the Ohio Valley and the Southwest. Finance, transportation, utilities, and, especially, services and government—each

AREAL FUNCTIONAL ORGANIZATION IN THE EASTERN UNITED STATES

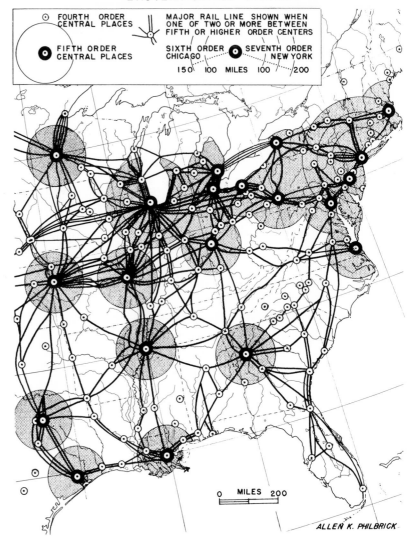

FIGURE 9-3   *Philbrick has divided the urban centers into orders of cities, all fitting into a hierarchy. The seventh-order center, New York, is an international capital as well as the primate city in the United States. Chicago is the primate city of the interior United States. Fifth-order cities are major focal points for clusters of large cities; commonly they are regional economic capitals with central banking functions. The concentration of these higher-order cities in the Commercial-Manufacturing Core is noteworthy. Fourth-order cities are transshipment points with commercial controls over only part of a state or over parts of several adjacent states.* [Allen K. Philbrick, "Principles of Areal Functional Organization in Regional Human Geography," ECONOMIC GEOGRAPHY, vol. 33 (1957), pp. 306–336.]

of these yields much more income than the crops, livestock, lumber, and minerals which first attracted settlers to the region. Much more important today in the regional economy are central location in relation to Anglo-American population, and the well-developed structure of transportation, communication, utility, and other networks.

THE LAKE ERIE PORTS

Transshipment points have provided logical sites for the development of great cities and

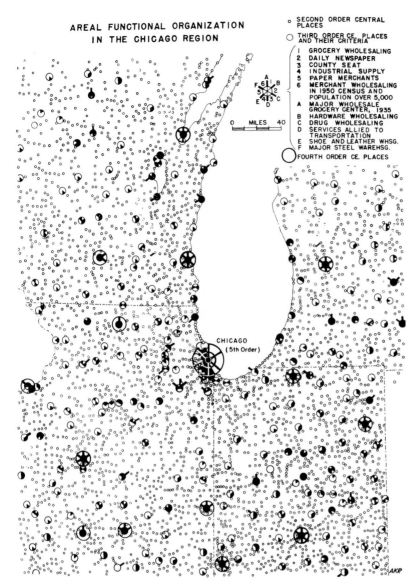

AREAL FUNCTIONAL ORGANIZATION
IN THE CHICAGO REGION

o SECOND ORDER CENTRAL
  PLACES
○ THIRD ORDER CE. PLACES
  AND THEIR CRITERIA
1 GROCERY WHOLESALING
2 DAILY NEWSPAPER
3 COUNTY SEAT
4 INDUSTRIAL SUPPLY
5 PAPER MERCHANTS
6 MERCHANT WHOLESALING
  IN 1950 CENSUS AND
  POPULATION OVER 5,000
A MAJOR WHOLESALE
  GROCERY CENTER, 1935
B HARDWARE WHOLESALING
C DRUG WHOLESALING
D SERVICES ALLIED TO
  TRANSPORTATION
E SHOE AND LEATHER WHSG.
F MAJOR STEEL WAREHSG.
◯ FOURTH ORDER CE. PLACES

0   MILES   40

CHICAGO
(5th Order)

FIGURE 9-4   *The regular distribution of small cities (second-order) is partly the result of the rectangular survey. The map shows also that these cities are lined up along railroad routes. Second-order cities have mostly local functions; third-order cities also possess wholesaling and other specialized functions. The classification of these cities is somewhat arbitrary; for example, Gary, Indiana, is classed as third-order, but it is fourth-order in some respects.* [Allen K. Philbrick, "Principles of Areal Functional Organization in Regional Human Geography," ECONOMIC GEOGRAPHY, vol. 33 (1957), pp. 306–336.]

the Lake Erie shore—especially those places which offered sheltered harbors—provided logical places for city development. The Erie ports received grain, lumber, and ores from the upper lakes and shipped bituminous coal to industrial Ontario and other lake ports. The Erie ports soon developed major wholesale, retailing, industrial, and financial centers, connected by major east-west railroads and highways paralleling the lakeshore which offered faster service than that provided by lake shipping. As the lakeside economies grew, the heavy industries benefiting by cheaper fuel and raw materials spawned other industries—especially machinery and consumer durables indus-

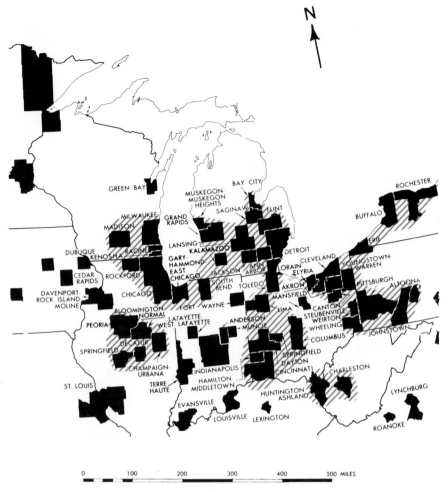

FIGURE 9-5   *The black areas are SMSAs according to the Bureau of the Census; the diagonal shading indicates those areas in the Great Lakes states which seem to be potential megalopolitan areas.*

tries. Light industries also developed: food packing and processing, partly for local markets, partly using nearby farm products, and partly using grain shipped in by lake.

Only major cities can be discussed in the following sections. In each case, it will be noted that their initial locating factor was either a local or nearby resource or a convenient location on water routes for transshipment. In most cities these locating factors are still reflected in the industrial structure, but all have added other activities, such as consumer goods manufacturing and service industries, which naturally arise from the growth of a large local market.

Potential Megalopolises

Several potential megalopolises (Figure 9-5) may focus on the Great Lakes region which in turn may be integrated into even broader urban developments. Thus a triangular area whose sides would be based on Lake Erie from Lorain to Buffalo and extending inland to Pittsburgh and Wheeling seems predictable based on local markets, access to basic raw materials, and fast routes to more distant markets. An adjacent possibility is an international megalopolis including Buffalo, Toronto, and Hamilton astride the Welland Canal and the ends of two of the lakes. It has been suggested that these megalopolises may connect with an Erie Canal megalopolis occupying a band from Buffalo to Albany. Westward potential megalopolises seem to be forming within a 75-mile radius of Detroit and around the southern end of Lake Michigan (Milwaukee–Chicago–Grand Rapids). Such urban developments, more predictable in general than in specific location, seem the logical outgrowth for an economy increasingly substituting urban technology for rural raw materials. The one raw material for which no substitute has been found is water; since in this the Great Lakes offer great potentialities, rapid urban expansion near their shores seems likely if pollution can be controlled.

The Buffalo SMSA

The diverse Buffalo SMSA includes fruit growing on Lakes Ontario and Erie; the tourist attractions of Niagara Falls; the electrochemical and other industries attracted by cheap Niagara power; the machinery, transportation equipment, and flour-milling industries of the central city; the commercial and financial services of the CBD and its adjacent well-sheltered harbor; and to the south the steel mills of Lackawanna. Primarily an industrial center producing durable goods and bulky nondurables (Figure 9-6), the SMSA owes its growth to its remarkable ability to combine skillfully raw materials, water, and power. This industrial function could be (and is) performed elsewhere along the lakes, but Buffalo has had unusual locational advantages. Starting with a natural harbor on

Buffalo Creek (now lined with flour mills), its port has been greatly expanded by breakwaters and docks along Lake Erie. After 1825 the Erie Canal made its harbor the logical point to transfer from canal to lake transport. Later with the advent of railroads, special rate concessions allowed grain to be processed at the port without losing the advantages of the through freight rate from inland points of origin to the Atlantic Coast. To this *milling-in-transit* privilege has been added *milling-in-bond* so that Canadian grain can be processed and reshipped without paying United States duty.

Lake transport provided grain, iron ore, lumber, and other Great Lakes raw mate-

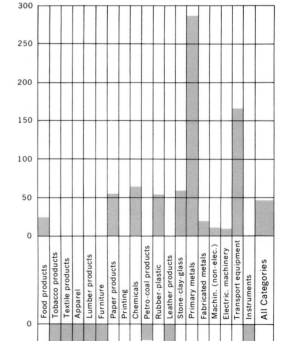

Deviation from U.S. per capita data, %

VALUE ADDED BY MANUFACTURING
Buffalo SMSA = .72% U.S. Pop.

FIGURE 9-6   The Buffalo SMSA has some industrial resemblance to Pittsburgh (Figure 8-5), but being on excellent rail, highway, and lake routes, it has attracted a greater variety of industries.

RAILROADS AND LAKE STEAMERS converge at the grain elevators and flour mills along Buffalo Creek, the locating feature for the Port of Buffalo. The original harbor has been greatly enlarged by dredging and by the construction of breakwaters and filled land. (Buffalo Area Chamber of Commerce.)

rials; natural gas and petroleum were piped in from nearby New York and Pennsylvania; coking coal came by rail from western Pennsylvania; and initially adequate electric power was available from the 326-foot drop of the Niagara River from Lake Erie to Lake Ontario. Today petroleum and natural gas from Pennsylvania are supplemented via pipelines from the Southwest, and Niagara power is supplemented by carboelectric power. As many of its industries require huge amounts of water, it is fortunate that the Buffalo pumping system can draw as much as 400 million gallons daily from Lake Erie.

Recently the Great Lakes–St. Lawrence Seaway has given Buffalo cheaper access to distant markets. Lakeside piers capable of handling ocean boats with a 25-foot draft have been constructed near an industrial district created on filled land. Waterborne shipments average annually 15 million tons valued at $1 billion.

The Cleveland Area

Cleveland is another port similar to Buffalo. The Cuyahoga River was the north-

ern link in the Ohio and Erie Canal which connected the Ohio Valley with Lake Erie and thence with the Erie Canal. As the largest city in Ohio, it controls the trade of a considerable number of industrial and commercial satellites.

Cleveland has suffered from congestion; its harbor on the Cuyahoga River has long been inadequate for over 15 million tons of inbound traffic, mostly iron ore and other bulky commodities. Docks, protected by a huge breakwater, now stretch along the lake, especially east of the river. Overseas trade already shows the effect of the Great Lakes–St. Lawrence Seaway, with iron ore coming from as far as Labrador, Liberia, and Chile.

Future growth Most American cities, laid out to service smaller populations and much less traffic, require considerable urban renewal; several projects in Cleveland illustrate what can be done. Iron capital has financed a project to modernize 163 acres in downtown Cleveland; this Erieville project will have 80 acres of parklike plaza, a 40-story office building, 10 apartments, houses, and other buildings. An expressway through the downtown area and 14-minute rapid-transit service from outlying parking lots are other parts of another effort to open up a congested city. At the same time Cleveland is expanding outwardly, and Cleveland planners are talking about *Cleveland Growthland,* a megalopolis to include Ashtabula, Akron, Elyria, and Lorain. West of Cleveland, the port of Lorain and its inland industrial satellite, Elyria, have characteristic lake-shore businesses; in the Lorain SMSA automobile assembly ranked second to steel among a diverse list of products, mostly heavy durable goods.

South of Cleveland in Akron more than half the industrial workers manufacture rubber products. Financial encouragement caused B. F. Goodrich to move there from Hastings, New York, in 1870. As late as 1910, Akron was mainly a farm-marketing center with diversified small industries. The growth of the automobile industry attracted other tire companies because Akron already had experience with this industry; hence by 1920 the city had nearly tripled its population. Akron was on the Ohio-Erie Canal but this had nothing to do with the rubber boom, caused mainly by the advantage of an early start.

The Toledo SMSA

Like Buffalo at the other end of Lake Erie, Toledo's rise was based in part on the junction of river and canal routes with the lake; there were, however, distinctive differences between the two ports in local resources and location which are reflected in the present industrial mix. The Maumee River Valley has changed functions within the last 125 years. Until 1827 when a road to Detroit was finally constructed across the swampy valley, the river mouth was occupied only by a fur-trading post. In 1836, the Erie and Kalamazoo Railroad started operation from Toledo and the

opening of the Wabash and Erie and the Miami and Erie canals in the 1840s multiplied Toledo's port business. The drainage of the swampy lacustrine soils in the 1850s added local farm trade to other Toledo business. In 1888 the first glass company was attracted to Toledo by the discovery of nearby oil, gas, and glass sand deposits, and today four major glass companies justify Toledo's claim to be "Glass Center of the World." Petroleum refining developed about the same time. These industries still remain although local resources have been exhausted, and so fuels and raw materials are now brought from Texas, Illinois, and West Virginia. The leading industry in terms of present employment is the automobile industry, producing Jeeps as well as parts for other cars. Toledo also has steel and other durable goods industries characteristic of the Lake Erie cities—in fact, durable goods employment is three times that of nondurable goods.

Some of Toledo's industrial development results from excellent transportation. With 11 railroads the SMSA claims third rank among United States rail centers, and its port recently has been close to first in tonnage on the Great Lakes. The port is the largest handler of soft coal in the world, shipping Appalachian coal to Canada and upper lakes ports. Toledo is also an importer of general cargo for western Ohio and Indiana and possesses the only United States free-trade zone on the Great Lakes.

MICHIGAN AND THE AUTOMOBILE INDUSTRY

Michigan has a per capita income about the average for the United States. That the figure is even this high is largely due to high income from durable goods manufacturing—especially the twentieth century automobile industry and industries that supply tools, raw materials, and parts for that industry. Although steel is the principal raw material in the automobile

FORD MOTOR COMPANY'S River Rouge manufacturing complex in Dearborn is the largest concentration of closely knit factories in the United States. The Rouge is the only Anglo-American plant at which iron ore, limestone, and coal are unloaded on the docks; smelted into iron; converted into steel; and transformed into engines, frames, bodies, and parts which are assembled into automobiles. (Ford Motor Company.)

today, the passenger automobile developed from the wooden carriage and the truck from the wooden wagon. The early automobile had a wooden body made of raw materials then plentiful in Michigan forests. Fortunately the iron ores of upper Minnesota supplied adequate materials for the steel bodies which replaced the wood. Although today automobile materials and parts are widely produced and assembled throughout the country, the business capital and design center for the American automobile remains in the Detroit area.

Detroit SMSA

Detroit (from a French phrase meaning *of the strait*), which had started as a French fur-trading post, became a port about 1830 for pioneers settling the well-drained area north of the swampy Maumee Valley. Farm trade; the exploitation of Michigan lumber; and farm machinery, wagon, and bicycle industries gave Detroit industrial importance long before the automobile entered the scene.

There was no impelling geographic reason why southeastern Michigan should become the American automobile region; in fact, early automobile manufacturing also did well at such widespread places as Bridgeport (Connecticut), Cleveland (Ohio), South Bend and Indianapolis (Indiana), and Kenosha (Wisconsin). Detroit, however, had such men as Ford, Olds, Buick, and Leland who were willing to risk their time and money on the new industry. Established vehicle and engine industries provided a trained labor supply. The major market was in the Midwest, and Detroit businessmen turned out products which captured that market. Today a multitude of towns and cities within a 200-mile radius of Detroit supply parts and subassemblies for the growing industry which in recent years has accounted for one-sixteenth of all United States industrial production.

Detroit has often been lopsidedly discussed as a one-industry city (Figure 9-7) because so much of its industry—steel, glass, machine tools, metal stampings, etc.—delivers much of its product to the automobile industry. But Detroit ranks fourth or fifth in most respects among the nation's SMSAs, being generally surpassed only by New York, Chicago, and Los Angeles. It is a major lake port, leading all others in tonnage received, although behind the iron-ore ports of Minnesota and the coal port of Toledo in shipments. It has over 10,000 workers each in its food, textile and clothing, printing, and chemical industries, and its government and service employees exceed employment in all vehicle industries. Its chemical industry was originally based on a rock salt deposit directly under the city.

Detroit's rapid growth, stimulated largely but not entirely by the automobile industry, has brought in a variety of ethnic groups. Canadians represent the largest foreign group. Hamtramck is a center of Polish settlement. As in New York City, there are distinct Italian, German, and Slavic sections. More recently large numbers of Southern Negroes and hillbillies from Appalachia have added to the cosmopolitan aspect of the city as well as to its social and economic problems. The prosperity of many of these new workers is uncertain because being employed largely in Detroit's "feast or famine" industries, they are the first to be laid off when markets for automobiles and machinery are poor.

Other Michigan Cities

It is difficult to find a Michigan city of any size that does not make an important contribution to automobile manufacture. Kalamazoo might seem to be an exception with papermaking, pharmaceuticals, and television tubes as leading industries; however, it also manufactures Checker taxicabs. Battle Creek, well known for its breakfast foods and sanitariums, also produces industrial trucks. Bay City, Jackson, Saginaw, and many others start their list of products with transportation equipment. Some are almost dominated by the motor companies. Pontiac has most of its industrial labor working for

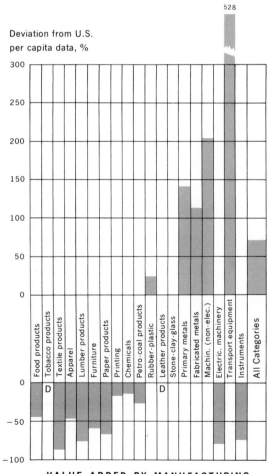

VALUE ADDED BY MANUFACTURING
Detroit SMSA = 2.05% U.S. Pop.

FIGURE 9-7 Nearly one-third of all Detroit's manufacturing employees are in the transportation equipment industry, and even more are in industries related to the automobile industry.

one automobile company. Flint might seem more diversified, only 42,500 of its 75,000 industrial workers being in the transportation equipment category; however, most of its other industries supply materials used in automobile manufacture, for example, automotive enamels and lacquers, and oil filters. The Lansing SMSA has 15,000 employees in Michigan State University and other state government agencies. The Oldsmobile–Fisher Body plants employ more than the state government, and other large factories are all related to the motor industry, those with over 1,000 employees being entirely automotive.

Grand Rapids SMSA   This, the only Michigan SMSA not dominated by Detroit, is the major business center in western Michigan. Located on a fall line, 30 miles up the navigable Grand River from Lake Michigan, Grand Rapids started as a lumber mill town. Later it symbolized furniture manufacturing, still an important industry, although more are now employed by automobile factories. In addition, its durable goods industries produce such items as business machines, refrigerators, and automatic merchandising machines. Located originally because of its local waterpower and water supply, the city now pumps part of its water from Lake Michigan, and gets gas and fuel oil by pipeline from the Southwest and some of its electricity from a generating plant on the Lake Michigan shore. The river is neglected for navigation, but water shipments may be made through Muskegon, a lake port and auto-parts manufacturing town.

THE UPPER LAKES

About 50 miles north of a line connecting Grand Rapids and Saginaw begins an area of cutover land with much infertile podzol soil. Along the eastern shore of Lake Michigan winter weather is moderated by the lake, thus encouraging fruit growing. Dairy-

ing is also a major rural activity. Eastward, potatoes, hay, and livestock are produced on the better soils, although the majority of the land is not in farms. The port of Alpena is noted for shipping the limestone used for flux in the Great Lakes steel industry. The remainder of northern lower Michigan is a wooded, lake-studded land which attracts the vacation trade in the summer and hunters in the autumn and winter.

The Lake Superior Area

Except for its extensive ores and somewhat poorer soils the Lake Superior area resembles the northern part of lower Michigan. It too has had difficulty recently in maintaining its economy. Its mammoth forests (about which the Paul Bunyon legends grew) have been cut over for at least a quarter century; their slow regrowth with inferior varieties of trees provides wood suitable mainly for pulping. The complicated metamorphic and igneous rocks underlying the forest were rich in ores, especially iron and copper, but the best of these are almost exhausted, and the other ores have difficulty in competing with cheaper ores from elsewhere. The infertile soil, mostly rocky or sandy podzols, is worth farming only where pockets of good soil provide some basis for dairying and potato farming. The numerous lakes and streams and the cool summers provide attractions for hunters, fishermen, and campers, but this business is highly seasonal. Rapid past development has been based on resources, largely shipped elsewhere for manufacture. Such a resource base provides a modest foundation for modern industrial growth.

Forestry   The lake region (defined by the Forest Service as Michigan, Minnesota, and Wisconsin) yielded 3.6 billion board feet of lumber in 1869, and almost 10 billion feet in 1899, but thereafter declined to less than 1 billion board feet in most years after 1930. The lumber companies made little attempt

THE SPACIOUS LAKEHEAD HARBOR, shared by Duluth and Superior, is sheltered by an 8-mile spit. (Gallagher's Studio from Duluth Chamber of Commerce.)

to replant the trees, usually abandoning title if the land lacked mineral resources. Fire destroyed huge areas. Today state governments are encouraging tree farming, and Wisconsin in 1965 claimed a possible sustained yield harvest nearly 10 percent higher than the current harvest.

Copper and iron   The earliest commercial copper mining was in 1844 in the Keweenaw peninsula of Michigan; iron ore mining began in 1846 in the Marquette Range. The prospects were sufficiently good in 1855 to justify the opening of the Sault Ste. Marie Canal, commonly called the Soo. Later ores were (and still are) shipped from the Menominee and the Gogebic ranges, using the ports of Marquette and Escanaba (Michigan) and Ashland (Wisconsin).

Minnesota ores, being more isolated from markets, were not tapped until nearly 40 years later, the first iron ore from the Vermilion Range being shipped by rail to Two Harbors in 1884, and the first Mesabi ore to Duluth in 1893. The 50 to 70 percent iron-content hematites, largely recoverable by open-pit mining, are now approaching exhaustion. The future hope of the iron mining industry depends on taconites (20 to 30 percent iron content) whose utilization has been slowed by the competition of richer ores and state taxes. Minnesota had

levied heavy taxes on *each ton* of iron ore mined; on taconite these taxes were almost prohibitive. In 1963, this tax was repealed; consequently an estimated half billion dollars has been invested in taconite-processing plants.

The Duluth-Superior SMSA   One-third of the subregional population is concentrated at the head of Lake Superior with its 19 square miles of sheltered harbor. Originally a fur-trading post, Duluth became a significant port when the railroad from St. Paul reached it in 1870. The slim prospects of Duluth were satirized in a speech by Congressman J. Proctor Knott on January 27, 1871, when in the House of Representatives he attacked a bill to provide land grants for a railroad to terminate at Bayfield, Wisconsin, 60 miles east of Duluth. Thinking that the railroad would serve Duluth, Knott aimed his barbs at that city, defeating the bill to the great joy of Duluth merchants. In 1890 a nearby town was named Proctorknott (now called Proctor). Knott's geography was imaginary but politically effective: "An area of over two million square miles, rich in every element of material wealth and commercial prosperity, all tributary to Duluth . . . inexhaustible mines, wide extended plains of richest pasturage, all embraced in this vast territory which must . . . empty the untold treasures of its commerce into the lap of Duluth."

Unlike most cities of its size, Duluth-Superior has little industry (8,000 employed in steel, flour milling, oil refining), being primarily a commercial and transshipment center. Its huge grain elevators and ore- and coal-loading docks are conspicuous; it is also a way station on the oil pipeline from Alberta to southwestern Ontario. The opening of the St. Lawrence Seaway brought ocean vessels to Duluth in 1963, but the 41,521,421 tons shipped by the port that year were largely Great Lakes traffic. More rapid growth for Duluth seems to depend on the dim chance of more trade from the spring wheat belt, an agricultural region of declining rural population and minute urban growth. Although Duluth showed a 9.4 percent population increase (1950–1960), the SMSA had a net out-migration of over 11,000.

The importance of the Great Lakes Duluth, connected by rail southward and westward to the interior, may be used to point out the importance of the Great Lakes to the Anglo-American interior. Before Minnesota ores were exploited, Duluth was exporting grain from the American and Canadian farms in the Red River Valley. Lumber from the upper lakes was the raw material used to build and furnish Midwestern farmsteads and cities. Ores from the Lake Superior area made possible the railway networks, the farm and industrial machinery, and the tall buildings of the cities. The greatest urban development took place, however, around the lower lakes where a network of railroads and roads carried the products of the farm to markets and distributed the manufactures of cities. In the twentieth century the direct contribution of mines, forests, and farms to the income of the Great Lakes states has been modest, but without the impulse to settlement provided by these resources, the economies of these states would have grown slowly and differently than they did.

THE POTENTIAL CHICAGO MEGALOPOLIS

The western section of the Great Lakes region focuses on Chicago, core of an urbanized lakeshore area extending 125 miles from Milwaukee, Wisconsin, to Gary, Indiana. This urban agglomeration slightly exceeds New York City (not the New York SMSA) in income and population. Like that city, it developed because its leaders took advantage of converging land and water routes. The southern Lake Michigan area had the additional advantage of being adjacent to the world's richest agricultural area; it had the handicap of being, before the opening of the Welland Canal and the St. Lawrence Seaway, at least 687 miles from ocean ports (see Table 7-3).

The population of the urbanized area extending from Milwaukee to Gary was estimated in 1967 at 9 million people, occupying an area slightly smaller than the states of Connecticut and Rhode Island. The 1950–1960 population growth rate approximated that for the United States as a whole, and, as in most metropolitan areas, averaged together declining populations in the central cities with rapid peripheral growth. Losing out in competition for second place in population to the exploding Los Angeles megalopolis, this region hopes because of seaway and air routes and more central location in Anglo-America to take over increasingly the functions of New York City.

The Physical Site of Chicago

An examination of Chicago's site makes it seem an almost inevitable location for a large city. A short portage across a low divide of unconsolidated sediments suggests several places where canals could be built to connect streams tributary to Lake Michigan with tributaries of the Illinois River. Even without dredging, lake channels pro-

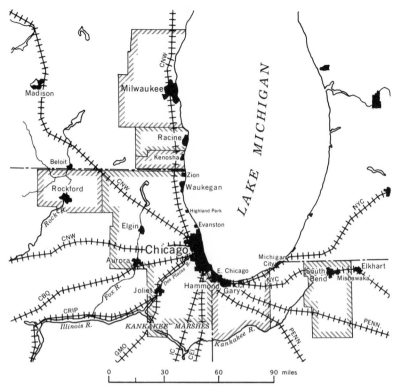

FIGURE 9-8   From Milwaukee to Michigan City SMSAs are continuous. The gap between the Calumet District and South Bend will be filled up with the development around Burns Ditch (Figure 9-10).

vided a navigable waterway eastward to Buffalo. The shore itself is flattish and fairly well drained in places, and consists either of lacustrine deposits formed when Lake Michigan had a higher level or of sand dune and morainal ridges which paralleled the shore. Lake Michigan provides an unlimited municipal water supply, and since it is slightly higher than the Illinois tributaries, its waters could be readily used to fill canals connecting with the Mississippi systems. To the west and southwest is a rich farmland. Finally Lake Michigan and the Kankakee marshes some miles south of the lake made it convenient for overland east-west routes to converge near Chicago.

The portage at Chicago, used in turn by the Indians and fur traders, later was dominated by Fort Dearborn. The growth of Chicago into a great city reflected the settlement (1830–1850) of the Illinois prairies, southern Wisconsin, and, later, of the lumbering areas around the upper lakes.

At its port farm goods were collected and shipped by water. Westward transportation was well underway before the rail link was completed eastward; thus the Illinois and Michigan Canal (1848) preceded by four years the first rail connection with New York City.

By 1860 Chicago had 112,000 people, and its grain elevators, stockyards, and sawmills were supplemented by factories processing raw materials and supplying farm implements and consumer goods. Heavier industry developed toward the end of the century, and railroads fanning out westward gave Chicago merchants control of a vast wholesale market, commonly selling goods which Chicago industries produced. Mail-order merchandizing extended its Midwestern retail market. The Chicago Board of Trade, leading Anglo-American exchange for farm products, became as influential in these commodities as Wall Street had become in securities.

Was the growth of Chicago inevitable?   The natural advantages of Chicago seem so obvious that its growth seems foreordained. However, if Eastern railroads, for example, had continued to build westward, thus avoiding the necessity of changing trains at Chicago, its railway business might be considerably less. If St. Louis had exploited its Mississippi and Western railway trade more effectively, that city might have remained, as it was until 1870, business capital of the Central Lowland. Greater leadership might have gone to Milwaukee or even Duluth in exploiting Wisconsin and Minnesota trade. Had Gary, Indiana, been founded a century earlier, the present business pattern would have been different. A full analysis of the rise of Chicago would require a book; its growth, not inevitable, depended on business leaders who utilized well its natural advantages.

The Loop and the railroads   The Chicago CBD grew up on a roughly rectangular peninsula, about a mile square, enclosed on the east by Lake Michigan, and on the west and north by the Chicago River. The major railway passenger terminals are on the fringe of this area, and rapid-transit lines travel around the Loop on elevated tracks (the major north-south line is now underground).

The view from the top of the Board of Trade Building shows: railroad tracks converging toward the Loop, the Union stockyards 4 miles to the south, the fashionable apartments along Lake Shore Drive, the smoke of heavy industries along the southwestern curve of Lake Michigan, and scattered industries along the rail lines and main highways. Along the northern and western edges of the Loop, boats and barges carry cargo along the Sanitary and Ship Canal, the flow of whose waters is regulated by locks close to the lake.

The Loop and adjacent parts of the CBD contain loft industries and other types of activity found similarly in the Manhattan CBD. The hotel-restaurant-theater area is clustered within the Loop and offers less variety than its New York counterpart. Libraries, museums, and educational institutions are found on the fringes of the Loop as well as in several outlying locations, for example, Evanston and Jackson Park. Port business, although large and growing by Great Lakes standards, is less conspicuous than in Manhattan, much of the bulky business being relegated to outlying waterway sites. On the other hand, railways and trucks are unavoidable and remind the visitor of the inland nature of Chicago business.[1]

Chicago industry   The Chicago SMSA includes almost every kind of industry and is not lacking in any main category. Its industries process raw materials for final consumption (for example, meat packing) or produce parts for assembly elsewhere. In terms of number employed, durable goods account for three-fifths of the employment. The leading industrial categories in order of number employed are: electric machinery, food processing, printing, and apparel. Employment in manufacturing is slightly more than one-third of the total and is almost equaled by commercial employment (trade, transportation, finance). Employment in professional, educational, and other services is also high, as is to be expected in a large metropolis.

Outlying Chicago   Like most metropolitan cities, Chicago includes many satellite communities, some of which have been incorporated into the city. Except for major roads

---

[1] Only an inland city would put as much of its centrally located lakefront in parks. Parks, public buildings, and fine residential areas occupy at least 43 of the 48 miles of shore from the Wisconsin line to the Indiana line. The Indiana shore in Lake County is entirely industrial.

THIS IS THE HEART of Chicago. The Loop can be identified by the high buildings
left of the harbor and Grant Park, and partly enclosed by the Chicago River and
its south branch. The railroad tracks approach the edge of the Loop from all sides
except due north and east. (Chicago Aerial Survey.)

which converge toward the CBD, the Chicago area street pattern is rectangular, thanks to the rectangular system of land survey. Belt expressways and railways connect the satellites, thus avoiding central city congestion. The suburbs vary in quality and local community spirit, some being dormitory towns for commuting workers, some being clustered around factories, a few being exclusive residential centers which have also educational institutions and "scientific" industries. Cities such as Elgin (watches, precision instruments), and Aurora (diversified industries), both located on the Fox River, a tributary of the Illinois; and Joliet (food, clothing, petroleum) on the Illinois,

FIGURE 9-10   Part of a topographic map shows the concentration of transport facilities characteristic of the southern end of Lake Michigan. The Burns Ditch project has been opposed by conservationists because it destroys parts of the sand dunes, a scenic feature along the southern lakeshore. Burns Ditch was originally a drainage project for the almost level lands to the south. The state-financed harbor to the east is expected to provide Indiana with its own port and adjacent warehouse facilities, as well as to encourage other industries nearby. NIPSCO (Northern Indiana Public Service) is already prepared to supply additional power. (Indiana Port Commission.)

were distinct urban centers before they were absorbed into the Chicago SMSA.

Chicago Satellites in Adjacent States

The Calumet area   East Chicago, Hammond, Gary, and smaller Indiana industrial suburbs of Chicago are locally referred to as the *Calumet,* named after the Calumet River. This booming heavy industrial area is essentially a continuation of the South Chicago industrial area to which most of the following remarks apply. Seventy-five years ago its alternate sand dunes and marshes were little used except by railroads converging on Chicago. About 1890 an oil refinery was built at Whiting and a steel plant at East Chicago; in 1905, after a careful survey, the United States Steel Corporation selected a sand dune site on which to build an integrated works to supply the Chicago market. The attractions of Gary (named for the corporation president, Elbert Gary) were obvious: excellent lake and railroad connections; unconsolidated materials which could be easily bulldozed into level land; harbors and unlimited fresh water; cheap access to Minnesota hematite, Michigan limestone, and Appalachian coal; central location amid growing automobile, farm machinery, and construction-steel

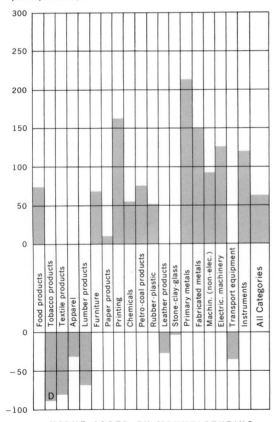

Deviation from U.S. per capita data, %

VALUE ADDED BY MANUFACTURING
Chicago – N.W. Indiana
Standard Consolidated Area = 3.76% U.S. Pop.

FIGURE 9-9   The industrial diversification of the Chicago area is outstanding. Compare this graph with those for New York (Figure 6-8) and Baltimore (Figure 7-7). Why the differences?

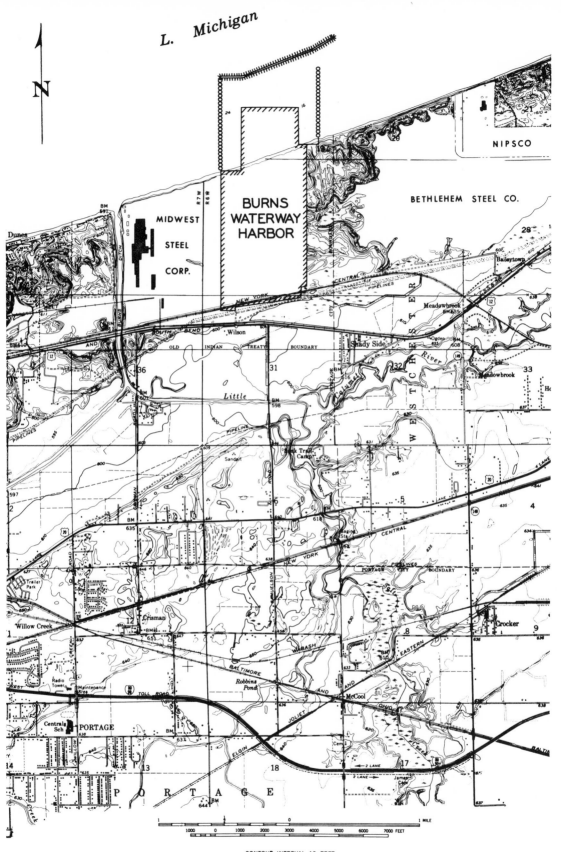

CONTOUR INTERVAL 10 FEET
DOTTED LINES REPRESENT 5-FOOT CONTOURS
DATUM IS MEAN SEA LEVEL

markets; and a huge potential labor supply. The lake at East Chicago has been linked with the Illinois Waterway by the Calumet-Sag Channel. All this proved ideal for industries producing heavy or bulky goods, and steel, cement, chemicals, and petroleum products, but employment is concentrated in a few cyclical industries; for example, over half the industrial workers are in the steel industry, about 20,000 being in the United States Steel works at Gary.

Burns Ditch and eastward A ditch constructed over 40 years ago to drain 20,000 acres of marsh, has given its name to a controversial project. Ten miles east of Gary between the 750-acre Midwest Steel site and the 3,300-acre Bethlehem Steel site, a 27-foot-deep harbor, with equipment to handle coal, iron ore, grain, petroleum, and refrigerated foodstuffs, and with space for industrial development, is being built for the state of Indiana. Opposition to this comes from conservationists who wish to preserve the sand dunes for recreational use.

In 1965 the 40-mile area between the proposed harbor and South Bend was largely rural with mainly artificially drained land producing truck, grain, soybean, dairy, and livestock products for nearby urban markets. Many of the farm residents worked at least part time in the cities. Advocates of the Burns Ditch Harbor expect urban and industrial development to expand eastward, at least absorbing South Bend, adjacent Mishawaka, and possibly Elkhart into the Chicago megalopolis. Figure 9-5 suggests greater eastward expansion.

South Bend SMSA has machinery, transportation equipment, and rubber products industries. The long-established Studebaker Corporation and other century-old metal industries developed here a reservoir of mechanical and metallurgical skills so attractive to new industries that even the departure of Studebaker led to only temporary employment readjustments.

The Milwaukee SMSA A lakeshore urbanized strip almost connects Chicago with Milwaukee. Urban centers, notably Kenosha with its automotive and textile industries, and Racine with machinery and household supplies industries, were localized initially by small river-mouth harbors. A larger harbor, formed by the junction of three streams close to the lakeshore and enlarged by dredging and breakwater construction, provided the initial site for Milwaukee. Railroads follow these converging valleys, along which cluster most of the earlier industries. This is the physical setting that attracted German and Polish immigrants during the middle decades of the last century. They built a port to process and ship the lumber, grain, and animal products produced in southern Wisconsin. Many of the immigrants were political refugees who, being technically more skilled and better educated than the average immigrant, founded the mechanical industries for which Milwaukee is noted. To supply the local market they established breweries whose premium products are now sold throughout the United States.

Milwaukee is the commercial center for Wisconsin, half of whose trade is in its 11 southeastern counties. The city also serves as a port and performs some shipping and wholesale services for northern Illinois, Iowa, Minnesota, and the upper peninsula of Michigan. Milwaukee and other Wisconsin ports are preparing terminal facilities to expand use of the Great Lakes and the St. Lawrence Seaway. Compared with Chicago, these ports have the advantage of less congestion, newer equipment, and a high-quality labor force drawn in part from nearby Wisconsin farms. Lake Michigan ferry services permit overland shipments eastward without passing through Chicago. Milwaukee offers a wide variety of commercial and educational services, but primarily it is an industrial city with emphasis on durable goods.

TABLE 9-1 Representative Products in Selected Eastern Wisconsin Cities

| | Population (in thousands) | | Representative |
City or SMSA	1960	1967	Products
Beloit	33	38	Engines, paper, machinery, shoes
Janesville	35	41	Auto assembly, pens
Madison SMSA	222	270	Meat, machinery, batteries
Sheboygan	46	47	Plumbing fixtures, furniture
Fond du Lac	33	34	Machine tools, outboard motors
Oshkosh	45	47	Metal, woodworking, textile
Appleton	48	57	Paper, dairy products
Manitowoc	32	35	Furniture, aluminum, shipbuilding
Green Bay SMSA	125	143	Paper, food, metalwork

SOURCE: Census data; and Editor and Publisher, *Market Guide*, 1967 Edition, New York.

Although nondurable goods, such as beer and meat, are Milwaukee products best known to consumers, they account for only one-tenth of its industrial labor force. The primary basic industry is steel, processed by local mills from scrap or from steel obtained from the South Chicago–Gary area. Milwaukee industry, the third largest user of steel in the country, has steel, fabricated metals, and nonelectrical machinery industries, accounting for nearly half of all industrial employment. Other major categories are electric machinery and transportation equipment. Together these six categories employ five-sixths of the industrial force.

Eastern Wisconsin cities and farmlands On the northern fringe of the Chicago megalopolis, eastern Wisconsin performs many services directed primarily toward Chicago. This is a green land of neat white farmsteads with tall silos, of scattered lakes and wooded ridges and hillocks, amid which a sprinkling of neat towns and small cities specialize in serving the adjacent countryside and manufacturing a few specialties. The largest towns are on the southeastern margin, and the country roads that lead into them are paved to support the heavy milk tank trucks which concentrate Wisconsin's well-known product at butter, powdered-milk, and cheese factories. In the center and north, industry is largely based on local raw materials; further south, more diversified industry is characteristic, as Table 9-1 suggests.

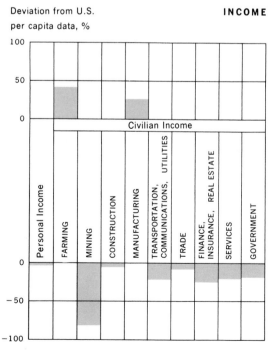

FIGURE 9-11 Wisconsin income data reflects the state's dual emphasis on dairy farming and diversified manufacturing. Most of Wisconsin's income arises from those southeastern counties which may become incorporated with the Chicago megalopolis (Figure 9-5).

THIS MODERN DAIRY FARM, with acres of corn and huge silos and barns, is located in Walworth County, southeastern Wisconsin. Although the total sale of farm products ($26 million in 1964) gives the county the highest per farm rate in Wisconsin ($15,000 per farm), the value added by manufacturing in the small cities of the county is about twice the farm sales. The manufacturing labor force is about twice the size of the farm labor force. Most farms are highly mechanized and require few full-time workers. The high farm-operator family level of living in southeastern Wisconsin is surpassed in few areas, notably in California. (USDA photograph.)

CONCLUSIONS

In the nineteenth century, access to the agricultural, lumber, and mineral products of the lakes was a tremendous commercial and industrial advantage which led to the rise of cities at lakeside transshipment points. The further rise of the Great Lakes region resulted from a high degree of human technology being applied along the world's greatest inland seas which are connected to the ocean by three great water routes, the St. Lawrence, the Erie Canal–Hudson, and the Illinois-Mississippi. Today these routes bring in raw materials from more distant points in Anglo-America and overseas. The machinery designed and built in the city has made possible the continued exploitation of natural wealth with a reduced labor supply. The cities, once service centers for the food and raw-material areas, are now major markets as well as transshipment points to broader world markets.

The urbanized area, both for residence and for lighter industries, has expanded inland, in places even into rich farmlands.

A 50- to 100-mile-wide zone of megalopolitan development is developing from Buffalo to west of Chicago–Milwaukee with possible spurs to Toronto, Pittsburgh, Cincinnati, and St. Louis. Urban growth has been most rapid near through routes on the lower Great Lakes; the upper lakes whose routes handle the bulky but low-value products of mines and forests have not participated in the national growth except in a few highly seasonal recreational activities. Although regional agricultural and mineral raw materials are still important in the Great Lakes region, the rapid growth of raw material, food, and fuel imports into the region may be more significant. As in other mature regions, human skills represent the greatest resource and make possible a high level of living.

SELECTED REFERENCES

ALEXANDERSSON, GUNNAR, and GORAN NORSTRUM: *World Shipping,* Wiley, New York, 1963, pp. 248–270.

DOXIADIS, CONSTANTINOS, and STAFF: *Emergence and Growth of an Urban Region: The Developing Urban Detroit Area,* Detroit Edison Company, Detroit, 1966, and later. A study that includes most of the Great Lakes region, although the focus is on Detroit.

GARLAND, JOHN H. (ed.) *The North American Midwest,* Wiley, 1955.

PHILBRICK, A. K.: "Principles of Areal Functional Organization in Regional Human Geography," *Economic Geography,* vol. 33 (1957), pp. 306–336. The examples in this study are mainly from the area around Lake Michigan.

REINEMANN, M. W.: "The Pattern and Distribution of Manufacturing in the Chicago Area," *Economic Geography,* vol. 36 (1960), pp. 139–144.

PART III
AGRICULTURAL AREAS IN TRANSITION

SOUTH AND WEST of the Commercial-Manufacturing Core are varied areas, once prosperous agricultural or raw-material producers, but now containing widespread areas of population decline. This decline has been precipitated in part by resource exhaustion, in part by the competition of newer regions, but most important, by the mechanization of modern agriculture, mining, and forestry, with consequent reduced labor requirements per unit of production.

The increasing demands for manufacturing, services, and recreation space may help provide compensating urban employment as it has in some cities in these areas. But much of the area is peripheral, and many of its people are untrained for the new activities. The training is poorest in the South where the outlook otherwise is more hopeful because mild Southern winters have attracted retirement homes, winter resort activities, and some industries. In contrast to the former advancing agricultural frontiers, the incursion of many activities seems more selective; thus, as has already been noted by many observers, progressive cities have developed amid broad areas of rural decline.

POWERED MACHINERY which so revolutionized manufacturing during the Industrial Revolution has more recently done the same for the farm, the mine, and the lumber camp. Machinery such as shown here, together with improved fertilization and weed and pest control, has increased wheat output 500 percent per man-hour in the last 30 years. (USDA photograph.)

FIGURE 10-1   Landforms of the Midwest. All the landform features are minor, consisting mostly of low hills, bluffs, water bodies, and marshes. Can you find a city not located on a stream? (Base map copyright by A. K. Lobeck. Reprinted with permission of The Geographical Press, Hammond, Inc.)

CHAPTER 10

AGRICULTURE AND URBAN GROWTH IN THE MIDWEST

This vast region of population decline and out-migration contains a relatively few urbanized counties whose population growth offsets the more widespread rural declines. The common rural out-migration is not caused by low productivity—indeed this is the world's rich agricultural area. The cause rather is technological: mechanized scientific agriculture is able to produce abundantly with a much smaller labor force. True, the need for farm machinery and other urban products demanded by the new agriculture has increased urban employment but not sufficiently to absorb surplus rural population in the urban-

BASIC DATA:

AREA INCLUDES	Population Change 1950-1960	1960 (millions)	1967 (millions)	Rural Farm 1960	Personal Income 1966 Total	Farm	Manufacturing (billions)	Mining
Illinois { partly outside	22.8%	10.1	10.8	5.6%	$38.1	$1.0	$10.9	$0.21
Wisconsin { the region	15.1	3.9	4.1	14.0	12.4	0.6	3.8	0.02
Minnesota	14.5%	3.4	3.6	17.2%	$10.4	$0.7	$ 2.1	$0.12
Iowa	5.2	2.8	2.9	24.0	8.3	1.3	1.6	0.02
Missouri	9.2	4.3	4.5	12.5	12.9	0.6	2.9	0.06
Kansas	14.3	2.2	2.4	14.7	6.5	0.6	1.2	0.09
Nebraska	6.5	1.4	1.5	21.9	4.2	0.7	0.5	0.13
South Dakota	4.3	0.7	0.7	30.2	1.6	0.4	0.1	0.20
North Dakota	2.1	0.6	0.6	32.3	1.5	0.3	0.1	0.12
Plains States	9.5%	15.4	16.2	18.4%	$45.4	$4.6	$ 8.4	$0.34

REGIONS

Land Area (thousand sq. mi.)

Plains (West North Central) States	509.6
Less Northeastern Minnesota (Great Lakes)	−27.1
Plus Western Wisconsin and Illinois	51.3
Total	533.8

Regional Population (1967): 17,700,000

AREA INCLUDES	Population Change 1950-1960	1960 (thousands)	1967 (thousands)	Employment 1960 Durable Goods	Nondurable Goods (thousands)	Trade
MAJOR SMSAS:						
Minneapolis–St. Paul	29%	1,482	1,620	85	65	122
Des Moines	18	266	280	9	14	23
Omaha	25	458	545	11	6	24
Kansas City	35	1,093	1,230	56	55	93
St. Louis	20	2,073	2,250	144	114	139

CLIMATE — *Humid continental to middle-latitude steppe, daily and seasonal weather extremely variable*

	Temperature (°F) Jan.	July	Precipitation (inches) Annual	Season
St. Louis	32	78	35	Slight summer maximum
Minneapolis	12	72	25	Summer maximum
Bismarck	10	72	15	Early summer maximum
Wichita	32	81	30	Early summer maximum

VEGETATION — Deciduous forest in the east and on river flood plains; coniferous forest to the northeast; medium-height grass in central Illinois and west to about 98–100°W; medium to short grass westward.

SOIL — Prairie soils, based on loess and/or glacial materials to about 97°W; thence chernozem to the short grass country where dark brown soils are common; soils fertile and nonacid except in extreme northeast and southeast.

MINERALS — Low-grade coal fairly common in Illinois, Missouri, and Iowa to eastern Kansas; lignite and oil in western North Dakota, oil and gas in southern and central Kansas and western Nebraska; lead, zinc, and iron ore in Missouri; cement rock, stone, sand, and gravel available in most of the region.

ized economies. Thus while the national 1950–1960 population growth was 18.5 percent, not one of the Plains states came near the national average; every one of the Plains states experienced a net out-migration. About 800,000 more people moved away from these states than moved into them in the 1950s. The problem has been less serious in the cities that were near the Commercial-Manufacturing Core which is pushing its boundaries westward and near national transportation centers such as Minneapolis and Kansas City. The problem is most severe in the rural areas where vast fertile stretches can be kept productive with fewer farmers and fewer rural centers than had once been believed possible.

Boundaries

The boundaries selected for this region (Figure 10-1) are not sharp and have been chosen in part for statistical convenience. Some of the agricultural regions (and their problems) discussed below extend well into the Great Lakes region and the Ohio Basin. Likewise there is no sharp change at the geometrical western borders of the Dakotas, Nebraska, and Kansas; the wheat farming of Kansas spills across northwestern Oklahoma into the northern panhandle of Texas. As the jet-age traveler flying across these borders can see for himself, the ranches, dry-farming areas, and irrigated areas send innumerable fingers across the boundaries so sharply depicted on generalized agricultural maps. On the western margin, land use varies from decade to decade, sometimes from year to year. The regional boundaries used, although far from ideal, are as good as any, more convenient than most.

The Rural Central Lowland

Aside from the small areas in cities, the American Central Lowland still is a land of farmers who till their lands with a maximum of machinery and a minimum of hired la-

bor. Theirs is a land of hot, rainy summers and cool to very cold winters, which in favorable seasons produces record-breaking yields for world markets, using city-built machinery, fertilizer, seed selection, and antibiotics so as to make it possible for the outstandingly successful farmer to become a wealthy man. Along with generous soil resources, the region has benefited from a wealth of timber, ores, and fossil fuels, one of the world's great natural waterways (the Mississippi system), and terrain level enough to encourage a development of a close network of roads and railroads.

The agricultural areas, laid out in 80- to 320-acre homesteads, have in recent decades become a land of rural problems. Their better farms have developed huge crop surpluses; many smaller farms are on the verge of bankruptcy. The forests to the east have been cut over, and many of the mines are increasingly unable to compete with other sources of ore and fuels. Even where sales of farm products have continued high, technology has replaced men with machines, and the rural land resources no longer support the land's population. Farming and the extractive industries account for only 8 percent of the income of the Plains states but support directly one-tenth of the civilian labor force and over one-tenth of the population.

The regional income attributable to farming, forestry, and mining does not adequately measure their total economic importance. Without these fundamental food and raw-material industries, many manufacturing, commercial, and professional sources of livelihood in the region would collapse. The present problem is much broader than the mere production of current incomes; it also includes the conservation and future use of good land which will be increasingly needed for the world's burgeoning populations. At present technology supplies the American economy with surpluses of food and raw materials. With the

MAJOR TYPES OF FARMING IN THE UNITED STATES

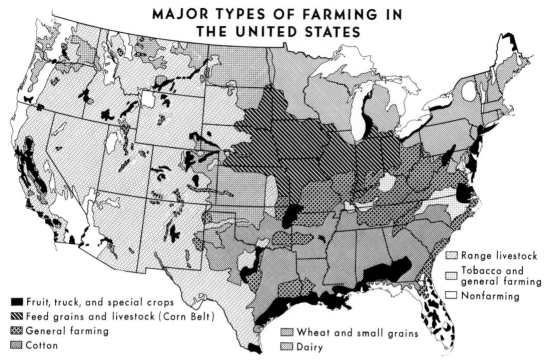

■ Fruit, truck, and special crops
▧ Feed grains and livestock (Corn Belt)
▨ General farming
▨ Cotton

▨ Wheat and small grains
▨ Dairy

▨ Range livestock
▨ Tobacco and general farming
▢ Nonfarming

FIGURE 10-2   This is a highly generalized picture of United States farming. The Corn Belt includes many local areas that do not engage in Corn Belt farming, and the cotton area includes many areas that do not now plant cotton. (USDA.)

future population growth in most countries ranging upward to 3 percent annually, the demand may once again exceed the supply; indeed human requirements do now but the overseas purchasing power is least where the need is greatest.

HUMID FARM REGIONS AND REPRESENTATIVE CITIES

Figure 10-2 shows the distribution of the type of farming regions mentioned below. Except in detail, the farm-centered discussions below are applicable to adjacent regions to the east, areas in which farming was discussed in preceding chapters only incidentally because it contributed relatively little to the regional income.

About one-ninth of the land of the United States (excluding Alaska) and about one-third of its cropland is included in an area of highly diversified farming featured by crop rotation, chemical weed control, fertilization, and the marketing of the bulk of its crops as livestock products. The out-

standing crop is corn which occupies one-fifth of the total acreage: somewhat more in the South (commonly called the "Corn Belt"), and somewhat less in the North (the "Dairy Belt"). The soils, generally derived from lime-rich glacial deposits or from windblown silts, were initially fertile, but when carelessly tilled, become leached and eroded. Local soil variations based on slope, nature of soil materials, and drainage conditions are common; fortunately most of the farmers are skilled in adjusting their tillage and crops to the varied soils in their fields. The rotation of cleanly cultivated corn and soybeans with such ground-covering crops as hay and small grains, and the common inclusion of nitrogen-depositing clover, alfalfa, or soybeans help to maintain soil fertility. However, the once universal system of soil management based on grain, liming legumes, and livestock has been re-

THE PLAINS ARE far from uniform. The field patterns in this wheat-flax-barley area of North Dakota are fairly regular considering the minor relief irregularities caused by glaciation. This photo was taken south of latitude 49° N at about 101° W. What does this location tell about the area? (USDA photograph.)

placed by highly scientific systems tailored to specific physical and market conditions.

The Corn Belt

The prairie soils that have developed under prairie vegetation are dark in color and high in organic and nitrogen content. This is the traditional Corn Belt with its rectangular grid of fields and local roads with hamlets spaced at convenient intervals, and numerous small cities (commonly county seats). Less regular are the railroad grids which focus on Chicago, St. Louis, and Kansas City.

Livestock farming Two related systems of farming occupy this agricultural region, and some of its farmers shift their emphasis from one system to the other as the market changes. East central Iowa illustrates the most widespread type: The farm that sells little or none of its crops and specializes in a variety of livestock.[1] A representative farm of 240 acres raises and markets 300 hogs and 40 Hereford steers each year. Additional animals include a dairy herd of 20 milk cows and calves, and chickens for home consumption. The basic fodder is

obtained from an annual rotation of corn, oats, and meadow with an extra year in meadow on the sloping land and an extra year in corn on especially flat land. Permanent pasture occupies the slopes along a small stream.

The loam soil was derived largely from loess (windblown material) in which humus from decomposed prairie grass roots is intermixed. The farm economy is based on maintaining soil fertility and humus by crop rotation and the application of manure and chemicals. In addition, some of the lowland fields must be drained by tile and may be terraced along the contours to prevent erosion. The work load for the farmer is fairly well spaced throughout the year because of the variety of tasks connected with cultivation, feeding, and breeding livestock, and maintaining buildings and equipment.

Such farming requires considerable working capital. Although many calves are raised on the farm, cash is needed to buy additional livestock from western ranches for "finishing." Fertilizer consumption may be high, especially on the mediocre soils where manure and crop rotation do not make up for the huge soil-nutrient requirements of high-yielding hybrid corn. Weed killers, antibiotics, and vitamins for livestock; machinery repairs and replacement; fuel for

[1] The data for the farm examples in this chapter have been taken largely from Edward Higbee, *American Agriculture*, Wiley, New York, 1958.

FOR BEEF CATTLE, this modern, mechanized, paved feedlot operation in Iowa has a capacity of 200 to 300 head. The actual feeding time is 20 to 30 minutes, depending on the amount of grain with the silage. (USDA photograph.)

farm machines; taxes; and a host of other items require cash. The farmer's business is no longer simple tillage and livestock feedings: In order to compete, his techniques must be scientific and his market judgment must be sound. He must maintain a set of books to calculate his costs for each product, and to satisfy his banker, the income tax collector, social security, and the Soil Conservation Service.

Such complications do not suit the inefficient small farmer. In central Iowa the value of land and farm buildings averages over $80,000 per farm, and several farms in each county exceed 1,000 acres. Over 90 percent of all Iowa farmers own tractors, and over half own trucks. Although manure and crop rotation are used, the average purchase of chemical fertilizer annually is 4 tons per farm. Most full-time farms sold over $10,000 of produce per year, and for the state as a whole, two-thirds of this was livestock.

Cash grain farming In east central Illinois and north central Iowa, both areas convenient to major markets, cash grain farming is more common. If the farm is near urban markets, for example near metropolitan Chicago, dairy farming may be added to or even monopolize the farm economy. The yields per acre obtained by some cash grain farmers are almost unbelievable. The *Farm Jour-*

nal (November, 1965) reports 125-bushel-per-acre wheat, 8-ton alfalfa, and whole counties averaging 120 bushels of corn. The same magazine gives an Illinois example of a farm averaging 200 bushels of corn (11,200 pounds of grain per acre) on 550 acres. How was this done? The farmer spaced his rows only 20 inches apart, applied 2 tons of limestone per acre every other year and 200 pounds of potash and 225 pounds of anhydrous ammonia per acre every year. His fertilizer bill was $36.80 per acre; in addition he applied $8.85 per acre of weed killer and pest inhibiters. The tools used included a tractor, plow, field cultivator, spike-tooth harrow, eight-row cultivator, sprayer, and four-row combine. After further fertilizer applications in the fall, the field was replanted the following April in corn.

Conditions are not quite so productive in central and northern Indiana and Ohio where glaciation has produced a great variety of gray-brown podzolic soils within a small area: sandy ridges, rolling areas of silt, and low-lying lands of muck soils. Much of the land has been drained by tile; in fact, the amount of drained land there exceeds that in the Mississippi flood plain. The basic crop remains corn, which with soybeans makes up about one-half the crop acreage. On this once wooded land, soils are more acid and less fertile than in the

Deviation from U.S.
per capita data, %

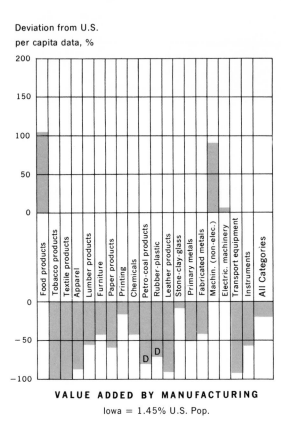

VALUE ADDED BY MANUFACTURING

Iowa = 1.45% U.S. Pop.

prairie; consequently larger applications of lime and fertilizer are needed to produce high yields. The combination of products varies from section to section and even from farm to farm, hogs being the principal product in the South, with more emphasis on dairy products northward.

Corn Belt Cities

Iowa cities   The Corn Belt encompasses all of Iowa, and as Table 10-1 indicates much of Iowa's industry processes food or produces farm equipment (Figure 10-3). As in most American states, Iowa's capital is approximately in the center of the state (or central to the populated area where the population is unevenly distributed). Des Moines, founded in 1843 as a military post, is at the junction of the Des Moines and Raccoon rivers, a fact then considered sig-

TABLE 10-1   Principal Industries in Iowa; Value Added by Manufacturing, 1954, 1958, 1963 (in millions of dollars)

	1954	*1958*	*1963*
ALL INDUSTRIES	1,236	1,684	2,285
Food and Kindred Products	361	540	653
Meat Products	167	230	282
Dairy Products	47	72	66
Grain Mill Products	93	144	177
Machinery (farm-related):			
Farm Machinery	N.A.[1]	190	287
Food Products Machinery	6	9	9
Machinery, Other Nonelectrical	N.A.	98	179
Machinery, Electric	N.A.	64	253
Transportation Equipment	30	31	27
Printing and Publishing	86	104	128
Chemical and Allied Products	77	93	152
Stone, Clay, and Glass Products	N.A.	83	96
Primary Metals	53	62	108
Fabricated Metals	67	94	98

[1] N.A.   Not available.

SOURCE: U.S. Bureau of the Census, *Census of Manufactures: 1958, 1963*, Washington, 1966.

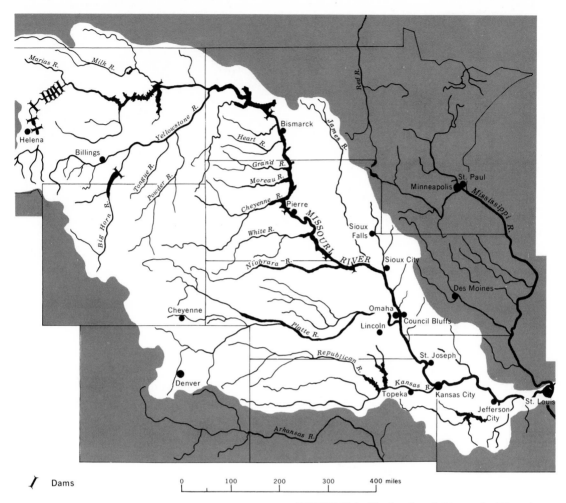

Dams

| 0 | 100 | 200 | 300 | 400 miles |

FIGURE 10-4   The location of cities on the Missouri River was originally due to river transportation, which today is of minor importance. The western tributaries of the Missouri were not navigable, but did provide water for early travelers across the plains.

nificant. Many of its modern activities are service industries including regional federal offices, universities, research centers, insurance offices, and the publication of farm journals. These and commercial activities far surpass industrial employment which is only one-fifth of the total. To its formerly farm-oriented industries have been added such non-farm items as jet engines.

Except for fewer government functions, a similar story could be told for other Iowa cities such as Burlington, Davenport, Cedar Rapids, Waterloo, and Cedar Falls. Most Iowa cities are commercially tributary to Chicago to which they are connected by a variety of rail and highway routes. Some of these cities are outliers of the Commercial-

Manufacturing Core, and the state is sufficiently close to its western edge to be absorbed into that belt in coming decades. The larger cities serve the more complicated needs of a host of smaller centers (Figure 9-4).

Missouri River cities   The Missouri, whose river traffic is just beginning to revive with the construction of dams and the dredging of its channel, was of major importance in the settlement of the Plains states and the West. Before the railways penetrated be-

THE KANSAS CITY STOCKYARDS represented a major function of the city after the surrounding area was settled. The city still claims that it is "the axle on which the hub of livestock activity turns," but the SMSA is more diversified than that, as Figure 10-6 shows. (Kansas City Chamber of Commerce.)

yond the Mississippi, fur traders, military detachments, and prospective settlers sailed by steamer to convenient places (Figure 10-4) on the Missouri, whence they outfitted themselves for the journey across the Plains. Kansas City, St. Joseph, Omaha, and Sioux City, founded to handle such business, later served as convenient collecting points from which Plains produce could be shipped eastward.

The growth of Council Bluffs and Omaha to more than local centers dates from 1863 when railway construction began westward on the first transcontinental line. Soon other railroads converged on Council Bluffs to make connections with the Union Pacific. Although Council Bluffs developed railroad shops and grain elevators, it has now become subordinate to Omaha to which two-fifths of its workers commute.

Omaha in 1940 was largely a railroad and meat-packing center, with some 39 insurance companies as a major secondary industry. Its location near the center of the continent caused it to be selected for the headquarters of the Strategic Air Command. The dredging of the river to 9 feet revived the shipment of farm products by barge. Meat packing and other food products remain the outstanding industries, but some new industries have been attracted, producing such diverse articles as telephone dials, machinery, and metal parts.

The Kansas City SMSA Founded as one of the Missouri River ports, this metropolis has grown into a major regional center. Its port is now of minor importance while its rail, highway, air, and financial connections have brought a growing business. Its Federal Reserve Bank, for example, serves an area to the west extending beyond the Rockies and southward into Oklahoma and northern New Mexico (Figure 10-5).

The location of Kansas City is significant because there the Missouri turns northward and the Kansas (Kaw) Valley provided a route westward (Figure 10-4). A number of historic towns are within the Kansas City SMSA (e.g., Independence and Westport). This was the eastern end of the Santa Fe and Oregon trails and, after the Civil War, the collecting point for the grain of the adjacent Corn Belt, the hard winter wheat of

Drawn by R.W. Galvin, Cart

—— Boundaries of Federal Reserve Districts ——Boundaries of Federal Reserve Branch Territories

✪ Board of Governors of the Federal Reserve System

◉ Federal Reserve Bank Cities   • Federal Reserve Branch Cities

FIGURE 10-5 The Federal Reserve Districts were delimited in 1914 after a careful study combined with the presentation of testimony by interested cities. Within a year after the districts were established, minor revisions proved necessary. Thus northern New Jersey was transferred from the Philadelphia to the New York district, and central Wisconsin was shifted from Minneapolis to Chicago. Note that most of the districts extend westward from the Federal Reserve Bank cities. Districts are supposed to reflect regional business connections. Would you suggest any further changes in district boundaries? (Note that Alaska and Hawaii are in the Twelfth District.) (Board of Governors, Federal Reserve System.)

Kansas, and the cattle of the Central Plains.

The elevators, flour mills, stockyards, and packing houses of Kansas City are still important, but the SMSA also caters to the more complicated needs of farmers and ranchers by manufacturing feeds, farm implements, portable storage bins, and farm buildings, and by serving as a headquarters for numerous farm organizations, for example, the American Hereford Association. Manufactures are not limited to farm goods; they range from automobile assembly and petroleum refining to aerospace industries.

Peoria   This medium-sized SMSA exemplifies a Corn Belt city on the edge of the Commercial-Manufacturing Core. It gained commercial importance because at its port Mississippi steamers transshipped their cargo to barges. To serve its grain and livestock market area, the city added industries related to farming: meat and dairy-product packing, distilling and brewing, farm machinery, wire fencing, and other industries that supplied farm needs. With strip coal mines near and oil available by waterway, Peoria has obtained additional industries, some completely unrelated to farming.

The General Farming Region and St. Louis

From northern Missouri southward the undulating prairie of the Corn Belt gradually changes to a prairie forest, then to a forested area. Southward the terrain becomes rougher, changing to open hills, then to the low but dissected Ozark Plateau. The rural population, human and animal, thins out, and a type of general farming, including corn, wheat, dairying, and root crops, replaces the more intensive, more scientific Corn Belt farming. This is the trans-Mississippi counterpart of the low plateaus adjoining the Ohio Valley. On the northeastern edge of this area is St. Louis, a city developed more in relation to trade than to a surrounding farm economy.

The St. Louis SMSA The new monumental arch at St. Louis memorializes its historic position as the "gateway to the West."

Deviation from U.S.
per capita data, %

VALUE ADDED BY MANUFACTURING
Kansas City SMSA = .62% U.S. Pop.

There in 1764 a French trading post was established where a bluff overlooks the Mississippi. A few miles upstream on the west bank, the Missouri provided a river route northwest to the Northern Rockies; a few miles farther north on the east bank the Illinois provided an easy route to the Great Lakes; and 140 miles downstream the Ohio joined the Mississippi.

The uses to which the St. Louis locational advantages have been put have varied in the last two centuries. Until 1817 St. Louis was primarily a fur-trading center. Then, with the beginning of steamboat traffic, it became a major river port where freight was transshipped from the smaller upstream boats to the larger river steamers. In the middle of the nineteenth century shallow draft vessels sailed 2,000 miles up the Missouri River while railroad construction was fanning out westward in Missouri. In 1857 the first railroad connected East St. Louis with the Atlantic Coast via Cincinnati, a line of great importance in shifting Union troops from Virginia to the Mississippi Valley. During the Civil War, St. Louis was a Union military base and a supplier of goods and munitions for Union armies down the valley.

After the war the city resumed its position as major trading center for the Mississippi Valley. The first bridge across the Mississippi was completed in 1874, and being located at a focus of Eastern and Western railroads on a major water route, St. Louis seemed destined to be the leading city of the Midwest. During the late 1870s Chicago, with an even greater focus of railroads combined with Great Lakes traffic, pulled ahead. At the same time St. Louis became the great wholesale and industrial center for the area to the south and southwest. Its direction of trade was recognized

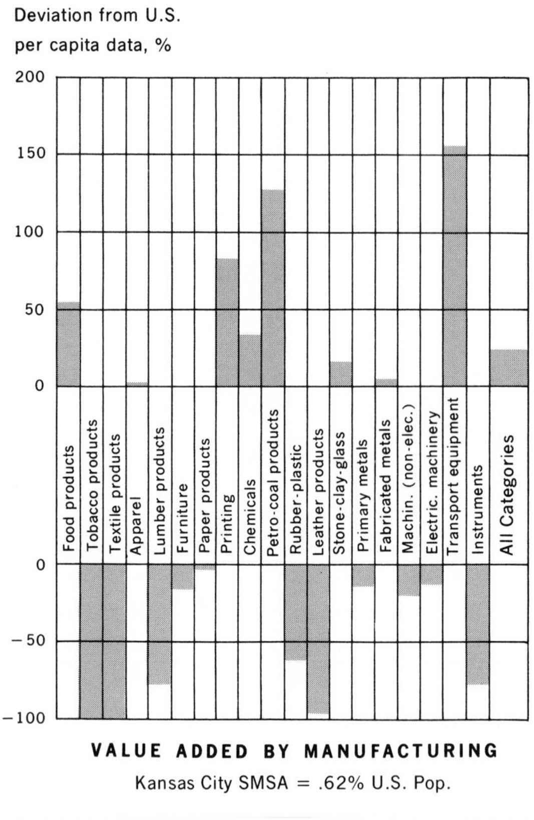

FIGURE 10-6   To what extent do Kansas City manufactures reflect the influence of raw materials? of transportation?

by the Federal Reserve System which assigned to the St. Louis Federal Reserve Bank most of Missouri, Arkansas, the Mississippi Valley to central Mississippi, and the Ohio Valley to Louisville.

The St. Louis SMSA is not lacking in natural resources. Adjacent southern Illinois has coal and oil; oil and natural gas are even more available in Oklahoma and southern Kansas. The Ozark Plateau south and southwest of Missouri provides lead, zinc, iron ore, timber, and hides. The better farmlands to the north and east and down the Mississippi provide a great variety of crops: cotton, corn, wheat, soybeans, and fruits, all used in St. Louis industries. The lighter products are commonly manufactured in St. Louis, Missouri: beer, meat products, textiles, shoes, electric machinery, aerospace parts, automobiles, paper products, and chemicals. The Illinois side of the SMSA generally has the heavier industries: oil refining, aluminum, steel, railroad equipment, explosives, glass and building materials.

Politically, the St. Louis SMSA with a population of nearly 2.25 million is much divided. The central city (1965) has only 769,000 inhabitants, whereas suburban St. Louis County consisting of a cluster of small cities has 830,000. The warehouses and older factories are clustered in the city, especially near the waterfront and along the railroads. The newer factories are sprinkled through the suburbs.

Across the river in Illinois the cities of the SMSA are scattered. East St. Louis, occupying a part of the flood plain protected by levees, was not large enough to be a city until 1865. Today it packs meat for Eastern markets and manufactures alumina, glass, and paints. To the southeast is Belle-

ville, an older industrial town on the edge of the southern Illinois coal fields. To the north is Granite City, a steel town founded in 1895. Ten miles north is Alton with a variety of heavy industries including explosives, oil refining, glass, and bricks.

The St. Louis SMSA is one of the most diversified metropolitan areas in the United States. Its distribution of employment by occupations is about the average for urban United States (Figure 10-7). It does not depend overmuch on one industry. Its largest industrial groups—food packing, transportation equipment, and machinery—are well diversified; for example, transportation equipment includes aircraft, motor vehicles, and railroad shops. Competing metropolitan

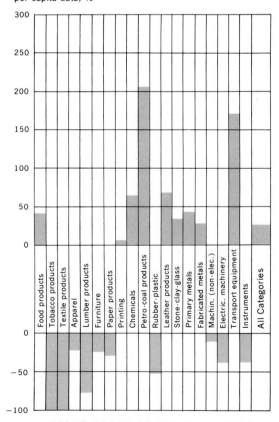

VALUE ADDED BY MANUFACTURING
St. Louis – E. St. Louis SMSA = 1.27% U.S. Pop.

FIGURE 10-7 Both St. Louis and Kansas City are river ports with excellent overland routes and access to raw materials and fuel. To what extent do they have similar industrial patterns?

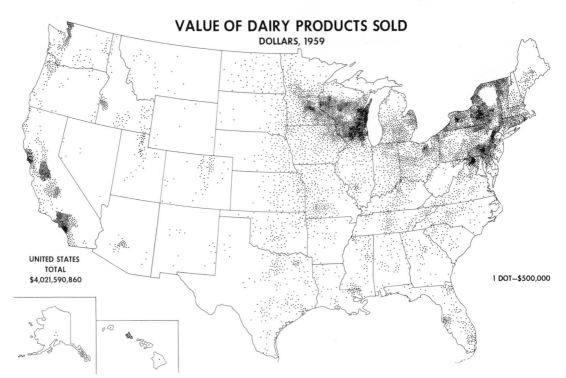

VALUE OF DAIRY PRODUCTS SOLD
DOLLARS, 1959

UNITED STATES
TOTAL
$4,021,590,860

1 DOT—$500,000

FIGURE 10-8   The map of dairying reflects two locating factors: cool, humid areas ideal for dairy cattle; nearness to urban markets. Which areas can be attributed to each? Are there any other factors that might enter into a complete explanation? (Bureau of the Census.)

areas are at least 250 miles away. Although St. Louis is not likely to compete for urban leadership with New York City, Chicago, or Los Angeles, it is the outstanding metropolis near the center of the United States population.

The Dairy Belt

In most of Michigan and Wisconsin, and along the Mississippi Valley north of Burlington, Iowa, the land is better suited for hay and pasture than for grain. Corn and other grains are grown there but mainly for fodder. This wooded area of low but rolling-to-rough relief is generally thought of as the "Dairy Belt." It is the domain of the cow; although beef cattle, hogs, and poultry are not uncommon, the Holstein and other dairy breeds are most conspicuous. Generally the soils are acid and require considerable liming and fertilizer; the winters are long, huge barns and tall silos being required to maintain the herds through the winter. The dairy farms represent a

much smaller investment than the larger Corn Belt farms, and the farmer makes a living by intensive year-round work. Higbee describes the situation of many of these farmers:

Dairymen of the Great Lakes states who do not maintain large specialized farms have found a way to compensate somewhat for the small returns obtained by dairying. Many raise extra cash crops. These cash crops require a large amount of labor per acre and heavy fertilization, but the income per acre is correspondingly high. The dairy herd provides manure which is useful in the fertilization program. Labor is available because farms and dairy herds are ordinarily small. Almost every farm has a few acres of choice land which can be set aside for the favored cash crop. On dairy farms in different parts of these states one may find tobacco, pepper-

mint, canning peas, cabbage for sauerkraut factories, cucumbers for pickling, sugar beets, potatoes, canning corn, market vegetables, orchard fruits, Concord grapes, dry onions, canning beans, and canning tomatoes. A few acres of these cash crops are vital to the economic solvency of small dairy farms producing Class 2 milk. Many of them also have subsidiary livestock enterprises—a small flock of laying hens and usually a few hogs fed on dairy by-products, pasture, and some grain.[2]

The dairy farmer's product varies with distance to the market. Farms near large metropolitan areas generally ship fresh milk although seasonal surpluses may be converted into cheese and dried milk. Cream is shipped to fairly distant markets, for example, from Wisconsin to New York City. More isolated farmers are likely to market most of their product as Class 2 milk, that is, milk to be processed into butter, cheese, or powdered or evaporated milk. From Wisconsin to New York City the freight for fluid milk is 36 to 38 percent of the wholesale price, for cream, milk powder, and evaporated milk about 7 percent, and for butter and cheese 2.5 percent of the wholesale price. The price per hundred pounds of Class 1 milk (whole milk delivered at the city plant) was about 25 percent higher in the New York Metropolitan Area than in northern Wisconsin. Class 2 milk sold in northern Wisconsin for about two-thirds the Class 1 price. Trade in milk and milk products illustrates clearly general rules for most staple commodities: prices are determined at major urban markets so that prices elsewhere are determined by these prices less freight. The form in which the product is marketed may also be determined by relation between freight costs and prices for each product.

Forestry is becoming more important in this subregion, partly because many of its soils are unsuitable for other uses. In central Wisconsin, for example, the parent soil materials are largely sandy or lime-poor glacial drift. About 40 percent of Wisconsin's forest lands are in the Dairy Belt, producing principally oak and pine. The bulk of these plantings is in northern Wisconsin and Minnesota where the dairy industry thins out and forests occupy an increasing share of the land.

St. Paul (Figure 10-9)   The northern counterpart of Kansas City is the Twin Cities SMSA, strategically situated to serve as the commercial center of the Ninth Federal Reserve District, often called the Upper Midwest. Fort Snelling, constructed in 1819 on a bluff overlooking the junction of the Minnesota and Mississippi rivers, guarded water routes leading to easy portages to Lake Superior up the Mississippi or via either river to the Red River of the North. The well-wooded countryside, studded with attractive lakes, provided valuable hardwoods; northward 100 miles the pine forests began; southward and westward the bison-stocked prairies offered potential pastures and fertile farmlands. Twenty years later, St. Paul was established downstream from Fort Snelling at the northward head of navigation on the Mississippi. Just before the Civil War steamboat arrivals there averaged nearly a thousand annually, mostly from downriver but some from the Minnesota tributary. Other shallower Mississippi tributaries, especially the Chippewa and St. Croix, offered convenient natural routes north and northeastward. St. Paul became the political capital, and its port the focus from which roads and railroads radiated into the new state (1858). Minnesota's subsequent settlement was jointly stimulated by the Homestead Act of 1862 and by the efforts of railroads to settle lands acquired by congressional land grants. Early settlers had been mainly from the older states, but for decades after the Civil War Scandina-

---

[2] Edward Higbee, *American Agriculture*, Wiley, New York, 1958, p. 269.

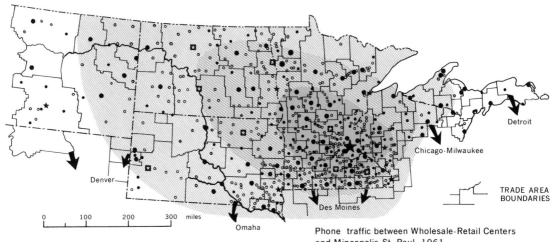

TRADE CENTER CLASS

★ Metropolitan Center of Minneapolis-St. Paul

★ Wholesale-Retail Center

▣ Secondary Wholesale Center

● Complete Shopping Center

• Partial Shopping Center

○ Convenience Center

Phone traffic between Wholesale-Retail Centers
and Mineapolis-St. Paul, 1961
(calls per 100 inhabitants at the Wholesale-Retail Center)

over 1000

400 to 1000

100 to 399

less than 100

*FIGURE 10-9   The Ninth (Minneapolis) Federal
Reserve District has a hierarchy of cities and towns
focused on the Twin Cities. The commercial influence
of the Twin Cities may be measured by the volume of
telephone calls from outlying areas. Would you expect
this urban hierarchy to function differently than in
the Chicago area (Figure 9-4)? Note that the two
hierarchies are plotted on slightly different criteria.
(Data from maps from The Upper Midwest Research and
Development Council.)*

vians poured into the commercial territory of St. Paul.

Minneapolis and St. Paul   Minneapolis, settled a decade later than St. Paul, started as a manufacturing town, utilizing the power of the falls of St. Anthony first to saw lumber and later to grind wheat from the prairies to the west and northwest. Today Minneapolis and St. Paul cooperate, sharing, for example, an airport, a baseball team, and a metropolitan planning commission; but in 1890 their rivalry was so bitter that both cities falsified census returns in an attempt to outdo each other.

St. Paul, now the state capital, possesses a mammoth stockyard and such industries as paper products, printing and publishing, household appliances, and automobile and farm-machinery assembly. Commercially its business is mainly eastward, including northwestern Minnesota and extreme western Michigan. Generally these are dairying,

lumbering, and mining areas with stagnant populations except near St. Paul itself.

Minneapolis, now somewhat larger in population and business, is the major financial and commercial center for a huge area extending north to Canada and west to central Montana. This commercial area has a declining rural and small city population; growth is in a few medium-sized centers and in areas adjoining the metropolis to the west and south. Although no longer the nation's leading flour-milling center, Minneapolis retains the head offices and research centers of most of the nation's grain-handling organizations; it now equals St. Paul as a rail-

MINNEAPOLIS ORIGINATED at the location of the falls of St. Anthony and was differentiated from downstream St. Paul because the latter was the head of navigation on the Mississippi. Man-made changes in the river make it hard to identify the falls and have given Minneapolis a harbor, which appears in the upper left of the picture. Man has also revised his own works: The former skid-row section near the railroad station has been cleaned up, and the business area at the top of the photo has been renovated under a comprehensive renewal plan. (Minneapolis Chamber of Commerce.)

road center, and the products of its electronic controls and mechanical industries are sold throughout the Plains states and westward.

The Twin Cities and Minnesota Like most metropolitan areas, the Twin Cities SMSA can also look inward for many sales of its goods and services. The metropolis accounts for 45 percent of Minnesota's population and 55 percent of its income. Although its 1950–1960 population growth was not sufficient to balance the out-migration from rural parts of the state, its growth was above average for all United States SMSAs. In spite of its prolonged winter and the decline of nearby rural industries, the Twin Cities metropolis is improving both the quality and quantity of its life; for example, 40 percent of the Minneapolis CBD has been completely rebuilt, and cultural institutions such as the Guthrie Theater have been established.

Smaller Minnesota cities have also shown growth based on industrial and service functions. For example, Rochester in southeastern Minnesota employs 3,500 people in world-famous medical centers (Mayo Clinic) and about 2,000 in business-machine manufacturing. St. Cloud to the northwest on the Mississippi River includes railways shops, and refrigeration and paper products factories. Most Minnesota cities have some manufacturing, some of which involves the processing of dairy, meat, or lumber products.

THE LESS HUMID FARM REGIONS

Westward between the 96th and 100th meridians, water becomes a scarce commodity away from streams fed by the melting snows of the Rocky Mountains. There farming changes from a business to a gamble. Indeed it must, if the farmer depends on rain which, for example, in one county in central South Dakota, ranged in 28 years from 9 to 26 inches annually; during the same period wheat yields varied from 3.0 to 15.8 bushels in 25 years; in the other 3 years the wheat crop failed completely. With high risks from drought, plant disease, locusts, hail, and wind erosion, not to mention fluctuating wheat prices, no wonder the farmer wants crop insurance, soil banks, price supports, and other forms of governmental aid. The farmer tries to spread his risk by using drought-resistant sorghum and rye grass, dry-farming techniques, cattle, and, where possible, some irrigation. Farms must be large since productivity per acre is low except on irrigated land. The average farm occupies about 1 square mile, but toward the western margin of the region the average size in some counties is many times greater: Thus Hughes County farms (central South Dakota) averaged 2 square miles in 1959, and Harding County farms (extreme northwestern South Dakota) averaged 7 square miles.

Types of Farming

Several types of farming have become characteristic of the less humid regions in the Midwest. *Dry farming* is the oldest, the term referring to any type of farming in which special techniques are used to conserve the limited soil water. The method used may be mulching, fallowing in alternate years, strip cropping, shelter belts, or terracing, or any combination of these. *Sidewalk farming* is done by farmers who live in town and hold jobs in town but drive out to their fields when farm work needs to be done.

Suitcase farming is done by the farmer who works on a number of farms, commonly in different latitudes, so the periods of heavy work come at different times of the year on each farm. A week at most suffices for the harvest on the average wheat farm. The suitcase farmer's equipment is transported by truck, and his family may move with him in mobile homes. By combining one or more winter-wheat farms with a spring-wheat farm, his labor is better distributed and his risk from local drought reduced. In many cases suitcase farm work is performed by migratory work groups who work on contract for absentee landlords. Much more intensive is *irrigation farming* in which water which fell as rain or snow on the mountains to the west is used to supplement the modest local precipitation. Most of this water is obtained from and used near transverse surface streams; less common but locally significant is irrigation water obtained either from artesian wells or pumped from underlying aquifers.

Stock farms provide another way of reducing risks. Such farms must be large and must have a dependable stream or underground water which can be pumped to the surface. Some land is devoted to crops including hay; grain crops which fail to mature may be used for fodder. Most farms in this region today have some cattle; whether a given farmer is classified as a stock farmer depends on whether his stress is primarily on beef rather than grain.

The Spring Wheat Belt

One of the great wheat surplus areas of the world is the Red River Valley, an area of rich black lacustrine soils. The farm products may be spring wheat, dairy cattle, potatoes, flax, sugar beets, soybeans, or clover, or more likely a combination of several of these. Drought is rare; in fact, the soils are often difficult to till in spring because of excessive moisture. The growing season is short, and the farmer must work fast to get the maximum from his extensive acres (average about 500 acres) before winter comes. Large machinery and mass production methods are conspicuous on the huge flat fields.

West of the Red River Valley, the land is rolling, and the tall grain elevators loom on the horizon long before the market towns become visible. In eastern North Dakota, the land is largely in spring wheat, grain being the principal source of income. To the west, cattle and sheep gradually become the predominant sources of income, and increasing parts of the crops are irrigated. Work in the region is highly concentrated in the summer season with underutilization of manpower during the winter. In North Dakota, industries are almost entirely related to agricultural and mineral raw materials. The two largest cities, Fargo and Grand Forks, are in the Red River Valley on the Minnesota border. In the center of the state, Bismarck, in addition to its functions as state capital, has a dozen small industries serving local markets. Much smaller is Williston whose 60 percent population increase (1950–1960) resulted from oil discoveries.

An Agricultural State

South Dakota, including parts of three farming regions, offers a good example of an agricultural economy. In 1966 its 719,000 people had a total personal income of $1,643 million, of which $372 million was classified as farm income. Another major source of income ($227 million) was trade, most of which was in farm products or in goods sold to farmers. South Dakota's industrial income ($91 million) is also related to farming; thus 71 percent of all industrial employment is in meat-packing and other food products industries. Thus, although in 1960 39 percent of the South Dakota population was urban and 30 percent was rural non-farm, most of these non-farm people

earned their living by performing services for farmers.

The state may also be studied by considering its distribution patterns. The western edge of South Dakota is ranch country bisected by the wooded Black Hills whose lumbering and gold mining activities add some diversity to the income (mining, $16 million; wood products industries, $5 million). Three railroad lines and six through highways handle west-east traffic including tourist and other through traffic. Except around the Black Hills the towns are small, and there are many sparsely populated counties, including two that lack county seats and organized local governments. Even the capital, Pierre on the Missouri River, has only 10,000 people and no sizable industries. Eastward the population density increases, crops become more important and ranching less important, the railroad and road net thickens, counties are smaller in size, and county seats are larger in population. The only SMSA, Sioux Falls (87,000), is on the eastern border of the state.

South Dakota may also be described in terms of family income and per capita retail sales, both of which are high in the counties with cities, especially in Minnehaha (Sioux Falls) and Pennington (Rapid City), and are extremely low (50 to 70 percent of the United States average) in the numerous counties containing Indian reservations. Washabaugh, the poorest county has been described in a federal pamphlet as: "Almost half as large as Rhode Island, this county in 1950 had only 12 taxpayers, no local government, not even a post office."

Thus South Dakota includes Corn Belt farms, Spring Wheat Belt farms, cattle ranches, Indian reservations, and the wooded, mineralized Black Hills. None of these provide an adequate basis for rapid growth in a modern industrial economy. One forecast as to future population is that

220

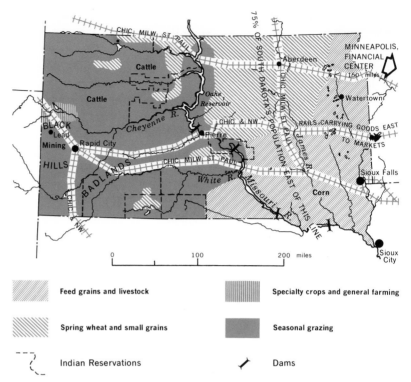

FIGURE 10-10 *An agricultural state such as South Dakota can be summed up more readily in a map than can more intensively developed states.*

the 1960 population of 688,000 may grow to 732,000 by 1975. With cold winters, drought-ridden summers, and somewhat isolated from Anglo-American population centers, South Dakota seems likely to continue to provide agricultural produce, a few minerals, and some tourist services; but its outlook for major urban growth seems poor.

The Winter Wheat Belt

Although the products of the two wheat belts are similar, the seasonal work schedules are different. In the Dakotas the winter is too severe for crops, whereas in Kansas wheat is planted in the fall and harvested in early summer. Corn, sorghum, and other summer crops may enter into the crop rotation. Generally hard winter wheat and beef cattle bring in cash income, other crops being used for fodder. As in the Dakotas, the farms become larger toward the west, and large machinery owned by traveling teams of farm workers is characteristic.

In western Kansas (and extending southward into Oklahoma), winter wheat is commonly planted in alternate years on each field. Experience has shown that if proper moisture conservation methods are used, more wheat per acre is obtained in this way. In Colby, Kansas, for example, records for 34 years showed that fields planted every year averaged 7.9 bushels per acre, whereas on adjacent fields fallowed in alternate years, crops were 18 bushels per acre per harvest or 1.1 bushels per acre more per year. This is the area in which suitcase farming is especially prevalent, many of the farms being owned by nonresidents and tilled by farmers who are hired to work the land at planting and harvest times.

Cities in the Winter Wheat Belt

The largest city is Wichita whose leading source of employment is durable goods manufacturing. The outstanding industry is aircraft assembly, attracted by the high percentage of days suitable for testing planes. Wichita claims that half of all planes flying in the world today have at least in part originated in its factories. The city also has an important air-conditioning equipment industry as well as industries to serve the surrounding countryside, for example, food packing and railroad shops.

The growth of Wichita suggests that industry may be able to counterbalance the decline in farm employment. In 1965 the Kansas City Federal Reserve Bank surveyed all cities of between 10,000 and 50,000 in its district. In the Corn Belt and the Winter Wheat Belt the great majority showed substantial increases in both population and employment. Many of these cities had small industries in addition to the food-processing industries normal in farm country. Small towns away from metropolitan areas were less successful in holding their populations. The rich oil fields of central and southern Kansas undoubtedly contributed to this development. Nevertheless, although the state experienced a 14.3 percent population increase from 1950 to 1960, it had a net out-migration of 121,000. It appears that many activities can be expanded in the Plains states away from the Commercial-Manufacturing Core, but so far such expansion has not sufficed to make up for the decline in farm employment.

Two Ranching Subregions

Much of western Nebraska consists of sand dunes which support an ample grass cover. The valleys have local water sup-

plies and meadows sufficiently damp to yield a good hay crop. This is beef cattle country, somewhat richer than most of the semi-arid grazing lands. It must not be forgotten that there are also many beef cattle in the Winter Wheat Belt grazing on lands too rough or infertile for cultivation.

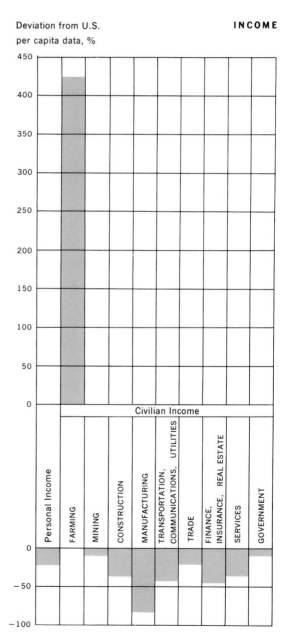

In the Flint Hills of eastern Kansas the country appears drier than it is, and the westward traveler seems to pass directly from the Corn Belt into a range of nearly 5 million acres. In part the stony soil is too thin for crops, but the rain suffices for a lush growth of bluestem grass; on the other hand, much tillable land is kept for grazing, being owned by ranchers affiliated with other ranchers to the southwest. Cattle, locally bred or fattened after arrival from Texas ranches, produce luscious steaks and contribute, along with the Corn Belt, to Kansas City stockyards and slaughter houses. "K.C." steaks are often featured in restaurants from Texas to the Rockies, being preferred to the leaner meat of range cattle.

Water on the Land

From the air the less humid farm and grazing regions show a surprising number of bodies of water. Small ponds dot the landscape, some created by damming streams, others fed by windmills. Large reservoirs are storing the floodwaters of rivers once noted for their undependable water supply. Along the Platte and other streams, ribbons of irrigated land appear dark green in summer, yielding fodder crops such as alfalfa. As farms and ranches are merged into larger units, most of the newer units contain some irrigated land.

The Missouri River is gradually being converted into a chain of lakes. The objective is partly flood control to prevent the repetition of the 1951 flood which drove half a million people from their homes. The Missouri project will also provide irrigation water to an additional 18,900 farms, 2.5 million kilowatts of electric power, and a barge channel on the river. Dams on the Missouri system should stabilize many domestic water systems which in the 1959 drought year proved inadequate. A by-product will be the creation of lakes suitable for recreation.

CONCLUSIONS

The leaders of the Plains states are not unaware of their problems: thus, an elaborate series of thoughtful studies has been prepared by the Upper Midwest Research and Development Council which analyzes the Minneapolis Federal Reserve District:

The Upper Midwest, like most major agricultural areas in the United States, had long been a population exporter. This trend has been intensified in the past thirty years by rapidly advancing farm technology and mechanization permitting substantial reductions in the numbers of farms through farm consolidation. This, of course, releases a steady flow of farm families from the land, which augments the traditional flow of farm youth.

This large outflow of people from the region, which has gone on now for decades, is likely to continue due to the large population still remaining on farms and in rural areas (but at a decreasing rate as that population diminishes). This fact alone—an abundant labor supply—represents the Upper Midwest's greatest natural resource for accelerating future growth.[3]

This quotation applies to most of the region discussed in this chapter. Population and economic growth have been mainly limited to a number of areas along major transport routes to the American Commercial-Manufacturing Core: notably in northwestern Illinois, northern Iowa, and southeastern Minnesota; also along routes from Chicago to St. Louis, Kansas City, and Wichita. Growth spots appear around most other cities, but commonly these represent a corresponding loss in surrounding rural regions.

Development agencies in each state are attempting to increase urban growth by attracting new activities to their cities.

[3] Larry A. Sjaastad, *Migration and Population Growth in the Upper Midwest: 1930–1960*, Study Paper 6, Upper Midwest Research and Development Council, Minneapolis, 1962, pp. i–ii.

Their success can be roughly measured by the increase in city (or SMSA) populations in the decade 1950–1960, a decade in which the United States population increased 18.5 percent and SMSA populations increased an average of 26 percent. In this decade 12 cities and SMSAs in the region grew less than 10 percent, 13 grew between 10 and 18.5 percent, 12 between 18.5 and 26 percent, and 2 over 26 percent. The cities with greatest growth were state capitals, or had large universities, or had secured booming industries, e.g., Wichita (aircraft). The ability of urban leaders to attract growth industry, whether this be based on skill or luck, explains differences in growth of cities with apparently equal attractions. Several SMSAs which have become regional metropolises (Minneapolis–St. Paul, Kansas City, and St. Louis) have developed an economic attraction which it is difficult for smaller competing cities to overcome.

The Midwest will no doubt continue to lose rural population. Certain of its cities will take on functions of the Commercial-Manufacturing Core which may in the future extend westward to a line from Minneapolis to Kansas City, thence eastward to somewhat south of St. Louis. Other outlying cities will no doubt develop in response to individual initiative, but there seems little reason to predict general growth. Although agriculturally productive, the produce of the plains can be obtained, indeed increased, with fewer people. Although centrally located in the nation, much of the Plains states is distant from the concentrated markets of the Core and from markets that are developing in the South and on the Pacific Coast. Certain business services will, of course, be performed in the plains for goods and passengers in transit across the country, but these will decline with the increasing use of air and nonstop freight hauls. One other chance remains for the development of the agricultural area—the ability of plentiful, well-trained labor to attract industries oriented to skilled labor rather than to market and raw materials.

SELECTED REFERENCES

BAUGHMAN, ROBERT W.: *Kansas in Maps,* Kansas State Historical Society, Topeka, 1961.

BROWN, ROBERT H., and PHILIP C. TIDEMAN: *Atlas of Minnesota Occupancy,* Minnesota Atlas Company, St. Cloud, 1961.

HIGBEE, EDWARD: *American Agriculture,* Wiley, New York, 1958. This book and the author's more popular book, *The American Oasis,* Knopf, New York, 1957, give a picture of American farming as it is today.

KNUDTSON, ARVID C., and REX W. COX: *Upper Midwest Agriculture: Structure and Problems,* Upper Midwest Research and Development Council and University of Minnesota, Minneapolis, 1962. Also other studies in this series.

KOLLMORGEN, W. M., and C. F. JENKS: "Suitcase Farming in Sully County, South Dakota," *Annals, A.A.G.,* vol. 48 (1958), pp. 27–40.

—— and D. S. SIMONETT: "Grazing Operations in the Flint Hills–Bluestem Pastures of Chase County, Kansas," *Annals, A.A.G.,* vol. 55 (1965), pp. 260–90.

MALIN, J. C.: *The Grassland of North America,* privately printed, Lawrence, Kansas, 1948.

MARSCHNER, F. J.: "Land Use and Its Patterns in the United States," *Agricultural Handbook,* no. 153, U. S. Department of Agriculture, Washington, 1959. Out of print but well worth searching for in libraries.

U.S. DEPARTMENT OF AGRICULTURE: *Soil,* Yearbook of Agriculture. Washington, 1957. This and other agricultural yearbooks provide excellent source materials. See also, *Power to Produce,* Yearbook of Agriculture, 1960, and for statistical details, *Agricultural Statistics* (annual), Washington.

WEAVER, JOHN C.: "Crop Combination Regions in the Middle West," *Geographical Review,* vol. 44 (1954), pp. 175–200.

Numerous publications of the state agricultural experiment stations are of value, e.g., *Soils of the North Central Region of the United States,* University of Wisconsin Agricultural Experiment Station Bulletin 544, Madison, 1960.

CHAPTER 11

THE SOUTHERN UPLANDS: PROBLEMS AND PROGRESS

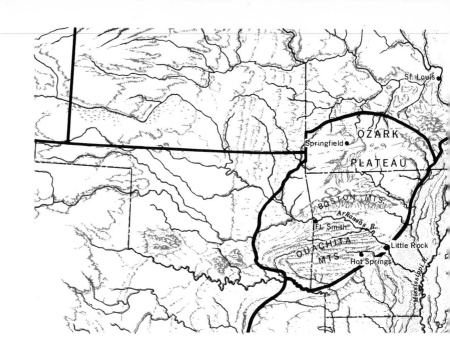

BASIC DATA: AREA INCLUDES	Land Area (thou-sand sq. mi.)	Change 1950-1960	Population 1960	1967	Personal Income 1967 (billions)
			(thousands)		
SOUTHERN UPLANDS	195.0	5.2%	13,484	14,765	$33.8
APPALACHIAN:					
Maryland (part)	1.1	− 5.6	105	110	0.3
West Virginia (part)	10.5	− 15.3	548	530	1.2
Virginia (part)	19.8	4.2	1,276	1,500	2.7
Kentucky (part)	5.7	− 21.9	399	315	0.5
North Carolina (part)	24.3	6.5	2,683	3,040	7.6
South Carolina (part)	10.6	8.0	966	1,070	2.6
Tennessee (part)	23.6	6.5	1,662	1,830	3.3
Georgia (part)	22.8	14.4	2,166	2,500	6.0
Alabama (part)	18.0	10.2	1,741	1,870	4.5
OZARK-OUACHITA:					
Arkansas (part)	26.0	− 4.5	1,090	1,050	2.3
Missouri (part)	18.5	− 1.2	534	550	1.3
Oklahoma (part)	14.1	− 13.1	314	380	0.5
MAJOR SMSAS:					
Greensboro-High Point	0.7	29.0%	246	295	$ 0.9
Charlotte	0.5	38.1	272	385	1.2
Atlanta	1.1	38.0	1,017	1,245	4.3
Chattanooga	1.0	14.9	283	295	0.9
Knoxville	1.4	9.2	368	400	1.1
Birmingham	1.1	13.6	635	680	2.0
Little Rock	0.8	23.5	243	300	0.8

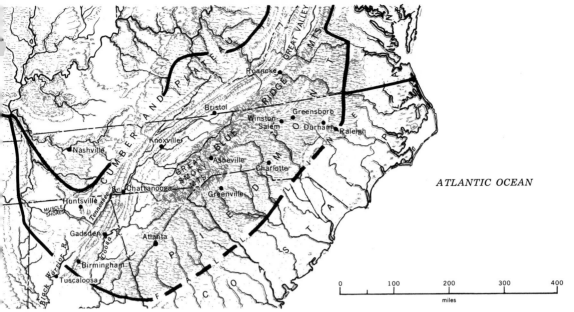

FIGURE 11-1 *Landforms of the Southern Uplands. The boundaries of the subdivisions discussed can be identified from the physiographic symbols. Note that a small part of the northeastern corner of the region has been omitted because of the awkward shape of the region.* (Base map copyright by A. K. Lobeck. Reprinted with permission of The Geographical Press, Hammond, Inc.)

CLIMATE   *Humid continental to humid subtropical, considerable local variation based on altitude and explosure.*

	Temperature (°F)		Precipitation (inches)	
	Jan.	July	Annual	Season
Charlotte	41	78	44	Summer maximum
Atlanta	44	79	48	Summer maximum
Knoxville	40	78	41	Summer maximum
Birmingham	47	80	54	Summer maximum
Little Rock	43	81	46	Summer maximum

VEGETATION   Hardwoods (oak, hickory, ash, maple, chestnut, yellow poplar); some pine.

SOIL   Transitional from gray-brown podzolic to red-yellow podzolic; much stony and steep land; considerable variation based on underlying rock and slope.

MINERALS   Coal and stone, iron ore, copper, lead in scattered localities.

THE SOUTH

This is the first of four chapters devoted to what is commonly called "the South," an extensive area considered as having long, hot summers and short, mild winters, producing cotton, tobacco, corn, peanuts, and sweet potatoes, and having a social system greatly influenced by the plantation and the legacy of the Civil War (War between the States). Such an area is difficult to define, and the criteria listed do not occur wrapped up in a neat regional package.

The broadest definition of the South (by the U.S. Census) includes 16 states and the District of Columbia, comprising the southeastern quarter of the nation's area and three-tenths of its people. Such a political region encompasses large areas that have already been discussed in this book as part of the Delaware-Chesapeake Gateways, and the Ohio Basin. The remaining parts of the "Census South" will be discussed in the following chapters (parts of which extend beyond the Census South):

Chapter 11: *The Southern Uplands,* essentially those upland areas drained by the Tennessee, the upper Kanawha, the Shenandoah, and the numerous small streams of the Southern Piedmont; included also are somewhat similar areas in the Ozark-Ouachita Uplands.

Chapter 12: *The Southeastern Coastal Plain,* an area including the fall-line cities and the sandy and locally marshy plain from North Carolina to Florida.

Chapter 13: *The Gulf South,* including the lowland areas tributary to the Mississippi and several smaller rivers debouching into the Gulf of Mexico.

Chapter 14: *The Southwest,* an area transitional between the Gulf South, the Plains states, and the High West, consisting of interior Texas, Oklahoma, New Mexico, and Arizona.

All four regions are in various stages of transition from an agricultural-raw-material economy to an industrial economy. No sharp boundaries separate these regions from one another, but the boundaries used bring together areas that have in common distinctive features, potentialities, and problems. Once no doubt these areas had somewhat distinctive culture features: the pioneer farmers of the Piedmont and the Appalachian valleys; the planter aristocracy of the Southeastern Plain; the planter aristocracy mixed with Spanish and French traditions in the Gulf South; the Mexican and Indian traditions and the semi-

arid conditions in the Southwest. Such traditional characteristics still provide a regional accent, but interregional bonds such as television, southward infiltration of Yankee industry and tourists, and northward shipments by pipeline and ship of southwestern minerals have broken down regional isolationism. Today many Southern cities look much like Northern cities except in carefully preserved older sections such as downtown Charleston, South Carolina. Nor are the Southern problems unique: the North and West also have race riots, rural and urban slums, traffic congestion, and urban renewal. The South has its prosperous industrial centers as well as a rural unemployment problem as serious as that in the Plains states. If income averages in Southern states are low, it is commonly because a larger proportion of regional employment is in low-paying activities.

Obviously economic and social progress in any environment depends on the abilities of its people (plus their inherited or developed skills) to develop local advantages and create both a prosperous economy and a satisfying society. Each region to be discussed has certain problems whose solution contains economic and social potentialities. The Southern Uplands, blessed with attractive settings, a mild climate, and adequate water resources, offer many homesites, industrial sites, and recreational possibilities. There, close to the worst Appalachia problem areas, amazing progress has been made in the present century with private industry, community leaders, and the TVA providing much intelligent leadership. On the Southeastern Coastal Plain the proper management of soil and water and a mild climate have attracted subtropical farming, lumber industries, and an influx of settlers desiring to avoid cold winters. The Gulf South has a wealth of alluvial soil whose produce has become in many subregions subordinate to industrial development stimulated by such resources as petroleum, nat-

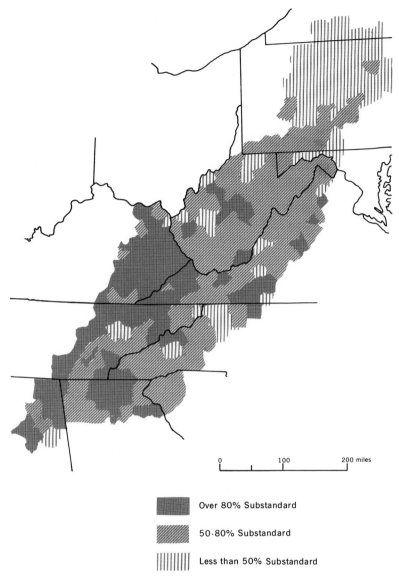

0   100   200 miles

Over 80% Substandard

50-80% Substandard

Less than 50% Substandard

FIGURE 11-2   Substandard housing in Appalachia. Note that the Appalachia area includes some areas not part of the Southern Uplands, which do not generally have as severe problems as most parts of that region. (After Maryland Department of Economic Development.)

ural gas, sulfur, salt, and lumber. In the Southwest petroleum and other minerals have speeded up development of ranch, dry, and irrigation farming, and of industrial and urban developments attractive to those fond of semi-arid environments. Finally an advantage that applies to the development of much of the South: its population exceeds that of either the Northeast or the Central Lowland, although its aggregate income is well below that of its northern neighbors. Even today the South repre-

sents a huge market, but when (and if) its levels of living can be raised to national levels, it will become the largest Anglo-American regional market. This in itself will develop huge demands for goods and services such as are already perceptible in progressive centers as Atlanta, New Orleans, and Houston.

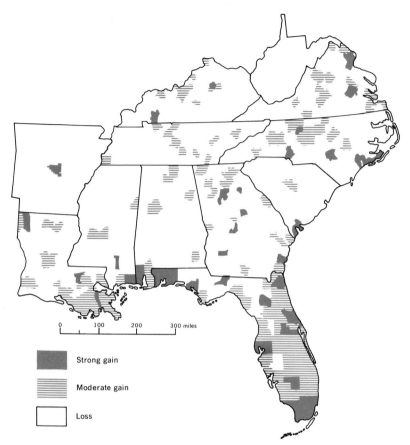

FIGURE 11-3   *Total net relative change in employment by counties in the Southeast: 1950–1960. The areas showing a moderate or strong gain are mainly urbanized areas. Can you find any exceptions to the preceding generalization?* (Map after O.B.E., Department of Commerce.)

Strong gain

Moderate gain

Loss

Employment Growth Patterns

How can the recent economic progress of the various parts of the South be measured? The Office of Business Economics has worked out a technique, analyzing employment growth patterns by counties,[1] states, and regions. For the states in the South, the growth as compared with the United States is shown in Table 11-1. The map (Figure 11-3) shows that the growth areas are mainly around cities and that although much loss is concentrated in the Appalachia area, there are also extensive areas in all Southeastern states (except Florida) which rate in the loss category. Such data show that although state figures may be of value, they average together considerable variety and may conceal detailed explanations.

[1] U.S. Office of Business Economics, *Growth Patterns in Employment by County: 1940–1950 and 1950–1960,* 8 vols., Washington, 1965.

O.B.E. data for all of North Carolina are reproduced in Table 11-2. The county tables in the O.B.E. studies enable the reasons for employment loss and gain to be pinpointed. Thus Mecklenburg County, North Carolina (including Charlotte), was rated (1950–1960) as a "strong-gain" area, its loss of employment in agriculture (1,596) and textiles (2,140) being more than made up by gains in vehicles and machinery manufacturing, trade, and services, for a net gain of 24,637 or relative gain of 11,248 compared with the national growth rate. In contrast, nearby Anson County rated in the lowest category with a rural loss of employment of 1,752 and a net relative loss of 2,207.

Table 11-2 also differentiates employment changes attributable to the state's share of national growth in employment from changes attributable to changes in the nation's proportions of employment in each industry. Thus the net loss in North Carolina agricultural employment in 1950–1960 is shown as 155,209, which is obtained by subtracting C from B in the first line of Table 11-2. On the basis of national growth in all employment, a gain of 55,747 (column J) in agriculture would be anticipated. However, because agricultural employment is declining rapidly, causing a change in the proportions of employed persons in agriculture (a change in the *industrial mix*), North Carolina agriculture on this basis should decline 194,263 (column K) or (K − J), a net decline of 138,516. Since the actual decline (M) was greater than this by 16,693, this is attributed to regional circum

stances; in other words, agricultural employment in North Carolina is declining more rapidly than in the nation ("strong loss" with a decline in both industrial mix and regional share). Note that other branches of North Carolina employment are rated in the strong gain category, for example, food and kindred products manufacturing. For all industries, North Carolina[2] is rated as having moderate net loss caused by an industrial mix so weak in growth industries that the high rate of growth in some of the state has not enabled it to keep up with the national rate of employment growth.

[2] It should be noted that in 1950–1960 of the 50 states only 8 (as a whole) showed a strong gain and 13 a moderate gain by the O.B.E. definition. In North Carolina, out of 100 counties, 5 showed a strong gain and 17 others a moderate gain. Most of the Piedmont counties containing cities over 25,000 showed a gain. The gains were reduced by high employment losses in agriculture and textiles, industries in which there has been a strong loss nationally as well as in the Southern Uplands.

TABLE 11-1 Relative Employment Growth: United States and Southern States, 1940–1960

	Percent Change		Rating Compared to United States	
Area	1940–1950	1950–1960	1940–1950	1950–1960
UNITED STATES	26.7	15.5	Base	Base
SOUTHEAST	20.6	12.6	Loss	Loss
West Virginia	21.1	− 14.3	Loss	Strong loss
Virginia	34.9	17.1	Gain	Strong gain
North Carolina	24.5	11.6	Loss	Loss
South Carolina	16.7	11.7	Loss	Loss
Georgia	16.7	12.2	Loss	Loss
Florida	53.8	70.9	Gain	Strong gain
Kentucky	15.3	− 0.3	Loss	Strong loss
Tennessee	22.5	8.1	Loss	Strong loss
Alabama	16.4	4.7	Loss	Loss
Mississippi	0.5	− 3.8	Strong loss	Strong loss
Louisiana	15.0	15.8	Strong loss	Gain
Arkansas	5.7	− 7.1	Strong loss	Strong loss
SOUTHWEST	32.5	23.6	Gain	Gain
Texas	33.8	21.7	Gain	Gain
Oklahoma	16.5	6.6	Strong loss	Strong loss
New Mexico	55.5	42.0	Gain	Gain
Arizona	63.8	81.6	Gain	Gain

SOURCE: U.S. Office of Business Economics, *Growth Patterns in Employment by County: 1940–1950 and 1950–1960*, vol. 5, *Southeast*, tables 2 and 4, Washington, 1965.

TABLE 11-2 North Carolina Employment Change by Industries, 1940–1960

	Employment in:			1950–1960 Changes Related to:			
				National Growth	Industrial Mix	Regional Share	Total Change
Industry	1940 (A)	1950 (B)	1960 (C)	(J)	(K)	(L)	(M)
Agriculture	405,923	360,097	204,888	55,747	−194,263	−16,693	−155,209
Forestry and Fisheries	3,127	3,901	3,130	604	−1,598	223	−771
Mining	2,914	3,134	3,531	485	−1,417	1,329	397
Contract Construction	46,971	86,388	98,224	13,374	−4,411	2,873	11,836
Food and Kindred Products	13,498	19,495	33,009	3,018	2,614	7,882	13,514
Textile Mill Products	189,974	215,129	221,726	33,304	−82,954	56,247	6,597
Apparel	6,327	14,612	33,010	2,262	−954	17,090	18,398
Lumber, Wood Products, and Furniture	57,977	82,895	80,749	12,833	−21,395	6,416	−2,146
Printing and Publishing	5,403	8,663	13,062	1,341	1,555	1,503	4,399
Chemicals and Allied Products	9,184	8,905	13,547	1,379	1,393	1,870	4,642
Electric and Other Machinery	2,933	9,529	38,197	1,475	2,964	24,228	28,667
Motor Vehicles and Equipment	798	1,146	1,619	177	−214	509	472
Other Transportation Equipment	507	617	3,707	96	536	2,459	3,091
Other and Miscellaneous Manufacturing	38,938	47,961	70,567	7,425	1,566	13,615	22,606
Railroads and Railway Express	15,388	17,905	11,557	2,772	−8,536	−584	−6,348
Trucking and Warehousing	8,947	15,061	23,909	2,332	2,144	4,373	8,849
Other Transportation	4,842	11,629	10,943	1,800	−1,481	−1,005	−686
Communications	4,525	9,498	12,952	1,470	−1	1,985	3,454
Utilities and Sanitary Service	7,421	12,595	15,225	1,950	−132	812	2,630
Wholesale Trade	17,778	32,782	43,736	5,075	−1,251	7,130	10,954
Food and Dairy Products Stores	25,155	38,290	40,446	5,928	−6,688	2,916	2,156
Eating and Drinking Places	12,963	23,415	27,552	3,625	−2,119	2,631	4,137
Other Retail Trade	70,816	114,952	145,523	17,796	2,202	10,573	30,571
Finance, Insurance and Real Estate	15,416	24,414	42,722	3,780	6,058	8,470	18,308
Hotels and Other Personal Services	34,021	43,929	45,773	6,801	−4,914	−42	1,845
Private Households	81,412	62,764	76,630	9,717	903	3,246	13,866
Business and Repair Services	13,371	24,580	27,564	3,805	1,763	−2,584	2,984
Entertainment and Recreation Services	5,717	8,889	7,995	1,376	−1,230	−1,041	−895
Medical and Other Professional Services	63,684	99,163	154,903	15,352	42,127	−1,738	55,741
Public Administration	21,495	38,469	49,762	5,955	4,579	759	11,293
Armed Forces	5,500	41,996	73,920	6,501	22,488	2,934	31,923
Industry Not Reported	15,765	22,545	49,320	3,490	43,755	−20,470	26,775
Total	1,208,690	1,505,348	1,679,398	233,045	−196,911	137,916	174,050

Total Net Relative Change (M): (sum of totals cols. K and L) — −58,995

SOURCE: U.S. Office of Business Economics, *Growth Patterns in Employment by County: 1940–1950 and 1950–1960*, vol. 5, *Southeast*, table 6-2, Washington, 1965.

THE SOUTHERN UPLANDS

Relief and Settlement

Political discussions of the Appalachia region have given Americans an oversimplified picture of the Southern Uplands. The highland areas are by no means uniform, in either physical features or human settlement. Thus the mountain region includes Oak Ridge (atomic research), mining towns, isolated farmsteads, and the huge aluminum plant at Alcoa, Tennessee; the Piedmont includes bustling Atlanta and Charlotte, prosperous poultry and cattle farms, and rundown farmsteads. Physically, the much dissected Piedmont Upland slopes upward toward the Blue Ridge, becoming hillier westward. Forests cover the rugged, narrow, sparsely settled Blue Ridge and its southwestward neighbor, the higher and largely unsettled Great Smokies, both providing a substantial barrier which even today slows traffic on the roads across the major gaps. Even these rugged areas in the past attracted settlers who liked the pioneer life with its self-sufficient farming supplemented by hunting and fishing. These crystalline masses slope abruptly west to the broad, well-settled Great Valley, land of limestone soils which, once the great corridor used by pioneers moving southwestward and westward, today includes a number of small, medium-sized, to moderately large cities with considerable commerce and industry. West of the Great Valley and locally easily connected with it are the narrower valleys of the folded Appalachians, adjoined to the west by the sharp edge of a locally coal-rich Cumberland Plateau. West of the Mississippi the highlands have somewhat the same pattern: the Ouachita roughly corresponding to the higher and more rugged Blue Ridge; the Arkansas Valley corresponding to the broader Great Valley; and the southern Ozark Plateau resembling the higher, more deeply dissected Cumberland Plateau.

Appalachia

The Southern Uplands include most of Appalachia, an area of some 360 counties in 11 states which are to be developed under the Appalachian Regional Development Act passed by Congress in 1965. The region delimited in this act, determined at least in part by political considerations, includes large areas already discussed under the Ohio Basin and as part of the Delaware-Chesapeake Gateways; it also includes a few counties with a net gain in the O.B.E. employment rating and a considerable number rated as "moderate loss" areas.

This brings up one of the problems resulting from sharp regional boundaries. Considering coal and water, both necessary commodities for the Ohio Basin, mountain West Virginia and eastern Kentucky are part of the Ohio Basin (Chapter 8). From the point of view of human geography and social problems, these areas belong with the Southern Uplands and Appalachia, and for this reason are considered in this chapter. Also to be considered here (but not included in the Appalachian Regional Development Act) is the Ozark-Ouachita area, a smaller western counterpart of the Appalachians. The act does not include some progressive upland areas to the south and southeast which depend on Appalachia for many raw materials and fuel, and which have received many migrants from Appalachia. These Piedmont (foot of the mountain) areas, worn-down parts of the older crystalline Appalachians, and the lower southwestern ends of the Appalachians are here included with the uplands. All these uplands represent not only a barrier zone which focuses north-south communication on the easier passes but also a transition zone between the South and the Central Lowlands. These uplands have other common features: a mild, rainy climate with sharp weather changes from day to day, an environment well suited for trees but less suited to row crops whose cultivation

THE HIGHEST TVA DAM, Fontana Dam in North Carolina, rises 480 feet and can produce 202,000 kilowatts of electricity. The Great Smokies are rounded, wooded mountains, soaked annually by heavy rains and well suited to store water for downstream use. There is little permanent settlement, but many pleasant acres for recreational use. (TVA.)

encourages soil leaching and erosion. Although the relief varies locally from 100 to over 1,000 feet, most of the land is intricately dissected. In human terms, most of the area is characterized by low rural incomes, declining rural employment, and considerable rural out-migration.

Appalachian problems The problems of Appalachia have not been unique in Anglo-America. Farm populations have declined and farmlands have gone out of cultivation there just as they have in the hills of New England and southern Indiana and in the Upper Lakes area. Coal mining has declined in production because of competing fuels, and even more in employment because of strip mining and mechanization, but this has also occurred in southern Illinois. Schooling has been backward, and public improvements have not kept up with the times, but this, too, has been common elsewhere where the tax base has been limited;

especially serious in the Appalachians has been the inadequacy of the roads, much more expensive to build than in level areas (Figure 11-4). Perhaps the most serious handicap of the mountain areas has been out-migration which, consisting of the better educated and more energetic, has lowered the average skill of the communities from which the migrants came.

However, the situation is not entirely gloomy; where conditions favor those urban industries and services that are part of the growth sector of the national economy, progress has taken place in Appalachia. Although rugged relief brought about isolation in the past, the populated parts of the area are no longer completely isolated. On the main roads it is possible to cross most of the highlands in an afternoon; on the poorer roads in a day. Interstate highways and other roads provided for by the Appalachian Regional Development Act should make most of the region accessible. The

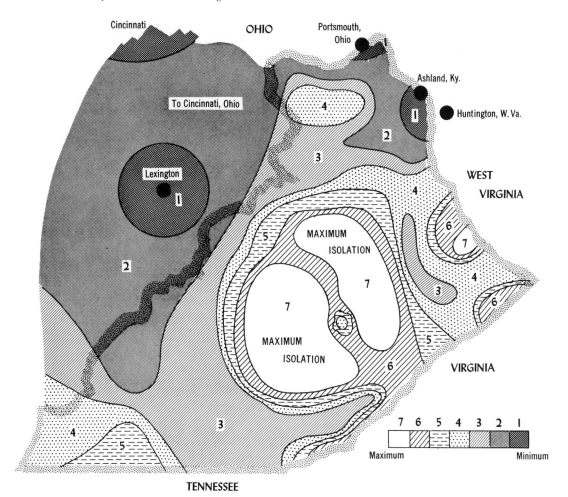

FIGURE 11-4   *Isolation contours in East Kentucky.
Although this map is only about six years old, its data
have already been changed by the construction of the
Mountain Parkway to the east and slightly south of
Lexington and by interstate highways connecting
Lexington with Cincinnati, Louisville, and south much
of the way to Knoxville, Tennessee. Such deluxe moun-
tain highways are obviously not supported by the
earning power of these uplands.* (Map from Mary J.
Bowman and W. Warren Haynes, RESOURCES AND PEOPLE IN
EAST KENTUCKY, published for Resources for the Future, Inc.,
Johns Hopkins, Baltimore, 1963.)

environmental setting, in latitudes guaran-
teeing mild winters, yet high enough to
moderate summer heat, and with enough
rain to keep the woods and pastures green,
is attractive both climatically and visually.

In an Anglo-America in which level land
for farming is at present in surplus, the
problem of the highlands is to obtain the
capital, leadership, and skill to develop
the advantages that the hills have to offer,
and not to try to rival the plains. The highlands located centrally amid the more populous half of the nation are supplied with a
variety of raw materials. The resources are
not lacking: The problem is rather to develop the human resources and integrate
them into the national economy.

The preceding analysis is not intended to
suggest that the region is free from physical
handicaps (although those who have traveled in Austria and Switzerland may consider these handicaps modest compared
with those already overcome in European
mountain areas). No doubt upland farmers
do suffer from the small and disconnected

areas of level land and from the length of roads necessary to connect modest beeline distances. In the more isolated areas the economy suffers from the lack of know-how to develop resources, attract industry, and develop resort business. Help, however, has not been lacking: for example, from the TVA starting in 1933, area redevelopment programs, such state projects as the Kentucky Mountain Parkway and the West Virginia Turnpike, and numerous privately endowed educational projects. With all this help, the reversal of a regional downtrend has not been easy, especially where the residual population is above average in age, below average in education, and lacking in capital.

Appalachian history and culture In part the retardation of the uplands must be explained in terms of the past. Toward the end of the eighteenth century, the lowlands in the coastal states were largely held in large estates. Smaller farms were available but at a price the pioneer could not afford. A farm in the Appalachians with 10 or 20 acres of tillable land, plus the forest's game, nuts, berries, and timber resources, sufficed to provide a standard of living well above that of the European peasant. Indians were few in much of the highlands, and the Cherokees to the south, friendly at first, learned much about farming from the pioneers. The earliest settlers selected the areas with limestone soils, but the others were not dissatisfied with their poorer holdings. Markets were distant, but corn could be concentrated into whiskey, and livestock could be driven to market for ready cash. A conservative society with many folk arts developed among people who had infrequent contact with lands and peoples beyond their valleys and coves. Through routes traversed the Great Valley and crossed major gaps to the Piedmont and the Bluegrass, but there was no network of paved roads to serve the back country before 1930. The

railroads extended the length of the Great Valley before the Civil War, and a few north-south lines developed soon after, but some local lines into the coalfields were not completed until World War II. Railroads speeded up the exploitation of the forests and the coalfields. These developments attracted immigrants who added diversity to the Scotch-Irish and English strains. Negroes, however, remained few, and there was little of the planter aristocracy found elsewhere in the South. The settlement of the Ouachita and Ozark highlands occurred decades later but followed the same general pattern.

The decline of this area exemplifies the effects of changing technologies and a changing national economy. With the demand for coal stagnating, not expanding with the national economy, the coal produced (Table 8-3) was mined by strip or auger mining, both using mining machinery that required less labor per ton. Rural activities, such as farming and lumbering, generally are submarginal, being unable to compete with similar activities elsewhere. The region is especially uncompetitive in the various activities that account increasingly for the lion's share of the national income: manufacturing involving technical skills, urban services, and recreation. An attempt has been made to open parts of the area by constructing the West Virginia Turnpike, but the tolls from this venture have proved insufficient to retire the bond issue that financed it.

Appalachian Valleys and the TVA

Tremendous progress has occurred in the Great Valley and parallel Appalachian Valleys from the eastern West Virginia to Alabama. Between the Blue Ridge and the Allegheny Front, an area of folded sedimentary rocks provides easy routeways southwestward. Steepsided ridges divided this area into parallel valleys, the widest (the Great Valley) being on the southeast.

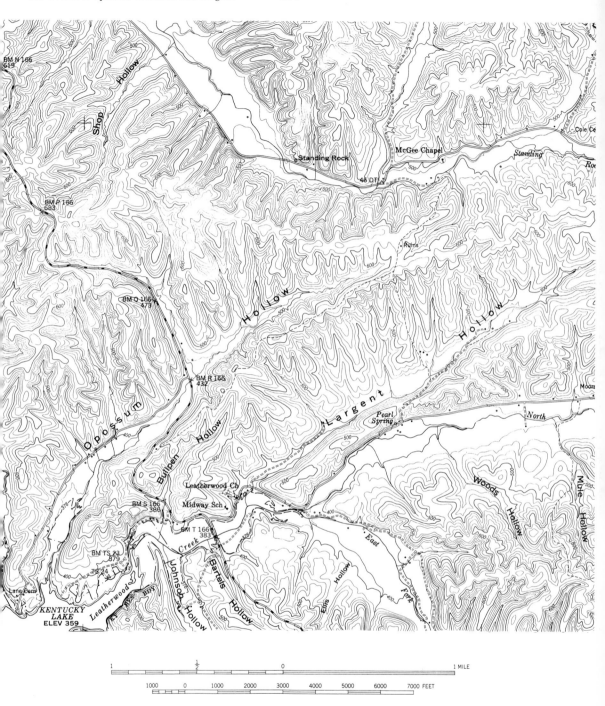

FIGURE 11-5   *This area in Stewart County, northern Tennessee, is adjacent to Kentucky Lake, created by the impounding of the lower Tennessee River by TVA. The map shows many of the characteristics of the poorer sections of Appalachia. The average income per household in this county is less than half that in Nashville; what basis is there for improving such low income?* (U.S. Geological Survey, Standing Rock, Tennessee, quadrangle.)

STRIP COAL MINING leaves mountain areas ugly and subject to erosion. The photo on the opposite page shows that something can be done about such scarred landscapes. (U.S. Department of Interior.)

These fertile valleys are formed on less resistant rock and many are drained by several streams. The many river gaps and some notches in the ridge tops provide narrow but relatively easy routes across the mountains on each side. Cities, such as Roanoke, Knoxville, and Chattanooga developed near each gap, are at junctions of valley routes with gap routes.

Although not isolated from the adjacent South, the Appalachian Valleys, at least as far south as Knoxville, were settled from the north. The wheat, corn, tobacco, hay, dairy products, and apples marketed there suggest a type of farming characteristic of southeastern Pennsylvania. Rich soils formed on limestone, ridges on indurated sandstone, and mediocre soils on shale characterize the land resource. Farming is mainly done by small farmers rather than planters, the rural and city populations are overwhelmingly white; facts that explain why many citizens of the southern

Appalachian Valleys were neutral or pro-Union during the Civil War.

Urban populations The valley population is mainly urban and rural non-farm, only 350,000 being classified as farm residents. Roanoke provides an example of the growth of the valley cities. Located strategically where the Roanoke River cuts a gap in the Blue Ridge, the town was unimportant until in 1882 the Norfolk and Western Railway established its western headquarters there, thence pushing its lines west into the Appalachian coalfields. Railroad shops and a junction with the Great Valley rail route stimulated further growth. Later, being in an area of declining rural population, Roanoke's modest wage level and labor surplus attracted industrialists producing such goods as textiles, furniture, and electric machinery. Labor surplus, cheap power, and low costs have also attracted a variety of industries to a cluster of small cities (Bristol,

AN APPALACHIAN AREA in Wise County, Virginia, three years after it was stripped and replanted shows that stripped land can be saved. (TVA.)

Johnson City, Kingsport, etc.) on the Virginia-Tennessee border, each producing relatively simple manufactures such as rayon, paper, furniture, and clothing—mostly based on local raw materials or cheap labor. These advantages are widely available in the region, but are only exploited where alert businessmen have integrated them so as to produce a marketable product.

Knoxville Another nodal center is Knoxville, metropolis of the upper Tennessee Valley, which was founded near a junction of the main tributaries of the Tennessee, developed later as a railroad junction, then as manufacturer of simple goods (especially clothing, furniture, and mine equipment), and as site of the University of Tennessee. Privately developed hydroelectric power was used by the Aluminum Company of America at nearby Alcoa to supply a huge aluminum-smelting plant. In the 1930s the Tennessee Valley Authority (TVA) established headquarters at Knoxville, and shortly afterward public power became available, being used in World War II for atomic energy production at Oak Ridge, 25 miles from the city. In contrast to most industries in the valley, Oak Ridge brought in a large proportion of highly trained scientists.

Chattanooga Southwest of Knoxville, the Tennessee leaves the Great Valley and enters a parallel valley in which lies the quite different city of Chattanooga, an industrial rather than political, commercial, and service center. During the Civil War this river port was the most strategic rail junction in the South. Large-scale textile manufacturing, based on cheap power and labor, boomed a half century later. Local wood produced raw material for woodworking industries and, in the last half century, for rayon factories. Nearby iron ore, coal, limestone, sulfur, and other minerals encouraged heavy industries, most of which today

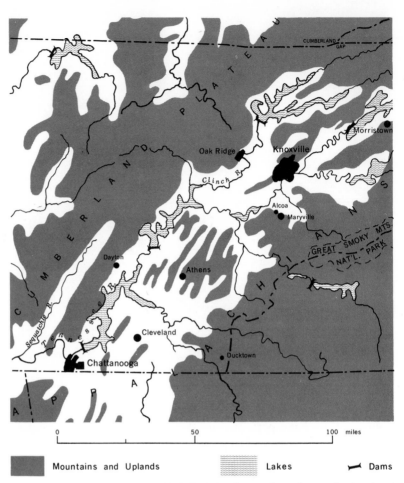

Mountains and Uplands   Lakes   Dams

FIGURE 11-6   The map shows the most developed area in the TVA project. Note that the valley here is subdivided by ridges and is by no means as flat as it appears on more generalized maps.

produce specialties such as stoves and pipe rather than basic iron and steel.

Birmingham   Although small iron industries had been established northward in the Great Valley earlier, the modern steel industry of northern Alabama is less than a century old. Birmingham, founded in 1871 by a railroad-backed land company, became a steel producer about a decade later. In few other places were coking coal, iron ore, and limestone so conveniently combined as in northern Alabama; all are mined within the Birmingham SMSA. The raw materials for cement, concrete, gypsum, and plaster are also available locally. Rail and road connections are excellent, but the Birmingham share of the Southern market for

heavy steel products is limited by competition from Baltimore and Pittsburgh, both of which use water transportation. The nearest port to Birmingham is at Birmingport, 20 miles from Birmingham on the 9-foot Black Warrior barge channel. Although its growth is attributed to the heavy industries Birmingham now obtains most of its income from commercial services for northern Alabama and by manufacturing diverse goods for the regional market (Figure 11-7).

The TVA   Industrial development in the Great Valley preceded the Tennessee Valley Authority by many decades; however,

TVA did stimulate further growth. Why was this valley chosen for a new experiment in American government? The Tennessee River, rising in the rainiest part of the Appalachians, was a major contributor of flood waters to the Ohio-Mississippi system. The river had been navigated during high water but its water levels had proved uncertain. Various local improvements, attempted over a period of a century, failed to solve the problems of shoals, floods, and low water. During World War I, the Muscle Shoals area of northern Alabama had been dammed to obtain power for nitrates. But a more comprehensive program was needed for flood control, navigation, and power development.

Revamping the river was no simple task: its headwaters originating in western Virginia, North Carolina, northern Georgia, and eastern Tennessee, converged on the Great Valley of southeastern Tennessee. Obviously a series of dams was needed to control the river, but these dams would flood the best farmlands, require locks for navigation, and could generate cheap power as a by-product. Obviously such a project was beyond the capacity of any state government or private company.

The Tennessee Valley Authority was authorized by Congress in May, 1933. In the following decade, it constructed 25 dams which converted the main stream and some tributaries into a chain of lakes (Figure 11-8); this created a 9-foot channel from Knoxville to the Ohio; the cheap power generated at the dams stimulated and modernized the valley economy, attracting so much activity that supplemental carbo-

electric plants have been necessary in recent decades to meet local power demands. TVA moved many farmers from the flooded lands, teaching them to use modern farm methods on their new lands to conserve the soil, and to plant forests on land unfit for tillage. All in all, it has been the greatest example of regional planning the world had seen, and it is not surprising that TVA aroused antagonism from private business, and was accused of "socialism," unfair competition, and worse by power and fuel producers. Whether these accusations were justified or not, it is now generally admitted that TVA has controlled floods, provided a needed waterway cheaply, and raised the regional level of living.

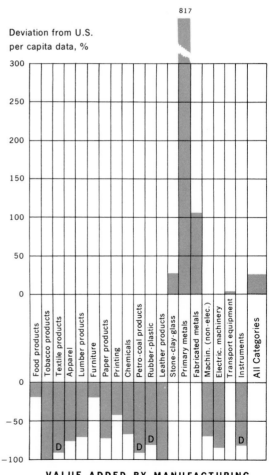

VALUE ADDED BY MANUFACTURING
Birmingham SMSA = .35% U.S. Pop.

FIGURE 11-7 Birmingham is sufficiently specialized in metals to make it above average in all categories, but its industry is well below the United States average in all but five categories. Although generally considered an industrial city, Birmingham is equally noteworthy as the major commercial and financial center for Alabama.

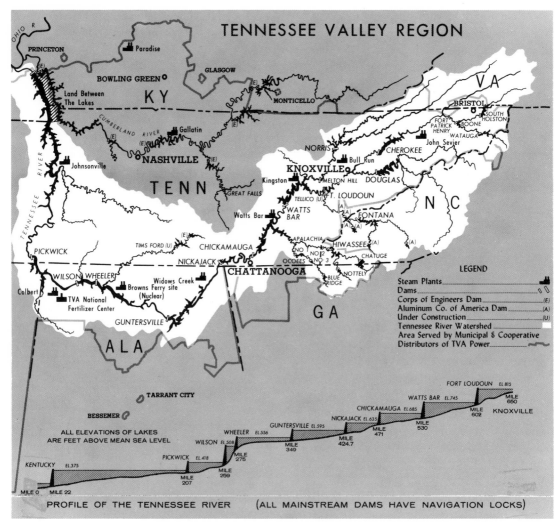

PROFILE OF THE TENNESSEE RIVER   (ALL MAINSTREAM DAMS HAVE NAVIGATION LOCKS)

FIGURE 11-8 *The Tennessee River rises in the rainier parts of the Appalachians and for this reason is a major contributor to Mississippi floods. The dams have converted much of the river into a series of lakes.* (TVA.)

The Tennessee River now provides a connecting link between the Ohio Valley and the interior South, shipping petroleum and grain upstream, coal and stone downstream. TVA has stimulated industrial centers already mentioned and caused the growth of smaller centers, most notably the missile center at Huntsville and the cluster of small industrial cities around Muscle Shoals, northern Alabama.

EAST OF THE GREAT VALLEY

The Blue Ridge and the Great Smokies

This tadpole-shaped area of rounded, wooded mountains, rising to over 5,000 feet, is largely a recreational area, with marginal farmlands in the valleys and on the lower slopes and widely scattered towns and small cities. Its resources are scenery and a mild but rainy climate, waterpower, lumber, and a few peripheral mineral deposits, most notably copper ore at Ducktown, Tennessee. The only metropolitan area is Asheville, the commercial metropolis for the southwestern North Carolina Piedmont, as well as a vacation and health resort.

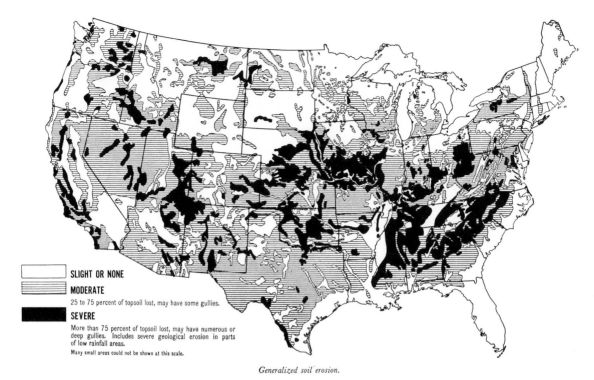

SLIGHT OR NONE

MODERATE
25 to 75 percent of topsoil lost, may have some gullies.

SEVERE
More than 75 percent of topsoil lost, may have numerous or deep gullies. Includes severe geological erosion in parts of low rainfall areas.
Many small areas could not be shown at this scale.

Generalized soil erosion.

FIGURE 11-9   Severe soil erosion is not limited to the Southeast, but with heavy, often torrential, rainfall and soil commonly unfrozen throughout the winter, it is not surprising that it is concentrated there. (USDA.)

The Southern Piedmont

The Piedmont stands out conspicuously on a map showing soil erosion (Figure 11-9). The region is not particularly high or hilly; it has rather the characteristics of an elevated plain which has been intricately dissected by streams. Its reddish soils, derived from quartz-rich crystalline rock, have had their sandy surface so eroded that the once underlying reddish clays now provide the characteristic surface soil.

Cotton, corn, forage crops, and oats are leading crops in the Piedmont, but their acreage is declining so that forest, pasture, and orchards are occupying an increasing share of the land. Many of the farmers entered the area from the North, and in contrast to the Southern plantation, the characteristic farm is small and owner-operated. The rural population is moderately dense, but full-time farming occupies only one-tenth of the population, most residents being classified as urban or rural non-farm. The larger cities tend to be within 40 miles of the mountains; many of the cities have a cluster of tributary industrial towns. On the population map the cities and towns form an irregular crescent from Raleigh, North Carolina, to Anderson, South Carolina, which is sometimes described as the "Piedmont Crescent of Industry" (Figure 11-10). Southeast of this crescent is an area of much sparser population which separates the interior Piedmont towns from the fall-line cities (to be discussed with the Coastal Plain). North and west of this crescent, other centers form industrial outliers.

Industrial growth   The industrial rise of the Piedmont during the present century has been attributed to such available local raw materials as wood, cotton, and tobacco, and to nearby coal and hydroelectric power. No doubt these have been advantageous, but generally the raw materials could have been

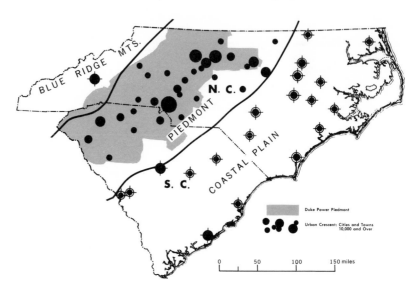

FIGURE 11-10   The Piedmont Crescent can be identified by the pattern of cities and less accurately by the area served by Duke Power. The relative size of the cities is suggested by the size of the dots. Cities outside the Piedmont have a cross and circle added to the dots. Does the pattern of these cities reflect the location of routes? (After a map by Duke Power Co.)

shipped to Northern markets as cheaply or more cheaply than could their products. Cheap, cooperative labor has been more important; even today among all states North Carolina ranked second only to Mississippi in low weekly earnings. True, low farm earnings account in part for this, but many farmers have already shifted to industrial work for modest wages which are low by standards elsewhere. Other attractions—less restrictive labor laws, moderate taxes, low land prices, newer and more modern factories and machinery—have been given credit by most economists for the southward migration of industry. At first the new industries were relatively simple: textiles, tobacco products, and furniture; in recent decades Piedmont industry has become increasingly diversified although textiles still account for half the industrial employment.

The Piedmont Industrial Crescent   The crescent-shaped area is commercially focused on Charlotte and Greensboro. Although it contains seven metropolitan areas, much of the industry is found in smaller cities and towns, and much of the industrial labor is rural non-farm. The industrial crescent is well connected by railroads and

by Interstate 85, locally nicknamed "the Textile Highway."

Several cities illustrate the variety and increasing maturity of industry in the crescent. Raleigh, once mainly a state capital and textile center, now also has woodworking and electrical industries. Durham, whose rise has been attributed to tobacco products, now employs more workers in textiles and food packing. The Greensboro–High Point SMSA has the greatest industrial employment; to the traditional food-packing, tobacco product, textile, and furniture industries have been added chemical, printing, fabricated metal, and machinery industries; neighboring Winston-Salem has experienced similar diversification. Charlotte, the most populous SMSA in the Carolinas, ranks only sixth in industrial employment, being more noted for regional sales offices and wholesaling and as a transportation center; its industries are highly diversified with nine major categories employing over 1,000

MANY CITIES ARE ATTEMPTING to reorganize their downtown sections to place businesses with similar functions together. This is a model for the rebuilding of the Greensboro, North Carolina, CBD. Notice the provision for parking on the rooftops. (Greensboro Chamber of Commerce.)

workers. Greenville is largely a textile city (20,000 out of 36,000 industrial workers are in textiles); nevertheless its textile-related activities are highly diversified, including clothing and textile machinery.

The boosters of the Piedmont Crescent have calculated that within a 600-mile radius live 71 percent of the nation's people, whereas only 45 percent live within the same radius of New York City. However, the mountain barrier to the west impedes access to about half of this area, and much of the market near the Carolinas has a per capita purchasing power below the national average. However, further industrialization may increase the local purchasing power since new industries are those offering more-skilled and higher-paid employment (Table 11-3) although the low-paying textile industry still dominates.

The Atlanta SMSA Atlanta is a latecomer among Southern cities, having been founded as a railroad town in 1836, destroyed by Sherman in 1864, and then re-

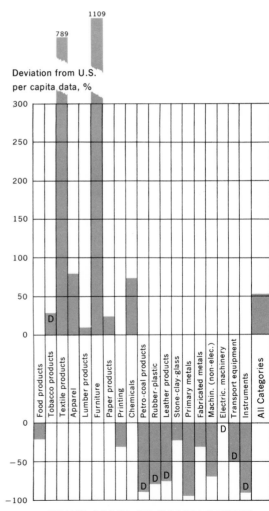

VALUE ADDED BY MANUFACTURING
Greensboro – High Point SMSA = .14% U.S. Pop.

FIGURE 11-11 The rise of the Carolina Piedmont as an industrial area resulted from a relatively few industries requiring cheap semiskilled labor. Greensboro–High Point SMSA has added a considerable variety of other industrial categories; smaller Piedmont towns would show much less diversification.

built to become the commercial hub of the Southeast. The city was strategically located at the southern tip of the Blue Ridge where a natural route extended north to the Great Valley at Chattanooga. At the time of the Civil War four railways connecting the South Atlantic area with the Gulf South passed through Atlanta. Today it remains the unchallenged rail, air, and highway crossroads of the Southeast, and its wholesale area includes at least the Georgia Piedmont while its financial and business services cover at least the area served by its Federal Reserve Bank with its branches at New Orleans, Birmingham, Nashville, and Jacksonville.

The five-county Atlanta SMSA, one of only three Southern SMSAs with over one million inhabitants, supports a variety of activities. Politically it serves the state, and its educational institutions serve a broader area. Its industries are highly diversified, being more related to Atlanta's function as a distributing center than to the traditional Piedmont industries. Of the 19 two-digit industrial categories used by the census, Atlanta is well represented in 15 (Figure 11-12). Atlanta's commercial and industrial services have brought in a generous income; it is surprising that an SMSA located in a state with below national average per capita income ranks twelfth among United States SMSAs in per household income, being ahead in this respect of New York, Baltimore, San Francisco, and Los Angeles. Atlanta and Georgia illustrate that the low economic averages of many parts of the South result from the combining of progressive cities with low-income rural areas.

THE OZARK-OUACHITA UPLANDS

Two hundred miles of Gulf Coastal Plain separates this subregion from the Appalachian area; yet the two separate sections

TABLE 11-3   Percentage Distribution of Industrial Employment in the Carolinas, 1950–1962

| | North Carolina | | South Carolina | |
	1950	1962	1950	1962
All Industries	100.0	100.0	100.0	100.0
Lumber and Wood	10.2	6.2	13.3	6.4
Furniture	7.8	8.6	0.9	1.4
Stone, Clay, Glass	1.6	2.0	1.8	2.8
Fabricated Metals	0.7	1.7	0.1	1.0
Machinery	1.4	7.4	1.1	4.8
Other Durable Goods	2.4	1.9	2.0	1.9
Subtotal: Durable Goods	24.1	27.8	18.2	18.3
Food and Kindred Products	4.7	6.7	4.8	4.6
Tobacco Manufactures	6.5	6.6		
Textile Mill Products	55.2	43.4	63.9	51.5
Apparel	3.2	7.4	5.8	13.1
Chemicals	2.3	2.8	2.3	5.8
Paper Products	1.9	2.7	2.7	3.4
Printing and Publishing	1.5	2.0	1.2	1.4
Other Nondurable Goods	1.8	0.7	1.9	1.9
Subtotal: Nondurable Goods	75.9	72.2	81.8	81.7

SOURCE: Federal Reserve Bank of Richmond, *North Carolina: An Economic Profile; South Carolina: An Economic Profile,* Richmond, 1964.

FROM THE BEGINNING ATLANTA has been a transportation hub, and it is hardly surprising that expressways, tracks, and parking lots are conspicuous in this view of a progressive Southern city. (Atlanta Chamber of Commerce.)

have so much in common that they should be analyzed together. The Ozark Plateau is the topographic counterpart of the Allegheny-Cumberland Plateau, but is less rugged and lacks its coal. Some coal is found in the Arkansas Valley whose relief resembles the Appalachian Valley of Tennessee, but the soils, in the western area, formed from sandstone rather than limestone, are fertile only on the narrow flood plains. South of the Arkansas Valley, the Ouachita Highlands rise less than 3,000 feet but contain areas almost as rugged as the Blue Ridge.

Like the Appalachian Uplands, the Ozark-Ouachita Upland is one of declining population with many isolated areas with submarginal land and peoples. The Arkansas Valley, traversed by several major highways and railroads, is above average for the region, but its commercial center, Fort Smith, lost population from 1950 to 1960, because the rural decline exceeded the modest growth in the central city, an industrial center specializing in furniture and small metal industries. The Ouachita Mountains are rimmed by coal on the northwest and bauxite deposits on the east, and there has been some resort growth around Hot Springs. But these resources did not offset rural decline, the population decreasing nearly one-eighth in the last decade. Like much of the Appalachians, this section seems suited to support a sparse population by forestry, cattle raising, and some resort business.

Little Rock In contrast to the Ozarks is the Little Rock SMSA which, like many major cities, is astride the regional boundary. Located in central Arkansas where routes from the Gulf Plain converge on the Arkansas Valley, it seems well located to be the state's capital and leading commercial center. Services, commercial, professional, and governmental, account for the majority of its employment; manufacturing is concentrated in industries related to local farming and lumbering, with some recent growth in small electronics industries. Unlike most of the rest of the state, Little Rock SMSA has a net in-migration, mostly from the surrounding countryside.

CONCLUSIONS

The Southern Uplands have a number of common problems: broad areas of mediocre soil made worse by leaching and erosion; rough-to-rolling relief which increases transport and construction costs; depleted resources (notably lumber and minerals) which are unable to support present populations; out-migration which has attracted many of the best workers cityward, especially toward the north. The nation has become so aware of these problems that a federal Appalachia program has been established to revitalize the area.

Not all of Appalachia is poverty-stricken. The Appalachian and Ozark plateaus and the Ouachita, Blue Ridge, and Great Smokies are largely problem areas. In the Appalachian Valleys the problems found are those of many rural regions—declining agricultural employment, out-migration, and the commercial and social consequences of these. There, however, the TVA has effectively stimulated activity—but most of the activity has been urban. In the Piedmont, there has been a rural transformation featuring contour terracing, tree crops, and livestock; these changes have not maintained rural employment, but regionally this has been offset by growth in the industrializing cities.

Although the problems of the present populations residual on submarginal lands cannot be overlooked, it may be economically better that these lands should be retired to such low-yield uses as forestry,

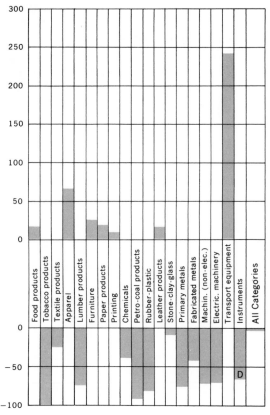

VALUE ADDED BY MANUFACTURING
Atlanta SMSA = .61% U.S. Pop.

FIGURE 11-12 In contrast to the Carolina Piedmont, Atlanta specializes more in consumer goods plus transportation equipment (aircraft and automobile assembly).

water control, and recreation, all suited to areas with rugged relief and mild humid climates. Investments of public and private capital could then be pinpointed on those areas with most promise—industrially and agriculturally. With an urban development in the Appalachian Valleys and the Piedmont comparable to that in the manufacturing belt, increasing demands for recreation and forest products might well solve the developmental problems of the adjacent rugged areas.

SELECTED REFERENCES

The three references preceded by an asterisk are also applicable to Chapters 12 to 14; they are old but still valuable.

ARKANSAS INDUSTRIAL DEVELOPMENT COMMISSION: *An Economic Atlas of Arkansas,* Little Rock, 1961.

BUREAU OF BUSINESS AND ECONOMIC RESEARCH: *The Carolina Economy,* University of South Carolina, Columbia, no date. One of the many pamphlets available from state agencies.

FEDERAL RESERVE BANK OF ATLANTA: Numerous publications including *Economic Characteristics of the Sixth Federal Reserve District,* Atlanta, 1963. (Revised every few years.)

FEDERAL RESERVE BANK OF RICHMOND: Numerous publications including *South Carolina: An Economic Profile,* 13, Richmond, 1964. Similar publications are available for West Virginia, Maryland, Virginia, and North Carolina.

FORD, THOMAS R. (ed.): *The Southern Appalachian Region: A Survey,* University of Kentucky Press, Lexington, 1962. A comprehensive study financed by the Ford Foundation.

KERSTEN, EARL W., JR.: "Changing Economy and Landscape in a Missouri Ozarks Area," *Annals A.A.G.,* vol. 48 (1958), pp. 398–418.

KYLE, JOHN H.: *The Building of the TVA,* Louisiana State University Press, Baton Rouge, 1958.

* MCLAUGHLIN, GLENN E., and STEFAN ROBOCK: *Why Industry Moves South,* National Planning Association, Washington, 1950.

* PARKINS, A. E.: *The South: Its Economic-Geographic Development,* Wiley, New York, 1938.

U.S. AREA REDEVELOPMENT ADMINISTRATION: Annual Report, Washington, 1962, and later years.

U.S. OFFICE OF BUSINESS ECONOMICS: *Growth Patterns in Employment by County: 1940–1950 and 1950–1960,* vol. 5, Washington, 1965.

* VANCE, R. B., and N. J. DEMERATH (eds.): *The Urban South,* University of North Carolina Press, Chapel Hill, 1954.

CHAPTER 12

SOILS AND DRAINAGE AND THE DEVELOPMENT OF THE SOUTHEASTERN PLAIN

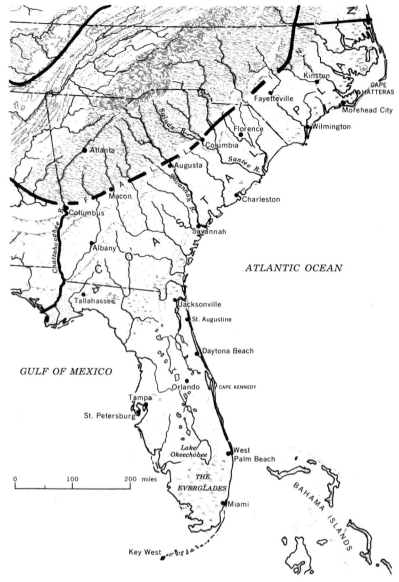

FIGURE 12-1 *The Southeastern Coastal Plain has been traditionally an area of water surplus with many swampy, marshy areas. Urbanization in SMSAs, especially in Florida, has locally changed the problem to one of water shortage.* (Base map copyright by A. K. Lobeck. Reprinted with permission of The Geographical Press, Hammond, Inc.)

Land-use patterns in the Southern Coastal Plain reflect interrelated soil and drainage conditions. This relationship is not limited to rural land use; the settlement pattern of many cities is related to drainage conditions, and much urban expansion has been preceded by artificial drainage. For convenience in treatment the Southern Plain has been divided into two regions: the Southeastern Plain including peninsular Florida, and the Gulf South centered on the Mississippi Valley. Both

BASIC DATA:

AREA INCLUDES	Land Area (thousand sq. mi.)	Population Change 1950-1960	1960 (thousands)	1967 (thousands)	Personal Income 1967 (billions)
SOUTHEASTERN					
PLAIN	127.6	29.2%	9,719	11,319	$28.4
North Carolina (part)	24.7	10.7	1,596	1,749	4.0
South Carolina (part)	20.3	15.0	1,423	1,522	3.1
Georgia (part)	36.5	14.5	1,792	1,908	5.2
Florida (part)	46.1	76.1	4,608	6,140	16.1
MAJOR SMSAS:					
Miami-Palm Beach	5.3	92.4%	1,497	1,895	$ 5.7
Tampa-St. Petersburg	1.3	88.8	772	930	2.5
Orlando	0.9	129.3	263	410	1.2
Jacksonville	0.8	49.8	455	550	1.7
Savannah	0.4	24.3	188	220	0.6
Charleston	0.9	31.3	255	305	0.7
Columbia	0.7	40.4	261	315	0.8

CLIMATE Humid subtropical to tropical in extreme south Florida.

	Temperature (°F) Jan.	July	Precipitation (inches) Annual	Season
Miami	67	82	60	Summer maximum
Jacksonville	56	83	53	Summer maximum
Charleston	50	81	40	Summer maximum
Raleigh	42	78	44	Slight summer maximum

VEGETATION Southern pine on better-drained land; cypress and marsh grass on poorly drained land; in Florida increasing proportion of palms southward on dry land, mangrove on swampy land.

SOIL Red-yellow podzolic soil, generally sandy or sandy loam; muck soils on poorly drained lands, former lagoons, and alluvium.

MINERALS Sand, limestone; phosphate in central Florida.

regions are subtropical in latitude, and this plus proximity to the sea ensures a mild, humid climate, often oppressive in summer and punctuated by occasional raw spells in winter.

The rather arbitrary dividing line, the Georgia-Alabama boundary and its southward continuation, the Appalachicola River in western Florida, is also the boundary between Eastern and Central Time. The two areas have much in common: extensive forests, swamps, and marshes; herds of cattle; and remnants of the plantation economy. The Southeastern Plain has more citrus fruit, tobacco, commercial vegetables, and resort activities. The Gulf South has more major mineral resources (petroleum, natural gas, salt, and sulfur), more fertile soils (alluvial and loessial), and more land in cotton, rice, and sugarcane. Both regions are commonly classified as being in the Cotton Belt, but the cotton fields are now relatively concentrated in the Mississippi Valley north of Vicksburg and on the Inner Coastal Plain.

SOIL AND RURAL PATTERNS IN THE SOUTHEAST

The relatively unconsolidated materials of the Southeastern Coastal Plain were formed mainly in or at the edge of the sea. In many areas seawater still infiltrates tidal marshes; elsewhere drainage conditions are greatly influenced by sea-laid terraces, underlying limestones formed from shells, and former sand dunes. Everywhere relief is slight, but even the small relief is significant because of drainage differences. Although sand is the prevailing constituent of the soil, locally the soil and drainage are greatly influenced by deposits of lagoon-formed clays and marls and by alluvium deposited by rivers originating on crystalline rocks inland.

In general, the cultivated soils of the Southeastern Plain are leached and especially lacking in phosphorus, nitrogen, lime, and humus. The soil remains unfrozen and unprotected throughout the winter; hence leaching and erosion continue all year. Many farmers, poor in both working capital and techniques, can harvest crops only at the expense of reducing their soil capital. One-quarter of all United States fertilizer is used in this region; more could profitably be applied. Although the long growing season and the generally humid weather aid crop growth, they also facilitate soil exhaustion and the multiplication of pests and plant diseases. To sum up, this region requires careful soil management, including possible drainage and supplementary irrigation, pest controls, and heavy fertilization

for successful farming; yet many farmers struggle along without such techniques.

Soil drainage and climatic differences obviously do not account for the present geography of Coastal Plain development. Demands for cotton, tobacco, peanuts, early vegetables, citrus fruit, phosphates, naval stores, timber, resort and retirement facilities, for example, as well as the position of the area in relation to the movements of peoples, have determined the timing of particular developments. Nevertheless, the localization of many of these activities (Figure 12-2) on the Coastal Plain can today be largely explained in terms of climate, soil, and drainage, even though the accidents of history and of local leaders should be considered in explaining the details of development. First, therefore, the physical framework of this flattish region (ranging from below mean sea level to about 300 feet) must be considered. The rural pattern is most conveniently described in soil belts which almost parallel the Atlantic Coast.

The Piedmont Edge

The innermost band is the southeastern edge of the Piedmont. Today the rolling red clay soils of the Piedmont Edge are less subject to erosion than in the past. Many of the streams, dammed up to form reservoirs, have reduced cutting power, and many sloping lands have been converted into woodland, peach orchards, pasture, or terraced fields. Adjacent to the Piedmont is a belt of once pine-clothed sand hills (in places rising higher than the adjacent Piedmont) which suffer from excessive soil drainage. In both areas the farms are irregular in size and shape and are being converted from cotton farming to diversified farming, yielding vegetables, fruit, dairy, and poultry products for fall-line cities. About three-fifths of the land is in commercial forest.

The Fall Line

Before roads and railroads were constructed, streams now considered too shallow for navigation were used to bring in immigrants and their supplies and to ship out the crops. The head of navigation was the edge of the Piedmont where falls or rapids blocked the streams. This fall line, where freight was transshipped, provided logical sites for inland commercial and political centers including Raleigh, Columbia, Augusta, Macon, Columbus, and Montgomery.

The Middle Coastal Plain

The typical soil is Norfolk, developed on gently rolling to slightly hilly topography from marine sands and clays. The surface soils, light colored and sandy, are underlain by reddish and yellowish layers of sands and clays. The open soil structure exposes it to leaching but also enables it to respond quickly to heavy fertilization. The natural vegetation is largely loblolly, longleaf, or slash pine; about half the land is in commercial forest.

On the Norfolk soils (the southward continuation of the sandy Sassafras soils of the Chesapeake Bay area), cotton and corn are common, and sweet potatoes and other subsistence crops are grown everywhere, at least for the local market. Areas with local specialties (which commonly extend into adjacent soil regions) are in North Carolina and southern Georgia, tobacco; in central Georgia, peaches; all across Georgia, peanuts and pecans; in South Carolina, truck crops.

Forest industries   The lumber industry (Figure 12-3) is conspicuous on the Coastal Plain; small commercial forests are common, and the well-labeled miles of forests owned by paper companies are even more noticeable. The long growing season matures pulpwood in a decade whereas saw

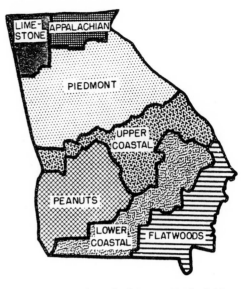

FIGURE 12-2   The Federal Reserve Bank of Atlanta divides Georgia into agricultural regions whose extent reflects largely the distribution of underlying rock, soil, or drainage conditions. (Federal Reserve Bank of Atlanta.)

timber takes two or three times as long. Used first for its naval stores (turpentine, pitch, and tar), then for cheap timber and as a raw material for making corrugated board and wrapping paper, southern pine now, thanks to modern chemistry, can be used for newsprint and other paper; indeed Southern forests are now the major producer of United States pulpwood. In many areas, forests also serve as recreation, grazing, and water-control areas.

The forest industries provide the manufactures for the relatively few cities in the Middle Coastal Plain. Lumber and woodworking, pulp and paper, naval stores, chemicals, and a few textile plants have caused cities such as Albany, Georgia, and Sumter, South Carolina, to become more than local agricultural centers. These industrial developments have been small; the growth of these cities has not offset rural out-migration, and not enough new jobs have been created to absorb the natural increase of population.

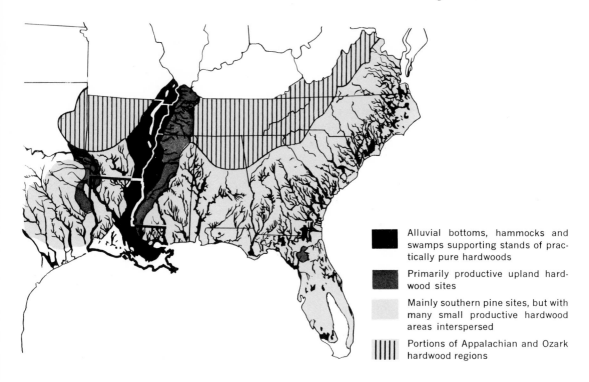

Alluvial bottoms, hammocks and swamps supporting stands of practically pure hardwoods

Primarily productive upland hardwood sites

Mainly southern pine sites, but with many small productive hardwood areas interspersed

Portions of Appalachian and Ozark hardwood regions

FIGURE 12-3   This map of the lumber resources of the South also serves to locate the alluvial areas and the Southern Uplands. Can you locate the fall line? (American Forest Products Industries, Inc.)

The Coastal Fringe

The coast is almost everywhere bordered by fringing bars and spits, backed by broad sounds, lagoons, tidal marshes, and swamps. The offshore bars have formed islands wide enough to be the sites of substantial resort cities: for example, Daytona Beach and Miami Beach. These sandy strips, formed by alongshore currents, may be 100 miles long, as in eastern Florida and on each side of Cape Hatteras where the fringing island is broken only by scattered inlets. Elsewhere, as in southwest Florida and the Sea Islands of Georgia and South Carolina, roughly oval islands make up the offshore barrier. The soil is either sands or in lagoons and near river mouths, peat and muck. The vegetation varies from southern pine (with some palmettos or palms south of Charleston) on the relatively dry land to marsh grass or cypress on the wet lands (mangrove in southern Florida). Almost every part of the coast has inlets adequate for small

boats; the larger river mouths and indentations have located the major ports. Inland the almost continuous line of lagoons and marshes made it relatively easy to construct the Intracoastal Waterway which extends the length of the Atlantic Coast and which shortly will connect across northern Florida with the Gulf of Mexico portion of a similar waterway.

The Flatwoods   The inner edge of the coastal fringe is known as the "Flatwoods." Its soil and drainage conditions are highly diversified, but extensive marshes and swamps appear mixed with infertile sandy areas, and some areas of good alluvial and muck soil. On this Flatwoods subregion, pines occupy the better-drained soils, and cypress the swampy soils, and there are scattered

BEAUFORT COUNTY, on one of the moister portions of the Coastal Plain of North Carolina, is cultivatable only because of an elaborate network of ditches and tile lines. Note the undrained and partly drained land to the right. (USDA photograph.)

areas of marsh grass and almost barren coastal dunes.

Too much water is the common problem. Although there is much good cropland in eastern South Carolina and southeastern North Carolina, on the whole only one-quarter of the land is cropped. Many of the old plantations which once raised rice and indigo on diked alluvial soils have gone out of cultivation, leaving the lumber industry to dominate the countryside with some supplementary income from resorts and fishing along the coast. The naval stores industry, once outstanding in the Carolinas, has now migrated to the newer lands of Georgia and northern Florida. Paper mills, rayon mills, and woodworking establishments occupy the towns. Farms producing corn, cotton, livestock, and truck crops are generally small except in the northern Flatwoods.

The rural Florida peninsula South of Jacksonville palms become common rather than rare; soils and land use change: the land and people gradually take on a new character. The peninsula, everywhere underlain by limestone and covered locally by sands or muck, rises at most to 200 feet. Five feet change in level is considered significant, and very modest relief has given rise to an

intricate system of two layers of underground fresh water upon which Florida depends. The Central Upland, underlain by slightly uparched limestone, collects much of the subsoil water which feeds the St. Johns River, Lake Okeechobee, and the Florida Everglades. So much water for domestic use has been pumped from these fresh water reservoirs that in some coastal areas salt water has invaded the underground reserves.

To the delicate balance of peninsular water must be added considerable variations in soil as well as minor but significant variations in climate. The long growing season justifies the clearing, cultivation, and intensive fertilization of infertile sands to produce berries, potatoes, and early vegetables. Nevertheless much of the land remains in pine forest. The exposed limestone in the slightly higher central upland forms a sandy, easily worked soil which is used for tobacco and general farming in northern Florida and for citrus fruits in the central peninsula.

In southern and central Florida, there are many sandy and limey areas, commonly rather marshy, whose lush grasses growing all year support huge herds of beef and dairy cattle. With proper drainage, these generally warm lands can be cultivated and, in extreme southeastern Florida, are used for tropical fruits and winter vegetables.

The interior of southern Florida consists of swamp, marsh, and bottomlands: muckland and peat lands south of Lake Okeechobee, and sandy lands in the Big Cypress Swamp to the southwest. How much of this land should be cultivated depends on the desirability of preserving wildlife and a wilderness national park, the cost of drainage, and the demand for its potential produce. At present, aside from scattered plots and some grazing, the main development is around and south of Lake Okeechobee where sugarcane and winter vegetables are dominant crops.

SETTLEMENT

Much of the Southeastern Plain was well settled by 1820. The demand for naval stores, tobacco, rice, and indigo, and later the ballooning demand for cotton spurred the extension of the plantations. Since it was believed that white labor could not do field work in the hot humid growing season, Negro slavery became so widespread that Negroes predominated in many counties. A white aristocracy developed a high degree of culture whose physical evidences still stand in fine town houses in Charleston and Savannah and planters' homes throughout the cotton area. After 1820 a migration set in—southward into northern Florida, and westward into the Gulf South. In part this represented normal frontier expansion; in part it reflected the abandonment of exhausted fields.

The above settlement pattern scarcely affected central and southern Florida which for half a century was commonly believed to be worthless swamp. Indeed the peninsula was too damp for cotton, then the dominant Southern cash crop. The citrus boom started in central Florida in the 1880s, and the railroad reached Tampa in 1884,

Miami in 1896. The Florida peninsula had little inheritance from Negro slavery, and today Negroes make up only 10 to 20 percent of the population. Many of the recent settlers in the peninsula are from the North so that the social atmosphere is clearly different than elsewhere on the Coastal Plain.

In settlement history, the Coastal Plain (except for the Florida peninsula) has much in common with the Plains states. With the relative decline of agriculture and its increased mechanization, rural population declined and the cities proved unable to absorb the surplus. The Negroes especially moved North to the industrial cities. Grazing, forestry, and fruits increasingly replaced crops with high labor requirements; it is possible today to drive for days in the Coastal Plain without seeing a cotton field.

Meanwhile the Coastal Plain was slow to develop industrially. Its manufactures during the last century were largely the processing of lumber, naval stores, cotton, and tobacco, or of imported materials mixed to provide fertilizers and other local needs. Such industries required little labor, and that labor needed to be only semiskilled. In recent decades, the picture has brightened: Migration to Florida (and to retirement areas northward) brought in new consumers. Industrialists have realized the advantages of modern, uncrowded factories on cheap land with year-round outdoor climates. The government has established numerous military bases and scientific stations (e.g., at Cape Kennedy). Consequently dormant cities have grown, and classic Southern mansions may be overshadowed by skyscrapers and factories.

EMPLOYMENT AND INCOME

A basic Southeastern problem has been the low level of living. Florida, the most prosperous state, had in 1960 a median family income $938 below that of the United States; in South Carolina, the same figure

THE LAKE DISTRICT of central Florida, pictured here southeast of Winter Haven, is a leading orange and grapefruit area. The climate characterized by adequate rainfall is almost frost-free; as a rule the occasional winter night frosts are not severe enough to damage the groves. Temperatures are moderated by the many lakes formed by solution in the limestone rock underlying the sandy soil. (USDA photograph.)

is $1,839 below the United States median. An examination of census data shows that there is considerable variation from one State Economic Area to another, and, in a single SEA, among urban, rural non-farm, and farm populations, and between white and nonwhite workers.[1] The highest median family incomes are in the Florida peninsula and in the urbanized areas throughout the region. Median incomes are lowest in the Middle Coastal Plain where urbanization is least advanced. In every area the median income for nonwhite males is sharply below

that for white males, for nonwhite females lower than all other groups.

The industrial distribution of employment is also significant. The areas with a high percentage of agricultural employment are low-income areas. In only two SEAs does agricultural employment exceed one-fifth of the total, whereas in 1950 about two-fifths of the workers were agricultural in all the Middle Coastal Plain areas. Everywhere the proportion in agricultural employment is declining. Manufacturing employment is predominantly in nondurable goods (except in a few areas with wood industries and in Florida around Cape Kennedy). In most areas commercial and service activities account for over half of all

[1] These data are conveniently arranged by State Economic Areas in U.S. Bureau of the Census, *Census of Population: 1960, Selected Area Reports, State Economic Areas*, Final report PC(3)-1A, Washington, 1963.

TABLE 12-1 Percentage Distribution of Employment by Industry: United States and Southern Florida, 1960

| Industry | United States | South Florida SEAs[1] | | | | South Florida SMSAs | |
		4	5	6	Orlando	St. Petersburg– Tampa	Miami– Palm Beach
Agriculture, Forestry, Fishing	6.5	7.3	15.0	10.7	8.1	3.6	4.9
Construction	6.0	10.3	8.7	12.4	10.6	10.1	8.4
Manufacturing:							
Durable Goods	15.2	11.6	4.2	4.1	10.3	6.8	5.3
Nondurable Goods	11.9	3.4	8.1	4.5	5.7	8.6	5.3
Transport, etc.	7.0	4.8	5.4	4.9	5.4	7.0	8.9
Trade	18.1	21.4	21.6	22.1	21.6	20.5	22.3
All Others	35.3	41.4	37.0	41.3	38.3	43.4	44.8
Total	100.0	100.0	100.0	100.0	100.0	100.0	100.0

[1] Florida SEA 4 is the Indian River Area; 5, the Central Florida Citrus Area; and 6, the South Florida Non-metropolitan Resorts Area.

SOURCE: Calculated from *County and City Data Book: 1962*, Washington, 1962.

employment. In a boom area such as the Florida peninsula with a strong emphasis on retirement and tourism, the demands for construction and other services are especially significant (Table 12-1).

NON-FARM OCCUPANCE

A general principle in land economics is: when land is equally suited for several uses, the most intensive use of the land pushes out the less intensive uses. In the Southeast as elsewhere in the United States, urban and urban-related uses take precedence over farming, ranching, and forestry; furthermore when urban development creates demands for rural products and services, specific rural occupance is distributed in relation to cities, providing them with dairy products and other bulky or perishable foodstuffs.

The pattern of urban distribution in this subregion differs from north to south. North of the Florida peninsula the cities and towns were originally seaports or local political centers and commercial centers. In recent decades many of these have added industrial and other functions. In the Florida peninsula (Figure 12-4) the early towns were mostly at first military posts, then resort and retirement centers, and development as agricultural, industrial, and metropolitan centers came much later, if at all.

The Miami–Palm Beach Megalopolis

Developed largely in recent decades, three SMSAs with a 1960 population of nearly 1.5 million form an almost continuous urbanized area about 5 miles wide extending 90 miles from north to south. The offshore bar has been settled mainly for resort and residential use. Behind the bar, a lagoon (or at least the Intracoastal Waterway) separates the resort area from the business and industrial portions of the megalopolis. Resort activities are not lacking west of the lagoon but tend to be concentrated along the waterways and along the north-south highways. The sandy area extending about 5 to 10 miles west of the urbanized area is devoted to dairying and other farm activities supplying the coastal cities. Westward the marshy or swampy Everglades repre-

FIGURE 12-4 Regional characteristics of the Florida peninsula. Although the peninsula is flattish, it has considerable variety in land use arising from small differences in drainage and temperature conditions.

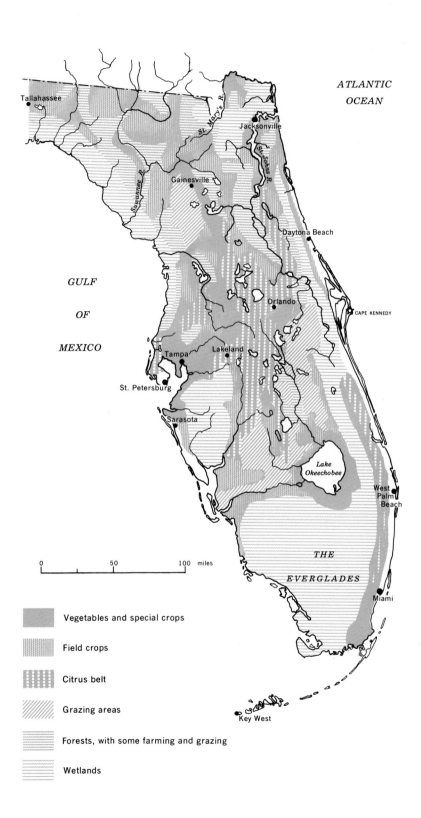

ON THE DRAINED MUCK SOILS of southern Florida, winter vegetables are a valuable crop, harvested with the latest machinery. This celery harvester travels 5 to 6 feet a minute, permitting the harvesting of 24 rows of celery. The machine and its crew cut, trim, wash, sort, and pack the celery in crates before it leaves the harvesting area. (USDA photograph.)

sent an almost uninhabited area except around Lake Okeechobee whose artificially drained muck shores provide the basis for a year-round agriculture.

The oldest city in the area is Fort Lauderdale, founded in 1837. Its seaport, Port Everglades, capable of handling most ocean shipping and by far the busiest port in southeastern Florida, receives petroleum, cement, and other raw materials not available on the peninsula.

To the north is stylish Palm Beach (on the offshore bar) and, across the lagoon, West Palm Beach. The development of this area began in 1892 with the construction of the Florida East Coast Railroad. Palm Beach is known for its palatial hotels, mansions, and large waterfront estates. West Palm Beach contains the county seat, the CBD, and a light manufacturing area.

The most populous SMSA is Miami with its satellite cities, Miami Beach on the bar, and to the south, Coral Gables, fronting on Biscayne Bay. Until the arrival of the railroad in 1896, the only settlement was a small Indian trading post. Rapid development began in the 1920s, and Miami soon became known as a resort center with accommodations to fit modest as well as deluxe budgets. At the same time Miami became the wholesale and banking center for the largely swampy area south and east of Lake Okeechobee.

The coming of the Air Age changed Miami from a peripheral to a central location. Miami International Airport became the focal point where air routes from Anglo-America connected with air routes from Mexico, Central America, the West Indies, and South America. With the rise of Castro, Miami became the destination of boat and plane loads of Cuban refugees; downtown Miami has become almost as Latin as it had been Anglo-Saxon.

Meanwhile Northerners had discovered Florida as a place to retire or even to seek employment. The population of southern Florida became more Northern and Cuban than Southern; Negroes make up less than one-fifth of the populace. On Lincoln Road, the main shopping street of Miami Beach, New York accents predominate in the tourist season; indeed Miami Beach resembles Atlantic City (plus palms). To serve more permanent residents, real estate promoters first laid out the sandy areas and then ditched the swampy areas, piling up the dredgings from the channels to provide each house with a dry site adjacent to its own boat landing. There and northward real estate offers were diverse: large lots or small? oceanfront, bay front, lagoon, lakefront or in a completely dry area? modest houses or swanky houses? houses for retirement or near jobs? houses near entertainment centers or on quiet side streets?—

everything was available for a price below comparable offerings in Northern cities.

All this construction and the needs of consumers required a multitude of goods and services—often goods especially designed for warm weather living: tropical furniture, sports clothes, packed foods, boats, fishing tackle, sporting equipment, and, of course, building supplies. Note the specialization of the Miami SMSA in Figure 12-5. Growth pyramided, and Miami, with only 5,471 in 1910, and 172,000 in 1940, had over 1 million in its SMSA in 1965, and the population of the Miami–Palm Beach megalopolis has reached nearly 2 million.

Tampa Bay and the West Central Peninsula

Well-sheltered Tampa Bay adjoined by much well-drained land would seem to have been an ideal place for settlement; yet Tampa had only 720 people in 1880. The coming of the railroad in 1884, combined with the orange boom and transfer of the cigar industry from Key West to Tampa, converted the village into a city. Its seaport was used to embark troops for the invasion of Cuba in 1898. In contrast to Miami, Tampa became primarily a commercial and industrial rather than resort city. Its major industry is food packing; rivals for second position are cigar-making and agricultural chemicals, the latter based on huge phosphate deposits east of the bay. Its port, the busiest in Florida, imports a variety of raw materials, especially petroleum and fertilizer materials for the chemical industries.

Although Tampa's resort and residential attractions are less important than its industry, the same is not true in much of its

FIGURE 12-5 Most of the workers in the Miami SMSA are there to provide services, not industrial labor. The single above-average category produces specialized furniture suited to an almost tropical environment.

trading area. West of the bay, St. Petersburg is noted for its large proportion of old people who can enjoy an inexpensive retirement there. More luxurious are many of the residences around Sarasota, 30 miles south of Tampa, and Lakeland, the same distance east of Tampa, is the gateway to a cluster of conservative residential towns in the lake and citrus area of central Florida.

Orlando and Its Trading Area

The first railroad to Tampa reached Orlando several years earlier, causing a citrus development in Orange County. Orlando, much less populous than the Tampa and Miami SMSAs, is nevertheless the largest city between Jacksonville and Fort Lauderdale. Attractively located amid several dozen lakes, large and small, it is an important junction for expressways and railroads. Until recently its trading area depended largely on citrus, retirement residences, and resorts, but the rise of the Cape Kennedy space center to the east has added numerous electronic, missile, and instrument industries to the older food-packing and consumer goods industries.

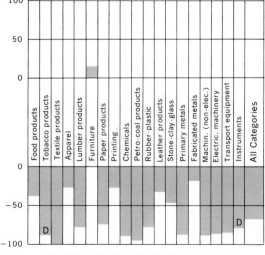

VALUE ADDED BY MANUFACTURING
Miami SMSA = .57% U.S. Pop.

FLORIDA HOMES FOR RETIRED people and others are available on all levels. At Ormond Beach the offshore bar provides level sites for a multitude of reasonably priced, standardized homes, each with access to boating, swimming, and fishing, as well as pleasant breezes. (Florida Development Commission.)

The Empty Spaces

Much of Florida—and indeed of the entire Coastal Plain—is lacking in population. The traveler passes rapidly from developed areas to marsh, pine forest, or extensive pasture. This almost deserted land has not been entirely disadvantageous: it has provided space for huge military bases and other government reservations, for paper company forests, for fishermen, and for the grazing of cattle. The empty area is especially conspicuous across the northern peninsula where it separates the commercial area of Jacksonville from the more tropical parts of Florida. There a Cross-Florida Barge Canal is being constructed which will connect the Atlantic Intercoastal Waterway and the St. Johns River with the Gulf of Mexico, encouraging in northern Florida, its promoters hope, industries using raw materials to be barged from the Texas-Louisiana Gulf Coast.

Jacksonville and Its Trading Area

Jacksonville is the southernmost of a number of ports which serve a moderately well-settled Coastal Plain characterized by few

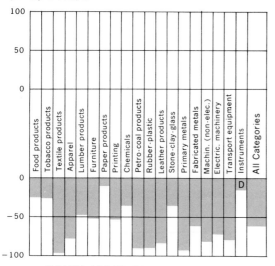

Deviation from U.S. per capita data, %

VALUE ADDED BY MANUFACTURING
Florida = 3.04% U.S. Pop.

FIGURE 12-6   Except in a few details, this graph resembles that for Miami. The negative deviations may be partly accounted for by the fact that Florida has 12 percent more people over 65 than the national average. What are other possible explanations?

large cities. Before the growth of an effi-cient rail and highway net, these inland areas depended on steamer and barge traffic on streams, now little used for this purpose; earlier Jacksonville and other river-mouth ports were major points of contact with the outside world. Later, road and railroad nets focused on the established ports and Jacksonville became the major commercial and banking center for all Florida (except the western panhandle) and for extreme southern Georgia.

Jacksonville was founded on the St. Johns Estuary, 20 miles east of the Atlantic, where the estuary turns abruptly southward. Its channel, dredged to 34 feet, is adequate for most ocean shipping and the port for a century and a half has shipped lumber and other naval stores as well as regional crops. Manufacturing is largely concerned with the processing of local raw materials (food products, wood products including paper), the processing of imports for regional markets (agricultural chemicals), with transportation equipment (ships), or with materials for local construction (concrete, metal parts). The metropolis, much more commercial than industrial, by use of efficient express-ways and distributing services facilitates the flow of people and goods to and from the peninsula. Resort business is modest, but many tourists pass through Jacksonville en route to the more tropical southern peninsula.

Although the Jacksonville trading area is noted for its lumber, tobacco, peanuts, and cattle, these raw materials contribute only about one-twentieth of the regional income. Trade and government each account for one-sixth of the income, manufacturing for one-ninth, service and miscellaneous for one-third. Aside from Jacksonville, the only

cities of any size in this region not already mentioned are Gainesville (University of Florida and light industry), Tallahassee (the capital of Florida), and Albany, Georgia, a food-packing and textile center.

Savannah and Its Trading Area

This long-established but smaller city is in many ways the Georgia counterpart of Jacksonville. Fifteen miles inland on a low bluff overlooking the 34-foot Savannah River channel, Savannah's docks line the river from 3 miles below to 7 miles above the city. Freighters calling there can load directly from rail and highway vehicles modest exports of cotton, lumber, and naval stores and unload heavier imports of petroleum, gypsum, sugar, fertilizer, and other raw materials. The major industries are food products, chemicals, and wood and paper products. An adjoining air base and the Savannah River Atomic Energy Plant upstream provide government income.

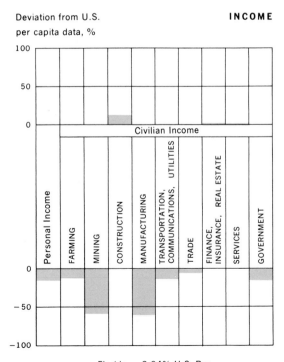

FIGURE 12-7 The above-average-construction bar suggests an expanding economy. How might you explain the length and direction of each of the other bars?

THE SAVANNAH RIVER offers port sites cut into the pine forest, each with deepwater docking, inland connections, warehousing, and necessary space for industrial processing. (Savannah District Authority.)

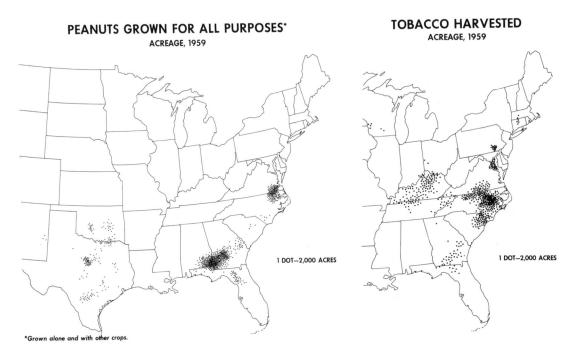

PEANUTS GROWN FOR ALL PURPOSES*
ACREAGE, 1959

1 DOT—2,000 ACRES

*Grown alone and with other crops.

TOBACCO HARVESTED
ACREAGE, 1959

1 DOT—2,000 ACRES

FIGURE 12-8   Do the peanut areas overlap the tobacco areas? Is tobacco exclusively a subtropical crop? Is there any relationship between tobacco growing and tobacco manufacturing? (Bureau of the Census.)

Savannah is more dependent than Jacksonville on industry and less dependent on government and transportation.

The Savannah trading area extends into central Georgia to the edge of the Piedmont, including three growing fall-line cities, Augusta, Macon, and Columbus, all of which also have major commercial bonds with Atlanta. These four SMSAs account for more than half the income of the trading area. Indeed the nonmetropolitan portions of the area generally have declining populations with rural activities shifting to larger farms using either mechanized agriculture or placing emphasis on livestock and tree farming. Augusta, at the head of barge navigation on the Savannah River, was primarily a textile city; recently government employment (at Camp Gordon and the Atomic Energy Plant) has taken first place. Macon, a textile, paper products, peach-marketing city, now has one-third of its urban workers employed on military projects. On the navigable Chattahoochee, Columbus, also a long-established textile and food products town, receives a major portion of its income from Fort Benning and its infantry school. In Georgia, where nearly one-fourth of all personal income originated from government sources (three-fourths of this from the federal government), government activity is becoming more important than agriculture in accounting for the distribution of people and business.

Charleston and Its Trading Area

In few American cities is the visitor so aware of the influence of the past as in downtown Charleston; on a tongue of land between the Ashley and Cooper estuaries, facing on a spacious bay guarded by the ruins of Fort Sumter, the pastel-colored houses of the antebellum and colonial periods have been charmingly maintained.[2]

The modern industries of Charleston, almost duplicates of those of Savannah, are further up the estuaries. There elevated expressways bring modern traffic to the busy modern port, industrial center, and naval and air bases. One expressway connects Charleston with Columbia, Greenville, and Spartansburg, South Carolina. Charleston business connections are inland and northward toward Charlotte and Richmond. The nonmetropolitan Coastal Plain areas, specializing in tree farming, cotton, tobacco, and vegetables, are only of modest importance to Charleston. A few small cities have more income than nearby rural counties; thus the largest, Florence, has 26,000 people but draws on the 87,000 people in Florence County for labor. Its many small industries, ranging from textiles to electronics, enable the county to earn $172 million, thus providing a median income nearly twice that of adjacent Calhoun, an agricultural Coastal Plain county.

Columbia   The fall-line city of Columbia, the state capital, is as populous and productive as Charleston. Its textile and other industries are modest; the city is primarily a governmental, commercial, and transportation center. The Saluda River, dammed to create a huge reservoir, provides power for the city.

---

[2] *Were the Low-Country plantation owner of the late 19th century to revisit South Carolina today, he would find broad fields planted in cotton and tobacco just as they were long ago, for farming is still a major business. But few other aspects of present-day social and economic life even remotely resemble those of his day. He could recapture a feeling of being in the state he knew by strolling down the avenue of oaks at Boone Hall Plantation or spending an afternoon in the formal gardens at Middleton Place, but he would have the company of vacationers who come from near and far to visit the many places reminiscent of the Old South which are still a part of the South Carolina scene. Quiet communities in the Piedmont where he used to take his family when summer brought hot, humid days to the Coastal Plain have been transformed into bustling manufacturing centers. Whereas cotton and tobacco were once the principal commodities loaded on ships bound for foreign markets, the range of export products handled by the state's ports has been broadened to include such diverse items as soybeans, peaches, lumber, wood pulp, paper, textiles, and clay products.*
Federal Reserve Bank of Richmond, SOUTH CAROLINA: AN ECONOMIC PROFILE, Richmond, 1964, p. 62.

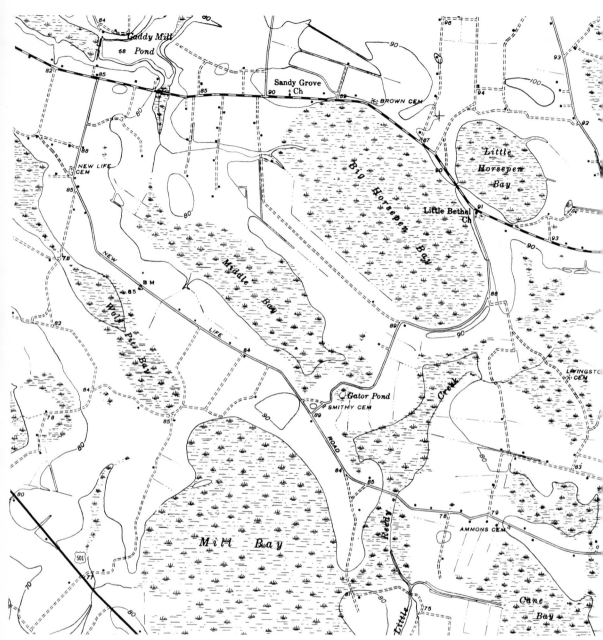

FIGURE 12-9 Extensive parts of the Carolina Coastal Plain are characterized by somewhat elliptical swamps and ponds, locally called "bays." The map has been reduced so that each inch represents one-half mile. Houses are represented by black dots. How many houses are on this map per square mile? (U.S. Geological Survey, Mullins, South Carolina, quadrangle.)

The Small Cities of the North Carolina Coastal Plain

When ships were smaller, North Carolina ports were of considerable significance, but their business has been modest compared with nearby Hampton Roads and Charleston. Northeastern North Carolina is separated from the sea by bars, shallow sounds, and extensive swamps. The ports of North Carolina are awkward to approach (Wilmington is 30 miles upriver), and much of the 5 million tons handled through Wilmington and Morehead City is coastwise or local. Over five-sixths of North Carolina exports by value are shipped through out-of-state ports, especially Norfolk.

The port of Wilmington has only 44,000 population; Morehead City has less than 10,000. The channels are as deep as at Charleston, the facilities are smaller but as modern; at Wilmington there is an industrialization that resembles Charleston in type if not in size. The major receipt has been petroleum; the major exports wood pulp and tobacco. North Carolina cotton, formerly shipped there, is now manufactured entirely within the state.

The agriculture of the North Carolina Coastal Plain continues productive with

major emphasis on flue-cured tobacco. Income rather than population growth has resulted from the industrialization of a dozen or more small cities, for example, Fayetteville (textiles, furniture, lumber). The only metropolitan area, Raleigh, is tied more closely with the Piedmont Industrial Crescent than with the Coastal Plain.

The Business and Growth of Coastal Plain Cities

John Fraser Hart in a study[3] based on census data for 1950 shows that the Coastal Plain cities were relatively wide spaced with

[3] "Functions and Occupational Structures of Cities of the American South," *Annals A.A.G.*, vol. 45 (1955), pp. 269-286.

TABLE 12-2   Employment Growth for SMSAs and Representative Smaller Cities in the Southeastern Plain, 1950-1960[1]

SMSA or City	Employment (in thousands) 1950	1960	Industries with Strong Gain
COASTAL:			
Miami	202	366	Food, printing, transportation, services, government
Fort Lauderdale	32	117	Food, chemicals, electrical, transportation, trade, services, government
Tampa–St. Petersburg	149	261	Food, printing, chemicals, electrical, trucking, services, government
Jacksonville	123	176	Food, electrical, trucking, finance, services
Savannah	57	68	Chemicals, finance, government, Armed Forces
Charleston	59	77	Services, government, Armed Forces
Wilmington	30	32	Miscellaneous manufactures, government, Armed Forces
FALL LINE:			
Columbus	60	81	Food, electrical, government
Macon	53	69	Food, printing, vehicles, trucking
Augusta	65	82	Government, Armed Forces
Columbia	69	102	Food, finance, services, government, Armed Forces
Raleigh	52	64	Electrical, trucking, government
OTHER:			
Tallahassee	19	29	Food, printing, finance, services, government
Albany	18	29	Food, miscellaneous manufacturing, government, Armed Forces
Fayetteville	43	60	Food, miscellaneous manufacturing, government
West Palm Beach	50	88	Food, miscellaneous manufacturing, trucking, finance, services, government
Orlando	54	118	Food, electrical, miscellaneous manufacturing, trucking, finance, services, government

[1] Data for smaller cities include all the county in which each is located.

SOURCE: U.S. Office of Business Economics, *Growth Patterns in Employment by County: 1940–1950 and 1950–1960*, vol. 5, *Southeast*, Washington, 1965.

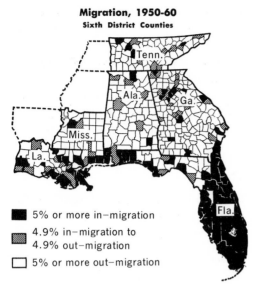

Migration, 1950-60
Sixth District Counties

- ■ 5% or more in–migration
- ▨ 4.9% in–migration to 4.9% out–migration
- ☐ 5% or more out–migration

FIGURE 12-10　Compare this map with Figure 11-3. Are people moving toward the counties offering employment opportunities? Toward the urbanized counties? (Federal Reserve Bank of Atlanta.)

only moderate interests in manufacturing. Table 12-2 uses Office of Business Economics data to pinpoint recent SMSA growth. It is apparent that employment growth varies from modest to spectacular with high growth being concentrated in areas benefiting from either the tourist-retirement business or government activities. It is also clear that the strong gains are limited to a few activities: food products, electronics, trade, and transportation, government, and Armed Forces. Miscellaneous manufactures which include both recreational goods and military and scientific equipment also rate high.

Within the region Florida is exceptional with its urban population doubling from 1950 to 1960 (Figure 12-10). As Table 12-2 indicates, this increase has provided increased employment in almost all urban activities, employment declines being limited to agriculture, forestry and fisheries, lumber, furniture manufacturing, and railroads. Coastal Plain areas outside Florida are also suitable for the growth of resorts

and retirement settlement, but unlike Florida this business is a small part of the total business in those states. Much of the Coastal Plain suffers from an industrial mix stressing low growth or declining opportunities for employment.

CONCLUSIONS

The development of the Coastal Plain has depended on the success of its settlers in developing areas handicapped by infertile or poorly drained soils. The contrast between the southern Florida peninsula and the Coastal Plain to the north is striking. Although both areas have similar flattish terrain with much poorly drained land, the more tropical peninsula has economically become almost a Yankee colony with a large and rapidly growing urban population and a stress on service activities. Elsewhere development is concentrated in a relatively few cities and SMSAs, mostly significant for commerce and relatively simple industries, and as service centers for nearby government bases and supply depots. The extensive areas of cheap land, at present almost worthless for agriculture, have provided space for forestry and grazing.

The Southeastern Plain has everywhere a growing season of at least eight months, and wintry spells are generally short and only moderately cold. The oppressive midday heat of the long summers can be overcome by air conditioning, and outdoor activities are possible most days of the year. Factory overhead is modest in this region of mild climate, cheap land, and moderate taxes; consequently the once stagnant cities have begun to experience industrial growth. In contrast to many regions formerly based primarily on farm and raw-material industries, the coastal counties in most of this area have grown in population in recent decades, but except in the Florida peninsula and the SMSAs, this population growth has not sufficed to absorb the natural population increase.

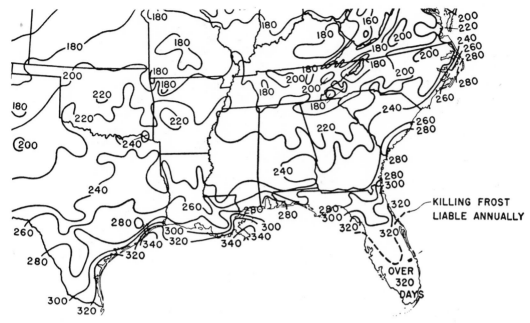

FIGURE 12-11   This map shows the length of the frost-free season in days in the average year. In the Southeastern Coastal Plain, the effect of proximity to water is conspicuous. (USDA.)

SELECTED REFERENCES

Many of the references for Chapter 11 are also applicable.

ANDERSON, JAMES R.: *Land Use and Development: Southeastern Coastal Plain,* Agricultural Information Bulletin no. 154, Washington, 1956.

BROWN, RALPH H.: *Historical Geography of the United States,* Harcourt, Brace & World, New York, 1948, especially chap. 8 and pp. 61–76.

FEDERAL RESERVE BANK OF ATLANTA: *Essays on Southern Economic Growth,* Atlanta, 1961.

———: *Population Change and Economic Change in the Southeast,* Atlanta, 1963.

GREENHUT, MELVIN L., and W. TATE WHITMAN: *Essays in Southern Economic Development,* University of North Carolina Press, Chapel Hill, 1964.

HART, JOHN FRASER: "Functions and Occupational Structures of Cities of the American South," *Annals A.A.G.,* vol. 45 (1955), pp. 269–286.

LONSDALE, RICHARD E.: *Atlas of North Carolina,* University of North Carolina Press, Chapel Hill, 1967.

———: "Two North Carolina Commuting Patterns," *Economic Geography,* vol. 42 (1966), pp. 114–138.

RAISZ, ERWIN: *Atlas of Florida,* University of Florida Press, Gainesville, 1964.

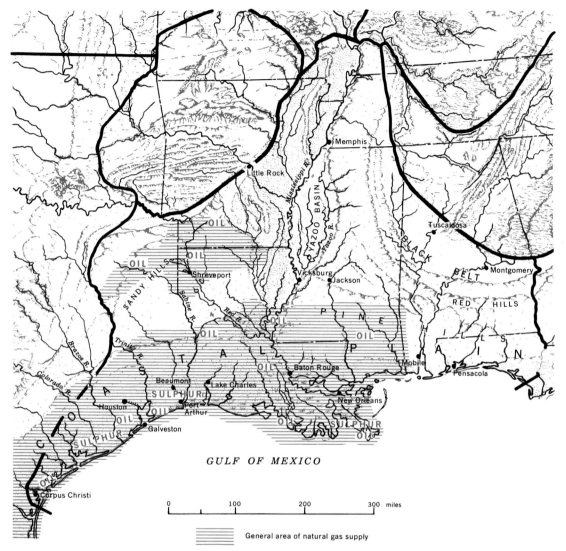

FIGURE 13-1 *Landforms of the Gulf South. Most of this area consists of alluvium or sands deposited in what was formerly a part of the Gulf of Mexico. As in the Southeastern Coastal Plain, groundwater conditions diversify local environments.*
(Base map copyright by A. K. Lobeck. Reprinted with permission of The Geographical Press, Hammond, Inc.)

CHAPTER 13

PLANTATIONS, MINERALS, AND INDUSTRY IN THE GULF SOUTH

This huge region, here called the Gulf South (Figure 13-1), has much physical resemblance to the Southeastern Plain. However, its location is more continental so that the Gulf South is somewhat more likely to suffer extreme heat in summer and severe cold spells in winter. Like the Southeastern Plain, amid many swampy and marshy coastal areas, the Gulf South is served by an Intracoastal Waterway and by bays which provide excellent natural harbors; an additional asset is the Mississippi system which provides a waterway unequaled in Anglo-America except by the Great Lakes–St. Lawrence Seaway. The flooding of the Mississippi plain has formed a broad wedge of

AREA INCLUDES	Land Area (thousand sq. mi.)	Population Change 1950-1960	Population 1960 (thousands)	Population 1967 (thousands)	Personal Income 1967 (billions)
GULF SOUTH	212.2	17.1%	12,304	14,075	$31.7
West Florida	8.1	51.6	391	485	1.0
Southern Alabama	33.1	3.0	1,526	1,630	3.1
Mississippi	47.2	0	2,178	2,400	4.4
Louisiana	45.1	21.4	3,257	3,720	8.5
East and south Arkansas	26.5	− 8.0	932	945	1.8
East Texas	41.9	30.4	2,864	3,485	9.4
West Tennessee	6.2	18.0	930	1,200	2.9
Southeast Missouri	4.1	− 9.6	226	210	0.6
MAJOR SMSAS					
Mobile	2.9	36.0%	363	410	$ 1.0
New Orleans	2.0	26.9	907	1,100	3.0
Baton Rouge	0.5	45.4	230	270	0.7
Memphis	1.4	30.2	674	800	2.0
Houston	1.7	54.1	1,243	1,800	5.3

CLIMATE — *Humid subtropical with brief cold winters inland from the Gulf.*

	Temperature (°F) Jan.	Temperature (°F) July	Precipitation (inches) Annual	Precipitation (inches) Season
Mobile	53	83	68	All year
New Orleans	56	83	63	All year
Memphis	42	81	50	Less rainy late summer
Houston	55	84	45	All year

VEGETATION — Pine near the Gulf grading inland into oak-pine; cypress on the alluvium; tall grass prairie near Louisiana-Texas coast and in the Black Belt of Alabama–Mississippi.

SOIL — Mostly red-yellow sandy loams except for alluvium of the flood plains and prairie soils underlying natural grasslands.

MINERALS — Petroleum and natural gas widespread south of Texarkana; sulfur and salt near Louisiana-Texas coast.

alluvium which today, as it has been for nearly two centuries, is the agricultural core of the region.

As in the Southeastern Plain, soil and related drainage patterns have been reflected in settlement patterns. The coastal marshes are largely unsettled except where fringing beaches have been suitable for resorts or where underlying oil, gas, salt, or sulfur has encouraged development. The larger ports are sited on well-drained land adjoining deep bays or on bluffs overlooking the rivers except for New

Orleans, situated on an artificially drained part of the Mississippi Delta. Inland much of the plain is occupied by Norfork-Ruston and related sandy soils; these are divided among croplands, pasture, and forest, with the forest being dominant on the poorly drained, hilly, and eroded areas. East of the Mississippi flood plain a broad band of soil formed from loess extends about 50 miles; locally the soil has been so much eroded that many of its once fertile croplands have been returned to forest and pasture. Finally, a number of prairie areas, such as the Black Belt of Alabama and Mississippi and the coastal prairies of western Louisiana and adjacent Texas, are largely grazed by cattle. On the better soils, the rural economy is based on livestock, fodder crops, cotton, vegetables, corn, and forest products, the exact proportion of each product varying with soil quality and the traditions of the farmer. Almost everywhere farm labor is migrating, either to other sections or to urban occupations, and the rural population is generally declining.

In the alluvial areas highly specialized agriculture continues with modernized plantation-type farming based on mechanization and fertilization. The alluvium is far from uniform, varying from well drained to swampy and in soil texture from sandy to clayey. Of the 42,000 square miles of Mississippi alluvium south of Illinois, about half is nonagricultural, being principally in swampy forest. The major crop varies from rice on level lands with poor drainage, sugarcane in the warm lands of south central Louisiana, to cotton or soybeans on the upper Delta. Yet the system differs mainly in detail—no matter what the cash crop, a large farm with a technically trained manager is necessary for economic agriculture.

NEW DEVELOPMENTS IN THE GULF SOUTH

The Plantation and the Neoplantation

An understanding of the present situation, both on the alluvium and on the sandier Coastal Plain, requires a discussion of the Southern plantation.[1] The antebellum plantation was found in relatively flat areas where large fields could be cultivated by slave gangs. Usually these plantations were much larger than Midwestern farms, units over 1,000 acres being fairly common. (Such large areas suitable for slave-gang or modern mechanized agriculture were scarce on the rougher surfaces of the Piedmont.) After the Civil War, the majority of the plantations were cultivated on a sharecropper basis (40 acres and a mule). Such a fragmented landscape was hardly suited to raising cotton with tractors and cotton-picking machinery, the introduction of which both caused and was stimulated by the out-migration of rural labor. The consequence was the development of what Prunty calls the *neoplantation* (Figure 13-2), centered around a tractor station, cultivated in large fields, and emphasizing high yields with a low labor cost per unit. The cultivation is managed by one farmer, the modest supply of labor is paid cash, not a share of the crop, and crop rotation (including livestock) is the rule where soil conditions permit. The small farmer has not been entirely eliminated by the spread of the neoplantation, but commonly his small farm earnings are supplemented by city work.

Employment and Income

As income figures by occupation are not available by subdivisions of states, Table 13-1 shows the income data for four states representative of the Gulf South. Although Mississippi is above average in the share of income received from farming, this item is still only one-seventh of the total income. In Louisiana, mining is relatively high, thus reflecting the oil, gas, and sulfur industries. Urban activities provide the bulk of the income in all four states although in 1960

[1] The articles of Merle Prunty, Jr., clearly portray the changes in Southern agriculture. This section is based largely on his "The Renaissance of the Southern Plantation," *Geographical Review*, vol. 45 (1955), pp. 459-491.

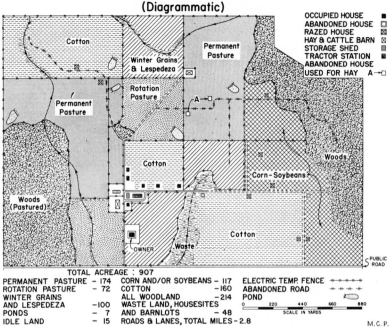

FIGURE 13-2   This generalized example of the neoplantation is in the cultivated part of the Mississippi
alluvium. Compared with the traditional Southern
plantation, the few workers' homes, the tractor stations,
and the crop diversification are noteworthy. [Merle C.
Prunty, Jr., "The Renaissance of the Southern Plantation," GEO-
GRAPHICAL REVIEW, vol. 45 (1955), pp. 459–491.]

TABLE 13-1   Industrial Sources of Civilian Income Received by Persons for Participation in Current
Production and Total Personal Income: Gulf States, 1966 (in millions of dollars[1])

Source	Ala.	La.	Miss.	Ark.
Farming	307	327	473	497
Mining	52	426	42	33
Construction	365	645	204	209
Manufacturing	1,747	1,173	837	731
Trade	908	1,154	495	498
Finance, etc.	226	286	119	121
Transport, etc.	363	587	180	221
Services	752	833	390	349
Government	1,020	879	459	378
Others	18	30	18	16
Total Civilian Income	5,758	6,341	3,216	3,054
Total Personal Income	7,254	8,235	4,153	3,931
Personal Income per capita	$2,039	$2,257	$1,751	$2,015

[1] Except Personal Income per Capita.

SOURCE: *Survey of Current Business*, vol. 47 (1967), no. 8, p. 37.

only 38 percent of the population was urban in Mississippi, 43 percent in Arkansas, 55 percent in Alabama, and 63 percent in Louisiana. In the cotton–soybean-growing section of the Delta, agricultural employment, which was 41 percent of all employment in 1950, had dropped to 24 percent in 1960; in the same period manufacturing employment rose from 8 to 16 percent, and trade employment from 16 to 17 percent. In areas near large cities increases in industrial employment are even more spectacular as many workers commute from as far as 40 miles to factories and offices.

The employment change in the Southeast[2] in nearly a century is shown by Table 13-2. The shift of labor from raw-material production to manufacturing and services is characteristic throughout all Anglo-America, but in the Southeast the shift has been relatively slow; in the four states largely within the Gulf South 12.6 percent was employed in agriculture compared with 6.5 percent for the nation as a whole.

Population Changes and Problems

The changes in the Gulf South economy have had striking effects on both the

[2] The above O.B.E. region includes not only the Gulf South but all the states from the Ohio and Potomac to Arkansas and Louisiana. Data for the Gulf South would not be very different.

economic and the social structure. Traditionally there were three groups: (1) the white planter–merchant–professional–clerical class; (2) the "poor white" class who worked as small farmers, and who later supplied much of the labor for Southern manufacturing, and (3) the Negro who worked as a domestic servant or common labor in the city, as farm labor or as a sharecropper in the country. Some of the poor whites rose to the upper class, and some Negroes rose to perform professional and commercial functions especially for the Negro community, but generally a shift upward economically and socially was more difficult than in the North and West.

Table 13-3 shows some of the changes that have occurred in four Gulf South states. In general, the poor industrial mix and slow rate of urbanization have been responsible for slow progress of this area. Good progress along the Gulf from Mobile to Houston averages in with the generally slow progress inland in the agricultural-forestry areas. Consequently heavy outmigration has occurred, especially among the Negroes and poorly trained whites whose opportunities have been lessened by mechanization in agriculture and other industries. In all these states the average income remains well below that for the

TABLE 13-2   Distribution by Industry of the Southeastern Labor Force, 1870–1960 (percent of total)

Census	Agriculture	Mining	Forestry and Fisheries	Manufacturing	Services and Others
1870	75.1	0.2	0.3	7.5	16.8
1880	75.4	0.3	0.3	7.8	16.2
1890	66.3	0.8	0.8	10.5	21.6
1900	64.9	1.3	0.9	11.3	21.5
1910	58.9	1.7	0.9	14.5	24.0
1920	49.5	2.7	0.9	18.4	28.5
1930	42.2	2.5	0.9	19.8	34.6
1940	33.4	2.6	1.0	15.4	47.6
1950	21.4	2.6	1.0	17.8	57.3
1960	9.9	1.5	0.3	22.3	66.0
United States, 1960	6.5	1.0	0.14	33.0	59.4

SOURCE: Harvey S. Perloff et al., *Regions, Resources, and Economic Growth,* published for Resources for the Future Inc., Johns Hopkins, Baltimore, 1960, pp. 176–267; and 1960 census data.

TABLE 13-3   Population Changes in Four Gulf States and the United States, 1940–1960

	Ala.	*La.*	*Miss.*	*Ark.*	*U.S.*
Population Change (percent):					
1940–1950	+8.1	+13.5	−0.2	−2.0	+14.5
1950–1960	+6.7	+21.4	0.0	+6.5	+18.5
Net Migration (thousands):					
1940–1950	−271	−112	−350	−320	1,035
1950–1960	−361	− 42	−433	−430	2,973
Nonwhite (percent):					
1940	35.1	36.1	49.0	27.7	10.2
1950	31.6	32.9	48.4	22.5	10.6
1960	30.1	32.1	42.3	21.9	11.4
Urban Residents (percent):					
1940	26.3	30.1	20.0	24.1	56.1
1950	43.8	54.8	27.9	33.0	64.0
1960	55.0	63.3	37.7	42.8	69.9
Per Capita Income:					
1940	$ 282	$ 363	$ 218	$ 256	$ 595
1950	880	1,120	755	825	1,496
1960	1,488	1,655	1,205	1,372	2,215

SOURCES: U.S. Bureau of the Census, *Statistical Abstract of the United States;* and *County and City Data Book: 1962,* Washington, 1962.

nation. It should be stressed again that these low state incomes result from the inclusion of large rural and small city populations. Incomes per household in the SMSAs are high to moderate: thus Memphis with an average per household income of nearly $10,000 ranks nineteenth among all SMSAs; Houston and Beaumont–Port Arthur have average household incomes over $9,000 while New Orleans, Baton Rouge, Jackson, and Mobile average about $7,000, approximately the average for Columbus, Ohio. The Mississippi average income per household ($5,650, 1965), for example, is pulled down by rural counties with averages close to the $3,000 poverty level: thus 13 Mississippi counties have more than half their families with incomes below $2,500 (Figure 13-3).

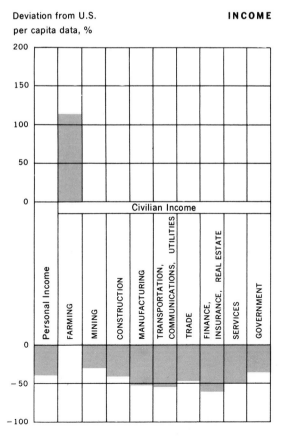

FIGURE 13-3   Mississippi has recently been lowest of the states in per capita personal income. The fact that farming is the only above-average source of income suggests that the state has a poor industrial mix. Mississippi cities have an average per capita income slightly above the average for the nation.

IN ASSUMPTION PARISH, Louisiana, the natural levees along the Bayou La Fourche form a ridge 15 to 20 feet high and 6 to 8 miles wide, with the river flowing on the crest. Drainage is away from the river. The fields were laid out long ago by French settlers whose homesteads formed elongated villages along the river road. The fertile fine sandy loam and silt soils are used for sugar and rice; the adjacent swamps and marshes breed muskrats. (USDA photograph.)

These figures explain why the four Gulf states have suffered from a net out-migration in spite of the urban-industrial advance which has multiplied the SMSA populations. The out-migrants come from all three classes, but the disproportionately large Negro group is reflected in the declining percentages of nonwhites in each state (Table 13-3). Developing urban occupations required more technically trained workers, but such training has been least available in those areas suffering from reduced rural employment.

MISSISSIPPI CHANNELS, ALLUVIUM, AND CITIES

The Mississippi flood plains provide homes for about 3.5 million people. The southern Delta was used by the French for cotton and sugar culture in the mid-eighteenth century; elsewhere the plain was used mainly as a commercial waterway—at first for furs, later for the shipment of Ohio Valley farm products to Southern planters, while the swampy plain remained in the hands of the trappers. Until 1840 when levees were started, the planters occupied the brown loess soils on and back of the bluffs overlooking the river from the east since fear of floods kept them from permanent exploitation of the alluvial wealth.

The changing, twisting channel of the Mississippi was a challenge to skilled pilots, as has been so vividly described by Mark Twain. The development of the shallow-draft steamboat made its navigation possible. The places where the channel cut into the eastern bluffs provided landing places for the steamers and sites for towns such as Natchez, Vicksburg, and Memphis. When the demand for cotton grew, the planters cleared the forests, built dikes, and planted fields that in most years were safe from the river. They did not clear all the land—even today many roads across the flood plain are largely adjoined by drainage canals beyond which are cypress, tupelo, and gum swamps.

Then, as today, the flood plain consisted of three kinds of soil commonly grouped together as alluvium. The broad flat basins have clay soils with poor internal drainage. The better soils for cotton are the sandy loams found on old natural levees or river channels, commonly 5 to 15 feet higher than the clay soils. The highest terraces include some loess soils. Intermediate are the silty loams usable for pasture when drained. Physically it is possible to convert most of the plain into drained lands; economically this is not feasible for half the area.

In terms of crops, the flood plain can be divided into three areas: (1) south of the 31° parallel the climate is too humid for profitable cotton production; (2) north of this and separated from it by a swampy, sparsely settled area is the Delta (so-called locally), a cotton-soybean area extending north to the mouth of the Ohio; (3) west of the above areas in southern Arkansas and in Louisiana are several heavy clay areas devoted largely to rice.

The total investment in protecting most of this alluvial land almost all of the time is about a half billion dollars for levees and ditches in the plain, but this does not count the investment in the TVA and other dams upriver along the Ohio, upper Mississippi, Missouri, and their tributaries. Heavy additional investments are required to cultivate the land with modern techniques: thus a cotton picker may cost $10,000. Economically this is no land for the poor small farmer who still occupies it in places for social rather than economic reasons.

The Delta Cotton Areas

Memphis Few SMSAs are so related to raw-material-oriented industries as Memphis, commercial metropolis for the north-

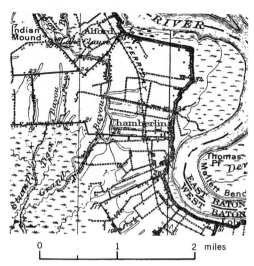

FIGURE 13-4 *This portion of the Bayou Sara, Louisiana, quadrangle shows how settlement is concentrated on the natural levee along the Mississippi River. The scale is about one mile to an inch; how wide is the river?* (U.S. Geological Survey, Bayou Sara, Louisiana, quadrangle.)

ern half of the flood plain and the higher areas in western Tennessee and northern Mississippi. This loess and alluvial area has a diversified agriculture focused on cotton but including soybeans, cattle, and hogs. Memphis has the largest inland cotton market in the country and also the largest hardwood lumber market. According to the 1963 *Census of Manufactures,* three raw-material-oriented industries (food, lumber and related furniture and paper, chemicals) each produced about one-fifth of the value added. There are also other industries— farm machinery, automobile assembly, metal products. High employment in government and transportation and the location there of a Federal Reserve Branch Bank indicate the significance of Memphis as a regional economic capital.

Delta problems With declining employment in agriculture, obviously some other source of employment must be sought for the rural counties. What remedies can be suggested for the purely rural counties such as Issa-

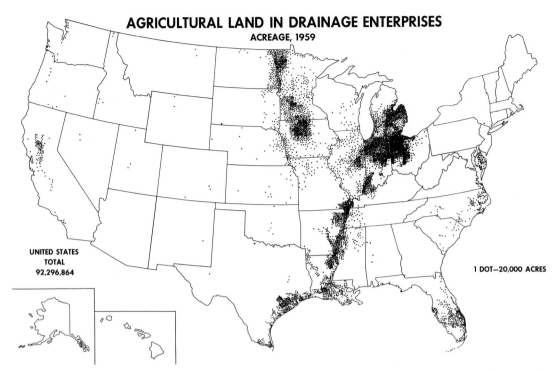

AGRICULTURAL LAND IN DRAINAGE ENTERPRISES
ACREAGE, 1959

UNITED STATES
TOTAL
92,296,864

1 DOT—20,000 ACRES

FIGURE 13-5   The dotted areas are almost entirely either glaciated areas or alluvial areas; can you identify those in each category? (Bureau of the Census.)

quena County, Mississippi, whose largest town had 800 inhabitants and no manufacturing? The median household income for the county in 1960 was $1,479, and agricultural employment had dropped (1940–1960) from 1,864 to 604. There were 22 farms over 1,000 acres, but most of the large landholders were not overprosperous as only 16 families had incomes over $10,000. The population of 2,954 (1960) was two-thirds Negro; the net out-migration (1950–1960) was 2,095. Although the average value of the 313 farms was $39,000 and 70 percent of the farms had tractors and trucks, the 42 percent of the alluvial land in farms did not produce much prosperity.

New Orleans and Southeastern Louisiana

Southern Louisiana seems to have been largely built, or at least rebuilt, by man. Its earliest settlement by Europeans was on the natural levees: On them in 1718 the French built the infant New Orleans primarily to open the trade of the Mississippi; on them

were laid out the French plantations. Even today the city and the farms seem embraced by marshes and swamps, and the bayous and drainage canals are conspicuous parts of the landscape; indeed extensive areas, almost roadless, can still be visited best by boat.

As the metropolis is 110 miles up the Mississippi, the countryside can be described by sectors radiating from the city (Figure 13-6). The area to the southeast is largely marshy with small truck crops on less than one-twentieth of the land. Recently this has been the state's most productive area in petroleum and sulfur and significant in natural gas. Production here is possible only because of new techniques devised to obtain the minerals first on swampy lands, later offshore. The half circle west of New Orleans alternates between swamp and sugar land with considerable fishing from the bayou ports; there too oil

Louisiana Forest Types

MAJOR TYPES IN LOUISIANA

|||| Loblolly-short leaf pine

Long leaf-slash pine

Oak-pine

⊗ Oak-hickory

Oak-gum-cypress

Nontyped, less than 10% forest

FIGURE 13-6   Forest types in the South reflect soil and drainage conditions; in Louisiana, especially the latter. Cotton is a significant crop, mainly in northern Louisiana, because the coastal areas are too humid. Other specialty-crop areas are shown by these symbols: R = rice, S = sugarcane. (State of Louisiana.)

and gas fields are common, being most productive to the southwest of New Orleans. North and northeast a sector is devoted mainly to truck crops, dairying, and winter strawberries; lumbering and paper are major nonagricultural activities.

New Orleans   The New Orleans SMSA, primarily a commercial and service center with manufactures largely related to commerce and regional consumption, has an unenviable site. The French Quarter, carefully preserved to attract tourists, is on the back slope of the natural levee; much of the more modern city is on drained land, and at high water the Mississippi flows above the street level. Hot and sticky much of the year and, until this century, often fever- and mosquito-ridden and drained by open sewers, the modern city is a prize example of the accomplishments of modern engineers. The water supply, formerly obtained from cisterns, is now obtained from purified, filtered river water. Numerous pumps drain the covered canals and eject the sewage into the sea. The older buildings were necessarily low, but the newer part of the city has skyscrapers and the new expressways and

bridges seem to tower over the low, older city. Hurricanes still bring flood problems at rare intervals.

New Orleans is becoming a largely air-conditioned, modern city. Trade, finance, and commercial services account for two-fifths of all employment; industry only for one-thirteenth. The major manufacture is food processing and packing, including the processing of imported foodstuffs such as bananas and coffee; second is transportation equipment, mainly shipbuilding. A rapidly growing industry is petroleum processing and petrochemicals, in part as a result of the recent oil and gas boom near the river mouth. Other industries are largely for the metropolitan market and the adjacent Gulf South (Figure 13-7).

In spite of the slow approach to the city, New Orleans has been and is among the leading American ports. In the first half of the last century, the Southern city rivaled and sometimes exceeded New York in value

NEW ORLEANS, a city with a low skyline, is acquiring a new profile as its expressways, skyscrapers, 45-story Plaza Tower, and 33-story International Trade Mart loom above the quaint Vieux Carre, the old French Quarter so attractive to tourists. (Chamber of Commerce of the New Orleans Area.)

and quantity of goods handled. Even today New Orleans has a rate advantage over North Atlantic and Pacific ports in an area extending from Florida to St. Paul and westward to the Rockies. Recently the city has taken great steps to service international trade, including a 33-story International Trade Mart at the foot of Canal Street. At present export and coastwise shipments are six times total receipts, an unbalanced situation which New Orleans would like to correct.

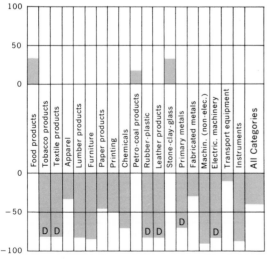

Deviation from U.S. per capita data, %

VALUE ADDED BY MANUFACTURING
New Orleans SMSA = .52% U.S. Pop.

FIGURE 13-7 The graph suggests that New Orleans is a port more than an industrial city. To what extent are the industries based on local resources? on products handled through the port by either ship or pipeline?

THE EASTERN COASTAL PLAINS AND GATEWAYS

East of the Mississippi, the Gulf South is another coastal plain like the Southeastern Plain consisting of coastal marshes fringed by offshore bars, spits, and islands; a flat, wooded area; and a sandy inland plain. Between this plain and the southwestern edge of the Piedmont is an arc of prairie, endowed with a rich, black limey soil. This is the "Black Belt," once an area of large cotton plantations but today shifting to beef and dairy cattle. This shift is not unique, for throughout the former Cotton Belt cattle have taken over depleted cotton lands or have been integrated into a diversified cotton-legume-cereal-livestock agriculture. Southwest of this Black Belt, timberland predominates, but cotton, poultry, and livestock farming are intermixed and occupy increasing parts of the land toward the Mississippi.

Eastern Mississippi and most of Alabama are drained by a number of small and moderate-sized rivers directly into the Gulf. The largest of these is the Alabama-Tombigbee system which flows into Mobile Bay with water from about half of Alabama, including almost all the Black Belt, the extreme southwestern end of the Appalachian Piedmont, and the ridge and valley country. Inland much of this terrain was cotton area which farmers were forced to diversify because of the incursions of the boll weevil (Figure 13-8). In southern Alabama, the farmers specialized in peanuts, plus some corn, cotton, cattle, and hogs. Enterprise, Alabama, so pleased by the financial results of this pest-stimulated farm diversification, erected a monument to the boll weevil. Closer to the Gulf Coast and including western Florida, the growing season is longer, the soils diverse. Much of the soil is suited mainly for pine forests, but a few areas have specialized successfully in early potatoes, truck crops, livestock, and poultry. The sandy coast, significant mainly

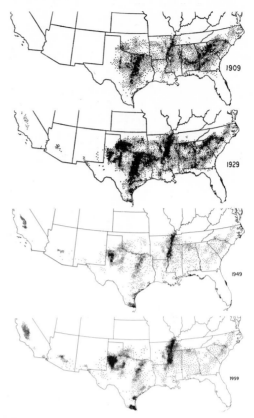

FIGURE 13-8 The distribution of cotton acreage for four dates for which maps are available. Cotton production has been moving west. To what extent has this move been influenced by the boll weevil? by the adoption of large-scale mechanized farming? by soil exhaustion? The much reduced acreage is partly offset by a tripling of cotton yields per acre. (USDA.)

for fishing and resort towns, is a dismal area out of season.

Mobile and Other Gateways

A series of small ports, each on an inlet on the Gulf Coast, includes Apalachicola, Panama City, Pensacola, Pascagoula, Biloxi, Gulfport; all have fishing, some shipping, vacation trade, a government base or hospital, and a few simple industries: lumber, paper, chemicals, synthetic fibers, or food packing. Only Mobile, located on a deeply indented bay, shows signs of becoming a mature commercial-industrial metropolis. Yet two-thirds of all Mobile manufacturing employment was in nondurable goods with

MOBILE BAY OFFERS a sheltered harbor which has been improved by the state docks developed by the State of Alabama. Railway and highway connections are immediately adjacent to the docks. (Parrott Photography from Mobile Area Chamber of Commerce.)

emphasis on food, chemicals, and paper. Its durable goods employment was mainly shipbuilding and wood products with relatively small employment in aluminum refining, fabricated metals, machinery, and electrical equipment.

The development of Mobile Although Mobile was founded by the French in 1711, its growth occurred largely in the second quarter of the nineteenth century when settlers, stimulated by soil exhaustion in the Southeastern Plain and by the increasing European demand for upland cotton, moved into Alabama. Carrying their household goods on wagons and driving their livestock before them, the immigrants arrived via three dirt roads, all converging on Mobile. The later shipment of supplies and the export of cotton depended on river traffic to Mobile down the Tombigbee from Demopolis and down the Alabama from Montgomery or even further upstream. The zone within 40 miles of the Gulf proved too rainy in autumn for cotton, but Gulf ports benefited by the output of huge cotton plantations

northward in the limey Black Belt and mixed medium-sized plantations and small farms of the rolling Coastal Plains. Mobile was the established commercial center of Alabama long before Birmingham, now the state's leading city, was founded; while Montgomery, more centrally located in the state and at the southeastern end of the Black Belt, became the political and social capital.

Later as railroads and paved roads focused on Mobile and Montgomery, inland water routes declined. About a half century ago the boll weevil entered the cotton fields from the Southwest and forced the diversification of the cotton plantations. Cattle displaced cotton in the Black Belt, and peanuts, fruit, corn, pecans, truck crops, and livestock shared the land with cotton and forestry on the sandy soils. While these changes were taking place on the plains, the Piedmont and Appalachian lands to the north were advancing industrially and continuing to produce cotton and other crops.

Other cities Although much of the industry is concentrated in Mobile, other urban activities are developing on the Coastal Plain. Many of these are associated with military bases; for example, one-third of the employment in Okaloosa County, Florida, and one-sixth of the employment in the adjacent Pensacola SMSA is "Armed Forces." Montgomery, capital of Alabama, has maintained a slow growth based on political activities, on such traditional industries as food and lumber processing, and on a few newer industries such as chemicals, glass, and forgings. Growth has been more rapid in Jackson, capital of Mississippi, where governmental employment has tripled in two decades, electrical industries have come in, and an oil field opened just to the south made Mississippi the ninth largest petroleum-producing state in 1966.

WEST OF THE MISSISSIPPI

Crossing the river does not bring any abrupt change in the types of physical features found in the Gulf South, but there is a change in the proportion of the land each occupies. Thus the loess bluffs which almost everywhere overlook the Mississippi alluvium east of the river occupy a negligible part of eastern Arkansas and southeastern Missouri. The swampy areas are much more extensive west of the river and extend in broad bands along the Gulf Coast and along the rivers. The longleaf pine forest occurs in west central Louisiana and eastern Texas, and, to the north, the oak-pine forest characteristic of the southern Piedmont reappears in northern Louisiana, Arkansas, and northeastern Texas. The black soils and tall grasslands of the Black Belt are found in a marshier version in the lush coastal prairies of the Texas–western Louisiana Gulf coast. Petroleum, natural gas, and salt deposits are much more productive here than east of the river.

Before the discovery of oil near Beaumont, Texas, in 1901, the western Gulf South was an unprogressive area producing lumber, cotton, rice, cattle, and, in the French-speaking area, sugarcane. Large-scale rice cultivation had already been introduced, being the foundation of an industry which today uses huge combine harvesters, elaborate systems of irrigation and drainage, with seeding and pest control by airplane. Muskrat trapping was a widespread industry as was the hardwood lumbering on the marshy areas and pine cutting on the sandy uplands. In this subregion, as in the Southeastern Coastal Plain, lumbering could be readily established on a sustained-yield basis because of the long growing season.

Mineral Wealth

Mineral exploitation of the western Gulf South transformed the area, providing capital for the development of cities and industries, and for pipelines, barge routes, and tanker services to ship its fuels and chemicals to eastern United States and Western Europe. The quantity of this mineral wealth is so large as to be hard to visualize. All the gold produced in California *since 1848* was valued at $2.4 billion, which is $225 million less than the oil and gas produced in Louisiana in *one year,* 1964. To this can be added the Louisiana production of sulfur ($55 million) and of salt ($36 million). Texas mineral production is greater, but much of its oil and gas production is west of the Gulf South region.

The value of this mineral wealth depended on the technical and market setting—it could hardly have been developed much before the early twentieth century. Earlier demands for petroleum and natural gas were limited to household use (kerosene, gas stoves, and gas light), and these markets were in the northeast, difficult to reach before the development of pipelines and tankers; then the market for fuel oil, gasoline, and the many petrochemicals had barely been touched. As for sulfur, the Frasch process which permitted the extraction of molten sulfur from the deep deposits in the salt domes was not introduced commercially until 1903. Salt, which underlies much of the Gulf South, was widely available, but only in recent decades has it been worthwhile to exploit such deep deposits. Finally the techniques for exploiting marshland and continental-shelf deposits have only been developed within the last quarter century. The result: Today the flow of fuels and raw materials by pipeline, rail, barge, and tanker from the Gulf South northeastward represents the leading trade route by tonnage in the nation. It has created a cluster of Gulf South cities—Baton Rouge, Shreveport, New Orleans, Lake Charles, Beaumont, Galveston–Texas City, Houston, and Corpus Christi—which to-

NETWORK OF MAJOR NATURAL GAS PIPELINES
As of December 31, 1966

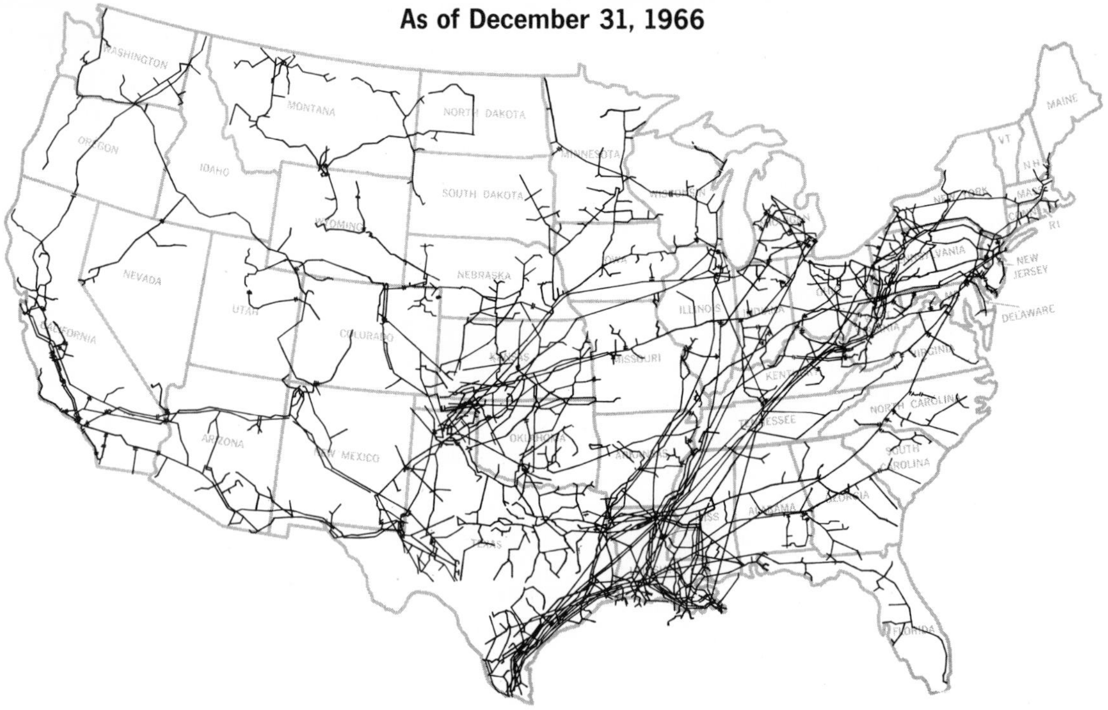

FIGURE 13-9   This map shows the conspicuous part played by the Gulf South in supplying the nation with natural gas. (Map by Federal Reserve Bank of Philadelphia.)

gether are called the "Petrochemical Empire." These use quantities of raw materials, and require elaborate and often highly automated machinery as well as elaborate networks of communication and transportation. From these have arisen a host of auxiliary manufacturing, business service, and professional activities.

The Houston-Galveston SMSAs

The economic capital of this Petrochemical Empire is Houston, founded at the head of navigation on Buffalo Bayou which drains into Galveston Bay. At first, it grew as a commercial outlet for the farms and ranches of southern Texas. In 1900 it was eighty-fourth among American cities; in 1960 it had advanced to seventh. Why? Largely, oil, and an aggressive policy by its leaders. Originally it was an inland city reachable only by small boats. With the increasing size of ocean vessels, Galveston on a long low island across the mouth of Galveston Bay

became its outport with the ships docking in the bay. A hurricane in 1900 swept water across low-lying Galveston, killing 5,000 and wrecking much of the city. Although Galveston rebuilt, protecting itself by a seawall, Houston excavated a 36-foot-deep channel, wide enough for all but the largest vessels, which led to a turning basin on Buffalo Bayou within the city. With the channel opened in 1914 and improved at intervals since, Houston now rivals New Orleans and Norfolk in tonnage shipped out. Although Galveston has gained some industries, the most rapid development has been along the ship channels in Galveston Bay and Buffalo Bayou. One-fifth of all Texans live in the Houston and Galveston SMSAs.

The country around this huge metropolis is a moist prairie sprinkled with oil and gas wells, herds of cattle, cotton and rice fields,

IN 1915 THE MAN-MADE *Houston Ship Channel converted Houston into an ocean port, a port primarily for the export of raw materials.* (Houston Chamber of Commerce.)

FIGURE 13-10 *The favorable combination of rail, highway, and water routes has been a major factor in the development of Houston's trade and industry. Nearby natural gas, petroleum, salt, and sulfur account for the specialized nature of Houston industry (Figure 13-12).* (Southern Pacific Company.)

+++ **SOUTHERN PACIFIC RAIL LINES** +++
Houston area industrial properties served by Southern Pacific

1. Kempwood Industrial Park
2. Eleventh Street
3. Beaumont Highway
4. Englewood
5. Bankers' Mortgage Industrial District
6. Galena Park Industrial District
7. Battleground Road
8. Rogers Road
9. Sharpstown
10. Post Oak Road
11. Roark Road

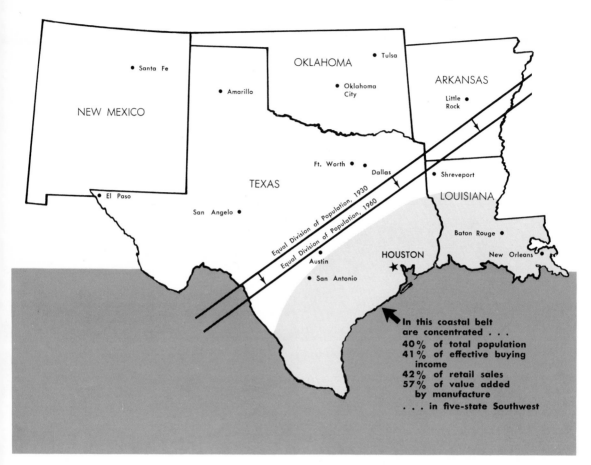

FIGURE 13-11   The Houston Chamber of Commerce
uses this map to stress the more rapid development near
the Gulf Coast.

with forest resources on its inner margin. Salt, sulfur, and lime (from shells) provide other available resources; iron ore is available 200 miles to the north and also imported from Labrador, Mexico, and South America; scrap iron is available locally.

The industrial economy of Houston is summarized by Figure 13-12. Every category of manufacturing is represented except tobacco and leather, but the petroleum and chemical products together account for half of the value added by manufacturing but only one-fourth of the industrial employment, thus reflecting the high degree of automation in these industries. Many of the other industries supply either consumer durable or nondurable goods for local con-

sumption or machinery for the basic industries. The presence of a billion-dollar spacecraft project and other defense activities is reflected in ordnance and machinery industries. As in any regional capital, the proportion of employment in trade, service, and government is high.

Other Cities

The other cities in the Petrochemical Empire are similar to Houston in that they have petrochemical industries and are located on navigable waterways. Generally they perform commercial and professional services for a more limited area and have a smaller variety of manufactures. All except Shreveport are connected with one another by the 12-foot or deeper Intracoastal Waterway or by the Mississippi; all are part of the network of oil and gas pipelines. In addition to oil and gas, many have secondary industries such as tin, zinc, and aluminum smelting based on the use of cheap gas. Baton Rouge also performs political functions as capital of Louisiana. Shreveport, in addition to oil, has industries related to nearby cotton and lumber production.

Water, Water Everywhere

The Gulf South is plentifully supplied with water; but is it good? The streams from the north are clogged with silt, sewage, and industrial wastes; the streams from the west and northwest are being drained upstream for irrigation and domestic use, and the waters returned to the stream are increasingly brackish and contaminated. Near the Texas Gulf Coast so much water is being pumped from wells that salt water is invading the aquifers. In the Petrochemical Empire salt water, oil wastes, and chemicals are contaminating the water. Thus, although precipitation is heavy, and hardly a stream lacks reservoirs and other forms of regulation, there is danger of inadequate *clean* water to serve the growing population, agriculture, forestry, and manufacturing. The water needs of productive enterprise are often overlooked: to grow southern pine may use as much as 2 gallons per board foot; to convert this pine into newsprint requires 26,000 gallons per ton; to manufacture steel for paper machinery requires as much as 65,000 gallons per ton of machinery. Add to this human consumption (drinking water, bathing, laundry, toilet, etc.) of 100 to 200 gallons per capita per

day, and it is understandable why there may not be adequate water for rice cultivation. Nevertheless, in this area rainfall is heavy, evaporation is low; compared to the western United States, this is a water-rich area. How will this resource be used most efficiently? The solution will involve huge capital investments and manifold restrictions on the carelessness of the inhabitants. To change human habits is rarely easy, and Americans, especially Easterners, have been accustomed to think of water as an unlimited resource.

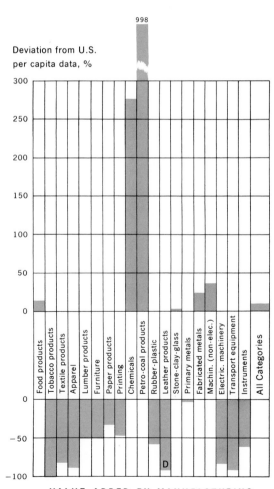

FIGURE 13-12   This graph is based on 1963 data. Since then, increasing maturity of the Houston economy has probably shortened some bars with negative deviations.

CONCLUSIONS

The Gulf South includes a number of the nation's most progressive cities whose development has been stimulated by petroleum, gas, salt, and sulfur. At the same time, social and technological revolutions have created serious tensions, especially in the rural areas. Farming has changed from a labor-intensive cultivation of a few staple crops to highly mechanized, more diversified agriculture which has little use for semiskilled labor. Emigration northward or cityward has provided some employment for displaced rural labor but generally not enough.

The urban geographic pattern of the region is largely determined by water routes and minerals; the rural patterns are more related to soils and associated drainage conditions. The combination of these sets of patterns results in a region in which intensive development is interspersed by areas of little or no development or of rural decay; of wealthy areas like the Houston SMSA interspersed with marshy and sandy wastes with poor farmsteads housing families in unpainted shacks. The soil wealth needs to be conserved to provide for permanent forestry and agriculture in a region of exceptionally favorable climate for plant growth. The mineral resources will be depleted, and meanwhile their wealth should provide capital for the further development of all the habitable lands.

SELECTED REFERENCES

ARBINGAST, STANLEY A., and LORRIN KENNAMER: *Atlas of Texas,* Bureau of Business Research, University of Texas, Austin, 1963.

GREENHUT, MELVIN L., and W. T. WHITMAN: *Essays in Southern Economic Development,* University of North Carolina Press, Chapel Hill, 1964.

JORDAN, TERRY G.: "The Imprint of the Upper and Lower South on Mid-nineteenth-century Texas," *Annals, A.A.G.,* vol. 57 (1967), pp. 667–690.

PRUNTY, MERLE, JR.: "Land Occupance in the Southeast: Landmarks and Forecasts," *Geographical Review,* vol. 42 (1952), pp. 439–461.

STOKES, GEORGE A.: "Lumbering and Western Louisiana Cultural Landscapes," *Annals, A.A.G.,* vol. 47 (1957), pp. 250–266.

U.S. FOREST SERVICE: *Timber Trends in the United States,* Washington, 1965.

See also references to Chapter 11.

PART IV

THE MATURING WEST

NO SHARP LINE forms the eastern boundary of the West: some scholars have selected the 98th meridian, others the 100th; still others have selected changes in rainfall or vegetation as criteria. Wherever the West is considered to start, it is a land of challenge and sharp contrast which has added a romantic note to American folklore, literature, song, and television. Its resources are patchy: isolated mines, limited oases, pastures and forests on steep mountains, and rivers winding across stark deserts.

Settlement required a gambler's fortitude and, in some parts of the West, still does: a new resource, a new boom—all too often followed by decline and abandonment; later renewed growth based on a discovered resource or possibly an old resource enhanced by new technology. Even the urban boom has hit the West spectacularly so that Los Angeles, having outgrown Chicago, now expects to surpass New York while orange groves fall to the subdivider. Where else but in the West can one find towering mountains adjacent to the cities; deserts and huge forests within metropolitan limits? The wilderness and the luxurious mansion are neighbors; the desert itself is subdivided where there is hope of getting water which sets the critical limit to Western expansion.

WATER IS THE KEY to Western development. Hoover Dam, the largest dam in the world, stores Colorado River waters in the largest artificial lake in Anglo-America. Power for California and Nevada, domestic water supply for California, irrigation water for California and Arizona, and recreational facilities for the nation are all products of this dam. (Las Vegas News Bureau.)

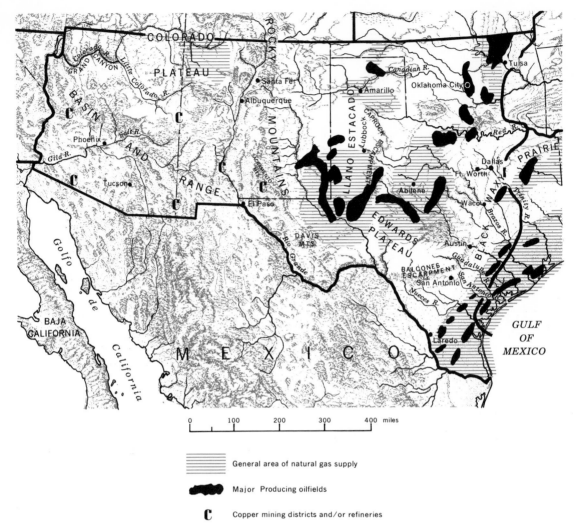

FIGURE 14-1 Landforms of the Southwest. This region is essentially a zone of transition among adjoining regions. Is this statement more true for this region than for other regions you have studied? What is the evidence in terms of landforms? climate? minerals? soils? products? economic development? (Base map copyright by A. K. Lobeck. Reprinted with permission of The Geographical Press, Hammond, Inc.)

CHAPTER 14

SOUTHWESTERN MINERALS, RANCHES, FARMS, AND FACTORIES

The one-seventh of the United States included in the Southwest (Figure 14-1) is a land of transition. Most of its subhumid to arid plains and tablelands have a mild climate; however, its eastern edges merge into the humid Gulf South, and its northeastern edges merge into the Winter Wheat and Corn belts. The area used is the same as the Southwest delimited by the Office of Business Economics except for the well-wooded portions of eastern Oklahoma and Texas and the industrialized Gulf Coast of Texas already described.

The population of the Southwest includes three minority groups which are generally inferior in education and income to the dominant

BASIC DATA:

AREA INCLUDES	Land Area (thousand sq. mi.)	Population Change 1950–1960	1960 (thousands)	1967 (thousands)	Personal Income 1967 (billions)
SOUTHWEST	532.9	15.8%	11,294	12,530	$32.9
Most of Texas	220.9	18.9	6,713	7,400	19.9
Most of Oklahoma	54.8	6.0	2,014	2,200	5.9
New Mexico	121.5	39.6	915	1,130	2.6
Arizona	113.6	11.5	1,302	1,800	4.5
MAJOR SMSAS					
Dallas–Fort Worth	5.3	45.8%	1,657	2,000	$ 6.6
San Antonio	1.9	37.1	716	850	2.0
Oklahoma City	2.1	30.4	512	575	1.5
Tulsa	3.8	27.8	419	440	1.2
El Paso	1.1	61.1	314	365	0.9
Albuquerque	1.2	80.0	262	340	0.9
Phoenix	9.2	100.0	664	970	2.5
Tucson	9.2	88.1	266	360	0.9

CLIMATE   *Humid subtropical grading westward into steppe and then into subtropical desert. Much variation because of altitude.*

	Temperature (°F) Jan.	July	Precipitation (inches) Annual	Season
Dallas	46	85	35	Spring maximum
Oklahoma City	37	83	31	Summer maximum
El Paso	43	82	8	Summer maximum
Albuquerque	35	79	8	Summer maximum
Phoenix	50	90	7	July–December

VEGETATION   Tall grass and oak-hickory forest in east, grading westward into short grass, and southwestward into mesquite, then creosote and cacti; on the western uplands open forest, mostly pine and juniper.

SOIL   Broad soil belts with limestone and prairie soils to the east, brown soils on the Plains, thin soils on mountains and plateaus, and coarse desert soils to the southwest.

MINERALS   Petroleum and natural gas east of the Rockies and in northwestern New Mexico; scattered deposits of low-grade coal and lignite; uranium in northwestern New Mexico; copper in southwestern New Mexico and southern Arizona; potash in eastern New Mexico.

white group. The Negroes, concentrated mostly in north and east Texas, range from highly educated professional workers to unskilled labor; these are Southern in culture.

In the southern part of the region, Spanish-speaking Mexicans (racially largely mestizo and culturally Mexican) represent a substantial minority. For many years it has been customary to bring in

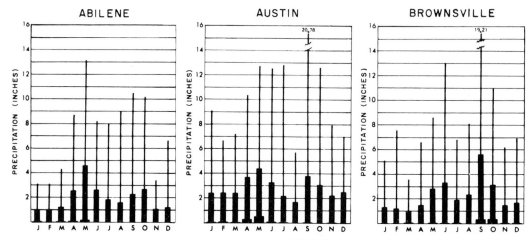

FIGURE 14-2   These bars show the monthly distribution of precipitation for representative Texas stations. The thin line indicates the highest precipitation on record, the bars the average precipitation, and the thickened bars the lowest on record. (THE REPORT OF THE U.S. STUDY COMMISSION: TEXAS, Austin, 1962.)

contract labor (braceros) to work seasonally harvesting the crops; other Mexicans have crossed the border legally, and perhaps more illegally, since the long border, consisting of the generally fordable Rio Grande in Texas and a geometrical boundary in New Mexico and Arizona, is not easily guarded.

The third minority consists of a variety of Indians, some living on reservations and others in towns, especially in northwestern New Mexico and Arizona. The culture of these people varies from considerable adherence to tribal tradition to diverse mixtures of Spanish, Indian, and American traits.

CHANGING SOUTHWESTERN RESOURCES

There is great diversity within this region, but its overriding characteristic, water shortage, is reflected in its vegetation (open or scrub woodland, mesquite, grass, creosote bush, and cactus), in its settlement pattern largely controlled by water resources, and in its planning for the future. Like neighboring regions to the east and north, its present economic development is still based on natural resources. In the Southwest key resources have been grass, soil, water, petroleum and natural gas, copper, and a sunny climate; without adequate water, the

other resources provide little basis for *permanent* development. Equally important, during the century and a quarter that the Southwest has been part of the United States, many of its natural resources have deteriorated in quantity and quality. Before subregional patterns are examined, the place of each resource in the settlement and development of the region will be briefly reviewed.

Grass

When the state was first settled, the natural pastures of Texas were much more lush than they are today. The Nueces Valley of south Texas, today classified as "mesquite and desert-grass savanna," was green all year when Spanish Americans introduced Andalusian cattle to the area. A half century later (about 1835) American farmers introduced eastern cattle into the area, thus upgrading the half-wild Texas breed. Within the next few decades these cattle were driven across the Southwest to California, creating a vast cowboy country which still lives in legend and western movies. After the Civil War, herds were driven north to the railheads of Kansas and to the Plains as far as Montana. What happened to the grass? Apparently it has deteriorated so that much good grassland has been invaded by mesquite trees, sage brush, juniper, and other plants unsuited for grazing.[1] Even areas uninvaded by these plants have had their turf injured by overgrazing.

Soil

The soil of the semi-arid and arid lands is commonly fertile, lacking mainly adequate humus and water. Spanish and Indian tillage of the soil was limited to a few easily irrigable areas. During the Texas Republic (1836–1845), German and American farmers established farms, but cotton farming did not enter the Southwest until just before the Civil War when it became the major crop on Houston clay, a prairie soil that extends approximately from San Antonio through Dallas into southern Oklahoma. Unfortunately the clean cultivation of this black soil and adjacent lighter soils to the west caused soil deterioration from leaching and water erosion; hence this once rich cotton land is being increasingly used for cattle, fodder crops, and poultry. Soil use further west is limited by lack of water; in some cases soil has been injured by underwatering causing alkali accumulation or overwatering causing an overhigh water table. Wind erosion is a further problem in the arid and semi-arid Southwest. All in all, the soil resource seems to have been considerably diminished by a century of use (a half century of use in most Southwestern irrigated areas).

Water

Sufficient water has always been a critical factor in the Southwest (Figures 14-3 and 14-4). The location of streams and water holes was of major concern to early explorers, cattlemen, and settlers. Even the presence of a river valley did not guarantee water, for many streams are dry during much of the year. Well-drilling machinery was a godsend, enabling underground water to be tapped. Yet this groundwater was not unlimited, and many areas today are discovering that the water table is dropping year after year. This is especially serious in Texas and Oklahoma where unlimited groundwater may be pumped by the owner of the surface although rights to surface water use are carefully regulated.

Assuming that water is conserved by storage reservoirs, retardation of evaporation, and efficient use, the problem of quality still remains. Some of the groundwater is saline or at least brackish. Much of the surface water carries a heavy load of silt so that reservoirs may fill up in a century or less. Irrigated lands must be drained to remove surplus alkali; this increases the salinity of the discharged water. Much more serious is contamination from municipal sewage, industrial wastes, and wastes from mining operations.

The easily available resources of the region are harnessed except for modest supplies of brackish water which may be desalinated. Further plans for each subregion involve water; for example, an elaborate study[2] made of eight river basins in Texas presented a plan for the utilization of the bulk of all Texas water through the year 2010. This involves flood and pollution control, hydroelectric power, drainage, irrigation, and municipal and industrial water supply, at a capital cost of $3 billion for an area with an estimated 2010 population of 20 million. The recommendations, comprehensive though they are, will not cure all the major water problems; for example, the fossil groundwater supply now being

---

[1] See David R. Harris, "Recent Plant Invasions in the Arid and Semi-arid Southwest of the United States," *Annals A.A.G.*, vol. 56 (1966), pp. 408–422; also James C. Malin, *The Grassland of North America*, privately printed, Lawrence, Kansas, 1948.

[2] *Report of U.S. Study Commission*, 4 parts, Austin, March, 1962; also available as 87th Cong., 2d Sess., H. Doc. 494, 1962.

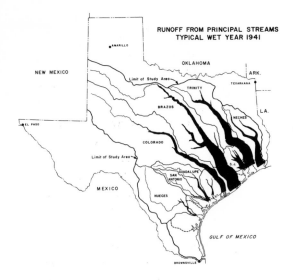

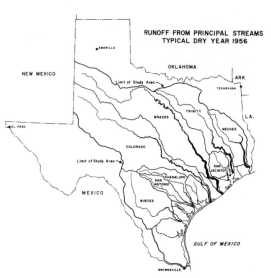

FIGURE 14-3 *Average climatic and climate-related data are apt to be misleading; hence data are given here for extreme rather than average years.* (THE REPORT OF THE U.S. STUDY COMMISSION: TEXAS, Austin, 1962.)

pumped to irrigate cotton on the High Plains will be largely used up by the year 2010.

Petroleum and Natural Gas

Although the first oil well drilled in Texas dates from 1866, the Texas-Oklahoma oil boom really began at the beginning of the present century. In recent years Southwest-

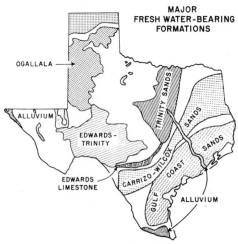

FIGURE 14-4 *In Texas, groundwater supplements streams as a source of water supply and in many areas is the major water source. The Ogallala formation is a water reserve that is not being replenished. The areas dependent on Gulf Coast sands are expected to supplement their supplies by distilling seawater.* (THE REPORT OF THE U.S. STUDY COMMISSION: TEXAS, Austin, 1962.)

ern minerals have accounted for over one-third of the value of United States mineral production; in the Southwest five-sixths of this value has been from petroleum and natural gas; in Texas and Oklahoma over nine-tenths of the value is from petroleum and gas. There is little doubt that much of the economic and population growth of the Southwest in recent decades is attributable to minerals and mineral-based industries.

Oil and/or natural gas are widespread in Texas (205 out of 254 counties), Oklahoma (66 out of 77 counties), and northwestern and southeastern New Mexico (8 out of 32 counties). This huge fuel resource should not be thought of as a unit; rather it consists of a number of fields (each of which might be divided into subunits) whose production rises rapidly with new discoveries and falls with depletion. Production is also controlled by state regulation to prevent flooding the market. The earliest oil discoveries were in the eastern parts of Texas and Oklahoma; the leading gas-and-oil-producing counties today are mostly in the Amarillo-Lubbock-Odessa area of

NORTHEAST OF AMARILLO, Texas, hard winter wheat shares the land with oil pumps. The latter occupy the smaller part of the area but produce the greater income. (Texas Highway Department.)

Texas, adjacent New Mexico, and the Oklahoma Panhandle. Obviously the future of the petroleum–natural gas industry depends on reserves, and Southwestern proved resources are high: half the nation's reserves or enough to equal 14 years current national production are in the Southwest. Proved reserves only indicate the resources the industry considers certain to exist; past experience indicates that actual reserves may greatly exceed the reserves considered "proved."

The extraction of petroleum and natural gas employs only about 150,000 out of 5 million in the Southwestern labor force. However, indirect employment in petrochemical manufacturing, equipment for oil wells, oil storage and shipment is much higher. In addition, the production of mineral fuels has yielded capital for economic growth, thus bringing in industries which may continue long after the oil and gas are exhausted.

Copper

The developing electrical industry has increased the use of copper and incidentally promoted the economic growth of southwestern New Mexico and southeastern Arizona. Copper, discovered at Bisbee, Arizona, in 1877 has produced four-fifths of all Arizona mineral wealth; it is the major source of income for Grant County in New Mexico, and Cochise, Greenlee, and Pinal counties in Arizona. The copper economy there as elsewhere is complicated because the profitability of exploiting its ores depends on competition from other areas; the recovery of by-products such as gold, silver, lead, and manganese; and changing costs resulting from technological advances. In Yavapai County, for example, the Jerome District, two decades ago the seventh largest copper producer in the United States, has been abandoned, while Bagdad, an isolated copper camp 60 miles to the west, is a growing minor producer that obtains silver and molybdenum as by-products. In contrast to petroleum and natural gas, copper has caused little industrial development in the two producing states, adjacent El Paso having benefited most from this type of business.

Sunny Climate

Now that air conditioning has lessened the problem of excessive summer heat, the advantages of this mild climate, frost-free from two-thirds to most of the year, attract many. Sunny days are characteristic, and the percent of possible sunshine received ranges from 70 (in central Texas) to 90 (in southwestern Arizona). Pure air is widely available, although unfortunately this con-

TABLE 14-1   Average Air Pollution—National Air Sampling Levels, 1963 and 1964

City	Suspended Particulate Matter (micrograms per cubic meter)		Benzene-soluble Organic Matter (micrograms per cubic meter)		Radioactivity (micromicrocuries per cubic meter)	
	1963	1964	1963	1964	1963	1964
CITIES IN THE SOUTHWEST:						
Dallas	88	97	6.6	8.4	5.6	1.3
Houston	100	97	7.8	6.2	6.7	1.2
San Antonio	77	104	5.7	5.4	6.6	1.4
Albuquerque	160	135	10.7	8.7	7.8	1.8
Phoenix	201	192	12.9	11.0	9.3	2.0
OTHER CITIES FOR COMPARISON:						
San Diego	87	84	10.2	6.6	7.1	1.5
Las Vegas	171	158	10.7	8.1	12.5	1.8
New York	215	197	17.1	12.2	8.6	1.4
St. Louis	118	148	8.4	8.1	7.0	1.2
Burlington, Vt.	38	71	3.4	2.8	6.2	1.2

SOURCE: U.S. Bureau of the Census, *Statistical Abstract of the United States*, Washington, 1965, p. 177; 1966, p. 180.

dition is disappearing in the metropolitan central cities (Table 14-1).

RESOURCES, EMPLOYMENT, AND INCOME

Table 14-2 shows that the four Southwestern states have had surprisingly little of their labor force employed in mineral production, although minerals have, no doubt, contributed much to Southwestern development. The availability of good grass, soil, and water rates much higher in employment statistics; but these directly account today for a modest and decreasing percentage of all employment. The bulge is in services including (for 1960) trade, 20.0 percent;

TABLE 14-2   Distribution by Industry of Southwestern[1] Labor Force, 1870–1960 (percent of total)

Census	Agriculture, Forestry, Fisheries	Mining	Manufacturing	Services and Others
1870	73.85	0.31	7.04	18.80
1880	72.62	1.29	6.41	19.68
1890	64.30	1.14	9.11	25.45
1900	67.14	1.65	8.35	22.86
1910	58.08	1.77	12.37	27.78
1920	45.11	3.49	15.62	35.68
1930	37.56	2.90	17.45	42.09
1940	29.49	3.47	8.11	58.93
1950	16.31	3.52	11.01	69.16
1960	8.40	3.38	14.42	73.80

[1] Note that data are for all the four states and include parts of Texas and Oklahoma not included in the Southwest as here defined.

SOURCES: Calculated from Harvey S. Perloff et al., *Regions, Resources, and Economic Growth*, published for Resources for the Future, Inc., Johns Hopkins, Baltimore, 1960, pp. 179, 270; and U.S. Bureau of the Census, *County and City Data Book: 1962*, Washington, 1962.

government including Armed Forces, 10.2 percent; medical and other professional services, 11.4 percent. How major activities contribute to income is shown in Table 14-3, and how the Southwestern income differs from that of the nation is shown in Figure 1-6.

THE EASTERN TRANSITION ZONE

A subhumid area, subject to wide fluctuations in precipitation, soil moisture, and stream flow, extends along the eastern edge of the Southwest. In the past this was a significant area for range cattle, for raising cotton, for farmers learning to adjust to conditions in the drier lands, and, in the present century, for oil fields. Physically this is the transition from the Coastal Plain to the Great Plains to the west, to the Central Lowland to the north. The soils are prairie soils, generally fertile and neither strongly acid nor alkaline; the vegetation is a transition from open forest to grassland in the Cross Timbers belt back again to open forest. Finally, this transition zone includes a line of major cities: San Antonio, Austin, Waco, Dallas–Fort Worth, Oklahoma City,

and Tulsa, each located where a river from the west or northwest cuts across the transition zone toward the Gulf (although the rivers were not the major reason for the location of each city).

San Antonio and Southern Texas

The oldest and southernmost of these large cities serves a huge ranchland and irrigated farmland area extending east to the Gulf and south and west to the Rio Grande and its irrigated winter garden of citrus and winter vegetables. North of the irrigated area are huge ranges including the 900,000-acre holdings of the King Ranch where Zebu cattle were bred with Herefords and other European breeds to produce high-grade cattle suited to tropical and subtropical weather. Northward the ranch area grades into a cotton-grain area amid which is San Antonio, founded by the Spanish as a political capital in 1718, later becoming a stockyard center, and recently a military and governmental center. Included also in the commercial area of San Antonio is the moister eastern part of the Edwards Plateau, edged by the Balcones Escarpment. Around San Antonio the visitor can see within 25

TABLE 14-3 Industrial Sources of Civilian Income Received by Persons for Participation in Current Production and Total Personal Income: Four Southwestern States, 1966 (in millions of dollars)

Source	Tex.	Okla.	N. Mex.	Ariz.	4 States
Farms	1,368	344	145	166	2,022
Mining	962	340	127	154	1,584
Construction	1,448	248	133	222	2,051
Manufacturing	4,335	763	121	583	5,801
Trade	4,096	814	293	556	5,759
Financial	1,138	226	78	179	1,620
Transport and Utilities	1,635	358	143	220	2,357
Services	2,881	578	353	486	4,298
Government	2,934	818	454	562	4,769
Other	68	15	5	11	99
Civilian Income	20,864	4,503	1,853	3,140	30,361
Personal Income	27,319	6,099	2,390	4,078	39,886

SOURCE: *Survey of Current Business*, vol. 47 (August, 1967), no. 8, p. 37.

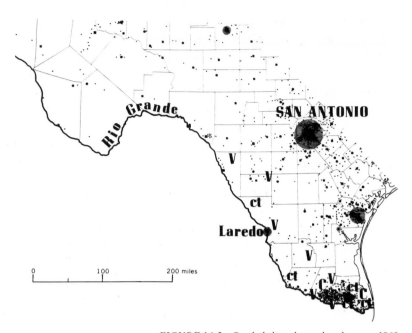

FIGURE 14-5   Symbols have been placed upon a 1960 population map of southern Texas to represent the specialties of the irrigated lower Rio Grande Valley: V = winter vegetables, C = citrus fruits, ct = cotton. (Base map from Bureau of the Census.)

miles the change from an open cattle range to the goat and sheep ranges on the plateau and to mechanized farming on the dark soils extending northeastward.

Austin and the Black Waxy Prairie

About 75 miles northeast of San Antonio is another governmental center, state rather than federal. Austin, capital of Texas, located where the Colorado River[3] crosses the Balcones Escarpment onto the prairie, is largely supported by state offices and institutions. Near Austin, the Black Waxy Prairie (or Blackland), named for its rich, limey soil, widens and forms an extensive, well-farmed area, once devoted to cotton but now highly diversified with mechanized cotton farming intermixed with dairying, beef cattle, poultry, hogs, grain, and vegetables. As in the Corn Belt, the cities are also developing manufactures. The largest of these cities, Waco on the Brazos River, produces, for example, tires, laundry machinery, rocket fuel, and clothing.

[3] Not to be confused with the Colorado River of Colorado, Utah, and Arizona. The name Colorado (Red) is a natural name where streams are colored with mud.

The Dallas–Fort Worth Megalopolis

These twin cities on the sometimes dry, sometimes flooded Trinity River include six counties and 2 million people in their contiguous SMSAs. Their urban activities now overshadow farming and ranching in the surrounding rural area they were created to serve. Fort Worth, after a few years as a military outpost on the edge of Indian country, became a market center for west Texas, gradually adding functions such as stockyards, meat packing, railroad center, and oil refining. During World War II aircraft factories were moved into the area from the Atlantic Coast to take advantage of a more defensible location. Much of the new industrial development took place between Fort Worth and Dallas.

Fort Worth was oriented westward; the older and much larger Dallas was originally oriented eastward, being more interested in Wall Street than in the livestock market.

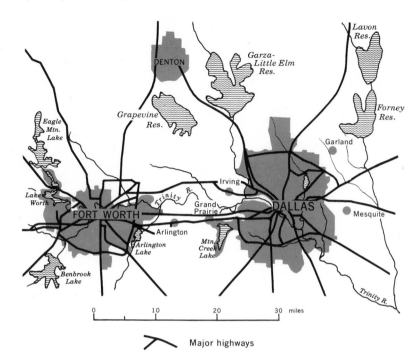

FIGURE 14-6 *As the twin cities of Dallas and Fort Worth grow, the problem of urban water supply becomes increasingly urgent, and as for most cities, related reservoirs expand in the surrounding area.*

The city started as the commercial center for the Black Waxy Prairie cotton area, specializing in cotton machinery, textiles, and, in recent decades, electrical machinery. Dallas is a Federal Reserve Bank city serving all of Texas and southern New Mexico and Arizona. Over one hundred insurance companies and innumerable regional sales offices are located there. Its shops are considered so outstanding that recently it has been recognized as a style center for ladies' clothing. Although most Anglo-American cities the size of Dallas offer a cosmopolitan range of activities, Dallas ranks not far below New York, Chicago, and Los Angeles in its diverse cultural and business interests.

Central Oklahoma

North of the Red River the land was deeded to the Indians; hence white settlers were (officially) kept out of Oklahoma until 1889. The prairie soils of Texas continue across the border; the topography is adequately described as rolling plain; the vegetation was originally mixed prairie and open for-

est. Climatically the area is the northern frontier of the land of cotton; economically most of the northern half of Oklahoma has proved more profitable in wheat, sorghum, and cattle.

Tulsa The major stimulus to east central Oklahoma development was oil. In 1901 oil was struck near the minor farm center of Tulsa on the Arkansas; several decades later the city with some truth claimed to be the "Oil Capital of the World." Although the center of Oklahoma petroleum production has moved southwest and west, the city flourishes as a center of research in oil technology; oil company offices; and oil-financing, oil-refining, and airline servicing. Manufacturing is highly diversified.

Oklahoma City Oklahoma City was founded as a boom town on April 22, 1889, the day this section of the territory was opened to settlement. It was made state capital in 1910, but its real boom began after 1928 with the discovery of oil around and in the city. In addition to its political and commercial functions, the capital soon added manufacturing, especially in lines related to oil and aircraft.

Population problems   As in the Plains states to the north (of which Oklahoma is essentially a continuation), Oklahoma has lost rural population steadily while the larger cities have grown. This urban growth has not sufficed to maintain the total population which in 1960 was 58,000 less than in 1930. In the 1950s 72 out of 77 counties had a net out-migration; 64 experienced a loss in population. Only five counties (within which are the cities of Bartlesville, Tulsa, Oklahoma City, Norman, and Lawton) had an employment pattern showing a net gain, 1950–1960, compared with the country as a whole. Oklahoma is no poorer in resources or human ability than other Anglo-American agricultural areas, but its good soil, petroleum, and natural gas alone have not be sufficient to ensure continued growth.

THE SOUTHERN PLAINS

The image of the Plains has changed greatly since they were first visited by American explorers. Damned by explorers Pike and Long as a vast desert and long classified on maps as the "Great American Desert," the Plains at first were an obstacle to be traversed rather than a land to be used. Later

FIGURES 14-7 and 14-8   These two SMSAs are close together; yet their industrial specialties are different. How might you account for the negative deviations in each?

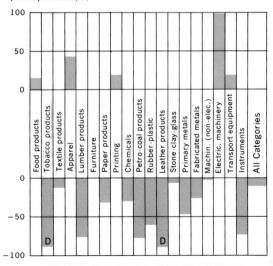

Deviation from U.S.
per capita data, %

VALUE ADDED BY MANUFACTURING
Fort Worth SMSA = .33% U.S. Pop.

VALUE ADDED BY MANUFACTURING
Dallas SMSA = .68% U.S. Pop.

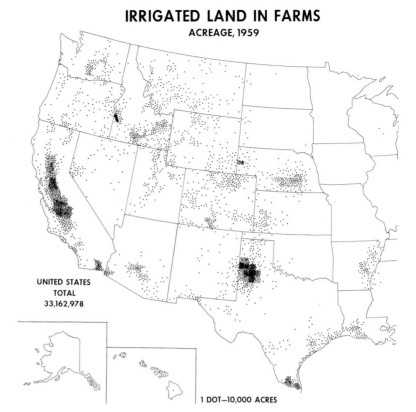

IRRIGATED LAND IN FARMS
ACREAGE, 1959

UNITED STATES
TOTAL
33,162,978

1 DOT—10,000 ACRES

FIGURE 14-9 *In the Southwest, the irrigated lands represent three types of irrigation: the ricelands of the Texas-Louisiana border; the river-irrigated lands of the Rio Grande, the Gila system, and the lower Colorado; and the well-irrigated cotton and other crops on the High Plains.* (Bureau of the Census.)

the transcontinental railroads, favored by a period of relatively rainy weather, were able to attract settlers to the fertile grasslands. Nevertheless, most settlement of the Texas-Oklahoma plains, except for open-range grazing, was deferred to the present century.

Edwards Plateau

This vast limestone upland, ranging from 1,000 to 4,000 feet in height, is bounded sharply to the south and east by the Balcones Escarpment and merges northward into the High Plains. A detached segment of the plateau is cut off from the main upland by the Pecos Valley. Essentially it is ranch country—cattle, sheep, and goats—with some farming in the valley to grow fodder. The underlying limestone stores water which can be recovered through wells. The widely scattered towns are small local service centers. The only cities large enough

to have daily newspapers are on the edge of the area; the largest, San Angelo, now an SMSA, is an oil center near an air force base. The plateau is somewhat larger than Indiana; yet its population is only 275,000, one-fourth of which is in the San Angelo SMSA.

The Rolling Plains

West of the Western Cross Timbers between the Colorado and the Canadian rivers lies a diverse section characterized by a mixture of grassland and scrub woodland. Its rainfall is barely enough for nonirrigated farming (cotton, wheat, sorghum), and water resources for irrigation are limited; the poorer lands are in cattle ranches. In com-

THIS AND THE PHOTOGRAPH on the facing page were taken at the same
place about 60 miles west of north from Lubbock, Texas. The High Plains (shown
above in November, 1941) are marked by shallow depressions filled with water from
recent rains. Another pattern consists of the square sections into which the land was
divided by the survey. The field patterns reflect the prevalent dry-farming practices
with plowing generally following the contours as a moisture-conservation practice.
(USDA photograph.)

mon with other Plains areas, most of the
counties are losing population while the
remaining farms are growing larger. The
subregion as a whole shows a slight increase
in population based on the rapid growth of
three SMSAs, the two Texas oil centers of
Abilene and Wichita Falls, and Lawton,
Oklahoma, whose growth is partly industrial
and partly stimulated by the Fort Sill Military Reservation.

The High Plains

The abrupt Cap Rock Escarpment separates
the Rolling Plains from a higher, flat area
underlain by a water-bearing layer of rock.
The soil is fertile; the rainfall suffices for
a turf of short grass. Surface water is scarce,
and early travelers called the Llano Estacado (Staked Plain) south of the Canadian
River the "Sahara of North America." The
bulk of the land is still primarily ranching
country, but those local areas suited for oil,
wheat, or cotton produce most of its
income.

Oil, cotton, and wheat   On the Llano Estacado
west of Lubbock, a dust bowl in the 1930s,
water is being pumped up several hundred
feet to supplement the 20-inch rainfall. The
main crop is cotton, but wheat, grain sorghum, and alfalfa are grown in rotation.
Irrigation triples the cotton yield, but this
may not be a permanent technique, for by
the end of the century groundwater will
only be adequate to supply the cities. The
basis for urban development is mainly
petroleum which is found throughout the
cotton area and to the south and southwest,
being especially plentiful around the neighboring Midland and Odessa SMSAs.

In the northern Texas Panhandle and the
adjacent Oklahoma Panhandle wheat and
grain sorghum replace cotton and extensive
dry farming and a limited amount of stream
and well irrigation. Petroleum and gas deposits are plentiful north and east of Amarillo, a growing transportation, oil-refining,
and air force center. Again the limiting
factor is water, the North Texas–Oklahoma

BY THE SPRING of 1953, the area shown opposite had been converted to pump irrigation, and cotton had become the dominant crop. The season was dry (note the lack of water in the depressions). The field patterns were mostly adjusted to straight-line irrigated farming rather than dry-farming techniques. (USDA photograph.)

plains having only one-third of the irrigated land in the cotton area, and the water in the recently built Canadian River reservoir, 10 miles north of Amarillo, being reserved mainly for urban expansion. Yet with all the potential water shortage, the Southern High Plains contain a large block of counties which are maintaining or increasing in population, largely because of oil and re-lated industries.

The Pecos Plains

A 75-mile-wide basin drained southward by the Pecos separates the High Plains of Texas from mountains of western Texas and cen-tral New Mexico. Irrigation farming (cotton, vegetables, fodder) supports a number of settlements along the river; desert grazing occupies that part of the basin where herb-age can be found. Growth, concentrated in a few cities, results from minerals: produc-tive petroleum and gas fields occupy most of the basin, while most of the United States potash production is mined east of Carls-bad, a small city best known for the nearby Carlsbad Caverns.

BASINS, RANGES, AND PLATEAUS

The Pecos Plains, bordered westward by discontinuous mountain blocks extending southward from the Rockies, is a sample of the much more extensive and generally higher basins, ranges, and plateaus west of the mountains. Both are water-deficit areas with populations concentrated by available water and highly localized mineral deposits; both are crossed by important east-west routes carrying passengers and freight across the areas rather than to them. Both contain considerable numbers of Indians and Mexicans who live on a lower standard than the average American.

There is somewhat more variety west of the mountains: the scenery is spectacular with its diverse combinations of colorful rock escarpments, deep canyons, purplish mountains on the horizon, sparse grassland, sage green shrubs, and open pine-juniper forests, all brightened by a brilliant sun shining in an intense blue sky. Except for a few mountain ranges such as the volcanic San Francisco Mountain (12,670 feet) near

WHEREVER THE LAND is flat, cotton is now harvested by machine. This photograph is on the High Plains of Texas where cotton is defoliated and picked clean. (USDA photograph.)

Flagstaff, Arizona, the surface rocks are generally horizontal, but faulting has cracked the original surfaces, raising huge blocks vertically in the Colorado Plateau and tilting them somewhat in the Basin and Range country to the south. The southern area generally consists of north-south trending ranges formed from uplifted blocks but complicated locally by igneous intrusions. Between the blocks extensive basins have been filled with silt, sands, and pebbles washed or blown from the higher surrounding areas and in a few cases filled by lava flows.

The Upper Rio Grande Valley

The greater part of the population of New Mexico and trans-Pecos Texas lives within the 5- to 25-mile-wide valleys occupied by the Rio Grande and its major tributary from the west, the San Jose. The irrigated lands form a narrow strip which is segmented where the Rio Grande flows in canyons. This country of Spanish and Pueblo Indian farmers was the objective of the Santa Fe Trail over which from 1822 until the completion of the Santa Fe Railroad Yankee traders hauled manufactures to be exchanged for New Mexican gold, silver, and furs. The Santa Fe Trail started at Inde-

pendence, Missouri, and followed alternative routes, approximately those of the railroad and U.S. 56.

Albuquerque and El Paso   Today the activity of the valley is centered around two SMSAs, Albuquerque and El Paso (Figure 14-10). The first of these is the commercial, transportation, and educational center of New Mexico. Its enterprises include the expected food and meat-packing industries based on regional resources to which have been added defense and atomic industries, an outgrowth of scientific work at the atomic center at Los Alamos, 50 miles to the north. The other center, El Paso in extreme western Texas, is a railroad maintenance center, a smelting and refining center for the New Mexico–Arizona copper mines, a Federal Reserve Branch Bank city, and a major port of entry from Mexico. The surrounding area is exceptionally barren so that the irrigated areas upstream and downstream from the city stand out conspicuously from the air.

The Colorado Plateau

Ascending the San Jose Valley west of Albuquerque, the traveler is soon aware that he is in an area of Indian reservations characterized by short grass, sagebrush, and

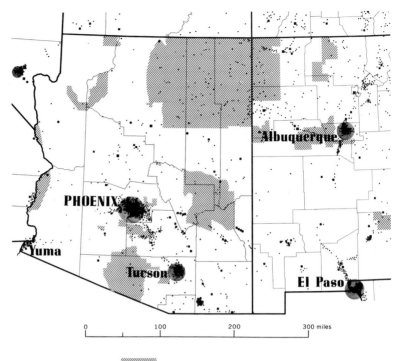

0   100   200   300 miles

▨▨▨ Indian Reservations

*FIGURE 14-10   The relation between population distri-
bution and available irrigation water in Arizona and New
Mexico seems obvious after examining Figure 14-9.
What other factors are needed for a complete explanation?* (Base map from Bureau of the Census.)

tablelands. Before one reaches Gallup, the
leading Indian center in the country, oil
refineries add an incongruous note, for
northwestern New Mexico is underlain by
oil and gas fields. Even this resource is
lacking in northeastern Arizona, a conspicuously empty area seen from either the
air or the ground. The northern counties of
Arizona, on about sixty-six thousand square
miles, support 172,000 persons, an average
of 2.7 people per square mile; most of these
live in towns along the Santa Fe Railroad
and between Flagstaff and Prescott (Figure
14-10).

Although Indian reservations are found
in all parts of Arizona and New Mexico, the
Indian population is concentrated on the
Colorado Plateau. Many of the Indians
work off the reservations and may be seen
in towns and working on highways and
other construction projects; others retain
Indian clothing to sell their services and
handicrafts to tourists; several Indian

groups have set up motels and factories, one
producing, for example, electronic parts. As
the reservation lands are held in trust by
the federal government for the tribes, oil
and other mineral discoveries benefit treas-
uries. Nevertheless Indian incomes are low:
in Arizona about one-third the average
income for the state.

The plateau surface ranges from 6,000
to 9,000 feet; consequently its precipitation
of 10 to 20 inches enables it to be classified
as semi-arid. The drier parts of the plateau
have a sparse grass or sagebrush cover; an
open scrub forest is common on the higher
levels; and the high, relatively moist areas,
like those around Flagstaff, support a forest
yielding excellent softwood. Groundwater is
not lacking but is in aquifers so deep that
pumping is rarely profitable. Major streams,

such as the Colorado, are incised as much as a mile deep so that at the Grand Canyon it was once considered cheaper to bring in water by tankcar than to pump it from the nearby river. The headwaters of the Little Colorado and other streams are at a higher level, but the irrigable area is only about 50 square miles. Ranchers and Indian shepherds dam up small valleys to impound modest supplies of water for their flocks and herds.

The income of this area is low, especially that of rural farmers and laborers. Only one-twentieth of the labor force is in farming and ranching; twice as many are employed on construction (roads and conservation projects), and half again as many engage in trade. Much employment is provided servicing tourists and freight passing through the area. Attractive though the area is physically, it has cold winter weather. Opportunities for making a good living are limited to a few towns and irrigable valleys—perhaps this is why so much of the land is still owned by the Indians.

The Basin and Range Country

The skyrocketing population that has made Arizona a boom state is concentrated in the Phoenix and Tucson SMSAs which accounted for 321,000 of the 327,000 net in-migration in the state. Northern Arizona, and especially its rural areas, had 19,000 net out-migration, which was more than offset by in-migration in two mining counties, Cochise and Pinal. The Arizona boom has been attributed to the four Cs: cattle, copper, cotton, and climate; the same might be said for the basin and range country of southwestern New Mexico. To these should be added, especially for the Phoenix-Tucson area, commerce, consumer goods, and in recent decades, retirement, electronic, and aircraft industries. Of these, cattle and copper are most concentrated in the highlands of southeastern Arizona and adjacent New Mexico, the other activities being found in

the irrigated areas of the Gila, the Salt, and other Gila tributaries.

As in most of the West, minerals were the original incentive for exploration and at least temporary settlement. Silver ores were first discovered by the Spanish in the late sixteenth century, but no major discoveries were made until the mid-nineteenth century when silver was exploited south of Tucson, and copper and gold between Tucson and the Colorado. Larger-scale operations developed in the highland ranges after 1875 as transcontinental railroads were constructed into the area. Gradually the emphasis shifted to copper (with lead, zinc, and silver as by-products), and since 1907 Arizona has been the leading copper-producing state in all but a few years. Adjacent New Mexico contributes about one-eighth as much copper—still sufficient to rank that state fourth among the nation's producers in 1965.

These minerals have not been necessarily produced continuously at one place. Ghost towns are common: for example, Jerome with its huge smelter at nearby Clarksdale, closed down operations in 1953 after producing 2.75 billion pounds of copper which, including gold, silver, and zinc by-products, were valued at $0.5 billion. All metallic ores produced since the beginning of mining are estimated at over $1.5 billion in New Mexico and nearly $10 billion in Arizona—a sizable chunk of capital for other developments.

Phoenix SMSA   Half the Arizona population is concentrated in the Salt River Valley around Phoenix. The growth of the city from a small irrigation center was stimulated by the construction of Roosevelt Dam (45 miles upstream), the first dam built under the Federal Reclamation Act. Cotton farming is the main farm activity, but there has been increasing diversification (vegetables, dairying, fodder) to meet market demands. Manufacturing, once limited to food products and metals, is now highly diversified (Figure 14-11) with electronics, miscellaneous manufactures, and aircraft each providing more employment than the previously mentioned industries. Above all, Phoenix is a service city, emphasizing trade, business, personal services, and government. The importance of tourist business is reflected in tourist expenditures equal to one-tenth of the state's personal income.

Tucson SMSA   The Santa Cruz tributary of the Gila waters an irrigated area north of Tucson, an outgrowth of an early Spanish settlement. In the nature of their business, the two Arizona metropolitan areas are similar except in size and in the greater emphasis of mine-connected business in Tucson. Industries including food and mineral processing, aircraft and missiles, and air conditioning account for one-sixth of the employment; more important are the diverse personal and business services offered.

In 1960 Arizona was greatly heartened by the U.S. Supreme Court's support of the state's contention that California was using a much greater quantity of Colorado River water than was permitted under the 1922 Colorado River Compact. This award makes possible the Central Arizona Project which will divert into the Salt-Gila irrigation area 1 million acre-feet of water, approximately the amount that California has taken in excess of its legal share. The regulation of the Colorado water supply has been greatly aided by the construction of a dam at Page, Arizona, which backs up the water in Glen and other canyons over one hundred miles.

FIGURE 14-11   Phoenix is not essentially a manufacturing center, but its residential attractions for trained people are such that its SMSA is attracting industries producing a high value added per ton.

CONCLUSIONS

It has been remarked that all the Southwest needs is more good water and more good people. Except for Oklahoma, which has suffered from the rural population decline characteristic of the Plains, the Southwest has been growing rapidly in population. Attempts have been made to conserve and store up more water for the growing population. This indeed is the limiting factor, for not only is water scarce; much of it is also being polluted. Reservoirs are not permanent resources; they fill up with silt, debris, and other pollutants; the prediction that water will become too scarce to be used for crops and will be reserved for people seems relevant for this region.

As important to regional development have been mineral resources—oil in the eastern Southwest, and metals elsewhere. These show no immediate prospect of exhaustion except in specific localities; new discoveries seem likely to be adequate to replace exhausted fields for at least a half century. Fortunately the wealth from oil,

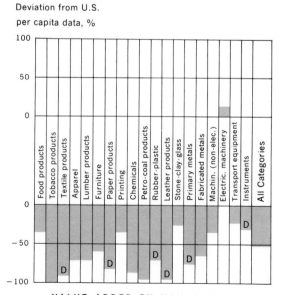

Deviation from U.S. per capita data, %

VALUE ADDED BY MANUFACTURING

Phoenix SMSA = .45% U.S. Pop.

gas, and copper have been largely capital-
ized in other industries, especially manufacturing and services. Here the mild climate with long scorching summers made
tolerable by air conditioning seems to favor
the milder southern two-thirds of the region.
As in the High West to be discussed next,
the Southwest contains many areas more
interesting to visit than able to provide a
good living; it also contains many spacious
sites suitable for uncrowded urban and
suburban development.

SELECTED REFERENCES

CROSS, JACK L., et al.: *Arizona: Its People and
Resources,* University of Arizona Press, Tucson, 1960.

FEDERAL RESERVE BANK OF DALLAS: *Monthly
Review;* contains articles of geographic significance in most issues.

GOLZÉ, ALFRED R.: *Reclamation in the United
States,* Caxton, Caldwell, Idaho, 1961.

HORGAN, PAUL: *Great River: The Rio Grande in
North American History,* Rinehart, New York,
1954. Volume 2 is especially valuable to the
historical geographer.

HUNDLEY, NORRIS, JR.: *Dividing the Waters,*
University of California Press, Berkeley and
Los Angeles, 1966.

OKLAHOMA STATE UNIVERSITY COLLEGE OF
BUSINESS: *The Oklahoma Economy,* Economic
Research Series No. 1, Stillwater, 1963.

The Report of the U.S. Study Commission, 4
parts, Austin, March, 1962; also available as
87th Cong., 2d Sess. H. Doc. 494, 1962.

ZIERER, CLIFFORD M. (ed.): *California and the
Southwest,* Wiley, New York, 1956.

FIGURE 15-1 *Landforms and railroads of the High West. The railroad symbols have been extended only to the edge of the region. Do either the landforms or the railroads actually stop at the regional boundary? If you were to revise this chapter, what regional boundaries would you select?* (Base map copyright by A. K. Lobeck. Reprinted with permission of The Geographical Press, Hammond, Inc.)

CHAPTER 15

THE SPARSELY SETTLED HIGH WEST

Scenically nature has been good to the High West: a land of spectacular mountains, colorful canyons, extensive tablelands, and gently sloping alluvial fans. Economically the region is less blessed: Water is scarce; exploitable minerals are in relatively small and scattered areas; and tourist income, concentrated in three months of the year, is important mainly near a dozen or so well-known attractions. The

BASIC DATA:

AREA INCLUDES	Land Area (thousand sq. mi.)	Population Change, 1950–1960	Population 1960 (thousands)	Population 1967 (thousands)	Personal Income 1967 (billions)
HIGH WEST	601.6	21.1%	4,292	5,039	$13.9
Montana	145.7	14.2	675	730	1.9
Idaho (part)	78.2	13.7	579	637	1.7
Wyoming	97.4	13.6	330	350	0.9
Colorado	103.9	32.4	1,754	2,200	6.5
Utah	82.3	29.3	891	1,045	2.6
Nevada (part)	92.6	7.6	63	77	0.3
MAJOR SMSAS					
Denver	3.7	51.8%	929	1,210	$ 3.9
Colorado Springs	2.2	92.9	144	200	0.6
Pueblo	2.4	31.6	118	138	0.3
Salt Lake City	0.8	39.3	448	555	1.6
Billings	2.6	41.4	79	85	0.3
Great Falls	2.7	38.5	73	86	0.3
Boise	1.0	32.3	93	105	0.3

CLIMATE — Generally semi-arid on the flatter areas, but much local variation based on altitude and exposure.

	Temperature (°F) Jan.	Temperature (°F) July	Precipitation (inches) Annual	Precipitation (inches) Season
Billings (3,117 ft)	23	71	13	Summer maximum
Butte (5,767 ft)	23	65	14	Summer maximum
Denver (5,280 ft)	29	73	15	Summer maximum
Leadville (10,200 ft)	18	56	20	Summer maximum
Salt Lake City (4,306 ft)	27	77	14	Cooler seasons
Boise (2,739 ft)	29	75	11	Cooler seasons

VEGETATION — Considerable local variation: Generally short grass on the Plains; open coniferous forest on the mountains and high plateaus; scattered shrubs in the interior basins (sagebrush, etc.).

SOIL — On the Plains, alkaline brown soils; on the mountains and high plateaus, mostly thin rocky soils; in the filled basins, desert soils productive when irrigated.

MINERALS — Coal and petroleum in the Plains; local concentrations of copper, gold, silver, lead, zinc, uranium, and salts in the mountains and plateaus; coal and petroleum on the northern Colorado Plateau.

population of this vast region is less than that of Indiana, whose area is only one-sixteenth as large. In per capita income the High West averages below the nation—only the Southern states have a lower average!

NATIVE VEGETATION

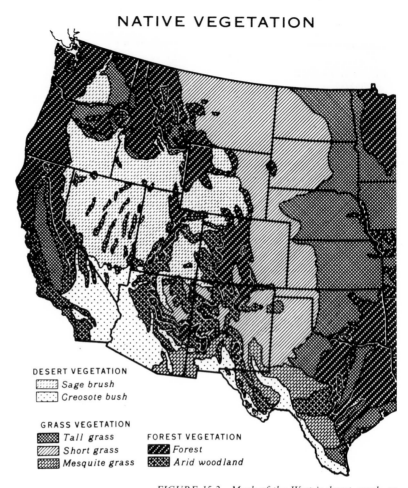

DESERT VEGETATION
⬜ Sage brush
⬜ Creosote bush

GRASS VEGETATION
⬛ Tall grass
⬛ Short grass
⬛ Mesquite grass

FOREST VEGETATION
⬛ Forest
⬛ Arid woodland

FIGURE 15-2   Much of the West is desert, scrub, or short grassland; its population (see front endpaper and Figure 18-2) is concentrated mainly near the wooded areas, especially where snowcapped and wooded mountains provide water for irrigation and domestic water supply. (USDA.)

The population of the High West is clustered in a few places: one-third lives in the Denver and Salt Lake City SMSAs. Aside from the urban and irrigation settlements along the Rocky Mountain Piedmonts of Colorado and Montana, along the Wasatch Piedmont in Utah, and on the Snake Plains of Idaho, towns are small, and rural settlement ranges from sparse to nil. Although many counties in the region exceeded the smaller Eastern states in area, in 1960, 79 out of 225 had less than 5,000 people; 11 less than 1,000.

More than half the land is government owned, and the proportion is this low only because most of the Plains area is privately owned. Government ownership accounts for 86 percent of the land in Nevada, 67

percent in Utah, and 64 percent in Idaho. Government disbursements (three-fifths federal) account for one-quarter of all personal income.

Boundaries

The High West has been delimited rather arbitrarily for statistical purposes by the use of political boundaries. The exact boundaries make only minor differences in terms of economic and human geography since the areas of dense population are well inside the arbitrary boundaries. The area described consists primarily of the Rocky Mountain region as delimited by the U.S. Office of Business Economics. To this have been added those counties of central and eastern Nevada which seem more related to the Mormon capital at Salt Lake City than to the Pacific Coast. On the other hand, five counties in western Idaho have been included with the Pacific Northwest because they are commercially tributary to Spokane.

The region is largely semi-arid except near the Rocky Mountains which make up its core (Figure 15-1). Eastward the higher and drier half of the Plains is included; westward the volcanic Snake Plains and most of the Great Basin. South and west of the Rockies the northern part of the Colorado Plateau adds considerable area but little population to the region. The southern parts of the plateau and of the Rockies have been treated as part of the Southwest (Chapter 14) because their commercial and cultural contacts have been generally southward.

THE REGIONAL ECONOMY

To what extent are the region's resources reflected in employment and income? Among early reasons for settlement were mineral resources: at first, gold and silver; later almost the whole range of minerals from stone, coal, and petroleum to uranium. Yet in 1965 mining provided only 3.3 percent of the employment and 3.7 percent of the income. The precious metals are now of minor importance compared with the fuels and copper (Table 15-1). Irrigation agriculture and ranching were less spectacular, but probably attracted more settlers; they provided 10.5 percent of the employment and 9 percent of the 1965 income. Location astride routes to the Pacific Coast can be considered as a resource since regional employment in both transportation and trade is higher here than the national average. Tourist trade and the management of public lands is reflected in the higher percentage of government employment, one-third above the national average. Man-

TABLE 15-1   Value of Mineral Production in the High West, 1965 (in millions of dollars)

Mineral	Colo.	Wyo.	Mont.	Idaho	Utah	Nev.	Total
Gold	1	*	1	*	15	8	25
Silver	3	*	14	24	7	1	49
Lead and Zinc	23	—	12	38	20	2	95
Copper	3	—	68	4	183	51	309
Iron Ore	1	25	*	*	14	5	45
Molybdenum	79	—	—	—	W	W	79
Stone, Sand, Gravel	31	11	24	18	17	16	117
Petroleum and Gas	117	358	82	—	75	W	632
Coal	24	10	1	—	32	—	67
Uranium	11	17	W	—	9	W	37
Subtotal	293	421	202	84	372	83	1,455
Total	331	499	229	105	431	100	1,596

*   Less than $500,000   *W*   Data withheld.

NOTE: Small parts of Idaho and Nevada (which are of modest importance in present mineral production) are included above although they are not in the High West as defined above.

SOURCE: U.S. Bureau of Mines, *Minerals Yearbook: 1965*, vol. 3, Washington, 1967.

ufacturing provides less than one-seventh of all employment, or about one-half the national average; food processing is the outstanding industry, but in the SMSAs there is a great variety of industry providing goods for local consumption as well as highly localized resource-based industries such as primary metals and lumber processing. There are also specialized machinery industries, e.g., mining machinery.

How the various sources of regional income compare with those of the country as a whole is shown in Figure 15-3. Although primary resources provide directly only one-seventh of the income as in most regions, these resources and, especially in recent decades, governmental expenditures are the foundation of the regional economy.

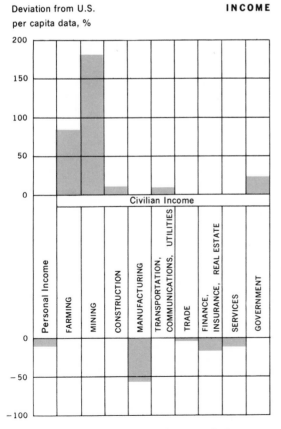

Rocky Mountain States = 2.46% U.S. Pop.

Economic History

The High West was settled piecemeal; nevertheless some generalizations can be made about its economic history. Table 15-2 shows the early importance of agriculture and mining, their gradual later decline, and the rise of the other occupations, mostly services such as trade, transportation, finance, and government. The first whites to settle the area were the Mormons who without previous experience started irrigating east of Great Salt Lake in 1847. Many pioneers crossed the region en route to Oregon or California without testing either its mineral or its agricultural potential. Gold was discovered near Denver in 1858 and shortly thereafter in the Colorado, Montana, and Idaho mountains. Cattle from Texas were driven into Colorado soon after, and by 1871 the first herds had reached Montana. Meanwhile in 1869 the Union Pacific bisected the region, and in 1870 several agricultural colonies started irrigating the Colorado Piedmont. Placer mining soon exhausted the easily available gold; subsequently milling machinery and complicated metallurgical processes requiring considerable capital were introduced. With the arrival of the railroad at Denver in 1872, this became an ideal spot both to manufacture machinery and to process the ore.

The advancing rail net led to the settlement of the Plains in the late 1880s, in part by ranchers who fenced their range, and in part by irrigation and dry farmers. The lush pastures in the Rocky Mountain parks were already settled, and many of the interior oases had been exploited by Mormon groups. Large irrigation projects awaited the help of the federal government, which, although granted by the Reclamation Act

FIGURE 15-3 The income pattern of the High West is remarkably similar to that of the Southwest (Figure 1-6).

THIS VIEW OF PAONIA DAM in west central Colorado (60 miles east of Grand Junction) shows forested slopes backed by snowcapped mountains. The problem is to get this water on the land where it will be used most productively. Some of this water will probably be used in Arizona and California. (U.S. Department of Interior.)

TABLE 15-2   Industrial Distribution of Rocky Mountain States Labor Force, 1870-1960 (percent of total)

Labor Force (thousands)	Census	Agriculture	Mining	Forestry	Manufacturing	Other
71	1870	33.6	26.5	0.8	12.9	26.1
188	1880	24.0	26.4	1.0	18.0	30.6
397	1890	26.5	12.7	1.2	20.0	39.6
525	1900	30.1	14.7	0.7	18.7	36.0
855	1910	29.9	8.5	0.7	20.5	40.4
964	1920	32.9	6.7	1.1	18.7	40.7
1,013	1930	31.0	5.2	1.0	18.1	44.7
1,107	1940	25.1	5.1	0.6	7.6	61.5
1,331	1950	17.8	3.4	0.5	9.4	68.8
1,501	1960	10.5	3.3	0.5	13.0	72.7

SOURCE: Harvey S. Perloff et al., *Regions, Resources, and Economic Growth,* published for Resources for the Future, Inc., Johns Hopkins, Baltimore, 1960, pp. 181, 270, 622-623.

SEASONAL USE OF WESTERN RANGE

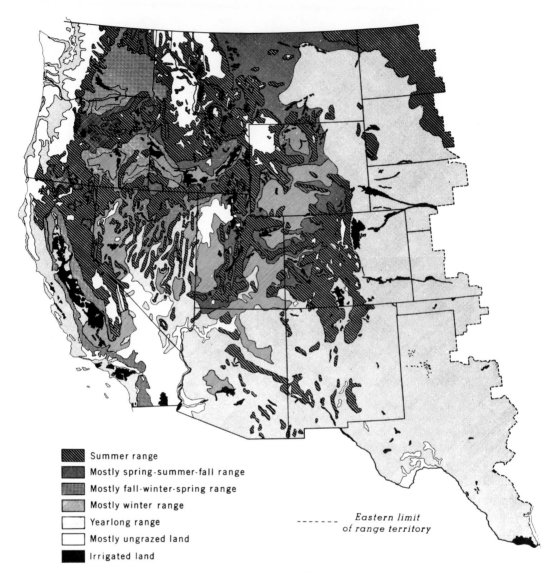

- Summer range
- Mostly spring-summer-fall range
- Mostly fall-winter-spring range
- Mostly winter range
- Yearlong range
- Mostly ungrazed land
- Irrigated land

- - - - - - - *Eastern limit*
of range territory

FIGURE 15-4   Although much of the West is commonly thought of as a vast potential ranch, there are significant differences in the quality of the range. The irrigated land provides supplementary fodder for animals inadequately nourished by the sparse natural herbage. (USDA.)

of 1902, did not produce much irrigable land for another decade. Meanwhile many gold and silver mines became exhausted, and ghost towns became a common feature; miners' attention was concentrated more on mineral raw materials and fuels, especially on copper, lead, zinc, alloy metals, petroleum, coal, and uranium. The national parks had been available for decades by rail, but the tourist business really boomed with the universal ownership of the auto-

mobile and the development of paved highways. Thus in less than a century the High West has changed from a primitive area strewn with mining camps and irrigation towns to a largely empty area crossed by a network of highways and punctuated by relatively small but modern cities.

Land and water titles The High West has devised many institutions which were new to settlers from the humid East. English common law, developed in a land of adequate water, developed the *riparian doctrine* under which the landowner has the full right to use any water flowing in or past his property, provided he does not diminish the volume of the stream. In contrast, 17 Western states use the *appropriation doctrine* under which the practice is "first come, first served." The settlers in each valley file with the state a claim to the right to use a certain amount of the water. If the claim is approved, the landlord has a perpetual right to this amount of surface water as long as he continues to use it for the purpose specified. The right of the earliest applicants has priority over that of later applicants so that if the stream is low, the rights of the later may have little value. The appropriation doctrine is followed everywhere in the states included in this region, as well as in Arizona, New Mexico, and California; it is a common practice in all the semi-arid and arid West.

Obviously such a system requires special organizations known as irrigation districts, conservancy districts, cooperative enterprises, water users' associations, and the like; there are also federal and state reclamation projects. All these distribute the cost of irrigation canals and reservoirs for the good of their members, and enforce the legal distribution of the available water. Underground water usually belongs to the owner of the surface who by pumping at will may seriously lower the water table. For this reason, in some areas pumping is restricted.

Large land units A second distinctive Western feature is the need for large farms, especially in grazing and dry-farming areas. The 160-acre homestead, well suited to the East, was quite inadequate; 40 acres of tillable land might be suitable for an irriga-

tion farmer, but 640 acres or more were needed for dry farming, many square miles for ranching. Even a large acreage did not suffice for a ranch if well or stream water was unavailable. Various acts after 1873 made it possible to acquire larger farms, and additional land could be obtained from grants to the railroads or by purchasing adjacent farms.[1] Consequently the average farm or ranch in the region encompasses several square miles, but there is considerable variation between states: the average farm in Idaho having 452 acres; in Nevada 4,649 acres. The counties vary even more: in irrigated Ada County (Boise SMSA) 2,093 farms average 151 acres while the 18 ranches in Esmeralda County, Nevada, average 115,929 acres (181 sq. miles).

The range A third distinctive Western feature arose from the changing use of the range. With the introduction of barbed wire, private ranches were fenced in, but, until 1934, public lands were open to unrestricted grazing. Since on poorer grazing lands a square mile suffices for only one to three steers, many public lands were consistently overgrazed. The Taylor Grazing Act of 1934 reduced such damage to the range by organizing the public land into grazing districts within which grazing is now regulated by permits.

Drainage basins The importance of water resources in the High West requires a regional analysis largely in terms of drainage basins. Each river originates in seasonally snow-covered high peaks whose relatively rainy slopes have at least an open forest; the headwaters of each are commonly impounded in water bodies, some natural but more man-made. Downstream, waters are used in mining, for urban use in Piedmont cities, and finally to feed streams, irrigation canals, and the underground waters on the

---

[1] For a summary account, see R. A. Billington, *Westward Expansion,* Macmillan, New York, 1967, pp. 698–704.

adjacent plains. The surfaces of these plains were built largely by erosional debris strewn over them by debouching mountain streams. These water-interlocked parts of each stream basin are becoming increasingly interrelated physically and chemically: mountain freshets depositing erosional and mining debris over good soils developed on alluvial fans and Piedmont urban sewage polluting the waters nourishing the Plains. Alternative water uses must be considered: a rough rule of thumb is that water needed to irrigate one acre will suffice for four to five urban families housing 18 people on the same area.[2] An urban acre in industrial or commercial activity can use much more water, the net consumption being greatly influenced by the amount of purification and recycling possible and being employed in each industry.

EAST OF THE CONTINENTAL DIVIDE

The Arkansas–Upper Rio Grande Valleys

The Rockies are commonly divided into three or more somewhat parallel ranges between which intermontane basins (called *parks*) are found. In southern Colorado the parks are generally semi-arid while the peaks receive 20 to 30 inches of precipitation. The ranges consist of complexly folded, faulted, and eroded sedimentary rocks adjoined, intruded into, or altered by igneous rocks which form the moutain cores. The sedimentary rocks on the Plains to the east locally contain lignite, coal, petroleum, and natural gas, all of which are also found on the Colorado Plateau to the west; the metallic ores are especially common in the central ranges and the west.

Leadville   The Arkansas River rises in the snows on the highest of all Rocky Mountain

peaks,[3] near Leadville. A long-established trail followed the river up to Tennessee Pass (10,240 feet) and thence down Eagle Creek to the upper Colorado Valley. Gold seekers en route to California by this route discovered gold near Leadville in the fall of 1859. Word of the strike spread, and by 1861 Oro City was the most populous town in Colorado. In a few years the placer gold was exhausted, the town deserted. In 1874 prospectors discovered silver-lead ore, and by 1878 the town was revived as "Leadville" and connected with Pueblo and Denver by rail.

Smelting was done near the mines, at first using local charcoal and thus destroying huge forest acreages. Water was essential in most mining processes, but the used water was returned to the streams, slightly contaminated. Much of the mining was underground, but mine dumps and deserted houses mar the landscape. The area mined is so small a part of the Rockies that this scarring detracts little from their recreational potential.

Figure 15-5 shows the ups and downs characteristic of mining towns and the changing nature of the ore exploited. In 1961 the last smelter at Leadville was closed, but mining continues at Climax, 12 miles northeast of Leadville, where a rich deposit of molybdenum ore now accounts for nearly one-quarter of all Colorado mineral production and nearly three-fourths of the nation's molybdenum production.

Irrigation settlements   The Arkansas Valley downstream is narrow; where possible, the flood plain is irrigated to produce fodder for livestock grazing the slopes. Salida, the largest town at a junction with routes westward over Monarch Pass and southward to San Luis Park, has only 4,500 people. Across a 9,011-foot pass (Salida, 7,050 feet)

[2] M. John Loeffler, "The Population Syndromes on the Colorado Piedmont," *Annals A.A.G.,* vol. 55 (1965), p. 66.

[3] The highest peak is Mount Elbert (14,431 feet), but this distinction is of little practical significance since 53 peaks in Colorado exceed 14,000 feet.

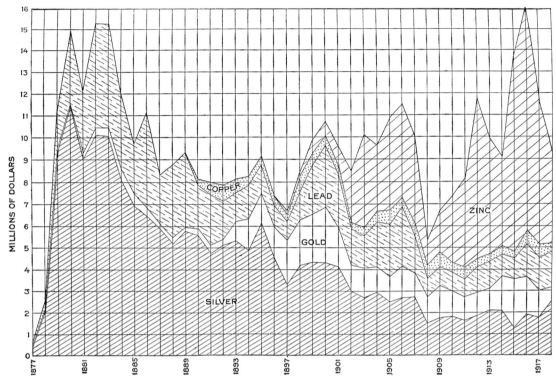

FIGURE 15-5   Lake County, Colorado, mineral production reflects the ups and downs of mining in the Leadville area. (U.S. Geological Survey Bulletin 707, p. 107.)

it is only 10 miles to the San Luis basin, about 75 miles long by 30 miles wide. Lacking minerals to attract Anglo-Saxon settlers, this basin, well irrigated by the headwaters of the Rio Grande, was settled by Spanish-speaking farmers a century ago. Vegetables and cattle are shipped out.

East of Salida the Arkansas has cut a narrow valley through a low section of the Rocky Front Range. The eastern and narrowest section is the renowned Royal Gorge; 18 miles northward is the Cripple Creek volcanic area whose mines yielded a half billion dollars of gold from 1890 until the last mine closed in 1962. Eastward the Arkansas flows across the Plains, first trenched amid a 40-mile stretch of pasture before reaching Pueblo at its junction with the Fountain River. There begins the narrow but productive irrigated area which extends eastward beyond the Kansas border, yielding sugar beets, fodder crops, vegetables, and cantaloupes. The key to

both urban and irrigated development is water, and the present supply is completely utilized—at times inadequate because of the uncertain flow of the Arkansas. Consequently the Frying Pan project has been started to divert water from the Frying Pan and Roaring Fork rivers, both tributaries of the Colorado, by tunneling under the continental divide, thus yielding additional power along the upper Arkansas before supplying water downstream.

Pueblo and Colorado Springs   Industrial Pueblo, once a fur-trading post, is now essentially a primary-metals center around which other functions, commercial, military, and service, have developed. Thanks to the foresight of the founders, the Colorado Fuel and Iron (incorporated 1872) has water rights in the Arkansas River. Its coking coal comes from near Trinidad 60 miles to the south, its

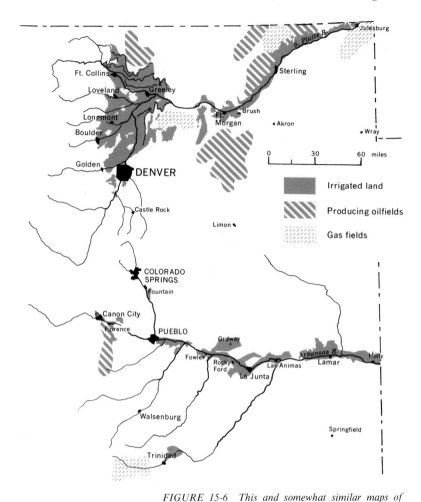

FIGURE 15-6 This and somewhat similar maps of Montana, Wyoming, and the Snake Plains of Idaho illustrate a repeating pattern in the High West: minerals; a stream for irrigation; level, irrigable farmlands; adjacent farmsteads; and modest commercial centers, a few of which have grown to have more than local importance. (After Loeffler.)

limestone from the mountains 40 miles to the west, and its iron ore from eastern Wyoming and southwestern Utah.

Colorado Springs on the Fountain River has a different history, having started as a resort center. Its industries are light (food, printing, and electronics), and its economy and growth are now dominated by the Armed Forces (Air Force Academy, Headquarters Continental Air Defense, Fort Carson) which account directly for a quarter of all employment and for even more of the purchasing power.

The South Platte and the Northern Colorado Piedmont

The South Platte, rising 15 miles east of the upper Arkansas, in its journey northeast-ward receives numerous tributaries from the High Plains to the south and from the Rockies to the northwest. Its source areas, once noted for precious minerals, today contain innumerable ghost towns, their principal mineral product now being the water that irrigates the agriculturally productive northern Colorado Piedmont. The glamour of Central City continues mainly as a tourist attraction but is overshadowed in fact as well as in metaphor by the adjacent Rockies with such attractions as Love-

THE BEAUTY OF Pikes Peak and the mineral springs was an obvious reason for the intitial development of Colorado Springs. After the 1890s, the city grew further as a commercial and smelting center for the Cripple Creek gold mining district 20 miles to the west. In recent decades military installations have further speeded growth so that Colorado Springs is now classified as an SMSA. (Colorado Springs Chamber of Commerce.)

land Pass and the Trail Ridge Road. The South Platte Valley downstream still has minerals, but the bulk of their yield is the natural gas, petroleum, coal, sand, and gravel of the plains.

Denver This mile-high city, founded to serve the adjacent mountains and the Plains, has outgrown its original hinterland. Located off through-transcontinental routes, at first it supplied urban services to the mines and to irrigated settlements which sold foodstuffs to the miners. Central to the state, it became state capital; central to the Rocky Mountain Front, it became a regional capital for an extensive region which, unfortunately for Denver, generated only a modest economy based on scattered settlements. Yet as the largest city in the High West, it attracted federal and corporation offices and developed a huge trade, so that the Moffat Tunnel and expensive highways were built through the highest part of the Rockies to give Denver direct connections westward. Business was also attracted from the Plains, and the 1963 Census showed that food products was second only to transportation equipment in manufacturing employment (Figure 15-7). The development of Denver reflects the varying eras of Colorado history classified by the University of Denver as mining (1870–1900), agriculture (1900–1940), and the Era of Defense (1940–   ).[4] Martin-Marietta's aircraft and

[4] *Economic Growth in Colorado,* Denver Research Institute, University of Denver, 1963, pp. 7-14.

missile production at Denver is mainly defense-connected, but it is by no means the only activity, data on many enterprises being classified.

The Northern Piedmont The Colorado Piedmont north and northeast of Denver supports a quarter million people. Because of the decline in agricultural employment, this is an area of modest growth. Educational centers and small manufacturing in the numerous small cities, and income from petroleum and natural gas, supplement the business generated by sugar beet, alfalfa, potato, beans, and vegetable production on this extensive outwash plain. As with the Arkansas Valley's Frying Pan project, the Big Thompson project pumps Colorado River water by tunnels under the continental divide into the Big Thompson, the central Platte tributary in the north Colorado Piedmont. Nor should the adjacent High Plains be forgotten, for its thousands of sparsely settled square miles, largely lacking water for irrigation, yield an impressive tonnage of wheat and beef in a continuation

of the farm-ranch economy of western Kansas.

The North Platte and the Yellowstone

The group of flattish intermontane basins separated by abrupt ranges, collectively known as the Wyoming Basin, divides the High Rockies so that the North Platte tributaries lead to several easy 7,500- to 8,500-foot passes employed by the major overland roads and by the fastest transcontinental railroad route. The semi-arid basins open to the north or northeast, so that the tributaries of the Platte and the Yellowstone in the High West swing north or northeast before flowing toward the Missouri.

This country was well described by a Crow chief:

The Crow country is a good country. The Great Spirit has put it exactly in the right place . . . whichever way you travel you fare worse. If you go to the south you have to wander over great barren plains . . . . To the north it is cold; the winters are long and bitter and there is no grass . . . . About the forks of the Missouri is a fine country; good water, good grass, plenty of buffalo. In summer it is almost as good as Crow country, but in winter it is cold; the grass is gone and there is no salt weed for the horses.

The Crow country has snowy mountains and sunny plains, all kinds of climate and good things for every season. When the summer heats scorch the prairies, you can draw up under the mountains where the air is sweet and cool, the grass fresh, and the bright streams come tumbling out of the snowbanks. There you can hunt the elk, the deer, and the antelope when their skins are fit for dressing; there you will find plenty of grizzlies and mountain sheep.

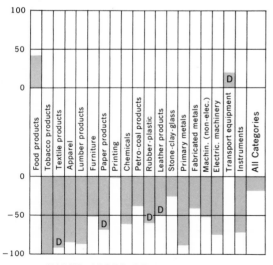

Deviation from U.S. per capita data, %

VALUE ADDED BY MANUFACTURING

Denver SMSA = .57% U.S. Pop.

FIGURE 15-7   Denver, like Phoenix, is not essentially a manufacturing city, but it is attracting some industries. The older industries processed regional products or supplied nearby markets; defense activities have brought in new industries including transportation equipment.

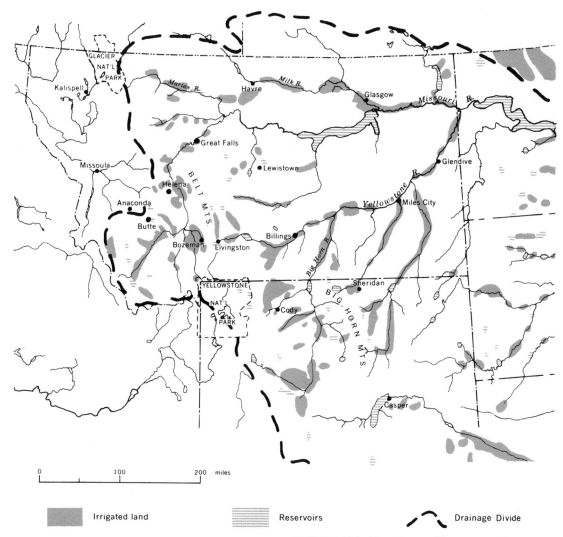

Irrigated land   Reservoirs   Drainage Divide

FIGURE 15-8 The Montana-Wyoming area has not had any urban development comparable to Denver; otherwise it has the same elements as eastern Colorado (Figure 15-6) with irrigation, dry farming, ranching, and petroleum on the Plains, and ores in the Rockies.

In the autumn when your horses are fat and strong from the mountain pastures you can go down into the plains and hunt the buffalo or trap beaver on the streams. And when winter comes on you can take shelter in the woody bottoms along the rivers; there you will find buffalo meat for yourselves and cottonwood bark for your horses, or you may winter in the Wind River Valley where there is salt weed in abundance . . . . There is no country like the Crow country.[5]

[5] From an interview by Lieut. James H. Bradley with Arapooish, Chief of the Crows, in *Contributions of the Historical Society of Montana*, vol. 9, 1923, pp. 306–307.

Today the bison are gone, and extensive reservations of relatively poor land remain to the Crow in Big Horn County, Montana, where Custer and his men were exterminated. Much of the Wyoming, Big Horn, and other basins consist of almost vacant lands with narrow oases along the streams, yielding alfalfa, sugar beets, winter wheat, hay, potatoes, and beans. In Wyoming livestock contributes four times as much as crops to the economy, and mining (largely petroleum) contributes more than farming and ranching together. Casper, slightly smaller than Cheyenne, the state capital and livestock market, is largely an oil-refining and wholesale center.

The Yellowstone   In Montana the Yellowstone River waters a narrow irrigated strip some 400 miles long amid a broad belt of sheep and cattle ranchland comparable to the mediocre range of northeastern Wyoming. Petroleum is found there too and now surpasses copper among Montana's mineral products. The commercial center for all this immense oil-ranch–oasis country is Billings, now one of the leading transportation and distributing centers of the High West. Upstream from Billings the country is rougher, more humid, and somewhat wooded. The main valley ascends to geyser-rich Yellowstone Park, so high that its narrow roads are safely snow-free for tourist travel only half of the year. West of the railroad and lumbering town of Livingston an easy pass, crossed by a transcontinental highway and the Northern Pacific, separates the Yellowstone from the ore-rich southwestern tributaries of the upper Missouri.

The upper Missouri   In the days when jets and interstate highways are taking away business from the Great Northern's *Empire Builder* and the Northern Pacific's *North Coast Limited,* it is difficult to realize that a century ago steamboats leaving St. Louis each spring were considered the easy way to get to Fort Benton, Montana. The trip took only 40 days and a wagon road completed in 1863 enabled the traveler to reach Walla Walla, Washington, whence a journey to the Pacific by the end of the summer was considered possible. Today the upper Missouri is so regulated by dams that much of it consists of wide lakes, largest of which is the 100-mile-long Fort Peck Reservoir whose creation greatly extended the poten-

tial irrigated area. Even without irrigation the Plains of northern Montana are humid enough in most years for hay and wheat farming supplemented by ranching. The population is sparse, and the towns are strung along the railroads. Settlement is denser toward the mountains; the second most populous SMSA in Montana has developed at Great Falls, where the Missouri produces power for copper, zinc, and aluminum processing.

In 1863 appreciable mountain settlement began with a gold rush at Virginia City (on the edge of the Missouri watershed, 35 miles northwest of Yellowstone Park). As in Colorado, placer gold was soon exhausted. In 1879 prospectors discovered the Butte District, an area of 8 square miles astride the continental divide on which the city of Butte is now located. Probably $3 billion worth of copper ore have been mined there with considerable silver, gold, lead, zinc, and some manganese as by-products.[6] The ore is smelted at Anaconda, 25 miles to the west, and also processed at Helena (settled in 1864 for placer gold) or at Great Falls. About 95 percent of the metallic ores mined in Montana originate in Silver Bow County in which Butte is located; the metals industry is almost entirely concentrated in an elongated triangle based on Butte and Anaconda with its apex at Great Falls. This triangle includes over half the population of all the upper Missouri Valley in Montana. Although mining employs only one-fortieth of the labor force of Montana (one-fifth of that in Silver Bow County), there is no doubt that minerals caused the development of the Missouri slope of the Rockies. Elsewhere in Montana, agriculture, which employs directly one-sixth of the state's labor force, was the motivating force for settlement. Although oil or natural gas exploitation is widespread in the Montana Plains, the total direct employment is small:

[6]The ore is expected to last another 30 to 50 years, by which time Butte hopes to develop industrially.

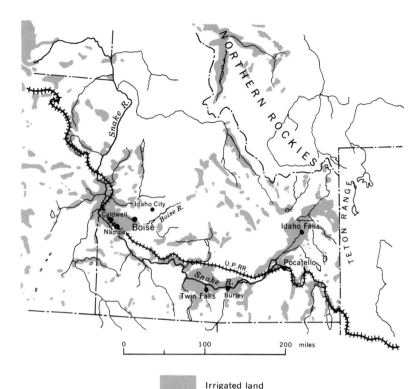

Irrigated land

FIGURE 15-9   The Snake Plains are trenched by the generally canyon-encased Snake River so that irrigation depends not only on fertile soil and level land but also on man's ability to channel water to the upland surface.

in 1960 about eighteen hundred workers for extraction and an additional twelve hundred for petroleum refining.

WEST OF THE CONTINENTAL DIVIDE

The Upper Columbia Watershed

An intricate trellis of streams separated by almost parallel ridges drains northwestern Montana and the Idaho Panhandle. The mountains are rugged, but by following the valleys draining to the Pacific or using easy passes, three transcontinental railroads and three major highways cross the area with little difficulty. More humid than the rest of Montana, this is a land of trees and recreation (Glacier Park); in the Coeur d'Alene section just across the boundary in Idaho, silver, lead, and zinc mining are added. This is the one section of the Rockies in which the lumbering industry is fully developed. Lumbering, mining, tourism, and agriculture in the broader valleys sum up

this attractive region which has much isolated and unsettled land off the main routes.

The Snake Watershed

Southern Idaho has been known for at least a century and a half, having been traversed first by fur traders and later by the Oregon Trail. Settlement was attracted by gold discoveries in the mountains north of Boise in 1862, followed by silver discoveries in southwest Idaho. Agricultural and ranch settlement was mainly to supply local markets until the construction of the Oregon Short Line (now Union Pacific) led to an irrigation boom in 1882. The cities, all modest in size, are mainly food-processing, transportation, and political centers.

A mass of granite mountains, some rising to over 12,000 feet and deeply dissected by canyons, effectively separates northern Idaho from the arid Snake Plains. Until 1927 the two parts of the state were unconnected by roads, and even today there is only one winding north-south trunk route entirely within the state. The flattish Snake Plain, whose volcanic rocks when decomposed form a fertile soil, is traversed by the Snake River incised in a canyon, 100 to 700 feet deep, until it swings north and cuts across rugged terrain in Hells Canyon, 5,500 feet deep. Sagebrush and bunchgrass occupy the soil except where water from the Snake and its northern tributaries has been pumped or diverted by canals from higher levels upstream. The irrigated area is concentrated in three main sections: around the Idaho Falls–Pocatello area, east of Twin Falls, and west of Boise. All three specialize in potatoes but sugar beets, fodder crops, vegetables, fruit, and wheat add diversity. Cattle and sheep are grazed on the nonirrigated lands; dairy herds in the cultivated areas.

The Upper Colorado Watershed

The Colorado and its eastern tributaries rise on the west slopes of the Southern Rockies; the only major northern tributary, the Green, flows in the unconsolidated sediments of the westernmost part of the Wyoming Basin, an area important mainly as a transportation bridge across the Rockies and as a grazing land. Recently, historic South Pass took on modern importance with the exploitation of iron ore nearby by use of the most modern technology developed with an investment of about $100 million. The bulk of the Colorado watershed is in the Colorado Plateau, an area of much faulted, deeply dissected upland capped by thick layers of almost horizontal sedimentary rocks. Until recently it was customary to dismiss this area as relatively valueless, suited only for Indian reservations, poor grazing, limited irrigation farming, and tourist development at the Grand Canyon,

Bryce, Zion, and Mesa Verde national parks.

This pessimistic outlook can be explained by comparing the Colorado Plateau with the equally arid Snake Plains. The latter ranges from 2,000 to 5,000 feet with volcanic or windblown soil-forming materials; the Colorado Plateau is generally over 5,000 feet, in a few places over 10,000 feet, and its soils are largely based on sandstone or other poor soil-forming materials. The Snake Plain, easily traversed from east to west, has been long used as a major route; the main routes in the Colorado Plateau either lead to the south of this region or, like the Denver, Rio Grande and Western, follow narrow, steepsided canyons. The Colorado area is largely enclosed within a horseshoe of rugged mountains: the Southern Rockies, the Uinta and the Wasatch; the Snake Plain is easily accessible from most directions except from due north. The Snake Plain contains much flatland with over half of the area consisting of gentle slopes; the Colorado Plateau is dissected by narrow, hemmed-in valleys, the gentle slopes being mainly on high uplands.

Minerals in the Colorado Plateau and in adjacent ranges may lead to further development. Rio Blanco County in northwestern Colorado produces over half the Colorado mineral production, and San Juan County in southwestern Utah produces most of Utah's petroleum. Oil shale and bituminous coal are widely distributed in the upper Colorado watershed and natural gas is available locally. Metallic ores, copper, lead, zinc, silver, and especially uranium, are being exploited in the plateau and in the Rockies west of the continental divide. Lumber is available for local development. The area is scenic with pleasantly warm summers and moderate winters—at least in the valleys. The major handicaps seem to be isolation from major markets and lack of accessible level land; water is available and flows through the region to Arizona and

TO THE RIGHT is the Wasatch Front of Utah; the city in the upper left is Logan. Water from the Logan River is stored in a reservoir, whence it is distributed as domestic water supply and to irrigation ditches. Livestock are grazed on the hills; fodder crops and cash crops such as fruits, vegetables, and sugar beets are cultivated on the irrigated lands. (USDA photograph.)

California. The handicaps mentioned seem least in southwestern Wyoming; yet in the 1950s this was an area of net out-migration.

The Great Basin and the Mormon Culture Region

Most of the Great Basin is unused by man—perhaps it is unusable. It generally has less than 10 inches of rainfall, and its drainage does not reach the sea; instead its limited flow of water is trapped in a series of basins, streams terminating in salt lakes or saline waste. These basins are separated from one another by huge uptilted blocks forming abrupt north-south ranges, some high enough to have a snowcap most of the year. Streams from these ranges bring alluvium to the foot of each range, creating huge alluvial fans which in places coalesce to form flattish, gently tilting surfaces. Wind plays a major part in erosion, commonly redistributing and smoothing the lighter debris so that flattish floors characterize many of the basins.

The basins, elevated 3,000 to 6,000 feet with adjacent mountain ridges commonly attaining 9,000 to 11,000 feet, are not excessively hot in summer and have winter temperatures averaging about freezing. Precipitation is heavier during the cooler months with some thunderstorms in summer. The vegetation ranges from sagebrush mixed sparsely with grass to open pine-juniper forest on the mountains. This is the West as portrayed by Hollywood; the land of great open spaces, scattered mines, ghost towns, horseback riders, widespread herds, flocks, and a few oases. Few natural routes cross the Great Basin, and even the least-used route depends on traveling from water hole to water hole. The major routes for immigrants followed the modest Humboldt River across northern Nevada or a series of small streams south and southwestward from the western foot of the Wasatch across southern Nevada to the Mojave River of California.

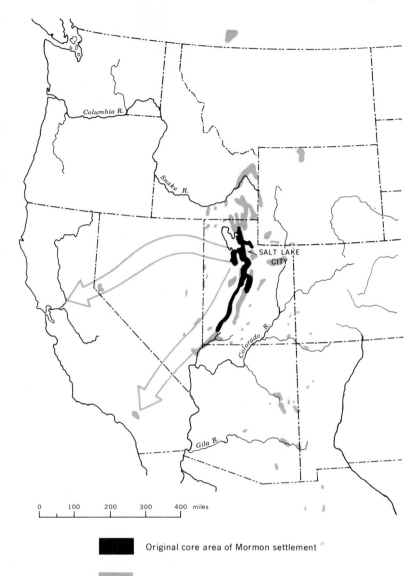

Original core area of Mormon settlement

Expansion in the first decade

FIGURE 15-10   The rapid expansion of a persecuted Mormon group in a region which had been despised by other settlers is part of the romance of the American West. (After Meinig.)

The Mormons From Salt Lake City, established in 1847 on the Jordan River, a stream flowing from Utah Lake to Great Salt Lake, the Mormons spread rapidly throughout the basin, converting the limited streams into a string of oases just west of the Wasatch and later expanding into eastern Nevada, Southern California, and southeastern Idaho. Hardened by persecution in the Midwest, unified by a new-found religious faith, these migrants worked miracles by prolonged cooperative effort. Ironically the

Mormons, having sought an isolated place in which to place their church-oriented society, characterized by discipline; abstention from tobacco, alcohol, and caffeine; and church-ruled government, soon found the Great Basin to be central amid the routes tapping the wealth of the West (Figure 15-10).

THIS GOLD-MINING OPERATION west of Carlin, Nevada, was developed by the Carlin Gold Mining Company during the 1960s. The company is a subsidiary of the Newmont Mining Corporation, an investment trust which specializes in the exploitation of newly discovered mineral deposits. The open pit mine is to the upper right, the mill is in the center, and the tailings pond in the foreground accumulates wastes. In the center foreground, a water-treatment plant neutralizes water overflowing from the tailings pond. Although close to the Overland Trail, the first transcontinental railroad, and a transcontinental highway, this mineral resource has only recently been utilized. (Newmont Mining Corporation.)

Salt Lake City remains the core of the Mormon culture region, based largely on a denomination which has over 1.6 million members in the United States, especially in the West. In contrast to outlying Great Basin areas the city contains an appreciable non-Mormon population.[7] Originally an agricultural center, it attracted converts to Mormonism who brought in a variety of industrial skills used to manufacture for Mormon consumption. Its raw-material-processing industries are mainly outside the city. As an industrial center the Salt Lake City SMSA is not outstanding; it has above the national average shares of employment only in the service industries.

Minerals and manufacturing Salt Lake City is well located in relation to minerals: A major American copper deposit is at Bingham on the edge of the metropolis; iron ore is available in Iron County 175 miles to the south, and coal and petroleum are widespread in the Colorado Plateau to the southeast. Ten miles south of Great Salt Lake, copper smelters and refineries, efficiently process low-grade ores yielding gold, silver, lead, zinc, and molybdenum as by-products. Iron ore is smelted and converted into steel

[7] Utah is 60 percent Mormon, and some counties have almost no non-Mormon population.

products at Geneva on Utah Lake. These metal industries and several defense industries have the only plants employing over 1,000 workers each. The Salt Lake SMSA has some production in every one of the 20 manufacturing categories except tobacco manufactures; however, most of the plants are small, 405 out of 593 plants employing less than 20 workers.

Irrigation The intensive irrigation agriculture on which Mormon settlement has been based is watered by a number of streams rising in the Wasatch Range, a rugged southwestern spur of the Rockies. This Piedmont area has nearly 50 percent more precipitation than the Great Basin as a whole. The crops are diverse, ranging from dry-farmed wheat and barley to irrigated fruits, vegetables, and sugar beets. Dairy cattle form a major part of oasis farming; beef cattle and sheep graze on adjacent dry lands. The oasis not only feeds its people but ships out fruit and vegetables, fresh, canned, or frozen.

The oases of central Utah contrast with the remainder of the Great Basin. Farms are moderate in size in Utah County; the average farm has 292 acres, but one-fourth of the farms have less than 10 acres each.

A Nevada county In contrast, consider Elko County, Nevada, a progressive grazing county: Its 238 ranches average 13,239 acres, and almost all of its $12 million product in 1959 was livestock. The county's 17,126 square miles are one-fourth larger than the three southernmost New England States combined. Elko with nearly 7,000 of the county's 12,000 population is the largest city in central and eastern Nevada. The county has eight tiny factories including a slaughterhouse, ice cream factory, bakery, several newspapers, and engine electrical equipment, altogether employing 78 people. Being on a transcontinental route, Elko County services transit trade with 681 em-

ployed by transportation, 584 by hotels and motels, 725 in retail trade. In addition, 792 are engaged in ranching, and slightly more in professional and governmental services. Such is the economy of the third[8] most populous county in Nevada—14 counties in Nevada and 21 in Utah have less population, and there was a net out-migration (1950–1960) from Elko County of 1,556. Yet the story is not all dark—it is a beautiful county, and the average income per household (1965) was the same as in San Francisco.

The Great Basin economy Economically the Great Basin is not a completely satisfactory unit. The parts of it around Reno and Las Vegas and adjacent eastern California are tied into the economies of San Francisco and Los Angeles. These areas in western Nevada account for over four-fifths of the income and employment of Nevada. On the other hand, the state of Utah, divided between the Great Basin and the Colorado Plateau, is focused on the eastern Great Basin. Its civilian income data show the relative unimportance of mine and farm products as a source of income (Table 15-3). Larger income sources were manufacturing, trade, and especially government. Much of the manufacturing was related to raw materials: for example, of a total industrial employment of about 64,000, about 9,200 were in food products, 8,000 in primary metals, and 5,900 in petroleum, wood, and other processing industries. The largest single group (17,000) is in the ordnance and transportation-equipment industry and related industries (fabricated metals and machinery are growing). These new defense-oriented industries are concentrated along the Wasatch Front, just as the similar Colorado industries are along the Rocky Mountain Front.

[8]The two more populous counties are those including Las Vegas and Reno, both west of the regional boundary.

FIGURE 15-11   *Government, especially the federal government, controls much of the land of Utah (and adjoining areas as well) largely because no one else wants it.*

CONCLUSIONS

The High West supports about 4 million people, 10 million cattle, and 10 million sheep; and includes 50 million acres of indifferent-to-good forest land and countless clumps of sagebrush. It has 7 people per square mile, but averages are misleading: The South Platte Valley has 75 per square mile and the well-settled irrigated core of Utah about 200 per square mile; huge areas lie empty. Metals have proved only a temporary resource; continuing growth has been most concentrated in the irrigated areas which contain significant commercial centers.

TABLE 15-3 Civilian Income by States and Industries, High West, 1966 (in millions of dollars)

Industry	Colo.	Wyo.	Mont.	Idaho	Utah	Nev.
Farms	226	66	248*	208	52	17
Mining	113	70	59	28	95	33
Construction	324	58	101	101	137	96
Manufacturing	755	48	160	222	360	58
Trade	850*	107	245	252*	368	190
Financial	249	25	54	53	86	52
Transport and Utilities	372	74	139	103	179	97
Services	682	83	173	181	255	503*
Government	800	132*	243	198	506*	187
Other	13	3	6	8	5	3
Civilian, income	4,383	665	1,428	1,355	2,043	1,237
Personal, income	5,700	874	1,842	1,704	2,502	1,507

* Major source of civilian income in each state.

SOURCE: *Survey of Current Business,* vol. 47 (August, 1967), no. 8, p. 37. Civilian income is that received by persons for participating in current production. Most of the Nevada income originates outside the region as here defined.

Water and water rights have proved limiting factors in both urban and rural expansion. Only the Colorado River appears to have much surplus water. All this apparent surplus has been assigned to states to the southwest, or to diversion projects across the continental divide; there would be a shortage if all the allocated water were actually used. Water pollution, from mining wastes, sewage, and alkalies flushed from the soil, is an increasing problem, not easily solved. By standards in most arid lands, the High West has adequate water for many times its population; by American standards of liberal domestic and industrial use, water scarcity is current and likely to increase in the future.

The population of the High West is growing more rapidly than the national average, but most of the growth is concentrated in the metropolitan areas. In the 1950s, 166 out of 228 counties had a net out-migration. This is not surprising since rural areas away from cities in much of the country have suffered a like out-migration. Perhaps a case could be made for a western Appalachia project! Nevertheless it seems amazing that in areas so sparsely settled and occupied generally less than a century, more opportunities have not been found. Certainly most of the High West is physically attractive; the difficulties rather have been in a poor industrial mix and in the isolation of many areas from those amenities that Americans increasingly expect. Possibly with the increasing amounts of leisure and better transportation, the spectacular mountains and great open spaces will be a refuge for tens of millions of noise- and-smog-bedeviled metropolitan workers. Perhaps, too, a few wilderness areas will be saved for those who wish to tramp through an America as nature made it.

SELECTED REFERENCES

FEDERAL RESERVE BANK OF KANSAS CITY: *Water Resources, Development and Use,* Kansas City, 1959.

GOLZÉ, ALFRED R.: *Reclamation in the United States,* Caxton, Caldwell, Idaho, 1961.

HELBURN, NICHOLAS, M. J. EDIE, and GORDON LIGHTFOOT: *Montana in Maps,* Research and Endowment Foundation, Montana State College, Missoula, 1962.

LOEFFLER, M. JOHN: "The Population Syndromes on the Colorado Piedmont," *Annals A.A.G.,* vol. 55 (1965), pp. 26–66.

MEINIG, D. W.: "The Mormon Culture Region: Strategies and Patterns in the Geography of the American West: 1847–1964," *Annals A.A.G.,* vol. 55 (1965), pp. 191–220.

QUINN, FRANK: "Water Transfers: Must the American West Be Won Again?," *Geographical Review,* vol. 58 (1968), pp. 108–132.

TAYLOR, ROBERT G.: *Cripple Creek,* Department of Geography, Indiana University, Bloomington, 1966.

U.S. DEPARTMENT OF INTERIOR: *Natural Resources of Colorado,* Washington, 1963. Similar pamphlets, available for all Western states, are especially good in portraying the work of federal agencies.

U.S. GEOLOGICAL SURVEY: *Guidebook to the Western United States:* Part A, *The Northern Pacific Route,* bulletin 611, part B, *The Overland Route,* bulletin 612; part E, *The Denver and Rio Grande Western Route,* bulletin 707, Washington, 1920–1922. These well-illustrated guidebooks are based on data a half century old but are invaluable for giving an impression of the natural background and historical development of sites along transcontinental railroads.

CHAPTER 16
THE DEVELOPING SOUTHERN CALIFORNIA MEGALOPOLIS

FIGURE 16-1 Landforms of California: Southern California. This region is so closely tied to the rest of California and adjacent Nevada that it is desirable to show the broader area; the names included are limited to the Southland. Massive mountain blocks of diverse length and height separated by alluvium-filled valleys are characteristic. (Base map by A. K. Lobeck. Reprinted with permission of The Geographical Press, Hammond, Inc.)

About thirteen million people reside in Southern California, a subtropical area of deserts, poor grasslands, and partly wooded, partly barren mountains which only two centuries ago barely supported about seventy thousand Indians. The physical setting (Figure 16-1) is little if any better than in most lands in the adjacent sparsely settled

BASIC DATA:

AREA INCLUDES	Land Area (thousand sq. mi.)	Population Change, 1950-1960	1960 (thousands)	1967 (thousands)	Personal Income 1967 (billions)
SOUTHERN CALIFORNIA	65.4	59.6%	9,732	12,765	$45.3
California (part)	57.5	58.1	9,605	12,490	44.5
Las Vegas SMSA	7.9	163.0	127	275	0.8
MAJOR SMSAS					
Los Angeles-Long Beach-Orange County	4.8	52.4%	6,038	8,320	$32.0
San Diego	4.3	85.5	1,033	1,220	3.8
San Bernardino-Riverside-Ontario	27.3	79.3	810	1,090	2.9
Bakersfield	8.2	27.9	292	345	1.1
Fresno	6.0	32.3	366	425	1.2

CLIMATE *Generally mild along the Coast with increasing daily and seasonal temperature range inland. Arid to subhumid; more humid in the mountains.*

	Temperature (°F)		Precipitation (inches)	
	Jan.	July	Annual	Season
Los Angeles	56	73	15	Summer drought
Palm Springs	54	91	7	Winter maximum
Fresno	45	82	9	Summer drought
San Diego	55	69	11	Winter maximum
Las Vegas	45	86	5	Winter maximum

VEGETATION Generally desert (creosote bush, cacti, Joshua trees) to shrubs and open evergreen oak forest with grassland near Coast; pine-juniper and other forests on the higher areas.

SOIL Great local variety: desert soils in the east; alluvial soils, stony soils; some brown and prairie soils in the west.

MINERALS Petroleum and natural gas, stone, gravel and sand, cement, borax and other salts; iron ore.

Southwest except in one important respect: it is near the sea. The Pacific modifies the climate, keeping the weather mild in winter, pleasantly warm in summer, and, at times, providing a fog or cloud cover which shields the brilliant subtropical sun. This world-renowned climate is found mainly in a narrow zone along the Coast; the populous area now extends inland where summers are hot and winters are mild and sunny.

Climate is not the only attraction that has brought millions to the California Southland. A succession of additions to the cultural landscape has made the region more attractive: the livestock and Mediterranean crops introduced from Spain by the missionaries, the commercial varieties of citrus fruit and dates introduced within the last century, and the shade-giving eucalyptus from Australia, the camphor tree from the Orient, and the pepper tree from Peru. Equally important were such water-management techniques as well drilling, irrigation, and the pumping of water which fell as rain on mountains a thousand miles away. These additions would have been of little economic significance without the railroads and highways which connect California with distant markets. More recently the glamor of Hollywood; the high levels of public education; the opportunities in science-oriented industries; the all-year, outdoor type of living have led to a forecast that California living may represent the type of life most men will achieve in the twenty-first century. Although not all Californians live in such an imagined paradise, the Southland today attracts more new settlers every two to three months than the total of its Indian population two centuries ago.

Boundaries

The boundaries of this booming region, based largely on integration into the developing Los Angeles–San Diego megalopolis, are somewhat more satisfactory than for many regions. The eastern boundary has been drawn to include the Las Vegas SMSA, Hoover Dam, and the Colorado River—all closely tied to the Southland economy. A good argument could be made for including an adjacent strip of Arizona, but the present development of the bordering Arizona counties is almost negligible. The southern boundary is the Mexican border, but Baja California—especially from Tijuana to Ensenada—serves largely as a recreation area for Californians. The northern boundary is based on the approximate limit of subtropical agriculture (especially cotton and citrus); this boundary also coincides with the transition between Los Angeles and San Francisco commercial

and financial predominance.[1] Owens Valley east of the Sierra Nevada is included because its waters are drained mainly into the Los Angeles Aqueduct.

THE PHYSICAL SETTING

In landforms, Southern California is very similar to Arizona and Nevada with their uplifted mountain blocks, intervening filled basins, and plateaus. In the California Southland, the major terrain feature is a series of diverse mountain blocks forming a vast arc from Point Conception to the Mexican border 50 miles east of San Diego. These abrupt ranges also form a boundary between the subhumid to semi-arid coastal areas and the interior deserts; their passes had a major influence on routes and early settlement. In the north the relatively low ranges parallel the Coast. To the east of Santa Barbara the mountain blocks, higher and more abrupt, trend east-west, and such passes as Tejon (4,183 feet), Soledad (3,225 feet), Cajon (4,301 feet), and San Gorgonio (1,500 feet) were used for major road and railroad routes. South of Riverside the ranges again trend along the Coast, but the higher ridges, 50 miles inland, are adjoined westward by lower mountains and hills separated by pleasant valleys. These ranges, together with at least several hundred miles of desert to the east, proved a major barrier to early travelers; nevertheless, the high ranges, well-wooded above 5,000 feet and with numerous streams and springs, must have been a welcome sight to those who had traveled from water hole to water hole for weeks.

South and west of these ranges, the coastal slopes are far from uniform: They include steep hills and low mountain ranges, alluvial fans, broad filled valleys, and some

---

[1] The Federal Reserve Bank includes only Kern and Inyo Counties in its Los Angeles subdistrict, thus excluding Fresno, Tulare, and Kings counties. The Greater San Francisco Chamber of Commerce claims even Kern County (Bakersfield SMSA) for its hinterland.

THIS SHOWS A TYPICAL rural Southern California landscape bisected by the freeway from Los Angeles to Bakersfield. Barren hills, productive fields, and pastures occur together on the edge of the Los Angeles–Long Beach SMSA. (California Division of Highways.)

marshy areas. The natural vegetation is varied, but evergreen shrubs predominate, forming a low tangle known as *chaparral.* Elsewhere there are stretches of short grassland, sagebrush, and some open groves of evergreen oak. Except after winter rains and along streams, the landscape ranges from brown or straw color to dull dark green.

Perhaps 70 percent of Southern California still has its original wild landscape (Figure 16-2), but on almost all the coastal slopes it has been modified. Palms, vineyards, shade trees, garden flowers and vegetables, grains, and even the common grasses were introduced by white settlers. Most marshes have been drained; and slopes have been fitted to the needs of the irrigator, the housing contractors, and the highway engineer. In recent decades the hillsides have been bulldozed into terraces for prestige housing with a view. Networks of roads, sewers, and utility lines traverse

the landscape. The oil and natural gas fields can be identified by derricks, oil pumps, and tank installations, but the rich fuel deposits of the Southland no longer suffice for its inhabitants; petroleum is imported by ship and gas is piped in from New Mexico and Texas.

In contrast, greatly altered areas occupy only a small fraction of the lands in the mountains and desert. The mountain slopes have been modified by lumbering, others even more by recreational centers, and most spectacularly by urban residential sections extending up the lower slopes. Yet most of the mountains remain wild. In dry weather large parts of the mountains are closed to hikers and campers because of the ever-present fire danger; viewed from an airplane, the most conspicuous features are the cleared firebreaks which follow the crests. The transformation of the desert is generally slight but is more thorough where transverse

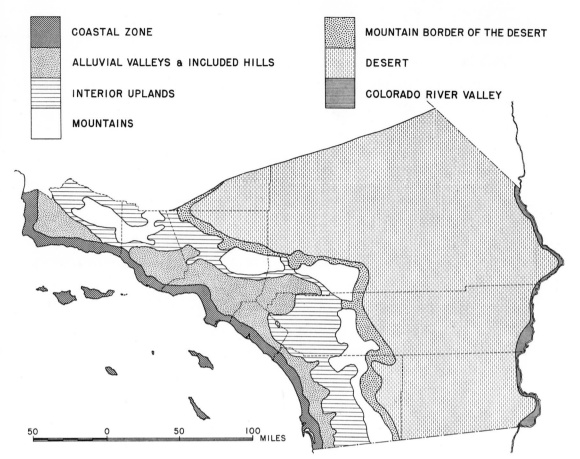

COASTAL ZONE

ALLUVIAL VALLEYS & INCLUDED HILLS

INTERIOR UPLANDS

MOUNTAINS

MOUNTAIN BORDER OF THE DESERT

DESERT

COLORADO RIVER VALLEY

50   0   50   100
                       MILES

FIGURE 16-2   Ecologic zones of Southern California. These zones differentiated Indian life and still influence settlement today. Indians in the Coastal Zone were largely dependent on marine animals; inland they lived more on edible roots, seeds, and acorns. The mountains were only occasionally visited by hunting parties. The eastern mountain border supported villages at the permanent springs. The desert had a sparse population, but agricultural tribes used spring floodwaters to farm the Colorado Valley. (Homer Aschmann, "The Evolution of a Wild Landscape and Its Persistence in Southern California," ANNALS A.A.G., vol. 49 (1959), no. 3, supplement, p. 50.)

routes, irrigation settlements, resorts, and mining operations have added buildings, roads, and green fields to the generally toasted landscape. Essentially the settlement of accessible desert land depends on water availability.

Climate and Weather

Differences in altitude, exposure, and distance from the sea cause great local differences in daily weather and climate. To these physical variables must be added a cultural factor—proximity to industrial and other sources of smog.[2] Since Southern California has great local variety in the weather-modifying variables, its climates differ

significantly within a few miles and its weather is often unusual for the season. The average climate in the coastal lowland is semi-arid with some rain in winter, warm enough for outdoor living most days of the year, with hot spells (but pleasant evenings) in late summer and brief cold spells with light frost in winter. Snow usually caps the higher mountains at least half of the year, and relief from summer heat is usually

[2] Smog is not limited to Southern California. Most large industrial cities have smog problems, but smog first attracted national attention in California.

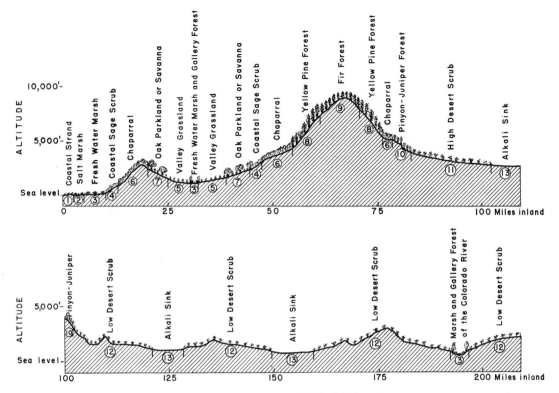

FIGURE 16-3   This is an idealized cross section showing the relief and vegetation encountered from the Pacific Ocean to the Colorado River. Only remnants of the wild vegetation remain unaltered except in the desert where half the land is in its original state. Even on the sparsely inhabited mountains and hills, the forests, shrubs, and grasses have been altered by visitors and settlers. (Homer Aschmann, "The Evolution of a Wild Landscape and Its Persistence in Southern California," ANNALS A.A.G., vol. 49 (1959), no. 3, supplement, p. 35.)

available near the shore or in the mountains.

Although these climatic characteristics are general, in summer it may be 20° hotter in San Bernardino than in San Diego and still another 10 to 20° hotter in the Imperial Valley. Considerable variations in temperature occur with distance from the sea, with altitude, between sun and shade, and even between the north and south sides of a hill. Rains sufficient to brighten the green of the hillside, common in early winter in some years, may not come until nearly spring in other years. Summer rains are more unusual but may be heavy enough locally to overburden the storm sewers. Frosts, showers, fogs and smog, and strong winds are often highly localized—indeed each part of each valley and slope has its individual variation from the general pattern. Land use and housing reflect these differences: Air conditioning is rarely needed along the Coast but is considered almost a necessity in San Fernando and other interior valleys; a lowland area west of San Bernardino, too frost-prone for citrus, specializes in wine grapes, vegetables, and dairy products; the Hollywood Bowl cools so rapidly on summer evenings that many concert goers carry blankets or warm coats.

The climate is much more extreme in the desert with notable changes from day to night, and with altitude. Winds and dust, sometimes strong enough to sandblast the paint off a car, are a common problem. Desert life can be very pleasant even in summer for those who like bright sunshine and can take refuge in air-conditioned

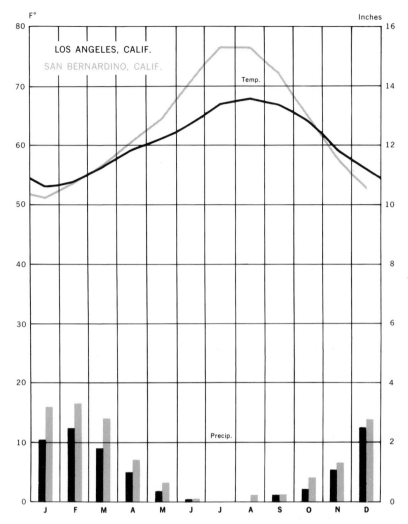

FIGURE 16-4   Los Angeles climate is represented by data for Los Angeles International Airport near the Pacific Ocean. As one travels eastward, the range of temperatures encountered gradually increases until extremes recorded are 17 and 116° F at San Bernardino, only 40 miles inland. East of the San Bernardino Range, even greater extremes are recorded, for example, Bagdad, 10 and 119 °.

quarters or swimming pools. In the winter the smog-free desert is commonly pleasant (50 to 75° during the day) and even during the rare cold snaps it is mild between sunrise and sunset.

Except in the mountains, Southland weather interferes surprisingly little with ordinary living—the smog in some localities being the principal annoyance. If watered, gardens bloom and lawns stay green all year; many homes are adequately heated by fireplaces and room gas heaters; the most modest homes lack central heating. Rubbers, umbrellas, raincoats, and overcoats are little used, and many Californians hardly know how to drive on wet or icy pavements.

Cool offshore currents make the Pacific too chilly for those accustomed to Atlantic beaches, but surfboarders and swimmers are seen even in midwinter. The dry, gravelly riverbeds rarely are filled; their waters have been diverted upstream into irrigation systems or for domestic water supplies. Yet flood-control reservoirs are kept empty because of the danger from rare cloudbursts.

FRUIT AND NUT ORCHARDS occupy a gentle slope south of Corona at the foot of the Santa Ana Mountains. The land lies within a Spanish grant; hence the few rectangular sections. The orchards are irrigated by runoff from the mountains, and the rows of trees follow the contours. Precipitation ranges from 15 to 20 inches, somewhat higher in the mountains. Good frost drainage on the slopes also aids the fruit industry. Note that the picture has been oriented so that south is toward the top of the page; this makes the relief more apparent. (USDA photograph.)

ECONOMIC HISTORY

The modern economy and society in the Southland is the result of past booms and transformations. About the time of the American Revolution, Spanish missionaries from Mexico established a line of missions from San Diego to San Francisco, spaced no more than a day's journey (by muleback) apart. The peaceful, primitive Indians brought into the missions were unusually skilled in using the nonagricultural aspects of their environment; they soon learned to till European crops and tend cattle and sheep. Less happily, the Indians also acquired European diseases so that few of them have survived.

During the next 70 years, the Spanish and Mexican governments assigned huge ranches to immigrants, some from Spain and Mexico, some from the United States. The only exportable products were hides and tallow which were sold to New England sea captains. After the California gold rush (1849), a new market for cattle, grain, and wine became available, encouraging the expansion of irrigation agriculture. New crops were introduced including the navel orange from Brazil (1873), lemon (1874), Valencia orange (1880), avocado (1910), and date (1912). Broader markets were opened when rail connections to the East via San Francisco were completed in 1876 and directly eastward in 1885.

At this time subtropical products were scarce in eastern United States (agricultural development was just starting in southern Florida); several techniques helped California produce reach the market: canning (1858), artificial dehydration (1870), and refrigerated freight cars (1880). The growing Eastern market attracted numerous farm settlers to Southern California who shifted the main crops on their irrigated land from grain for cattle to fruit and vegetables. Although the increased agricultural activity resulted in some growth in urban activities, Southern California remained agriculturally oriented until about 1918.

The Shift to Industry

Successive developments changed the economy of the coastal zone from agriculture to industry. Large quantities of oil were discovered in the Los Angeles Basin between 1920 and 1924, providing a surplus product which could be shipped east through the Panama Canal. About the same time, major moving picture studios moved to the Hollywood area to take advantage of the bright light and the diverse landscapes available nearby. Large-scale aircraft manufacturers which could assemble their product outdoors started in 1920. The automobile assembly industry also started in the 1920s, several decades before its product dominated the regional settlement pattern. All these manufacturers brought a flock of auxiliary industries to supply their needs and an even greater number of industries to supply the homes and consumer goods required by the burgeoning population.

Between the two world wars, maturing Southern California consisted of Los Angeles and San Diego and a sprinkling of small cities and towns, all connected by roads, railroads, and the Pacific Electric interurban lines. Each city spread over a large area because single houses predominated and even the so-called "apartments" usually rose only two floors. In contrast to most American cities, the CBDs had low buildings since maximum heights were limited to 150 feet because of supposed earthquake danger. Several hundred thousand acres of orange groves dotted the landscape, sharing the nonurbanized land with cattle ranches, dairy farms, vineyards, and gardens. The automobile numbers and industrial employ-

ment were growing, but smog and freeways were still nonexistent.

World War II brought a new industrial growth, involving military activities, aircraft, munitions, steel, and other supplies needed for the Pacific war; after the war many scientific, aerospace, instrumental, and consumer-goods industries were added. Along with these developments came a tremendous suburban expansion into areas unreached by public transport and distant from the new factories. The automobile became the accepted form of transportation. The rapid-transit lines were deserted by most of their customers, and some of the first freeways were constructed along the abandoned Pacific Electric right-of-way. The demand for more skilled workers seemed insatiable; the daily papers in California and elsewhere advertised many openings for engineers, artisans, and skilled technicians. When their families arrived from the East, they required new housing, new shopping centers, and new schools.

Although at first there was adequate well water from the mountains stored in underlying sediments, an aqueduct from Owens Valley was started in 1908, completed in 1913. In 1939 additional water was pumped from the Colorado River. In the 1960s an aqueduct was being constructed to tap Feather River water from the northern Sierras. Experiments with the desalting of seawater are also very advanced. Meanwhile orange groves and other farms are being replaced with houses in the exploding urbanized area. Florida and Arizona citrus products have appeared in Southland markets; dairy farming is being concentrated on dry lots which stable cows shoulder to shoulder before a food trough on perhaps the world's most valuable agricultural land— some worth more than $25,000 per acre. It has even been suggested that Southern California may need to restrict its agriculture further to make more water available for industry and people.

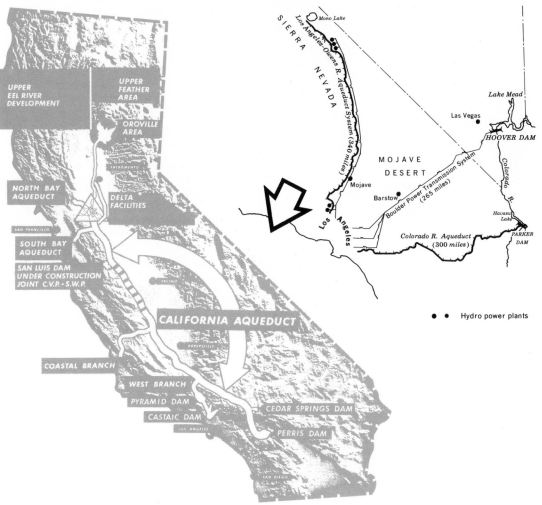

FIGURE 16-5   Southern California at first derived its water from local mountain streams and from wells driven into valley sediments. This map shows the plan now being implemented to ship northern California water southward. (California Department of Water Resources.)

Income and Employment

Although California boasts that in value of agricultural products it is the most productive of the 50 states, only a small percentage of Southern California income can be attributed to agriculture. Likewise its extractive industries, oil and gas; the mining of salts, stone, and iron ore; and lumbering, provide little employment. Over one-third of the income and employment arises from manufacturing and construction; most of the rest is in trade and services (Table 16-1) which are perhaps more elaborate there than elsewhere in Anglo-America.

Who are the California workers? The basic stock was Spanish and Yankee with a minor amount of Indian blood. Orientals were added to the early population but usually did not marry outside their own group. These early settlers were overwhelmed by large numbers from Texas, the Mississippi Valley, and Western Europe, including many with rural backgrounds. Employment opportunities have brought in many Mexicans and, in recent decades, a considerable Negro population, as well as whites from Atlantic Coast cities. The region is much more of a melting pot than the

DOWNTOWN LOS ANGELES is being increasingly divided between monumental buildings, such as those of the civic center shown here, and streets, freeways, and parking lots. (Los Angeles Chamber of Commerce.)

United States interior; its present college and university population includes large numbers from all ethnic groups.

THE LOS ANGELES AREA

History

The nation's second metropolis started as a Spanish colonial village one-half mile west of the Los Angeles River whose waters were used to irrigate the surrounding fields. The location was strategic; the river valley led upstream to the San Fernando and San Gabriel valleys and downstream to a poorly sheltered bay at San Pedro. To the south, a broad lowland extended at least 15 miles to the southeast. Like the Indian settlements

TABLE 16-1   Major Sources of Employment and Income in California, 1963 (thousands omitted)

Source	State	Southern California	Los Angeles Area	Civilian Income, 1966
Agriculture	259*	153*	36*	$ 1,555,000
Construction	329	200	145	3,242,000
Manufacturing	1,398	992	845	13,183,000
Transport and Utilities	310	175	131	3,584,000
Trade	1,169	758	565	9,085,000
Financial	277	172	139	2,838,000
Services	661	436	336	8,406,000
Government and Education	671*	390*	239*	8,281,000

* 1960 data.

SOURCES: Department of Employment, State of California, *County and City Data Book: 1962*, Washington, 1962. Income data from *Survey of Current Business*, vol. 47 (August, 1967), no. 8, p. 37.

FIGURE 16-6 Industrial Los Angeles is as scattered as commercial and residential Los Angeles. At first factories were located near railroads; later the harbor became an important localizing factor; and in recent decades freeways, other major highways, and available space for large factories have been major considerations.

and other early Spanish towns, Los Angeles was located where water was available at the edge of the hills; San Pedro, the outport from colonial days, long remained a small town.

With the building of the railroads and the consequent agricultural boom in the closing decades of the nineteenth century, Los Angeles grew, its CBD extending a mile south and southwestward while the residential district expanded to the west. In 1892 oil was discovered in the city, and oil processing was added to food processing and consumer goods as a major industry. The original industrial section was to the south in nearby Vernon, but industrial growth is now common throughout the metropolitan area, being especially concentrated along the rail lines and freeways (Figure 16-6).

The 1920s saw the growth of residential suburbs while the older residential part of the city developed into low-class housing

areas, some of which deteriorated into slums. Glendale and Pasadena to the north and northeast had grown into upper-class residential suburbs with the completion of Pacific Electric tracks to the central terminal. Another line extended northwestward to Hollywood on the south slopes of the Santa Monica Mountains where the new motion picture industry constructed studios over vast areas of cheap land. Shortly Hollywood and much of the San Fernando Valley joined Los Angeles to take advantage of Owens Valley water. The most important development was to the southward to San Pedro Bay where huge artificial harbors were constructed by Los Angeles and Long Beach. To give the city control of port

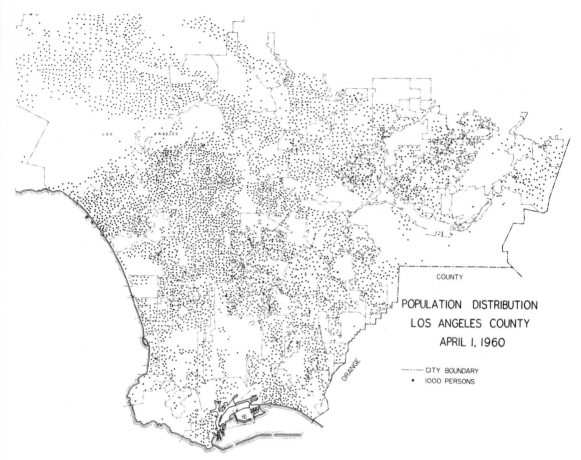

POPULATION DISTRIBUTION
LOS ANGELES COUNTY
APRIL 1, 1960

----·- CITY BOUNDARY
  •   1000 PERSONS

FIGURE 16-7 In contrast to eastern SMSAs, the population of the Los Angeles SMSA is rather evenly distributed, a pattern that makes it difficult to design a high-speed rapid-transit system. The white areas, mostly possessing rugged relief, are gradually being bulldozed into terraced residential sites. (Regional Planning Commission, County of Los Angeles.)

facilities and related industries, Los Angeles annexed a 20-mile "shoestring" of land extending to San Pedro. The shoestring and adjacent areas now include several major industrial zones.

The Metropolitan Pattern

The present period of expansion began during World War II, with special emphasis on aircraft, missiles, aerospace, electronics, and consumer-goods industries, all widely scattered throughout the metropolis. This scattering of industry is also characteristic of the other functions usually found in the CBD. The Los Angeles–Long Beach SMSA has a number of CBDs, and in retail trade the outlying CBDs now surpass the original central city. As a result of the residential sections spreading over a large area, there

was a need for the establishment of commercial and service centers near the suburbs. Therefore business offices, financial activities, skyscrapers, theaters, and concert halls are developing in many centers away from the central city. With surprising speed the metropolis expanded into the remaining lowlands to create new residential subdivisions, many so far from established transit lines that the automobile became the only means of getting to work. The first freeway, the winding Pasadena Freeway, was opened in 1940; other routes were laid out in the next decades. Industry and auto exhausts

GRISSOM ISLAND is one of four artificial islands constructed off Long Beach to serve as a base for offshore oil exploitation without spoiling the beauty of the coastal area. (Long Beach Promotion, Inc.)

increasingly converted fog into smog. Fashionable suburbs were laid out above the smog zone, increasingly developing on terraced hillsides which a few decades earlier seemed destined to remain in chaparral.

A regional grouping of urban functions has grown up. Sparsely or lightly settled hilly areas still compartment the lowland. The low Santa Monica Mountains separate the long-settled Hollywood–Santa Monica plain west of downtown Los Angeles from the new, expanding San Fernando Valley subdivisions. The Baldwin Hills, partly residential and partly occupied by oil derricks, separate Hollywood from newer southwest Los Angeles with its international airport and growing industries. To the south the urbanized city extends almost to the independent industrial and port city of Long Beach. Southeast of central Los Angeles the railroads to San Diego and the parallel Santa Ana Freeway serve an almost continuous urban belt into Orange County, which is separated on the north by low hills from Pasadena and adjoining San Gabriel Valley cities.

The harbor area   Each of these outlying areas has a distinctive history. The harbor area of Long Beach was a resort town of less than

3,000 in 1900. Oil was discovered there in the early 1920s; the once fashionable suburb of Signal Hill attained worldwide notoriety for its forest of oil derricks—one on each city lot—and the artificial Long Beach Harbor was constructed from the profits of 500 city-owned wells. The quietness of the resort-fishing city was further upset by the creation of a naval base there in 1925. Long Beach today is a major port and industrial center specializing in aircraft and automobile parts, oil refining, oil-well equipment, and seafood canning.

The histories of smaller Wilmington and San Pedro, the former towns annexed to form the Los Angeles port, are different only in detail. Most of the San Pedro–Wilmington industries are related to the port. Until 1910 when the breakwater was constructed, the port was primitive. Between 1912 and 1914 the harbor was carved out of the marsh in time to serve the Pacific Coast trade resulting from the opening of the Panama Canal. Trade has expanded since then with imports of lumber, petroleum, scrap metal, and tropical commodities. Exports include manufactures and iron ore destined for Japan. San Pedro is also a fishing port, and Wilmington has had petroleum industries since 1934 when one of the most productive California oil fields was discovered nearby.

The San Gabriel Valley This lowland was occupied by Spanish missionaries (San Gabriel Mission, 1771) and by Mexican ranchers on seven huge estates. Intensive utilization is less than a century old. Pasadena, the principal city, was founded in 1874 by a group from Indianapolis who started raising irrigated oranges. The entire valley was converted into irrigated farms among which arose a number of commercial and residential towns. Pasadena, only 11 miles from downtown Los Angeles, was especially noted for its fine homes, resort hotels, and such institutions as the Huntington Library and the California Institute of Technology. Since World War II, the towns in San Gabriel Valley have grown together and spread up the slopes of adjacent hills. The orange groves have disappeared, and industry, especially that involving scientific skills, is gradually infiltrating the once quiet valley. Because the major transcontinental rail lines and several freeways cross the valley, further industrialization is to be expected.

The San Fernando Valley and northward Two cities at the mouth of the San Fernando Valley, Glendale and Burbank, were founded as agricultural centers during the railroad expansion of the 1880s; later both became commuting towns. With industrial growth first in moving pictures, and later in aircraft, Burbank became an industrial city. Glendale acquired an industrial area along the Southern Pacific tracks. The western two-thirds of the San Fernando Valley remained agricultural until the 1950s when, with the growth of the freeway system, the valley provided space for suburban residences and for industries such as electronics and automobile assembly. Most of its towns, still referred to locally by name, have been annexed by Los Angeles.

Megalopolitan expansion is also expected to incorporate the equally attractive coast and hills northward to Santa Barbara and possibly to San Luis Obispo, thus including the missile-testing facilities at Vandenberg Air Force Base. This coastal zone to the north consists of small plains and valleys separated by steep hills and backed by mountain wilderness. Without earthmoving machinery, such an area could have had limited development; shortly its hillside locations may be carved into house sites, each above the smog and with a view of the Pacific.

Whether megalopolitan settlement will move inland is more doubtful. However, freeways now connect Los Angeles both with the Bakersfield end of the Central Valley and with Antelope Valley at the western end of the Mojave Desert. Although expansion in these directions will likely be limited to favored spots en route, in the light of California history it would be rash to predict any limit to growth there.

Los Angeles Becomes the Second SMSA

Although San Francisco developed earlier as a commercial, financial, and industrial center, there is no doubt that the Los Angeles SMSA is the primate metropolis in California. Its industrial output approaches that of Chicago and is about half that of the New York–Northeastern New Jersey Consolidated Area. This is a tremendous accomplishment for a relatively new metropolis whose original CBD is located 20 miles from its artificial harbor, and isolated from the American Commercial-Industrial Core by over 1,500 miles of mountain, desert, or sparsely settled farmland. Modern communication and transportation made this expansion possible by providing markets for Los Angeles oranges, oil, motion pictures, instruments, aircraft, and aerospace products elsewhere. The conquest of the friction of distance made it possible for Los Angeles to become second only to New York among American SMSAs.

Deviation from U.S.
per capita data, %

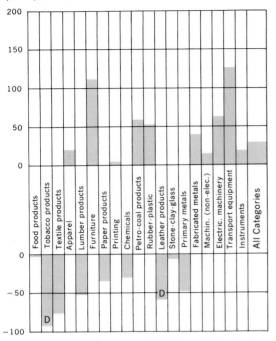

VALUE ADDED BY MANUFACTURING
Los Angeles – Long Beach SMSA = 3.54% U.S. Pop.

Figure 16-8   Compared with other SMSAs analyzed so far in the West, Los Angeles has a broad distribution over the various industrial categories. The low rating of "primary metals" would be improved if the large steel plant 10 miles east of the SMSA boundary were included. Industrial emphasis in the Southland is on industries requiring skill and technology.

history of the county parallels that of Los Angeles County—inland irrigation farms and coastal resort and fishing villages. Oil and industrialization along rail lines caused widespread developments. The exploitation of southern Orange County, however, was restricted by the 90,000-acre Irvine Ranch whose wealthy owners began to encourage urban development only in the 1960s.

SOUTH AND EAST OF THE LOS ANGELES SMSA

San Diego

It is tempting to think of San Diego as a smaller edition of Los Angeles: Both SMSAs started as agricultural centers; both have mammoth aircraft and military industries, suburbs connected by freeways, and a considerable retired population. Their

Orange County

This county was considered part of the Los Angeles SMSA in 1960; in 1963 the Bureau of the Census created from it the new Anaheim-Santa Ana-Garden Grove SMSA. Economically Orange County is part of the Los Angeles–Long Beach SMSA and has been included with it in the Basic Data. Orange County has the fastest growth rate in the Los Angeles area (233 percent, 1950–1960), a fact that should not surprise the geographer since much level and rolling land is available for development. The early

FIGURE 16-9   San Diego has so large an employment in naval, commercial, service, and construction that its manufacturing employment is small for its population. The food-products industry is based on the processing of local fruits, vegetables, and fish; the large aircraft assembly industry does not show up on the graph because it is part of the transportation equipment category (which includes automobiles which are not manufactured in the SMSA).

Deviation from U.S.
per capita data, %

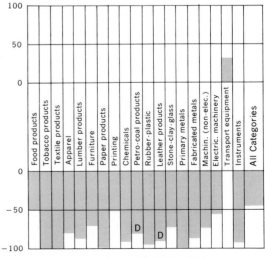

VALUE ADDED BY MANUFACTURING
San Diego SMSA = .62% U.S. Pop.

differences are equally striking. San Diego is a seaport located on a fine natural harbor; its hinterland is less extensive and poorer in natural resources, lacking oil, natural gas, and water from streams rising in snow-capped mountains. Its location south of the main transcontinental lines has been a further handicap; its through rail traffic is commonly routed via Los Angeles. Much of the city is on a mesa (low tableland), compartmented by canyons instead of on an extensive lowland as is Los Angeles.

The rise of modern San Diego has been attributed to its selection as a major naval base in 1907. Its excellent harbor is used mostly for naval purposes. Much of the nearby coast is used by the Navy and the Marine Corps. Its industries are reported to be 70 percent defense-oriented although some of them, e.g., aircraft and electronics, produce for both civilian and government markets. Seafood canning and shipbuilding, the other sizable industries, are small compared with aerospace and ordnance.

With a climate more equable than Los Angeles, it is not surprising that a number of residential towns have grown up between Los Angeles and San Diego. Settlement in this area has been slowed by water shortages, extensive military reservations, and such huge landholdings as Irvine Ranch. Judging from past growth in the Southland, this area should fill up during the 1970s.

San Bernardino–San Jacinto Lowlands

Another area expected to experience urban expansion shortly is separated from the Coast by the rugged, almost unsettled Santa Ana Mountains. This semi-arid to desert area, forming an equilateral triangle 50 miles on a side, still contains much farmland and ranchland. It is drained (when there is any surplus water to drain) by the Santa Ana River, which leaves the lowland through a canyon cut across the low northern end of the Santa Ana Mountains. The major crop of the San Bernardino Lowland

is oranges, but it also has extensive vine-yards, orchards, dairy farms, and truck gardens. The SMSA comprises the more densely settled portions of the immense San Bernardino–Riverside–Ontario urbanized area but also includes much uninhabited desert east of the mountains.

The principal city, San Bernardino, was founded by the Mormons in 1851 on a broad alluvial fan, watered by streams from the San Gabriel Mountains. The site was a focus for the routes over Cajon Pass and was on or near the routes of all the railroads serving the Los Angeles area. In addition to its long-established railroad shops, after World War II it acquired metal fabrication industries, aided by the proximity of Kaiser Steel, the first integrated steel mill near the Pacific. This mill obtains its iron ore from Eagle Mountain in the southern Mojave desert, its coal from Utah, and its limestone from west of the San Bernardino Mountains. These raw materials are brought together close to the huge Los Angeles industrial market.

Other major cities in the lowland are Riverside, an orange-growing educational and light-industrial center, and Claremont and Pomona, adjacent residential and commercial cities noted for the Claremont group of colleges. South of Riverside is the desert-like San Jacinto Basin whose streams rarely reach the sea. Parts of this basin remain in the hands of the Indians; small areas are intensively irrigated, as indeed most of the lowlands could be if water becomes available. The largest town in the San Jacinto Basin is Hemet with only 6,000 people in 1960.

THE DESERTS

The once-dreaded desert has taken on considerable glamour. Now that water can be pumped long distances and air conditioning tempers excessive heat, many people are finding the pure warm desert air a relief from the smog-bathed city. Farmers, too, find that steady sunshine, an almost year-long growing season, and a controlled water supply give huge yields of quality products salable at top prices.

The Colorado Desert

The warmest part of the desert—with very few frosty nights in winter—occupies a depression extending from San Gorgonio Pass 100 miles southeast to the Mexican border. Until the last century, this desolate area was crossed as quickly as possible by stagecoach and later by rail. Irrigation, using water from the Colorado River, began in the below-sea-level Imperial Valley in 1901, but in 1905 the river got out of control and flooded the formerly dry Salton Sea. Controlled irrigation was soon reestablished, and scientific agriculture using cheap Mexican labor proved very profitable, partly because two or more crops can be raised each year. Crops included cotton, winter vegetables, sugar beets, alfalfa, and cantaloupes. Agriculture expanded in 1910 to the Coachella Valley, northwest of Salton Sea, where artesian water was discovered and used to grow dates, grapefruit, seedless grapes, and truck crops.

The desert became of nonagricultural importance with the growth of Palm Springs as a fashionable winter resort in the 1920s. In the 1960s desert resorts have been built throughout the Coachella Valley, including several fishing resorts on the shores of the Salton Sea.

The Mojave Desert

The broad filled basins of the Mojave, being generally at altitudes of over 1,000 feet and locally supplied by the Mojave River and other streams from adjacent high mountains, appeared less barren to early travelers than the Colorado Desert. Agriculture is limited to the narrow Colorado Valley and to the back slopes of the San Bernardino and San Gabriel ranges. More important are the services of towns to railroads and highway travelers crossing the desert. Minerals, especially iron ore from Eagle Mountain, limestone, borates, potash, salt, and tungsten, account for the existence of scattered small towns. Within recent decades, the liberal gambling laws of Nevada made Las Vegas a major recreational center for people from Southern California. Another use of large desert areas is military maneuvers and supply depots; even empty space has its value in crowded Southern California!

The dams which regulate the lower Colorado River are in the eastern Mojave. They attempt to distribute its waters in accord with the interstate Colorado River Compact of 1922 and with treaties with Mexico. Hoover Dam, tallest of the world's dams, created Lake Mead whose waters are used primarily to generate hydroelectric power; Parker Dam diverts water into the Colorado Aqueduct which supplies all the southern coastal zone of California; Imperial Dam diverts water into the All-American Canal which serves Imperial and Coachella valleys. The Colorado water situation has become critical because Southern California has been drawing more than its share of water under the interstate compact; with Arizona now demanding its full share for expansion, the state of California is building aqueducts to carry water southward from the northern Sierra Nevada.

The Trans-Sierra

This northern desert, sparsely inhabited, is included with Southern California because most of its water is pumped to Los Angeles. Owens Lake, terminus of Owens River whose headwaters feed the Aqueduct, is a source of soda ash. Death Valley also is a modest source of minerals. But most of the business is concerned with servicing travelers, either tourists or others using U.S. 395.

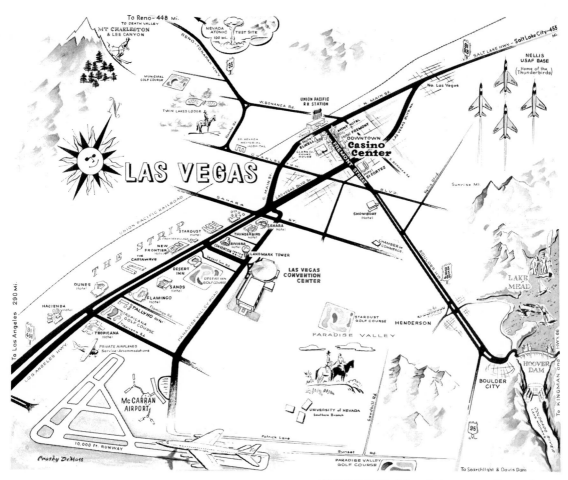

FIGURE 16-10   The artist has portrayed (somewhat out of scale) the attractions of Las Vegas which suggest what imaginative and energetic men have done to convert a desert environment into sources of income. (Las Vegas Chamber of Commerce.)

The Southern Central Valley

This is another desert except where it is irrigated by water from the Sierra Nevada. The central and western portion of the valley is low and, especially in the valley trough, flat. Dissected terraces, largely of alluvium, rim the trough. In the east the land surface is hilly and rises gradually up the granite Sierra Nevada block whose crest is generally 10,000 to 14,000 feet high. Irrigation water for the southern end of the valley, once obtained mainly from wells, now is also derived from the Kings and Kern rivers.

The development of the southern Central Valley can be expressed largely in terms of cattle, grain, raisin grapes, oil, and cotton. The subregion was settled by farmers with

a cattle-and-grain economy based on huge land holdings. Grapes and other subtropical fruits entered the picture mainly in the present century. Petroleum production became significant on the southern and western edges after 1900. Irrigated cotton, grown in huge fields and cultivated by machinery, became the major crop in the 1920s. There is considerable crop variety, partly because cotton is rotated with alfalfa, barley, potatoes, and other vegetables.

Although there are many small farms, large corporations control the majority of the land. For example, the Kern County

The Salton Sea and most of the Colorado Desert as seen from Gemini V on August 22, 1965. The sea is in the center of the photograph, the Coachella Valley to the left, and the Imperial Valley to the right. Although the photograph was taken at least 100 miles away, some of the irrigated fields can be identified. The Colorado River can be located by the irrigated strip which is visible in the upper righthand corner. (NASA photograph.)

Land Company, founded by a successful exploiter of the silver-rich Comstock lode, started as a cattle company with hundreds of thousands of acres. The company has water rights in the Kern River and now engages in irrigated agriculture, bringing in additional cattle for fattening; it also controls major oil properties. Di Giorgio Fruit Company, another example, claiming to be the nation's largest combined producer of fresh deciduous and citrus fruit, has ex-

panded its business into the Pacific Northwest and Florida.

Two SMSAs Fresno and Bakersfield are the two SMSAs controlling the trade of this region. Bakersfield at the northern exit of Tejon Pass deals primarily in oil and cotton; the larger city of Fresno, more concerned with fruit and fruit processing, also handles the wholesale trade of the central San Joaquin Valley. The other cities are small, local

LAND IN FRUIT ORCHARDS, GROVES, VINEYARDS, AND PLANTED NUT TREES

ACREAGE, 1959

UNITED STATES
TOTAL
4,119,826

1 DOT—2,000 ACRES

FIGURE 16-11   *Although fruits and nuts are produced throughout most of the United States, most of the commercial crop comes from a few major areas—most notably in California.* (Bureau of the Census.)

centers whose business is largely based on agricultural products.

CONCLUSIONS

It has been estimated that California may have a population of 40 to 50 million by the end of this century with perhaps 25 to 35 million in Southern California. By the year 2000 the coastal zone may be too valuable for agriculture which may expand into the desert. Within the coastal zone, housing will extend up the slopes and fill in thinly settled areas between Santa Barbara and San Diego; apartments and tall buildings will increase the urban population density and create CBDs with skylines like Eastern cities. Such focal points will be connected by efficient rapid transit. Water will remain a problem, but additional water will be made available by desalting seawater and reclaiming sewage, two processes already being tested in the Southland by pilot plants. The smog problem may be eased by the increasing use of electric power—probably atomically generated. The mountains will remain largely unsettled but not unvisited since the demand for recreational areas will increase more rapidly than the population as a result of the shorter work week anticipated by most economists. The vast Southland population will be a large enough market to encourage the production within the region of almost all the manufactures and services it will require; possibly there will be more than the regional share of electronic and other highly technical industries because of the concentration of skill for such industries as well as large markets for its products.

Continued in-migration and areal expansion seem guaranteed by the nature of the Southland, a beautiful setting in which (smog or fog permitting) high mountains can be seen from the beaches 40 miles

OIL AND IRRIGATED FIELDS (*background*) *are the backbone of the economy of the southern Central Valley.* (Jon Brenneis and Standard Oil Company of California.)

away; tall palms, flowering trees, and green lawns flourish all year; and the bright cultivated spots contrast with the dull flora on the slopes. Man has brought much of the beauty and productivity to this setting, building modern factories which are often attractive, and beautiful suburbs served by luxurious shopping centers. But man has also organized this into a hodgepodge of municipalities, each with its own street pattern and diverse laws. Aside from proximity, these diverse towns and cities are joined together by noisy freeways and boulevards, and by common dependence on imported water. The majority of the industries are no longer related to local resources: The movie studios are air-conditioned and film their output under klieg lights; the instrumental, electronic, and aerospace industries using imported parts (or at least raw materials) add great value by employing the skilled labor Californians have developed. The part of Southern California still dependent on primary industries is the less-populated inland area—the desert.

SELECTED REFERENCES

ASCHMANN, HOMER: "Purpose in the Southern California Landscape," *Journal of Geography,* vol. 66 (1967), pp. 311–317.

CUNNINGHAM, GLENN (ed.): *Day Tours, Geographical Journeys in the Los Angeles Areas,* Los Angeles Geographical Society, Pacific Books, Palo Alto, 1964. Fourteen tours written by Southland geographers which are worth reading about even if you cannot take the tours.

DURRENBERGER, R. W.: *Patterns on the Land,* Aegeus Publishing Co., Woodland Hills, California, 1965. An interesting atlas.

FOGELSON, ROBERT M.: *The Fragmented Metropolis, Los Angeles, 1850–1930,* Harvard University Press, Cambridge, 1967.

GRIFFIN, P. F., and R. N. YOUNG: *California: The New Empire State,* Fearon, San Francisco, 1957. Similar to the following reference but older and less detailed.

LANTIS, D. W., R. STEINER, and A. E. KARINEN: *California: Land of Contrast,* Wadsworth, Belmont, California, 1963. A detailed regional geography for use in California colleges.

LARGE, DAVID C.: "Cotton in the San Joaquin Valley," *Geographical Review,* vol. 47 (1957), pp. 365–380.

RAUP, H. F.: *San Bernardino, California: Settlement and Growth of a Pass-site City,* University of California Publications in Geography, vol. 8, no. 1, University of California Press, Berkeley, 1940. An interesting study in historical geography.

THOMAS, WILLIAM L., JR. (ed.): "Man, Time, and Space in Southern California," *Annals A.A.G.,* vol. 49, no. 3 (September, 1959), supplement. A superb overview stressing the historical approach.

THROWER, NORMAN J. W.: "California Population: Distribution in 1960," *Annals A.A.G.,* vol. 56, no. 2, 1966, map supplement. A detailed dot map on a physiographic base.

ZIERER, CLIFFORD M. (ed.): *California and the Southwest,* Wiley, New York, 1956. A systematic analysis of the region by 32 geographers.

CHAPTER 17

FOCUS ON SAN FRANCISCO BAY

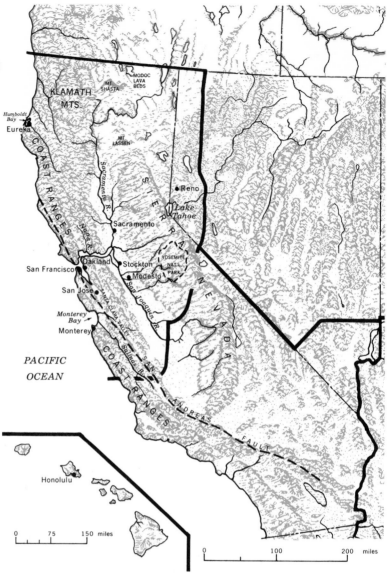

FIGURE 17-1 Landforms of the region that focuses commercially on San Francisco Bay. The influence of the San Francisco Federal Reserve Bank extends much further: east as far as the Rockies and north across Alaska. (Base map copyright by A. K. Lobeck. Reprinted with permission of The Geographical Press, Hammond, Inc.)

The northern two-thirds of California (Figure 17-1) differs physically from the Southland only in degree: Both regions include high wooded mountains, sharp lower ridges, and less humid, alluvium-filled valleys; both have dry, warm to hot summers and more humid, mild winters; both have sharp climatic and vegetative contrasts between the coastal zone and the interior; between lowlands and highlands. Adjoining the

BASIC DATA:

AREA INCLUDES	Land Area (thousand sq. mi.)	Population Change, 1950-1960	1960 (thousands)	1967 (thousands)	Personal Income 1967 (billions)
ENTIRE REGION	114.8	33.4%	6,836	7,938	$29.1
California (part)	99.1	34.1	6,108	7,050	26.2
Adjacent Nevada	9.3	68.0	95	143	0.6
Hawaii	6.4	26.6	633	745	2.3
MAJOR SMSAS					
San Francisco-Oakland	3.3	24.2%	2,783	3,150	$12.5
Sacramento	3.4	76.3	625	830	2.8
San Jose	1.3	121.1	642	990	3.5
Stockton	1.4	24.5	250	285	1.0
Reno	6.3	68.8	85	127	0.5
Honolulu	0.6	41.8	500	620	2.0

CLIMATE Mild and humid along the Coast with increasing aridity and temperature extremes inland. Rain irregular, mostly in winter.

	Temperature (°F) Jan.	July	Precipitation (inches) Annual	Season
San Francisco	51	59	21	Cooler months
Sacramento	46	74	18	Cooler months
Eureka	47	56	38	Summer drought
Reno (4,397 ft)	30	68	7	Winter maximum

VEGETATION Short grass in the Central Valley, evergreen oak and scrub on the lower slopes; Douglas fir and redwood to the northwest; and pine-juniper with some sequoia on the Sierra Nevada.

SOIL Alluvial soils in the valleys, extensive prairie soils; gray-brown podzolic soils in northwest; shallow stony soils on mountains and near eastern border.

MINERALS Natural gas, salt, stone, gravel, sand, gypsum, cement, gold.

interregional boundary is a broad transition zone between the more subtropical vegetation and mild middle-latitude vegetation. Both regions are suited for outdoor living most of the year. The transition in climate continues in Northern California, where the weather is more humid in winter and cooler in summer, thus gradually taking on the climatic character of the Pacific Northwest.

The relatively small economic differences between this region and the California Southland result from minor but significant differences in resources. The most notable of these was gold, first discovered east of the site of Sacramento in 1848. This first gold rush in Anglo-American history converted the then insignificant village of San Francisco, with one of the world's finest but hitherto little used harbors, into a major port. The focus of the region became San Francisco Bay which, in addition to its 4,500-foot-wide Golden Gate to the Pacific, offered a north-south navigable length of 45 miles connected by navigable streams to Sacramento and Stockton. In contrast to the inland orientation of early Los Angeles, Northern California, blessed with natural harbors from Monterey Bay to Humboldt Bay (Eureka), was bound to the sea. By 1869 San Francisco Bay became the terminus of the first transcontinental railroad and of roads from all the Pacific shores and interior valleys. Soon the Bay Area took on financial and commercial functions for most of the Far West, and, in addition, manufactured for western consumption a variety of products, including the refining of Hawaiian sugar.

THE PHYSICAL SETTING[1]

The major physical difference between Southern and Northern California is that the latter region, being more exposed to moisture-laden air masses from the Pacific, has a surplus of water. The variety of moisture conditions within Northern California is mostly related to relief.

Landforms

As in the Southland, the characteristic landform consists of tilted blocks, of either metamorphic or igneous rocks, between which are valleys, some narrow and some broad, but all filled to considerable depths by debris washed down from the mountain blocks. This structure has resulted partly from a long history of earthquakes which have been particularly severe in the last century along the San Andreas Fault extending from San Francisco southeastward to the Imperial Valley. In contrast, the northeastern corner of California, into

[1] Although both California and Hawaii are similar in the mildness of their climates and their suitability for outdoor living, they are otherwise so different that discussion of the latter is deferred to the end of this chapter.

which extends the southern end of the Cascades, is largely volcanic, its surface being characterized by lava flows and volcanic cones.

The Coast Ranges, much lower but no less abrupt than the ranges on the inland edge of the Southland coastal zone, roughly parallel the Coast. They are, however, arranged *en échelon,* that is, each range terminates as a headland projecting into the Pacific so that the valley between the range and the next parallel range inland drains northward to the Coast. Each coastal valley has tended to become a separate, small agricultural region. There are a number of exceptions to this general pattern, the principal one being at San Francisco Bay where the streams of the Central Valley converge into the lower Sacramento River, and send their waters through the Golden Gate, the major break in the Coast Ranges.

A much larger block is the Sierra Nevada, extending 400 miles from south of Mount Lassen to Tejon Pass; the latter carries the main route from Los Angeles to the Central Valley. This block, some 60 miles wide and tilted upward toward the east where its abrupt crest overlooks the Great Basin, is a major barrier. Even today no railroad or highway crosses the High Sierras for 150 miles, and transverse routes both to the north and south have steep grades and tortuous curves, and, in the north, snow hazards in winter. The peaks of the crest show the scars of past glaciation, and the deep valleys to the west are commonly U-shaped, forming spectacular scenery as in Yosemite National Park.

The gentle westward slope of the Sierra block continues beneath the Central Valley whose alluvium, largely derived from the Sierra, is as much as 2,000 feet thick. The streams from the Sierra Nevada and the Cascades to the north drain into the Sacramento–San Joaquin system after depositing much of their load of gravel, sand, and silt on alluvial fans on the eastern side of the

SAN FRANCISCO BAY *from above Oakland. Note the artificial lake in the foreground and the filled land occupied by the airport and harbor installations.* (R. L. Copeland from Oakland Chamber of Commerce.)

valley. Groundwater for wells used to be plentiful in these alluvial deposits. The valley trough, naturally poorly drained, consisted of a series of tule (rushes) marshes when first discovered.

In addition to the volcanic Cascades, the northern edge of the region includes the Klamath Mountains, a complicated cluster of folded and faulted ranges mostly of crystalline rock. East of the Cascades are the Modoc Lava Beds and the northwestern edge of the basin and range area; parts of these features extend into extreme western Nevada which is included in this region because its business is dominated by California. Settlement in these mountain areas is sparse compared with the high rural densities in the Central Valley.

Climate and Vegetation

The climate, far from uniform but generally mild, is usually classified as Mediterranean, so named because its dry summers and more humid winters resemble climates around the Mediterranean Sea (Figure 17-2). As in its European counterpart and in Southern California, climate and vegetation in Northern California vary greatly with altitude, exposure, and distance from the ocean.

The coastal zone, often foggy and with only about 10° seasonal range, has a moderate rainfall which is extremely effective in promoting tree growth. This is the land of the redwood forest. Around and south of San Francisco Bay the marine influence

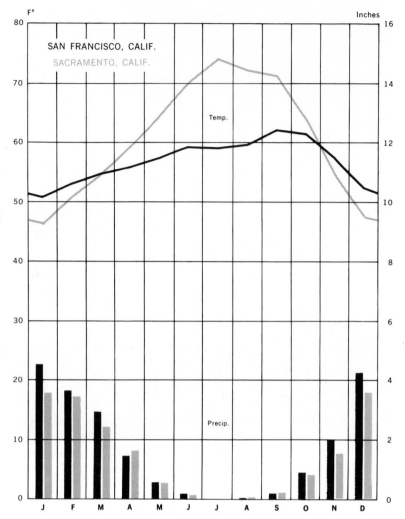

F°   Inches

80   16

   SAN FRANCISCO, CALIF.

   SACRAMENTO, CALIF.

70   14

                              Temp.

60   12

50   10

40   8

30   6

20   4

                              Precip.

10   2

0   0
   J   F   M   A   M   J   J   A   S   O   N   D

FIGURE 17-2   As in Southern California, the climate includes greater ranges in temperature and rainfall inland. Sacramento is 80 miles from the Pacific.

extends 40 to 50 miles inland, the weather gradually becoming less foggy, with daily and seasonal temperature extremes greater, and rainfall less than along the Coast. Thin prairie with scattered oak trees replaces the redwood forest, but chaparral is common where soil moisture is poor. Agriculture was not hampered and delayed by problems of forest clearing in the Central Valley, as in the valleys northward in Oregon.

Inland from the north coast, altitude increases the rainfall, and there is a greater seasonal temperature range. Douglas fir, mixed with the redwood along the Coast, dominates the forest inland and has become the basis for a well-developed logging in-

dustry. In turn, the firs give way in the less humid uplands to pines, mixed in many areas with white fir and incense cedar. These species are also characteristic of the California Cascades and much of the Sierra Nevada. South of Yosemite National Park, giant sequoias are an obvious part of the landscape. This upland area is cooler with higher altitude and has pleasant summers above 3,000 feet. Its snow accumulation is a major California resource, providing water for the valleys during the thirsty summers.

The climates of the smaller valleys vary greatly with exposure to wind, sun, and marine influence, whereas the Central Valley is sufficiently broad and level to permit climatic generalizations to be made. Rainfall increases to the northward and up the slopes of the Sierra with averages in the valley ranging from less than 10 inches (desert) to 30 inches (subhumid). Because the rainy season is in the cooler half of the year, the rains are relatively effective although not too dependable. The natural vegetation (except in the tule marshes) was originally prairie (bunchgrass and other herbaceous plants); on the slopes and in the extreme north, scattered oaks and other broad-leaved trees were common. The growing season is long—from 300 days in the south to 200 days in the north. Except where the influence of the sea enters through San Francisco Bay, summers are scorching hot but rarely humid. Winters are mild with average temperatures of 44 to 46° in most of the lowland. Foggy spells and subfreezing nights (20 to 30°) are characteristic in midwinter. Although it has a few handicaps, this is a favorable climate for human settlement.

ECONOMIC HISTORY

The Spanish-Mexican history in central California includes the same elements as in the South—mission agriculture and cattle ranches—but settlement came somewhat later. Monterey became the capital of Alta California (upper California, north of San Diego). Spanish-Mexican settlement extended about 30 miles north of San Francisco Bay, but ranching did not spread into the Central Valley until 1836. The gold rush, centered first east of Sacramento and later throughout the Mother Lode country adjacent to the Sierra, brought immigrants from many parts of the world, providing employment in trade, crafts, ranching, and services, for the great majority who did not find gold. The North Coast (north of San Francisco Bay), at first thinly settled by trappers, became after the gold rush a source of lumber, dairy products, beef, and other foods, and in a few places, gold.

After the Gold Rush

The importance of gold in the American settlement of California can hardly be overestimated; yet the gold rush lasted less than a decade—thereafter gold was exploited by large-scale operations. Individual prospectors seeking claims moved northward to British Columbia in 1858, eastward to Nevada, and northeastward and eastward to the Rockies in the next year. Sacramento, founded as a river port for the gold fields, became the state capital in 1852, while San Francisco, the ocean port, became the financial center for most of the area west of the Rockies. Several decades later, San Francisco became a processor and shipper of agricultural products from the Central Coast and Central Valley. The shift to agriculture was especially rapid in the last quarter of the nineteenth century: dry-farmed wheat first took over the extensive ranchlands, somewhat later, irrigation farmers developed vineyards, orchards, and truck farms whose crops were marketed outside the state by both rail and ship. The various microclimates and the generous water supply made the northern two-thirds of California outstanding for the variety, quantity, and quality of its agricultural products shipped to distant markets: dehydrated, bottled, canned, chilled, or frozen.

Industrial Development

At first industrial plants depended on local raw materials; food processing was the dominant industry until World War II. Some consumer-goods industries were established early in the San Francisco area, being encouraged by the high cost of freight from Eastern factories. Port industries, such as oil refining, coffee roasting and blending,

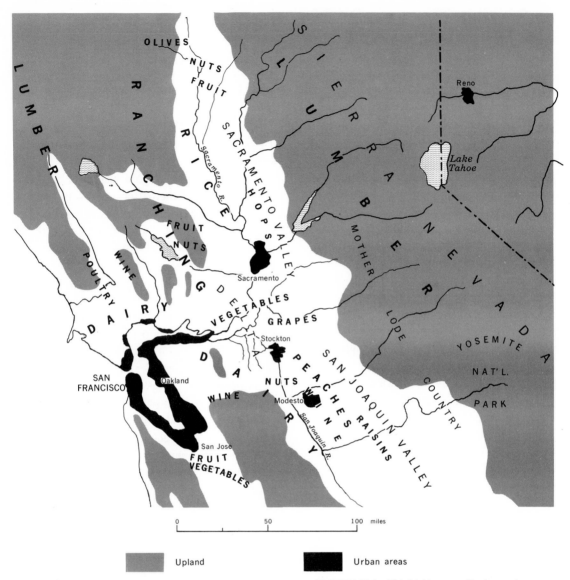

Upland   Urban areas

FIGURE 17-3   *This highly generalized map gives some idea of the variety of crop specialties found in central California.*

were gradually added. Before World War II a small steel industry and railway-equipment and automobile-assembly plants had been established. During World War II industrial diversification speeded up as a consequence of huge military demands in the Pacific area; primary and fabricated metals, machinery, electronics, and cement industries expanded in the Bay Area outside the central city.

Recent growth in the northern two-thirds of California has been well above average for the United States but less than in the Southland. San Francisco, once superior to its rival, Los Angeles, in cultural, service, and industrial leadership, still has a high per capita rating in these activities but the much more populous Los Angeles metropolis leads in each respect, at least in quantity of activity. San Francisco still retains the head offices of many western enterprises, including the Twelfth District Federal Reserve Bank.

Sources of Income

As in most urbanizing areas, this region gets the great bulk of its income from urban activities (Figure 17-4). About three-fourths of its income is concentrated in the 13-county area around San Francisco Bay which includes Sacramento, Stockton, and San Jose, as well as the numerous cities in the San Francisco–Oakland SMSA. For the 13-county area only 3 percent of the workers are agricultural, 27 percent are in manufacturing and construction, and 18 percent in trade; thus more than half are employed in various kinds of services, including government, education, professional, domestic, transportation, and utilities. Compared with the Los Angeles–Long Beach SMSA, the Bay Area employment is 9 percent lower in manufacturing and construction (36 percent for Los Angeles–Long Beach), about the same in trade, but about 8 percent higher in services.

SAN FRANCISCO AND THE BAY AREA [2]

Why the Site of San Francisco?

The location of San Francisco on a rocky, hilly peninsula with a business section adjacent to a spacious, well-sheltered harbor seems an obvious selection of the best site in the Bay Area. In 1849 equally usable sites might have been developed at San Mateo, Sausalito, Oakland, Berkeley, Richmond, Pittsburg, and elsewhere on the bay. Since the warehouse function was fundamental to

[2] The following section owes much to James E. Vance, Jr., "Geography and Urban Evolution in the San Francisco Bay Area," in *The San Francisco Bay Area; Its Problems and Future*, University of California, Berkeley, 1963.

FIGURE 17-4 California is the leading state in farm income; yet it cannot produce enough food to feed its growing population. It does, however, produce a surplus of some of its specialties: for example, grapes, avocados, and winter vegetables. The high personal income and the above-average bars for construction and services suggest an expanding and progressive economy.

early San Francisco business, the direction of the currents through Golden Gate and the firm bottom of Yerba Buena Cove facilitated the unloading of supply ships there. Even so, a long wharf was required to reach deep water, and the foggy site was considered a handicap by many. When the port facilities were built, small steamers found them convenient starting points from which to ascend rivers southward well into the present Fresno County and northward to Red Bluff; other steamers served smaller ports on the bay. Thus San Francisco became a boatman's city and, in anticipation of future port growth, land speculation became common.

Specialized Land Use

San Francisco was not only a central place to serve central California; it also grew as the result of its increasing population, requiring more workers to serve the needs of the local population. Consequently specialized land use within the city evolved to

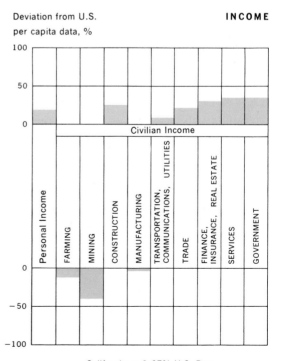

Deviation from U.S. per capita data, %

INCOME

California = 9.67% U.S. Pop.

perform services for both the regional trading area and the inhabitants of the city. Flatlands were built artificially along the harbor to provide sites for the wholesale district, while the financial district (Montgomery Street) became established on the slopes several blocks inland. South of this a retail shopping district arose along Market Street, a wide thoroughfare connecting the main landing (Embarcadero) with Dolores Mission near Twin Peaks. South of the shopping district a light-industrial district grew up on fairly level land around the railroad terminals, and residential districts were built on the hills and on the gently sloping areas on the western side of the peninsula.

Changing land-use patterns In the 1860s and 1870s the railroad modified this land-use pattern, especially because early routes terminated not in San Francisco but rather at places across the bay and connected with the central city by ferry. As railroads took over more traffic, and as navigable streams lost some of their water to irrigation projects, the paddle-wheel steamers and barges shortened their routes. Bulky interior products such as wheat might be sold in San Francisco, but they were loaded onto ocean ships at railroad terminals east of the bay. New town sites were no longer limited to waterfronts; they sprang up along the railroads. After the introduction of the electric traction motor (1887), trolley-car suburbs were added to San Francisco's railroad suburbs with retail zones arising along the streets carrying the trolley-car tracks. As suburbs sprawled out along these inland routes, San Francisco lost some of its early unity; further decentralization occurred in the early twentieth century when the East Bay established business centers which began to perform shopping and other functions formerly almost a monopoly of downtown San Francisco.

The automobile speeded the formation of outlying centers and led to a filling in of spaces between rail and trolley routes with residential, industrial, and neighborhood commercial developments. As parking within the central city became scarce, some central-city functions moved to the suburbs. Further suburban expansion resulted from the increased economic activity of World War II and postwar American involvement in Asia; these factors expanded trans-Pacific shipping and industrial facilities near Pacific ports. The freeway-bridge age, beginning in the 1950s, destroyed most of the remaining local water traffic. Yet the skeletons of the former land uses remained apparent in the street and railroad grids, in land uses, and in local traditions. Recently the concept of urban renewal has arisen: and the Bay Area is preparing to rebuild to fit contemporary needs. The new patterns will not be entirely novel because the grain of the hills, the water bodies, and the huge investments in structures will have a conservative influence; the twenty-first-century Bay Area will retain many of the features of the mid-twentieth century.

Metropolitan patterns Like most metropolitan areas built on uneven terrain, the Bay Area consists of a number of incongruous street grids inherited from towns that have since grown together. The industrial patterns show a more logical development. Lighter industries, including food processing and consumer-goods manufactures, are common in San Francisco, whereas the heavier industries are located along the railroad lines, behind the docks along the western bay shore, and also along the eastern bay shore. More recently established light industries, including publishing and science-oriented industries, are growing in many of the suburbs. Southward, industrial buildings are displacing the intensively developed farms which cannot compete profitwise with in-

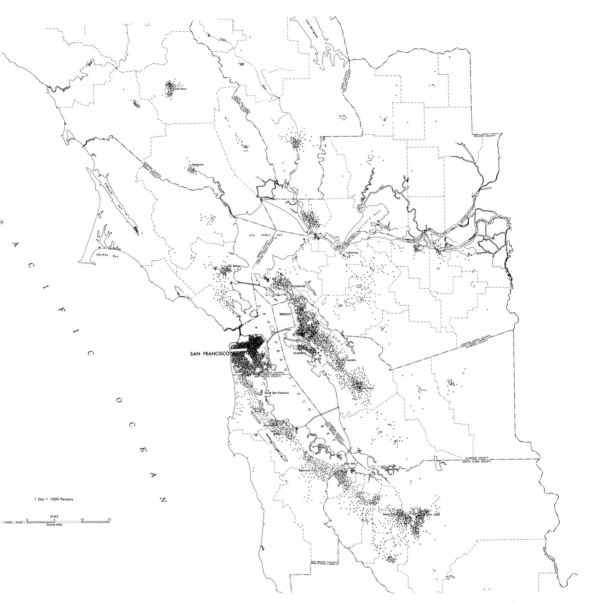

FIGURE 17-5   This population map suggests that there is much vacant land in the San Francisco Bay Area; the people are concentrated on the better-drained lowlands and on the adjacent slopes. (Office of Area Development, FUTURE DEVELOPMENT OF THE SAN FRANCISCO BAY AREA: 1960–2020, Washington, 1959.)

dustrial and residential use. Thus the Santa Clara Valley, noted for its orchards and vegetable gardens, is gradually converting to an economy based on electronic and science-oriented industries and supplying the residential and other needs of workers in these industries.

When in 1914 the Federal Reserve System selected San Francisco as the location for the Twelfth District Federal Reserve

Bank, it was recognizing the widely known financial and commercial dominance of this city in most of the area west of the Rockies. Today San Francisco ranks third in financial strength among the 12 Federal Reserve Banks, and although Southern California outranks Northern California in population and income, the Bay Area retains Western commercial and financial leadership. Why did San Francisco become the leader in the West, and why has it retained this position? The answer involves the site and locational advantages discussed above, perhaps even more the accidents of history, and the tendency of business to follow established channels until a change seems likely to result in outstanding economies.

San Francisco, Los Angeles, and New York

In most respects the Bay Area contrasts with the Los Angeles metropolitan area. The San Francisco area was never a major agricultural community, and it lacked local resources such as oil and natural gas. It developed initially as a focal point with many natural routeways and harbors, whereas Los Angeles had to develop its harbor and many of its routes in spite of natural handicaps. In the Bay Area residential districts grew initially on the slopes and later expanded onto the flatter, once marshy lands, whereas the Southland communities were first laid out on the flatlands and expanded later into the hills. The bay and river systems provided San Francisco with regional connections, and Southern California depended first on railways and later on roads and expressways to integrate its regional economy. Economically San Francisco started and has remained primarily a commercial center, whereas Los Angeles emphasized more the production of foodstuffs, raw materials, and manufactures. Of course, Los Angeles, in common with all metropolises, has developed important commercial and financial functions, but these represent a relatively smaller part of its overall economy compared with that of the Bay Area.

A Pacific Coast New York San Francisco has been thought of as the New York of the Pacific Coast, both metropolises having tall buildings, outstanding commercial functions, and spacious harbors lined with docks, warehouses, and factories. Both at first found the enclosed waterways a major convenience for regional communication and later replaced most of the ferry services

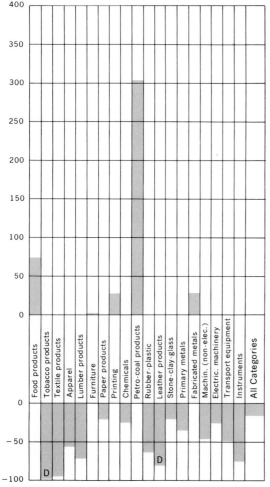

Deviation from U.S. per capita data, %

VALUE ADDED BY MANUFACTURING
San Francisco – Oakland SMSA = 1.55% U.S. Pop.

FIGURE 17-6 The entrepôt nature of much San Francisco–Oakland business is reflected in its manufacturing emphasis on industries processing petroleum and food products, both imported and to be shipped out. Compare with Los Angeles (Figure 16-8).

with bridges or tunnels. Both commercial centers depended for development on the resources of outlying rather than local hinterlands; both have important business ties overseas and in distant states. Both have compact Central Business Districts within which most high-level commercial and financial functions are performed. Both had and still have some nearby undeveloped areas of marshy and rugged lands.

Industrially the Bay Area has a smaller local market and a less mature industrial development than the New York area; furthermore, it stands more by itself, not yet being fully integrated into larger units, as New York is integrated into the Atlantic Megalopolis and the American Commercial-Industrial Core. Note in Figure 17-6 how much the San Francisco–Oakland SMSA departs from the United States average in most industrial categories. Recent industrial trends show that these deviations are lessening. With a larger local market and greater industrial maturity San Francisco is likely to grow closer to the national industrial averages.

Potential Growth and Integration

It has been predicted that the nine-county area around San Francisco Bay will grow into a megalopolis and that by 2020 the Bay Area will have a population of 14 million. The Office of Area Development study[3] which makes this prediction includes maps for 1960 (Figure 17-8) showing land use, as well as maps showing predicted land use for each decade, 1970–2020. Such predictions are likely to be greatly in error, as already

[3]U.S. Department of Commerce, Office of Area Development, *Future Development of the San Francisco Bay Area: 1960–2020*, Washington, 1959.

FIGURE 17-7   San Jose was once known for its canned fruits and vegetables, but recently it has developed an electric machinery industry based on a technologically trained labor force.

has been noted in Chapter 8, because of changes in human technology and objectives.

The Department of Commerce study did not consider the possible integration of the Bay Area with Sacramento and Stockton SMSAs, each less than 60 miles from the bay and now connected with it by 32-foot channels navigable by ocean freighters. Sacramento, the capital of California, started as a gold rush trading town, acquired status as state capital in 1852, and thereafter developed also as an agricultural trading center. The city is at the junction of the American and Sacramento rivers and formerly suffered from floods. To the north the water is controlled for use in rice fields, and modern dams now impound the headwaters of most streams. In addition to rice, the Sacramento trading area produces a wide variety of agricultural products ranging from beef cattle to walnuts. Industrially the

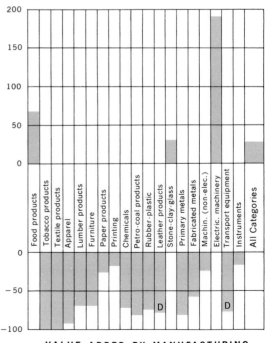

Deviation from U.S. per capita data, %

VALUE ADDED BY MANUFACTURING

San Jose SMSA = .46% U.S. Pop.

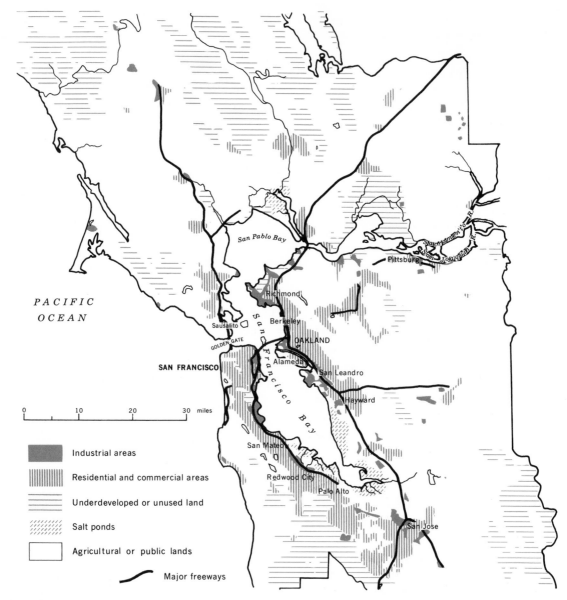

FIGURE 17-8 *Compare this 1960 map with Figure 17-5.* (After a map by the Corps of Engineers.)

city's long-established food-packing and railroad-shop industries have been supplemented by defense-oriented industries such as missile fuels and signal corps and air force equipment. Stockton's industries remain closely related to agriculture, and the exports from its port are mainly packed foods.

The conversion of agricultural areas between the adjacent Stockton-Sacramento SMSAs and the Bay Area into urban land would appreciably reduce farm production. However, urban activities are so much more intensive per acre than agriculture that there is little doubt that such activities can outbid the farmer for land. The area is strategically located near the San Francisco focus and possesses the mild winters and pleasantly warm summers that have attracted migrants from the East and Midwest.

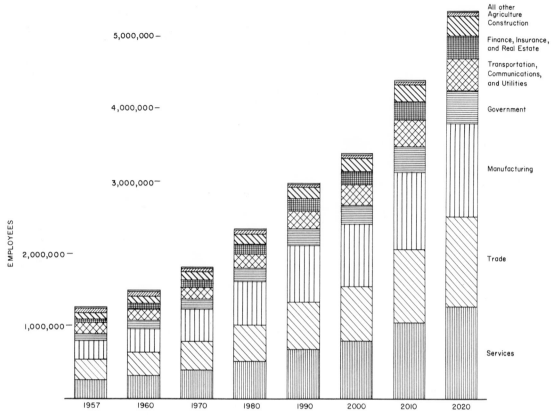

FIGURE 17-9   *Predicted growth of employment, 1957–2020, in the San Francisco Bay Area. The forecast obviously reflects the expected increased growth of population, but as in any maturing economy, it also shows a more rapid growth in urban-based activities, especially commercial and services employment.* (Office of Area Development, FUTURE DEVELOPMENT OF THE SAN FRANCISCO BAY AREA: 1960–2020, Washington, 1959.)

Sacramento, well established as a trading focus for the Sacramento Valley and Stockton, with a similar position in the lower San Joaquin Valley, seems likely to grow toward San Francisco, just as many Southern California cities have become satellites of Los Angeles.

Water resources   The future urban growth of California is related to the overall water problem. All except Northern California and a few mountain ranges are water-deficit areas. How can the local surpluses be distributed to the deficit areas? The total water available in stream runoff in an average year is sufficient to cover 71 million acres to a depth of one foot; this is sufficient to cover all the land area of California with 8 inches of water. About 42 percent of this drains into the Pacific north of San Fran-

cisco Bay; one-third drains into the Sacramento Valley, and one-ninth into the San Joaquin Valley. The remainder represents small streams in the Southland. The California state water project (Figure 16-5), at a cost of about $3 billion, plans to harness a water supply of an additional 4,221,000 acre-feet with a yield (as a by-product) of 6 billion kilowatts of electric power annually. Over half this water will go to the California Southland, in part to compensate for the partial loss of Colorado River water to Arizona as the result of the June, 1963, U.S. Supreme Court decision.

SACRAMENTO IS IN THE MIDST of the fields of the Central Valley. The winding course of the Sacramento River has been supplemented by a canal and harbor installations which make Sacramento a seaport. (Port of Sacramento.)

AGRICULTURE IN THE VALLEYS

California agriculture is highly specialized. This is well illustrated in the coastal areas south of the San Francisco area. The Coast is spectacular with small resort towns, oil-shipping ports, and farms in narrow valleys specializing in one or two crops. The Salinas Valley concentrates on head lettuce and artichokes with other specialties near the

THIS PIE-SHAPED CORRAL LAYOUT in central California is designed to facilitate the movement of dairy cows to the milking facility at the hub. Baled hay, brought in from a distance, is easily unloaded at the feed bunks around the perimeter. Compare this with the Wisconsin dairy farms described in Chapters 9 and 10. (USDA photograph.)

THE TRANSFER OF WATER in California is definitely big business. This photograph shows a part of the Central Valley Project Canal (252 feet wide at the top, 110 feet wide at the bottom, and 32 feet deep). The Das Amigas Pumping Plant shown here powers the flow of water along the flattish valley floor. (California Department of Water Resources.)

foggy valley mouth, for example, onions, carrots, and broccoli. The drier and warmer interior of this valley raises tomatoes, beans, fodder, and sheep. Inland, closer to the Central Valley than to the Pacific, is the Guyama Valley, dependent for income mainly on sheep and well-irrigation farming until oil was discovered in 1948. In contrast to the monotonous Central Valley, the Coastal Ranges offer changes in view and in climate every few miles along the road.

The Central Valley Specialization is also apparent in the Central Valley (Figure 17-3), although a few farm products are widely distributed, for example, cattle, chickens, fodder crops, and grains. Vegetables tend to be concentrated in a few localities, partly because of proximity to packing plants, and partly because highly specialized machinery is used in harvesting, thus encouraging large-scale operations. The largest concentration of vegetables is around Stockton. Fruits and nuts are likewise concentrated in particular regions. The distribution of grapes depends on the product being grown, whether market grapes, raisins, or wine grapes; the nature of the product is greatly influenced by small differences in climate

and soil. Lands unsuited for special crops may be used for hay and grazing.

THE WATER-RICH AREAS

The Northwest

This moist tenth of California has two resources—trees and enough water to export. Most of its waters flow, with little use, into the Pacific. Often the region has suffered from destructive floods because in this area, as in most of California, precipitation fluctuates widely. This is green California: trees, undergrowth, and lawns are verdant without irrigation. The landscapes appear moist and cool, in contrast to the semi-arid parts of California where forest fires and grass fires are an ever-present danger, and where drab browns and yellows are relieved by bright flowers and by brilliant sunlight.

There are no large cities in the northwest, Eureka with 28,000 being the most populous. It does not take many workers with power saws and tractors to harvest the lumber or even to cut the redwood, Douglas fir, and yellow pine into boards. Nor do the thousand small fishing vessels require mammoth crews. There is little agriculture along the Coast; inland much of the land is in national forest. The best-developed agriculture is in the transition zone between the northwest and the northern end of the Central Valley where grazing and middle-latitude orchards flourish; there also natural gas discoveries have created a modest growth. Another transition zone is in valleys southward merging into the Bay Area where poultry, dairy farming, orchards, and vineyards supply San Francisco markets. Napa Valley, mostly in the Bay Area, has achieved renown by producing dry European-type wines.

The Sierra Nevada

These mountains can be considered as impediments to travel, as recreational areas, as sources of timber, and as collectors of water. Of these, it is the last function that helps to make California habitable by tens of millions rather than by hundreds of thousands. Snowfall near the summits is commonly 200 to 400 inches (equal to 20 to 40 inches of rain), and much higher figures have been reported. Most of the snow meltwater flowing down the eastern slope is piped to Los Angeles. Meltwater descending the western slopes feeds the streams and replenishes the groundwater tapped by wells a century before extensive surface irrigation systems were constructed. At present, streams from the southern Sierra are fed into a canal to irrigate the Fresno-Bakersfield area. Two aqueducts from the Central Sierras bring water across the Central Valley to serve the bay cities; other streams supply water to the northern two-thirds of the valley.

Western Nevada   Watered largely by streams from the eastern slope of the Sierra Nevada, the Nevada counties adjacent to northern and central California are historically and economically tied to the larger state. They were first explored by hunters, army officers, and emigrants en route to California. The exploitation of precious metals was by California miners who reasoned correctly that if alluvial gold came from the Sierra Nevada block, veins might also be found on the eastern slope and adjacent mountains. In 1859 the Comstock lode, including gold and silver ores worth nearly $14,000 a ton, was discovered and people flocked in. Nevada became a territory in 1861, a state in 1864; its population reached 42,491 in 1870, and 62,266 in 1880, and then declined to 42,335 in 1900. In recent years Nevada mining employs only 3,000 to 4,000 people, very few of whom are in the western border counties. Copper, sand and gravel, and iron ore all surpass precious metals in value of output.

Tourist trade based on gambling, floor shows, and outdoor living provides the present economic backbone of western Nevada. Liberal laws are responsible for most of the income of Washoe County (Reno SMSA); even the 1 percent of the income attributable to mining is largely from sand and gravel used in the construction of roads and urban buildings. Lake Tahoe in Washoe, Ormsby, and Douglas counties, all once known for the mining of precious metals, now offers water sports along with wilder indoor amusements.

HAWAII

It is nearly 2,100 nautical miles (2,400 statute miles) from San Francisco Bay to Honolulu; the four-hour trip by jet involves a change of 16° equatorward in latitude and two hours change in time. These startlingly beautiful volcanic islands are the summits of a volcanic mass rising somewhat east and north of the center of the Pacific, but centrally enough located to serve as a focus of trans-Pacific air and shipping routes. Tropical heat is so moderated by the ocean that temperatures are pleasant, averaging 71° in January and 77° in July in Honolulu, with extremes of 52 and 90°. Even the midday heat is moderated by the almost constant

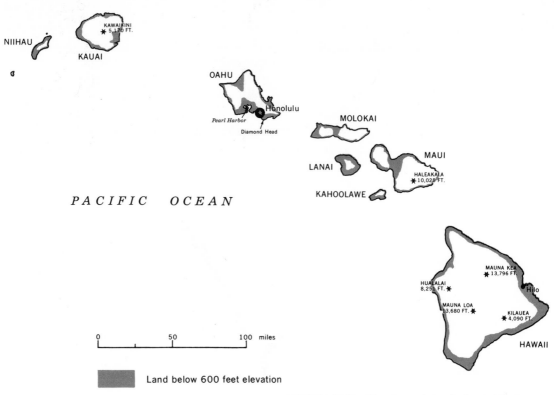

NIIHAU

KAWAIKINI
★ 5,170 FT.

KAUAI

OAHU

Honolulu

Pearl Harbor

Diamond Head

MOLOKAI

MAUI

LANAI

HALEAKALA
★ 10,025 FT.

KAHOOLAWE

P A C I F I C   O C E A N

MAUNA KEA
★ 13,796 FT.

HUALALAI
8,251 FT. ★

Hilo

MAUNA LOA
13,680 FT. ★

KILAUEA
★ 4,090 FT.

HAWAII

0   50   100 miles

Land below 600 feet elevation

FIGURE 17-10   Hawaii is a chain of volcanic islands, mostly mountainous, but each producing several specialties. The principal specialty of Oahu is services: military, commercial, and tourist.

trade winds. The major variable is the rainfall which is low on the leeward side and high on the windward side, so that surplus water in the latter is canalized to irrigate drier areas. Pleasant beaches, a lush tropical vegetation, a great variety of peoples, active but quiescent volcanoes, a choice of luxury and medium-priced hotels have made these islands one of the world's great resorts.

Not the least of the attractions of the islands has been their multiracial society. The Polynesians found by Captain Cook have blended in turn with American, Chinese, Japanese, Filipino, Portuguese, and other immigrants. Some of each group retain its distinctive cultural characteristics; many in each group have intermarried; in either case there is a spirit of tolerance. Outwardly at least most peoples seem to be highly americanized, especially in their business relationships.

The state is still noted for its tropical products: sugar, pineapples, coffee, and papaya; yet agriculture contributes less than one-twentieth of the personal income. Most of the farms producing for shipment to the mainland are large, highly mechanized, and managed by corporations. Sugar cultivation is so outstanding for its high yields per acre and per worker that delegations from many tropical countries have inspected the sugar plantations and adjoining factories to learn how this high productivity is accomplished.

Honolulu

About five-sixths of the people and income are concentrated on Oahu which includes one-eleventh of the state's land within the Honolulu SMSA. On this island are found most of the military, naval, and air force bases; the commercial and shipping facilities; and the tourist activities. Manufacturing is modest, consisting mainly of the

ON LANAI ISLAND, HAWAII, pineapples are picked by hand, but the conveyors enable the crew to harvest 25,000 per hour which are mechanically packed into crates on the truck. The crates are shipped by barge to Oahu for canning. (USDA photograph.)

processing of export crops, tourist goods, and bulky goods for local consumption; defense-oriented industries are a relatively new but growing development. Government, especially federal, directly accounts for one-third of the income, and probably more indirectly.

CONCLUSIONS

Almost every county in this region as well as in the California Southland is growing rapidly in population. The few counties showing a net out-migration are in the more rugged areas. This widespread growth reflects the tendency of people and industries to seek milder climates for homes and factories. Foodstuffs and raw materials, once the major attraction of these regions, still play a significant part in the total economy but, if the forecasts for the San Francisco Bay area are correct, will play a decreasing role both as raw materials and as a base for industry. Both California and Hawaii are investing heavily in education aimed at supporting a society based on technology and automation rather than on muscle and raw materials. The former handicap of distance from markets has been overcome by jet flights and by the accelerating growth of mammoth markets in the Pacific states and across the Pacific.

The population of California today is close to 20 million, and already highways, campsites, and tourist attractions are jammed literally bumper to bumper on weekends. What will it be like when there are 50 million or even 75 million Californians? One humorist has predicted that in a cen-

Deviation from U.S.
per capita data, %

INCOME

FIGURE 17-11 Compared with the income deviations in other states, Hawaii seems a paradox. Although its economy is booming (as suggested by the construction bar), its trade is below average. Its farming is exceptionally high for an urbanizing economy; its manufacturing exceptionally low. Much of this is explained by the important part government activity plays in the state's economy.

Hawaii = .38% U.S. Pop.

tury every acre of California will be used for one of four categories: business, residential, roads, or parking. Fortunately, much of California is too rugged for such intensive use. Actually very little of the Sierra is now being used for recreation, and all but a few thousand people keep to within some hundred yards of the highways. The less-used mountains are not unattractive; the most modest peak would be a mammoth tourist attraction if located near Chicago. The problem is how to pay for the roads in order to make the California mountains accessible to weak-legged urbanites.

The problem of water is also serious (although northwestern California still possesses little-used reserves). To what extent will the state build more extensive distribution systems? Will desalted seawater and reclaimed sewage add to the water supply? Will increased urban use lead to a limitation on irrigation agriculture? The answers to these questions may be politically rather than geographically motivated.

Indian California and Polynesian Hawaii have in a century been greatly altered and in many ways improved by the dynamism of an exotic Anglo-Saxon culture. Will the California environment remain attractive, or will its natural beauties be overwhelmed by smog, noise, and urban sprawl? There is also a cultural problem, for some of the populace seems unable to fit into a technological, highly automated society because of lack of education, lack of ability, or prejudice. Will the anticipated population explosion result in further improvement, or in dirt, congestion, and chaos?

SELECTED REFERENCES

In addition to relevant references in Chap. 16, consult:

GREGOR, H. F.: "The Plantation in California," *Professional Geographer,* vol. 14 (March, 1962) pp. 1–4.

GRIFFIN, PAUL F., and RONALD L. CHATHAM: "Urban Impact on Agriculture in Santa Clara County, California," *Annals A.A.G.,* vol. 48 (1958), pp. 195–208.

HIGBEE, EDWARD: *American Agriculture,* Wiley, New York, 1958, pp. 84–91.

MCCANN, WILBUR: *California's Economic Diversity,* Crocker-Citizens National Bank, Montgomery Street, San Francisco, no date. The variety of publications issued by California banks, chambers of commerce, state offices, and other promotion agencies is tremendous.

STATE OF CALIFORNIA, THE RESOURCES AGENCY, DEPARTMENT OF WATER RESOURCES: *The California State Water Project in 1967,* Sacramento, 1967.

U.S. DEPARTMENT OF COMMERCE, OFFICE OF AREA DEVELOPMENT: *Future Development of the San Francisco Bay Area: 1960–2020,* U.S. Army Engineer District, San Francisco Corps of Engineers, Washington, 1959.

UNIVERSITY OF CALIFORNIA INSTITUTE OF GOVERNMENTAL STUDIES: *The San Francisco Bay Area: Its Problems and Future,* Franklin K. Lane, Berkeley, 1966. This is a reprint of 13 studies originally printed in 1963 and reassembled in two volumes, the second of which is of special interest to geographers. Included are reports on demography, regional planning, air resource management, housing, urban transportation, and managing the environment. James E. Vance, Jr., contributed a report on "Geography and Urban Evolution in the San Francisco Bay Area."

FIGURE 18-1   The landforms of the Pacific Northwest. Alaska, Washington, and
Oregon have been placed together in this unusual way to stress the huge size of
Alaska. Much of the Pacific Northwest is too rugged, too dry, or too cold for intensive
economic development. (Base map copyright by A. K. Lobeck. Reprinted with permission of The
Geographical Press, Hammond, Inc.)

CHAPTER 18
THE PACIFIC NORTHWEST AND ALASKA

The Pacific Northwest (Figure 18-1), a region rich in water, lumber, and fish, consists of a number of specialized subregions, each with one or two outstanding economic activities. A major problem is lack of local diversification which makes each subregion vulnerable to any depression within its specialized industries. The most widespread industry west of the Cascades is lumbering, along with related material-oriented wood products and paper industries; the much less

BASIC DATA:

AREA INCLUDES	Land Area (thousand sq. mi.)	Population Change, 1950–1960	1960 (thousands)	1967 (thousands)	Personal Income (billions)
PACIFIC NORTHWEST	738.5	20.0%	4,936	5,495	$17.5
Oregon	96.2	16.3	1,769	1,950	6.5
Washington	66.7	19.9	2,853	3,180	9.8
Idaho (part)	4.5	11.8	88	90	0.2
Alaska	571.1	75.8	226	275	1.0
MAJOR SMSAS					
Portland	3.7	16.6%	822	910	$3.0
Seattle-Everett	4.2	31.1	1,107	1,260	4.5
Tacoma	1.7	16.6	322	365	1.0
Spokane	1.8	25.6	278	305	0.9

CLIMATE   *Humid and cloudy near Coast; drier with greater temperature ranges east of mountains; rain largely in cooler half of year.*

	Temperature (°F) Jan.	July	Precipitation (inches) Annual	Season
Seattle	41	63	34	Winter maximum
Portland	39	67	39	Summer drought
Spokane	27	69	15	Winter maximum
Juneau	28	57	83	Fall maximum
Fairbanks	−11	60	12	Summer maximum

VEGETATION Largely coniferous forest with low grasses and some sagebrush areas on interior plateaus; in Alaska broad tundra areas along the Bering and Arctic coasts and on the higher mountains.

SOIL   Generally rocky and podzolic, except for fertile grassland soils on the Columbia Plateau and the diverse alluvial and glacial soils of the Willamette-Puget Sound lowlands.

MINERALS   Oregon and Washington produce mainly sand, gravel, stone, and small amounts of nickel, lead, zinc, copper, uranium, and coal. Alaska, once noted for gold, produces mainly petroleum, natural gas, sand, and gravel, but is believed to possess a variety of undiscovered ores.

important fishing industry is significant in some ports. The other major industry, concentrated around Seattle, is the manufacture of aircraft, located there by historical accident in an area only marginally suited for aircraft production. Inland are the irrigated apple industry, irrigated pasture and associated cattle, the Palouse wheat farms, and the material-oriented manufactures of Spokane. Northward, aside from government-dominated activities, the Alaskan economy has material-oriented industries based on fishing and wood, similar to those of western Oregon and Washington.

THE PHYSICAL SETTING AND SETTLEMENT

The well-settled part of the region is, with a few exceptions, within 100 miles of the Pacific. This is a misty land of cloud-filtered sunshine, with relative freedom from extreme heat in summer and extreme cold in winter—an area in climate and indented coasts more like northwestern Europe than other parts of Anglo-America. Coniferous forest is the characteristic flora, in places lush enough to be described as a "temperate rain forest." Where cleared, the soil is likely to become leached and, on the slopes, eroded. It is a land of green pastures and meadows, with dairying, orchards, and berry patches, and such truck crops as potatoes. Grain can be grown but is profitable only in special areas.

East of the Cascades, the landscape changes within a few miles. The forests thin out and then disappear. The sunshine can be bright, and the air is at times bitter in winter, and sometimes hot and dusty in summer; the land resembles the High West with its contrasts of yellowed grasslands and wheat fields, drab green sagebrush, dark green orchards, and bright green irrigated fields. Water from streams rising in the snowcapped Cascades and in the Northern Rockies makes the land habitable. In Alaska, the trip from the mild, wooded southern coasts across the mountains leads to other forested lands with climatic extremes and with tundra on the heights; beyond, in the far north is a broad arctic meadow with myriads of insects in summer, a frozen waste in winter.

Not least among the resources is the scenic beauty of the land: the multicolored mesas, plateaus, and canyons of the volcanic Columbia Plateau; the cool, green forested slopes and valleys of the Cascades topped by white-capped volcanic cones, the pastoral landscapes of the Willamette and Cowlitz lowlands terminating northward in the dark-toned embayments of Puget Sound; westward the wooded Coast Ranges descend to a foggy, rocky Pacific Coast or end in the spectacular Olympic Mountains overlooking the Strait of Juan de Fuca. Even grander is the Alaskan scenery: the fjorded southeastern coast backed by peaks, surpassing the best Norway has to offer; the towering Alaska Range, the roof of the continent; the broad, somewhat swampy Yukon Valley separated by the icy, saw-toothed Brooks Range from the treeless arctic tundra of northern Alaska. Well stocked with game and fish, these are lands to attract the adventurer and the sportsman more than the agricultural settler. Somewhat isolated until the age of modern transportation (including the airplane), much of this land was unoccupied until a few decades ago, and even today little of it is crowded.

Settlement

For the aborigines, this had been the gateway to the New World. Aboriginal life was diverse in culture and, in many tribes, high in quality (although agriculture was commonly lacking). The most intricate cultures were based on seafood, elaborate wooden boats, wooden houses, artistic carving, and basketry. Along the tundra coasts, the Eskimos and Aleuts developed a culture based on the sea, with crafts using hides, bone, stone, and driftwood. Fishing was the economic base along the inland rivers; hunting and trapping were the occupations on the semi-arid Columbia Plateau and in the interior Alaskan woodlands. Although aboriginal economic life can be broadly categorized in the above terms, there were dozens of languages and distinctive cultures —even the individual villages commonly had distinctive cultural traits.

European trappers and fur traders reached the Pacific Northwest before the

MOUNT HOOD, most conspicuous of the Oregon Cascades, provides water for this reservoir which feeds a power plant. The fir forest is being logged off in patches as part of the U.S. Forest Service sustained-yield program. (Oregon State Highway Department.)

end of the eighteenth century. China-bound clippers from New England traded along the Coast for sea otter and other furs in demand in Chinese markets. During the first half of the nineteenth century, American and British fur traders came overland to establish forts which later were helpful to immigrants. The traders from Canada, troubled by long supply lines, turned to farming and discovered the productive capacity of the virgin soil. In the 1840s, thousands of American pioneers came overland over the famous Oregon Trail, settling mainly in the Willamette Valley. The Cowlitz Valley and Puget Sound area to the north were occupied a decade later when the forests of the Northwest began to supply lumber to California, Hawaii, and other lands touching the Pacific.

The gold rush in California also stimulated the Northwest; after the California boom, miners ventured north and northeast seeking new gold fields. Some gold was found in the Coast Ranges, but even more precious metals were found at the eastern edge of the Inland Empire—in Idaho, northeastern Washington, and western Montana. Many Oregonians joined the search and, if minerals were not always found, at least the interior was explored. Although stagecoaches, river steamboats, and coastwise services reduced Northwestern isolation, intensive development awaited the railroad.

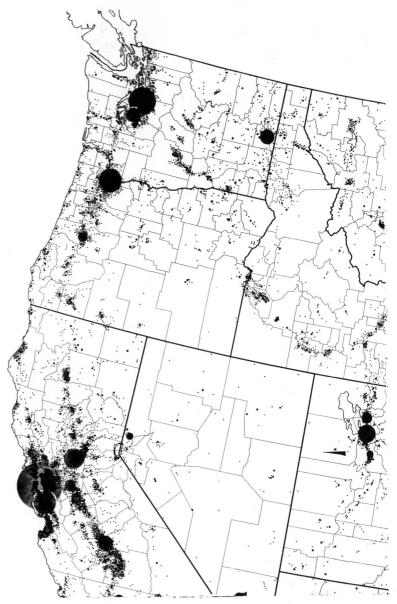

FIGURE 18-2   A population map of the northwestern United States, 1960. The concentration of population in relatively small parts of the area is clearly shown. (Bureau of the Census.)

In 1880 the Pacific Northwest had only a quarter of a million people; the railroads and the expanding lumber industry increased settlement. The Northern Pacific Railroad reached Puget Sound in 1883, the Great Northern in 1893, the Milwaukee in 1909. All three lines converged at Spokane, whence a spur service was operated to Portland. In 1884 Portland received more direct connection eastward via the Oregon Short Line, now part of the Union Pacific. Re-

source expansion was not only in lumber; fish canneries in the ports, fruit packing in the mountain valleys, wheat farming on the Columbia Plateau also contributed to a diversifying economy. During World War I, shipbuilding became a major industry, but was important thereafter mainly during periods of military activity. More significant was the rise of the Boeing Aircraft Company which expanded its factories to meet United States World War I demands. Hydroelectric power and related irrigation projects developed rapidly after World War I and made possible later power-based industries (aluminum and other metal refining) significant in World War II.

The history of Alaskan settlement likewise is related to furs, minerals, fish, lumber, and military activities but on a smaller scale. Vitus Bering discovered Alaska for the Russians in 1741 and started fur trading. The purchase of Alaska by the United States in 1867 for about $12 per square mile led to the development of a few scattered resources: the seal and salmon fisheries, a few gold mines, and a lumber industry in the southern panhandle. Settlers who came to Alaska before 1940 lived mainly in coastal towns. The only sizable area of agricultural settlement was in the Matanuska Valley. Fairbanks was the only town of significance in the interior. The Klondike and other gold strikes, although centered across the Canadian border in Yukon, attracted a peak Alaskan population of nearly 65,000 in 1900; thereafter the population dropped and remained small until World War II. Meanwhile the airplane speeded up exploration and transportation, making the territory ready for a defense-induced population explosion totaling a quarter million people, mostly located near several small cities.

EMPLOYMENT AND INCOME

More than half of both the regional population (Figure 18-3) and income is concen-

trated in four SMSAs representing one-sixty-seventh of the total area. Sixty percent of the population and 70 percent of the income are in the narrow 250-mile-long lowland including the Puget Sound region, and the lower Columbia Valley and its tributary valleys, the Cowlitz and the Willamette. Thus the business of the vast Inland Empire and Alaska accounts for a small part of the prosperity of Seattle and Portland whose present income is derived largely from the area between the Cascades and the Pacific.

Table 18-1 shows the importance of government expenditure in the Pacific Northwest. Table 18-2 shows how concentrated manufacturing can be in a few industrial groups.

PORTLAND AND WESTERN OREGON

Portland

The site of Portland seems destined for a commercial city. Located where the Colum-

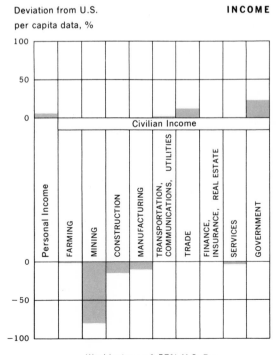

FIGURE 18-3   As in many Western states, government is an important source of income. Aside from this and the low income from mining, Washington is close to the national average. Oregon shows similar deviations except for a positive deviation in farming. For Alaskan data, see Figure 18-9.

TABLE 18-1 Personal Income and Civilian Income from Current Production: Oregon, Washington, and Alaska, 1966 (in millions of dollars)

Civilian Income	Oreg.	Wash.	Alaska
Farms	214	375	1
Mining	16	17	18
Construction	334	566	84
Manufacturing	1,249	2,232	43
Trade	913	1,386	90
Financial	214	377	23
Transport and Utilities	404	552	74
Services	607	994	75
Government	691	1,224	253
Other	21	39	20
Civilian Income	4,663	7,765	683
Personal Income	5,578	9,797	907

NOTE: Logging is classified in federal statistics as a subdivision of lumber and wood products manufacturing.

SOURCE: *Survey of Current Business*, vol. 47 (August 1967), no. 8, p. 37.

bia provided a gateway through the Cascades to a wedge-shaped fertile lowland with a river entering from the south and the Columbia itself giving access to the north before it cuts through the Coast Range to the Pacific, Portland seems an ideal crossroads. Yet tiny Portland in 1845 had rivals and handicaps. Oregon City (formerly Willam-

ette Falls), 12 miles up the Willamette River, had both waterpower and a location at the head of downstream navigation. Vancouver, Washington, on the Columbia River, was several miles closer to the Pacific. Salem, long the capital of Oregon, was more centrally located among the Willamette settlements. Portland's location on a tributary of

TABLE 18-2 Value Added by Manufacturing in Washington, Oregon, and Alaska, 1963 (in millions of dollars)

Category		Wash.	Oreg.	Alaska
20	Food and Kindred Products	360	235	40
24	Lumber and Wood Products	361	700	10
241	Logging Camps and Contractors	80	136	7
242	Sawmills and Planing Mills	165	252	—
243	Millwork and Plywood	98	284	—
25	Furniture and Fixtures	21	21	—
26	Paper, etc.	330	117	—
28	Chemicals	238	34	—
33	Primary Metals	202	W	—
35 and 36	Machinery	103	125	—
37	Transport Equipment	1,058	51	—
	All Other Categories	355	297	34
Total		3,028	1,580	84

W Data withheld.

SOURCE: U.S. Bureau of the Census, *Census of Manufactures: 1963*, Washington, 1966.

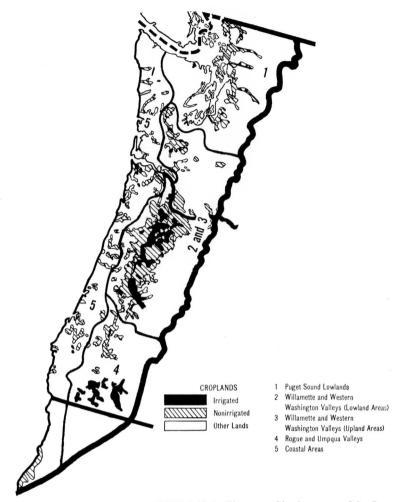

CROPLANDS
- ▮ Irrigated
- ▨ Nonirrigated
- ☐ Other Lands

1 Puget Sound Lowlands
2 Willamette and Western
   Washington Valleys (Lowland Areas)
3 Willamette and Western
   Washington Valleys (Upland Areas)
4 Rogue and Umpqua Valleys
5 Coastal Areas

FIGURE 18-4   This map of land use west of the Cascades identifies the land suitable for agriculture. One inch on the map represents about 75 miles; about how many square miles are available for farming? (After a USDA map in SOIL, Yearbook of Agriculture: 1957.)

the Columbia was influenced by the swamps and flood danger in the tongue of land between the Columbia and lower Willamette. Nor was Portland's connection with the Pacific always satisfactory until the channel was improved in 1877. Yet today with a 101-mile, 35-foot channel to the Pacific, with locks permitting barge traffic up the Columbia and Willamette, and with Oregon City and Vancouver absorbed into its SMSA, Portland is outstanding as a wholesaling, shipping, and financial center for Oregon and parts of Washington and Idaho.

Industries Portland's industrial development came late, and its specialties are closely tied to the resources of its hinterland. Paper-products and other wood-products industries account for one-quarter of the value added by manufacturing. Food products, some for metropolitan consumption but including packed fish, fruits, and vegetables for shipment eastward, make up one-sixth of the value added. Primary metals, especially aluminum, are based on cheap electric power, as is, in part, also the electric machinery industry. Machinery other than electrical, is largely of the special-industry type designed for other regional industries

THE WILLAMETTE VALLEY is not everywhere a flat trough; it includes hilly areas as in this section to the west of Portland. Here are dairy farms and poultry farms as well as the orchards so obvious in the photo. (USDA photograph.)

such as logging and paper. Transportation equipment means mainly ship repairs and, at times, shipbuilding. Other industrial categories are present but generally only suffice to supply part of the local demand (Figure 18-5). Portland's commercial functions are almost as important as its industries. Portland is the chief shopping and professional center of Oregon and supplies services not found elsewhere on the West Coast between Seattle and San Francisco.

Much of the swampy area along the Columbia has been drained (Portland International Airport is located there) so that the urbanized area extends to the Vancouver area across the Columbia. Residential Portland has also expanded westward into the foothills of the Coast Range. Portland's expansion has been slower than that of most Pacific Coast SMSAs, possibly because the economy of its hinterland is too largely based on industries with declining employment, such as food products and lumbering.

Western Oregon

Wood products dominate western Oregon industry, coming from a horseshoe-shaped mountain area. These mountains include the rounded but locally steep Coast Ranges, in which only a few summits rise above 3,000 feet, the higher and more rugged Klamath Mountains on the California border, and the still higher volcanoes of the Cascades rising above a platform of older rocks. Douglas fir is the dominant tree, with hemlock, cedar, and spruce being added along the Pacific; redwood in the western Klamaths; and sugar pine in the eastern Klamaths. Several easily traversed valley routes cut through the Coast Range, following tributaries of the Willamette and other rivers to the south. The Klamath and Cascades mountains (except at the Columbia Gorge) are more formidable, being crossed only by relatively high passes.

Lumbering More than half the lumber being harvested is from virgin and old second-growth timber. Trees are cleared in patches across the hillsides to permit the unharvested forest to reseed the cleared land. The logs may be conveyed to the sawmills by truck, water, rail, or overhead steel cable; some modern mills are portable and are moved to convenient central places in the forest. Logging supports a scattered and relatively small population in the forested hills, and the largest groups of forestry people work in the large sawmills which are found in all the main cities.

The lumbering industry has long been criticized for its wasteful practices. Optimum tree growth has been prevented by the failure to thin forests. Much small timber has been burned in huge refuse burners, other wood being unused in cleared areas. Many mature timber areas remained untouched because of lack of roads. Such wasteful practices have become rare; scrap wood is now used for hardboard or paper pulp, while fir veneer enables a thin board to do a job once requiring many more board feet.

Many Oregonians are worried about their major industry which in 1963 accounted for $817 million out of $1,578 million value added by manufacturing. By the year 2000 the allowable cut from Oregon forests is expected to drop 9 percent, at the same time that lumber consumption is increasing in adjacent California. One remedy being adopted is tree farming, started in Oregon in 1941. The 5 million acres in Oregon tree farms in 1966 represents about one-fifth of all Oregon forest land.

Farming Western Oregon produces specialized agricultural crops. The rainy, foggy lands along the Coast specialize in dairying,

including cheese. Pears and berries are grown in the narrow valleys of southwestern Oregon (Rogue, Umpqua). Farms in the narrow upper Willamette Valley produce cherries, walnuts, hops, and sheep. Northward near Eugene the valley is an alluvium-filled trough, and agricultural acreage is large, with some land suitable for every kind of middle-latitude fruit and berries, as well as dairying, nuts, flower and grass seed, potatoes, and vegetables. Although the Willamette Valley is classified as humid, precipitation is largely in the cooler half of the year; thus irrigation is increasingly employed during the dry summers. There is a considerable agricultural surplus for

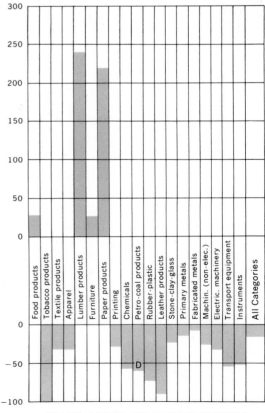

VALUE ADDED BY MANUFACTURING
Portland SMSA = .46% U.S. Pop.

FIGURE 18-5 Unbalanced industrial activity seems typical of the Pacific Northwest, as this chart for Portland indicates.

THIS FIRE IS IN the Douglas fir forest of western Oregon. The area in the foreground has been recently logged and, if the fire can be kept out, will grow a thick second-growth forest of fir and hemlock. (American Forest Product Industries.)

export south and east; hence food packing is characteristic in every Willamette city. Some industrial diversification has occurred in the Eugene SMSA, but employment in these new fields is modest compared with that in the material-oriented and service industries. Wood-products manufacturing is universal. Population growth has been especially rapid in the almost adjacent central cities, Eugene and Springfield.

WESTERN WASHINGTON AND THE PUGET SOUND CITIES

There is considerable resemblance between western Oregon and western Washington, but the latter has more leached and glaciated soils, better harbors with more fishing and shipping, an older and currently less productive lumber industry, and an indus-trial mix in which the aircraft industry overshadows the food products and forest-based industries so important in both states.

Lumbering

Lumber was among the earliest of Washington's export commodities, being second only to furs. The Hudson's Bay Company in the 1830s shipped lumber to the Hawaiian Islands; in 1847 the first American sawmill in the Northwest was erected at Tumwater near the southwestern end of Puget Sound. Because the Douglas fir forest was readily accessible, exploitation grew with the demand, and a peak production of about 7 billion board feet was achieved in 1925; production in the 1960s has averaged about half that figure, but even this lower figure is about one-tenth of the national timber production. Meanwhile

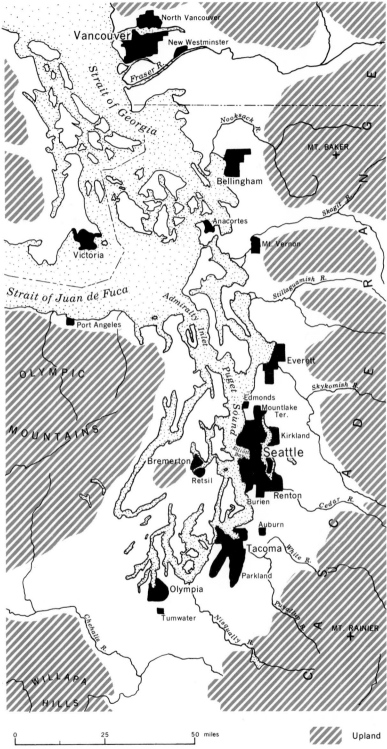

FIGURE 18-6 *The great commercial advantage of the Puget Sound Area is its wealth of navigable channels penetrating into the land.*

cleared forest lands have been converted into tree farms which in 1965 occupied about half the privately owned forest land in the state. Assuming that the trees are allowed to grow to full size, these farms will be ready for harvesting 50 to 100 years after planting. On this basis, the U.S. Forest Service predicts a 34 percent allowable increase in cut in the year 2000. Meanwhile Washington forests are much less productive than forests in Oregon.

Farming

Figure 18-4 shows the small extent of farmland in western Washington. Owing to the large urban markets nearby, emphasis is on dairying and poultry with some intensively cultivated areas devoted to flowers, vegetables, and berries. Ironically some of the lands that require drainage in the cool season need irrigation for best results in the summer; almost all tilled land requires liming. In contrast to Oregon, almost all farm produce in the Puget Sound Lowland is shipped to the larger urban markets within the state.

A Future Puget Sound Megalopolis

Nearly three-quarters of the people of western Washington are in sizable cities; more than half live in the Seattle–Everett SMSA. There is much more land available for urban development by those who like a cool climate similar to that of Western Europe. Most of the potential urban land is accessible to Puget Sound, a water body with fjordlike channels much subdivided by islands and peninsulas. Urban businesses, factories, and dwellings occupy the coastal strip from Everett to the north through Seattle, and Tacoma to Olympia in the southwest. The Puget Sound region is comparable to the New York–Northeastern New Jersey Consolidated Area in area and in its number of inland waterways and is superior to the New York district in climate. The main weakness of the Puget Sound

region is the lack of a densely populated hinterland. But should future trans-Pacific trade grow to equal the volume of trans-Atlantic trade, would not the Puget Sound region become one of the leading American ports?

Seattle   The city of Seattle has a spectacular site, located on a low but steep ridge between Puget Sound and glacial Lake Washington. The city has grown rather spasmodically. Lumber was the first industrial base (a major street, Yesler Way, is named for an early lumber king); then canned salmon became a second resource-based industry at the end of the last century. The discovery of coal in King County (a mineral now of minor importance) gave fuel for metallurgy. The original town concentrated on the well-drained uplands, leaving the swampy lowlands for railroad tracks connecting with the docks on Ellicott Bay. Like the San Francisco Bay Area, the Seattle SMSA expanded areally by means of a network of ferries and bridges; its residential and business sections reflect the ability of bulldozers to level hills and fill valleys.

The early growth of Seattle came decades before the aircraft industry which nourishes the metropolis today. Seattle is an important transshipment center. Four transcontinental railroads terminated there and, before the nylon era, oriental silk was transshipped from fast liners to fast freights to eastern hosiery factories. Seattle was the gateway to Alaska, but before 1940 the Alaskan economy supported few people, and therefore the flow of supplies through Seattle was a minor part of the port's activity. The annual value added by transportation-equipment manufacturing in Seattle exceeds the annual personal income of Alaska. Much greater are the potentialities of trans-Pacific trade and of manufactures for east Asian markets.

The relative unimportance of raw materials in the ultimate growth of large cities has been noted in preceding chapters. If lumber, berries, salmon, and Alaskan gold were the sole bases of Seattle growth, it might have had a population of 100,000 to 200,000 instead of over one million. Let a doctoral dissertation from Columbia University tell the story:

Preeminent among the industries which originated in the Northwest without regard to available raw materials, labor force, or markets, is the Boeing Airplane Company. This colossus, far and away the greatest industrial employer in the Northwest, with a labor force at times exceeding 25,000, owes its presence in the State of Washington to the chance fact that a wealthy young Seattleite named William Boeing became interested in flying and learned to pilot his own plane for pleasure. A repair shop he opened on Lake Union to take care of his private airplanes had by 1916 developed into a small plant for their manufacture. The United States Army was then procuring planes for the First World War, and Boeing was already in a position to meet their requirements. Thereafter, with the exception of a brief hiatus following the war, Boeing has been turning out airplanes continuously . . . .[1]

Table 18-2 indicates the importance of transportation-equipment manufactures to the state of Washington. In the Seattle-Everett SMSA, transportation equipment in 1963 accounted for nearly 60 percent of both the value added by manufacturing and manufacturing employment.

Tacoma   Tacoma is a smaller Seattle without an aircraft industry, although many Tacoma residents work in the Seattle aircraft plants. Tacoma, when it became the first terminal of the Northern Pacific, was a rival of Seattle; now it is noted for its copper and aluminum refining and related chemical

industries, its wood- and paper-products industries, and its food packing. Its port does not have the quantity and variety of facilities and installations of the Seattle waterfront.

THE INLAND EMPIRE

The Columbia Bond

The Columbia River is significant in binding together the economies of the Pacific Northwest. In pioneer days it provided an easy route through the mountains; more recently it has provided irrigation water for the farms of the interior and power for the cities. Its tributaries drain the eastern slopes of the Cascades, the northern Rockies, and even a few ice fields of the Canadian Rockies. The Inland Empire, watered by the Columbia, is not a lush land, but its environment is better than that of the deserts of Nevada, southern Utah, and western Arizona. Commercially the Inland Empire might include Idaho and northwestern Montana, areas already discussed with the High West. The transitional zone between these regions, like many arbitrary regional boundaries, is not sharply defined. The hinterland of the Inland Empire did not create the coastal settlements which were developed first; rather the inland region was settled in part from the Coast after routes had been established across it to serve the Coast. Later the produce of that Inland Empire provided some power, foods, and raw materials which stimulated further coastal urban growth.

Diverse Environments

To the traveler the Inland Empire seems to have everything, but his overall impression will vary according to his route (Figure 15-2). Thus the traverse from Idaho across northern Oregon is subhumid to semi-arid with extensive areas of pine-clad mountains and rolling prairies. Change the route to southeastern Oregon, and one encounters

---

[1] Edwin J. Cohn, Jr., *Industry in the Pacific Northwest and the Location Theory,* Columbia University Press, New York, 1954, pp. 161–162.

sagebrush and water scarcity. A northern route from Spokane across central Washington crosses grasslands and grain farms reminiscent of the prairies of eastern North Dakota or scenery suited for a "wild-western" movie. Toward the Canadian border the Rockies are close to the Cascades; open pine forests of the Rockies continue into the eastern slope forest of the Cascades. In these vast spaces between the Northern Rockies and the Cascades, precious minerals are rare and the mineral production of many counties consists only of stone, sand, and gravel. The major mineral to be husbanded, to be channeled into productive activity, is water; and the story of the Inland Empire is mainly the story of water development.

The Spokane area   Spokane, located at a falls on the Spokane River, was a good site for sawing the lumber being cut a few miles to the east, as well as a natural focus for rail routes debouching from passes in the Northern Rockies. Spokane is primarily a commercial center for the surrounding area, with additional processing industries based on power and regional raw materials: flour milling, meat packing, paper, millwork, and primary metals (especially aluminum). South of Spokane the Palouse (grassland) area with its fertile windblown silts is rich in organic matter and thus able to store water. The Palouse, originally used for ranchland, was discovered in the late nineteenth century to possess a soil able to grow grain and dried peas for the lumbermen and the miners of the nearby mountains; later it proved adaptable to highly mechanized agriculture.

Eastern Oregon   Eastern Oregon, across which the historic Oregon Trail passes, has a variety of landscapes: desert to the south, with a few irrigated areas as in other parts of the Great Basin—a northward continuation of Nevadan landscapes. Northeastern Ore-

gon includes the forested Blue Mountains and adjacent areas suited for dry farming, irrigation, grazing, or tourist scenery. In contrast, the eastern slopes of the Cascades in both Oregon and Washington have excellent ponderosa and other pines, as well as a number of irrigated areas. The Hood River and Yakima, Wenatchee, and Okanogan valleys are widely known for their irrigated apples; less known for fodder crops, cattle, and vegetables sold within the Pacific Northwest.

The Columbia as a Water Resource

Most of the irrigated areas noted above are on tributaries of the Columbia instead of on the main stream which in the last 30 years has been harnessed by federal engineers. The problem of water use has been complicated by the salmon that returned upstream to spawn; thus dams would destroy a valuable fishing industry. The Bonneville Dam (completed 1938) in the Columbia Gorge 30 miles east of Portland provided fish ladders so that salmon could jump from pool to pool upstream. However, few salmon now spawn in the Columbia River tributaries. Bonneville was primarily built for power, whereas dams further upstream were dual purpose: power and irrigation. Of the dozens of dams constructed, the largest was the Grand Coulee and its associated Columbia Basin Project (Figure 18-7).

Grand Coulee   The Grand Coulee is a former drainage channel of the Columbia River which forms a trough, $1\frac{1}{2}$ to 4 miles wide, across an arid volcanic plateau. During the last ice age, a glacier blocked the present channel of the Columbia River, forcing it to carve a valley east of the ice-choked area. After the ice retreated, the Columbia returned to its old channel but left behind a

FIGURE 18-7   The Grand Coulee Project integrates waterpower, irrigation water, and fertile soil on a scale difficult for anyone other than the federal government to handle.

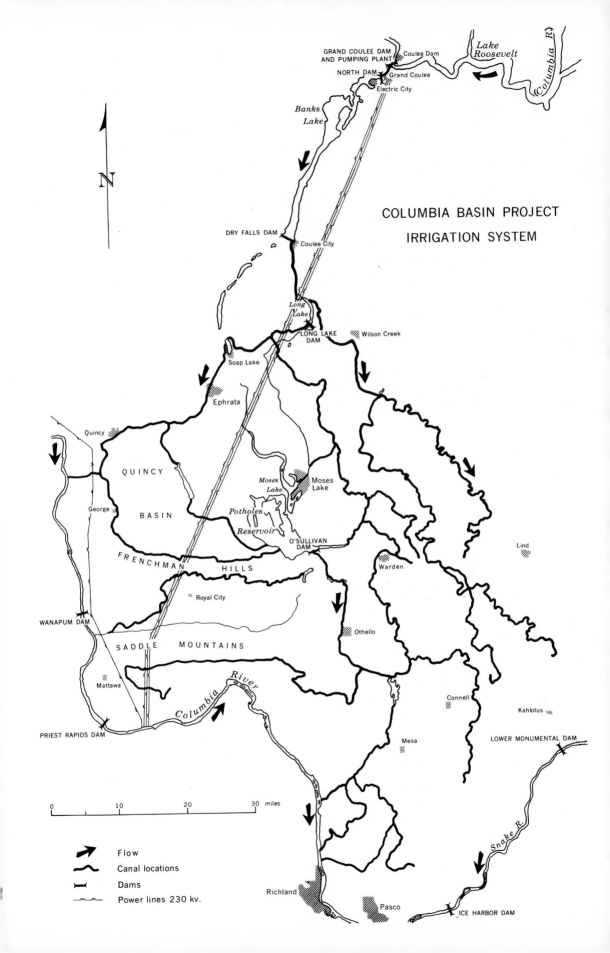

THE GRAND COULEE DAM blocks the Columbia River and generates power, part of which is used to pump water into the Grand Coulee (background) from which water is supplied to irrigated fields to the south. (U.S. Department of Interior.)

high-level channel (coulee) including a "dry falls." In 1918 a group of Ephrata businessmen proposed damming the Columbia just below the head of Grand Coulee, thus sending some of its waters through the Coulee to a fertile million-acre irrigable section. In 1935 the project was authorized by Congress with some modifications. The irrigated area begins about 27 miles south of the dam; the major crops are grain, dry beans, and cattle fodder. The relatively high density of farm settlement in the irrigated sections contrasts with the sparse population of the adjoining grasslands. The largest dam in the world, at that time, was constructed, including within it a mammoth power plant with an installed capacity of nearly 2 million kilowatts. Part of this power is used to pump water into the Grand Coulee and connecting irrigation canals; the remainder is transmitted into power grids which supply Spokane, Seattle, and other cities in the Pacific Northwest.

Future of the Inland Empire The Inland Empire, as here defined, has less than one-quarter of the population of the Pacific Northwest region. Aside from Spokane and the area stimulated by the Columbia Basin Project, the population of its counties ranges from modest growth to net out-migration. Further development from irrigation is likely to be modest since local markets are not large and this irrigated land has to compete with the crops grown in other irrigated areas of the Cordillera and High Plains. Population expansion seems to depend on the development of urban activities—not an impossibility if cool, crisp winters and sunny, mild summers become attractive to Americans. Perhaps there are attractions there for another southwest Arizona–type boom.

Alaska's income rises at accelerated pace in recent years . . .
future depends on expansion of new industries and transport network

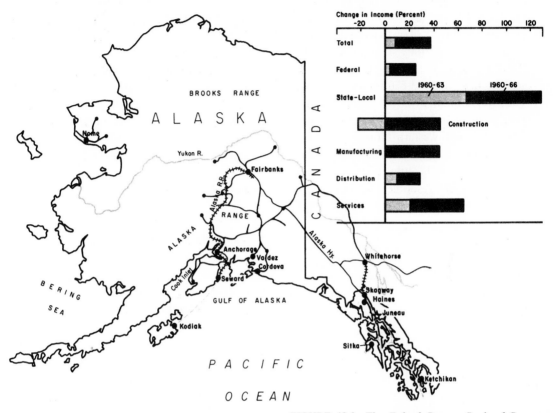

FIGURE 18-8   The Federal Reserve Bank of San Francisco rather optimistically portrays the progress of Alaska in the 1960s with this map and graph. Some of the spectacular percentage increases are due to infusions of government money; others arise from the smallness of the original base.

ALASKA

It is difficult to appreciate the immensity and emptiness of Alaska; it is twice the size of Texas with enough land left over to more than equal Louisiana. From the tip of southeastern Alaska to Bering Strait is several hundred miles farther than from Seattle to Los Angeles (Figure 18-8). Although its 1950–1960 population increased at a percentage growth rate approximating that of Florida, it still has a low population density— only 0.4 per square mile. The First and Third Judicial divisions, comprising a 2,400-mile arc from British Columbia to the tip of the Aleutians have over 200,000 inhabitants, most of whom are urban dwellers living in or near Anchorage, Juneau, Sitka, or Ketchikan. The majority of the remaining 70,000 live within 100 miles of Fairbanks.

In 1967 Alaskan households had the highest average annual income figure of any state, nearly $11,000. Of course the cost of living is equally high because of the high freight costs for everything shipped in. Goods and people reach Alaska by coastal ship or plane or via the largely gravel Alaska Highway. Travelers to areas not served by scheduled airlines generally go by chartered planes; skilled pilots will taxi passengers to the most distant outposts.

A Permanent Frontier?

It has been suggested that Alaska provides the United States with a permanent frontier; after a century of ownership the United States has settled only a small fraction of the land, and the principal reasons for settlement seem to be military bases and other government activities. Yet it has often been pointed out that southeastern Alaska resembles southwestern Norway, and that the Anchorage-Fairbanks area is climatically similar to well-settled parts of Finland. Several types of resources, including gold, coal, petroleum, lumber, furs, and fish, have been found and exploited; yet, in 1960, of the 91,000 employed 42,000 were in armed forces or public administration, and 5,000 in construction (Figure 18-9). Although the U.S. Department of the Interior in 1952 predicted an ultimate Alaskan population of 5 to 10 million, the first million seems a long time off. A more conservative study by George W. Rogers,[2] a resident of Alaska, concluded that land hunger cannot be counted on to settle Alaska, but that steady growth may result from training the Alaskan natives and by developing highly specialized industries using large amounts of power.

Southeastern Alaska

The earliest development was in the southeastern panhandle, an area as large as New England, having a narrow mountainous mainland, large offshore islands, and numerous inland passages. The southeast has been the major fishing area, the site of the Juneau gold rush, and the gateway to the Klondike gold field. Today mining is small; the emphasis is on fish, lumber, and tourism. Fishing for salmon, in part operated with Indian labor, employs less than a thousand people seasonally, plus an equal number in seafood packing. Forestry and wood products provide comparable employment. The large forest reserves on the slopes of the Coast mountains and islands are beginning to be used. For example, a pulp mill now operates at Ketchikan. Although the temperatures of this southeastern area are mild, heavy precipitation and the scarcity of flat or gently sloping land are inhibiting factors against future development.

[2] George W. Rogers, *The Future of Alaska*, published for Resources for the Future, Inc., Johns Hopkins, Baltimore, 1962.

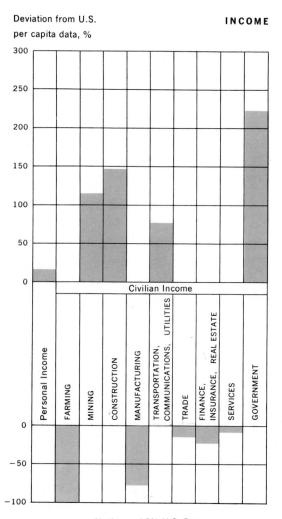

Deviation from U.S. per capita data, %

INCOME

Alaska = .13% U.S. Pop.

FIGURE 18-9   The influence of government activity is apparent not only in the government bar, but also in the construction, transportation, communications, and utilities bars which represent considerable government activity. The high personal incomes are negated by the high price level.

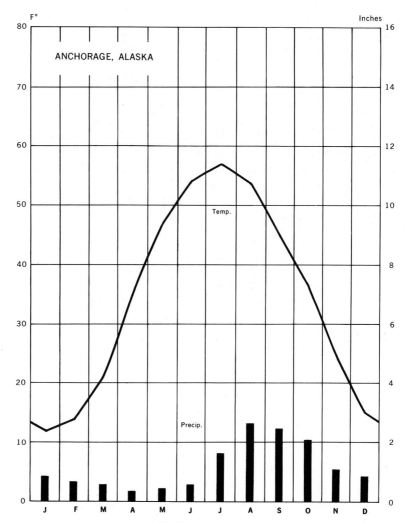

ANCHORAGE, ALASKA

Temp.

Precip.

J F M A M J J A S O N D

FIGURE 18-10   Compared to many well-settled parts of the world, Anchorage climate is not severe; its January temperatures are slightly colder than at Moscow, which is 5° further south. Anchorage is a city of 50,000 persons, many of whom are stationed there in military or other government service.

The Seward-Anchorage-Fairbanks Axis

More rapid economic growth has occurred along the government-owned Alaska Railroad and the Seward-Anchorage-Fairbanks Highway. South of the Alaska Range, mild summers with moderate precipitation totals are suitable for the farms which supply local markets (Figure 18-10). North of the mountains, January temperatures average below zero, and at Fairbanks the first killing fall frost occurs, on the average, on August 26; the last spring frost on May 29. Anchorage, the largest city in Alaska, with a good harbor and large airport, owes its rapid growth to military activities, as does the much smaller Fairbanks on the Tanana tributary of the Yukon. These cities are the commercial centers for an immense area of which only that portion east of the Alaska Railroad is accessible by a few roads, including the Alaska Highway connecting with the Prairie Provinces of Canada. The central portion is accessible in summer by navigation of the Yukon-Tanana waterways.

SOUTHEASTERN ALASKA *has little level land so that many small settlements are better reached by seaplane taxi than by overland routes. Note the low level of the snow line.* (Alaska Travel Division.)

Resource Potential?

What is there to develop, and how much of it is worth developing in this rigorous, isolated setting? Only valuable minerals, particularly those near seaports which can stand transportation to distant markets, have economic potential. At present oil (with associated natural gas) accounts for 40 percent of the mineral production; a small field near Point Barrow is reserved for naval use; other fields on Kenai Peninsula are available for the Alaskan market. Sand and gravel, used in construction, are second in value of mineral production. Coal is available along the Alaska Railroad and elsewhere, but is little used. Gold, historically so important, is of minor value, consisting mostly of that dredged in the Yukon Valley. Copper, iron (200 miles southwest of Anchorage), and many minor metals have all been discovered, but commercial output has been negligible, possibly because of transport and climate.[3] Yet considering the incomplete prospecting and present difficulties of exploitation and transportation, Alaskan mineral potentialities may surpass those of Washington and Oregon, even though present production is modest (Table 18-3).

Forest products, especially lumber, pulpwood, and furs, offer other possibilities for resource expansion. Fur trapping is likely to remain a small industry, but fur farming offers greater possibilities. Forest reserves are ample, both on coastal slopes and across the interior basin of the Yukon, but much of the forest is not economically accessible. Transportation would have to be built for some other purposes because the harvested forest would not regenerate itself in a century. Could the cleared land be used for agriculture? Such possible agricultural pro-

[3] The general problem of developing the subarctic and arctic regions will be discussed in Chap. 22.

duce would be competitive only in the small local markets.

Hydroelectric power is a major resource, with an estimated potential of 15 million kilowatts under the most adverse conditions. The largest single proposal is the Rampart Project, which would involve the construction of a dam 3,000 feet long and 500 feet high across Rampart Canyon on the central Yukon River. Such a dam could create a reservoir larger than Lake Erie with a power capacity $2\frac{1}{2}$ times as great as the output of Grand Coulee. Such a project might cost as much as $1.5 billion and could equal the 1965 electric capacity of the state of Missouri, but it might take 15 to 25 years to construct. Furthermore, it would require a huge market provided by such yet-to-be-born Alaskan industries as aluminum, elemental phosphorus, enriched uranium, electrolytic zinc, electrolytic steel, and rayon. With so many economic difficulties to be overcome, it is doubtful whether this large power source will be used in the near future.

And perhaps nuclear power will remove the need for developing marginal hydroelectric power sites.

CONCLUSIONS

Compared with California and Arizona, the recent population and economic growth of the Pacific Northwest has been modest. In each settled area a series of developments has resulted in a high degree of local specialization and a consequent vulnerability to economic fluctuations. Lumber, fish, wheat, livestock, gold, aircraft, irrigation projects, hydroelectric power, shipbuilding, and military bases have played major parts but have not developed well-integrated local economies. A withdrawal of government or airline contracts, a closing of military bases, the exhaustion of forests, a change in reclamation policy—any one of these could be catastrophic to certain parts of the region.

If it is assumed that a desirable environment for living rather than the mere pres-

TABLE 18-3   Value of Mineral Production of Pacific Northwest States, 1965 (in thousands of dollars)

Mineral	Alaska	Oreg.	Wash.
Cement	—	—	22,552
Clay	—	—	211
Coal (*bituminous*)	6,095	—	497
Copper	23	W	21
Gold	1,479	17	W
Lead	3	—	1,974
Lime	—	1,853	W
Mercury	W	779	W
Natural Gas	1,799	—	—
Peat	16	—	131
Petroleum	34,073	—	—
Pumice	—	1,181	W
Sand and Gravel	34,467	32,849	27,234
Stone	W	27,301	17,446
Uranium	W	—	1,871
Zinc	—	W	6,491
Value of Items That Cannot Be Disclosed	5,489	18,967	7,723
Total	83,455	82,967	86,172

W   Data withheld.

SOURCE: U.S. Bureau of Mines, *Minerals Yearbook: 1965*, vol. 3, Washington, 1967.

ence of raw materials will determine the population distribution of the next century, the Pacific Northwest has a promising future. Its climates include those in which Western Europeans have flourished; its scenery is attractive; and, except possibly for northern Alaska, the region is accessible to world trade. Waterpower is available, along with oil and gas from western Canada and Alaska; the forests and fisheries could be exploited so as to be permanent resources. But above all, it offers fine sites for a Pacific urban civilization to benefit from the anticipated rise of trans-Pacific economies.

SELECTED REFERENCES

COHN, EDWIN J., JR.: *Industry in the Pacific Northwest and the Location Theory,* Columbia University Press, New York, 1954.

DICKEN, SAMUEL N.: *Oregon Geography,* 4th ed., University of Oregon Cooperative Bookstore, Eugene, 1965.

FREEMAN, O. W., and H. H. MARTIN: *The Pacific Northwest,* Wiley, New York, 1954.

GOLZÉ, ALFRED R.: *Reclamation in the United States,* Caxton, Caldwell, Idaho, 1961.

HIGHSMITH, RICHARD M., JR.: *Atlas of the Pacific Northwest Resources and Development,* Corvallis, Oreg., 1962.

HIGHSMITH, RICHARD M., JR. (ed.): *Case Studies in World Geography: Occupance and Economy Types,* Prentice-Hall, Englewood Cliffs, N. J., 1961. Includes three studies (nos. 11, 12, and 23) of localities in the Inland Empire.

MACHINKO, G.: "The Columbia Basin Project," *Geographical Review,* vol. 53 (1963), pp. 185–199.

MARTS, M. E., and W. R. D. SEWELL: "The Conflict between Fish and Power Resources in the Pacific Northwest," *Annals A.A.G.,* vol. 50 (1960), pp. 42–50.

ROGERS, GEORGE W.: *The Future of Alaska,* published for Resources for the Future, Inc., Johns Hopkins, Baltimore, 1962.

SIDDALL, WILLIAM R.: "Seattle: Regional Capital of Alaska," *Annals A.A.G.,* vol. 47 (1957), pp. 277–284.

Transport Requirements for the Growth of Northwest North America, 87th Cong., 1st Sess., H. Doc. 176, 1961, 3 vols.

WINTHER, OSCAR O.: *The Great Northwest,* Knopf, New York, 1947. History and settlement by a historian especially interested in Western transportation.

PART V
CANADA

CANADA IS LARGE in area but relatively small in population. Canadians occupy a narrow strip across the southern part of their vast country. In this occupied zone, urban and rural life is very much like that of the adjoining parts of the United States: Seventy-five percent of Canadians live in urban places in which the factories, stores, and houses look the same as those in most American cities; likewise the rural landscape is similar to the farmlands of northern United States. North of the more densely occupied zone a resource-oriented exploitive economy is gradually extending northward, dominated by mining, forestry, and water-power developments. Canada differs from the United States in having a disproportionately large northern area of arctic and subarctic climate in which there are now few people and apparently little resource potential. Despite some notable differences in the physical environment of the two Anglo-American countries, the patterns of human use and occupation have many similarities.

CHARACTERISTIC SMALL "OUTPOST" SETTLEMENT, Fogo Island, Newfoundland. Note the low, rocky hills barren of trees. Houses are dispersed around the harbor, and connected by one winding road. There are many small family docks but no large port facilities. (National Film Board of Canada photo by G. Hunter.)

CHAPTER 19

THE ATLANTIC GATEWAYS

FIGURE 19-1   Landforms of the Atlantic Gateways. Compare with Figure 20-2 which names regions based largely on these landforms. (Base map copyright by A. K. Lobeck. Reprinted with permission of The Geographical Press, Hammond, Inc.)

THE CANADIAN IDENTITY

The land of Canada, particularly in the southern parts, has many characteristics which are like the surface features in the United States; the economies of the two countries differ very little from each other and, in fact, have many across-the-border linkages; most of the people of the two nations come from the same ethnic and national origins in Europe. Despite the many similarities, Canadians feel that they are different from Americans and are sometimes overly sensitive to these poorly defined differences.

The assumption that Canada is culturally distinctive from the United States—an assumption which lies at the heart of Canadian nationhood,

BASIC DATA:

AREA INCLUDES	Land Area (thousand sq. mi.)	Population Change, 1951–1961	1961 (thousands)	1966 (thousands)	Personal Income 1967 (billion Canadian dollars)
ENTIRE REGION	717.3	25.6%	7,156	7,757	$14.9
Nova Scotia	20.4	14.7	737	756	1.4
New Brunswick	27.8	15.9	598	617	1.0
Prince Edward Island	2.2	6.3	104	109	0.2
Newfoundland	143.0	26.7	458	494	0.7
Quebec	523.9	29.7	5,259	5,781	11.6
METROPOLITAN AREAS					
Halifax, N.S.		37.3%	186	198	$0.41
Saint John, N.B.		22.0	97	101	0.16
St. John's, Nfld.		32.4	92	101	0.14
Quebec, Que.		29.4	362	413	0.71
Montreal, Que.		43.3	2,150	2,437	5.00

CLIMATE   Humid continental with considerable fog and marine influences near the Coast; subarctic to arctic in Labrador and Ungava peninsula of Quebec; precipitation well distributed seasonally.

	Temperature (°F) Jan.	July	Precipitation Annual (rainfall equivalent)	(inches of snow)
St. John's, Nfld.	24	60	53	114
Nain, Nfld. (Labrador)	−3	50	30	128
Halifax, N.S.	24	65	54	64
Saint John, N.B.	20	62	47	80
Charlottetown, P.E.I.	19	67	43	112
Montreal, Quebec	15	70	42	100
Schefferville, Quebec	−12	55	28	128

VEGETATION   Mixture of conifers and deciduous trees in south, coniferous forest north of Quebec City; forest thins northward; tundra in the north and on higher areas.

SOIL   Mainly podzolic soils except in the lower St. Lawrence and Ottawa valleys; rocky, shallow, or bog soils occupy most of the land north of 48° except for a few basins.

MINERALS   A wide variety of minerals is found in the Canadian Shield, the most significant being iron, copper, gold, molybdenum, and titanium; the Atlantic Provinces produce coal, gypsum, rock salt, and base metals.

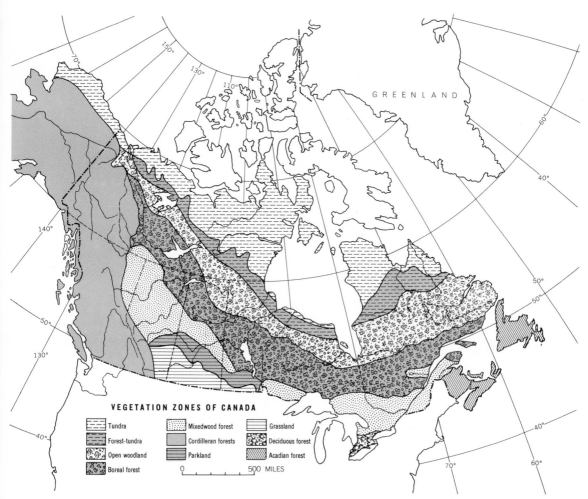

VEGETATION ZONES OF CANADA

Tundra	Mixedwood forest	Grassland
Forest-tundra	Cordilleran forests	Deciduous forest
Open woodland	Parkland	Acadian forest
Boreal forest	0 500 MILES	

FIGURE 19-2   The vegetation map indicates the tree-less nature of much of Canada, but also the large areas of forest cover. Areas described as "Open woodland" and "Forest tundra" contain insufficient timber per square mile to justify harvesting for markets to the south. The "Cordilleran forests" include many treeless areas which are above the treeline. (Otis W. Freeman and John W. Morris, WORLD GEOGRAPHY, McGraw-Hill, New York, 1965, p. 139.)

historically and today—is a large and nebulous subject, notoriously difficult to specify and delineate. The differences of taste, preferences, attitudes, institutions, and so forth within the various regions of Canada seem to be larger than those between Canada and the contiguous areas of the United States . . . . If there is such a thing as a distinctive Canadian way of life, it has yet to be crystallized sufficiently to be clearly identified.[1]

Although there are many common elements between the two Anglo-American environments, there are differences in the

[1] Geroge W. Wilson et al., *Canada: An Appraisal of Its Needs and Resources*, Twentieth Century Fund, New York, 1965, p. 401.

ways and proportions in which the diverse ingredients are combined. These different areal patterns result in distinctive geographies of the United States and Canada. Thus Canada has:

1 A much larger proportion of both barren and forested land than the United States (Table 19-1). Much of this land has little likelihood of future agricultural settlement.

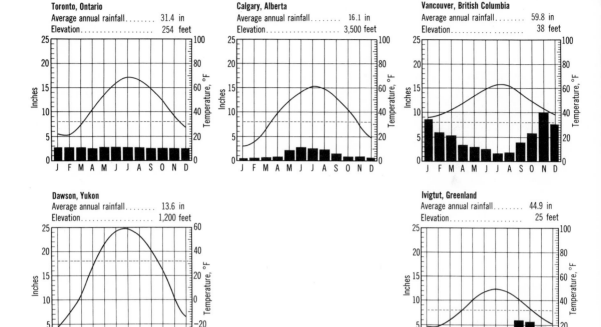

FIGURE 19-3 Climate graphs of northern North America. Compare the graphs of the three metropolitan areas in the top row with those in the subarctic and arctic areas. (Otis W. Freeman and John W. Morris, WORLD GEOGRAPHY, McGraw-Hill, New York, 1958, p. 117.)

2 Larger climatic areas in which long periods of cold weather handicap outdoor activity.

3 Four major population clusters which are more isolated from one another than from adjacent population clusters in the United States.

4 Greater dependence on distant markets, both domestic and foreign, and on transportation to these markets.

5 A more resource-oriented economy, in which many raw materials are exported in only semiprocessed form.

6 Most important, only one-tenth as much population and one-thirteenth as much personal income as the United States.

TABLE 19-1 Canadian Land Use by Political Regions and Comparable United States Land Use (in thousands of square miles)

Land Use	Atlantic Provinces	Que.	Ont.	Prairie Provinces	B.C.	Yukon and N.W.T.	Can.	U.S.
Agricultural	8	22	29	202	7	0.013	270	1,743
Forested	129	378	262	398	268	275	1,710	750
Other Land	60	130	58	89	86	1,183	1,606	1,056
Total Land	193	524	344	681	359	1,459	3,560	3,549
People per Square Mile (1961)	9.8	10.0	18.1	4.7	4.5	0.03	5.1	50.5

NOTE: Agricultural land includes land in farms or ranches and may include some woodland. Not all forested land is productive land. "Other Land" includes urban land (about 1% of all land in the United States), muskeg, bare rock, scrubland unsuited for grazing, etc.

SOURCES: Data calculated from *Canada Year Book: 1966*, Queen's Printer, Ottawa, 1966, p. 445; *County and City Data Book: 1962*, Washington, 1962; and Marion Clawson et al., *Land for the Future*, published for Resources for the Future, Inc., Johns Hopkins, Baltimore, 1960, p. 442.

For all these reasons, the Canadian economy operates with fewer benefits from the economies of large-scale production, with less diversification of products, and with a smaller per capita income to cope with a somewhat more severe environment. Nevertheless, although Canadians may feel overwhelmed by their more prosperous neighbor (Table 1-1), economically Canada is in most respects equal or superior to nations outside Anglo-America.

Resources and Landform Regions

Because Canada has so much land per capita and because many of its resources have been exploited only recently, it is not surprising that it has raw-material surpluses to export. Indeed the location of some of its resources is more suitable for export than for supplying distant Canadian needs.

Several Canadian landform regions (Figure 19-1) are continuations of those of northern United States. The Appalachians arc across southern Quebec and form the backbone of the Atlantic Provinces. These low, glaciated ranges were less a barrier to inland movement than were the American Appalachians, mainly because they were cut through by the water highway of the Gulf of St. Lawrence. The hills and valleys of the Appalachians in eastern Canada had as good a resource base as that of adjoining New England, but the Canadian Appalachians never attained the population densities or industrial development of New England. The natural resources of the Atlantic Provinces and southern Quebec include excellent coniferous forests, with some hardwoods; useful minerals, ranging from coal and asbestos to iron ore; productive offshore and alongshore fisheries; and valleys with soils suitable for agriculture. But from the time of early settlement the Canadian region always had fewer people and therefore a smaller local market; in addition, it never developed the level of technology of adjoining New England.

North of the gulf and estuary of the St. Lawrence and extending halfway across Canada is the Canadian Shield. This glacier-scoured mass of very old, largely granitic rock—the stubs of ancient mountains now eroded down to a rolling upland—has been called "the mineral storehouse" of Canada. The Shield also has forests of potential pulpwood across its southern half. Within the forest innumerable small sections of bare rock, swamps, muskegs, lakes, and a short frost-free season severely limit the area of potential agricultural settlement. Abundant hydroelectric power from the many rivers has been available to run machinery in the pulp and paper mills and in the mines, as well as to supply electricity to the cities south of the Shield.

Neither the Shield nor Appalachian Canada offered an easy living to nineteenth-century settlers who were looking mainly for agricultural land. A Canadian historian described his country as "one of the largest, harshest, and most intimidating countries on earth"[2]—a generalization that applies to about 80 percent of Canada and that helps to explain why only the southern part of the country is densely occupied.

A more favorable environmental area of southern Canada is the St. Lawrence–Great Lakes Lowland, a northeastern extension of the Central Lowlands of the United States. These rolling, glacial-deposited lowlands support most of the agriculture of southern Quebec and southern Ontario, and are similar to the subdued landforms of the states south of the Great Lakes. The lowland has a large area in Canada with the best combination of favorable environmental conditions for agriculture. Within the region the resources of minerals, forests, and waterpower are minor. This landform region is the "heartland" of Canada, having more than half the Canadian population, producing about 75 percent of the value

[2]W. L. Morton, *The Canadian Identity*, University of Wisconsin Press, Madison, 1964, p. 114.

added by Canadian manufacturing, and dominated by 35 of the 62 Canadian cities that had more than 30,000 population in 1961.

The Central Lowlands and the Great Plains extend northward, to the west of the Canadian Shield, being known in Canada as the Interior Plains. These plains, about 800 miles wide at the 49th parallel international boundary, narrow to the north in the Mackenzie Valley. Natural grassland covers the southern part of the Interior Plains, and this vegetation characteristic gave its name to the Prairie Provinces. Most agricultural settlement is in the prairie section of the Interior Plains, but large areas of the Prairie Provinces have forests, similar to those eastward on the Canadian Shield. The Interior Plains possess most of Canada's petroleum, natural gas, and potash as well as enormous coal reserves.

The Western Cordillera continues northward into mountainous British Columbia. The Rockies form the eastern wall of mountains, and on the west the Coast Mountains are the northward continuation of the volcanic Cascades. The Canadian Cordillera is more compressed than its American equivalent; from Calgary, on the Plains, to Vancouver is only half the distance from Denver to San Francisco. The Canadian section is richer in forests, waterpower, and ores but has much less tillable land than its American counterpart. The resources of the Canadian Cordillera are far from markets in eastern Anglo-America, and there is only a small local market. Development has therefore been more recent and is related to interior accessibility and external markets.

Income and Employment

Primary production accounts for a declining proportion of all Canadian employment (Table 19-2) and directly represents only 10.7 percent of the 1965 gross domestic product.[3] As in the United States, most Canadian employment is in urban places. The Canadian census defines an *urban place* as any incorporated place with more than 1,000 persons. About 75 percent of Canadians live in such urban centers. Many small towns may therefore house workers who are engaged in primary production in, for example, mines or sawmills. More complex manufacturing takes place in the larger cities. In 1966 Canada had 20 metropolitan

[3] The gross domestic product is roughly similar to the United States GNP (gross national product), but excludes indirect taxes and subsidies as well as income paid to or received from nonresidents.

TABLE 19-2　Canadian Industrial Groups Employment and Gross Domestic Product (percent of total)

Source	Employment Groups		Gross Domestic Product
	1946	*1964*	*1965*
Agriculture	25.4	9.5	5.1
Other Primary Industries	4.0	3.0	5.6
Construction	4.8	6.2	5.8
Manufacturing	26.0	25.0	26.3
Transportation and Utilities	8.1	8.9	11.9
Trade	12.3	16.7	13.4
Finance, Insurance, etc.	2.7	4.0	10.2
Services (including government)	16.8	26.7	21.7
Total	100.0	100.0	100.0

SOURCES: *Canada Year Book: 1966*, Queen's Printer, Ottawa, 1966, p. 729; and *Survey of 1966–67 Markets*, The Financial Post, Toronto, 1966, p. 247.

centers, each with a population larger than 100,000 persons, and these cities together held almost 50 percent of the population of Canada.

Much urban employment deals with the relatively simple processing and shipping of raw materials: Over one-third of all value added by manufacturing in Canada deals with the first-stage processing of materials: nearly half of this preliminary processing is accounted for by food processing and slightly less by wood, wood pulp, and paper products. Agricultural and forest products are therefore very important in Canadian manufacturing. Raw materials constitute about one-third of the value of Canadian export trade; partially manufactured exports such as wood pulp account for an additional three-tenths. This high level of exports, amounting to nearly one-fifth of the gross domestic product, enables Canada to import foodstuffs and raw materials not available internally (e.g., coffee, cotton, bauxite) and also some manufactures which cannot at present be produced economically. These manufactures account for three-fourths of all Canadian import trade, and most of the manufactured goods are imported from the United States.

THE ATLANTIC PROVINCES [4]

In landforms, population, and economic development the Atlantic Provinces are similar to the American Appalachia. This Canadian region has been experiencing a net out-migration of people and has had an income well below the Canadian average. Each province has an industrial mix which specializes in one or more of the primary industries of agriculture, fishing, mining, or forestry—all of which have experienced declining employment because of mechanization. Just as Appalachia has relatively

[4] The Atlantic Provinces are Newfoundland (including Labrador on the mainland), which joined Canada in 1949, and the three Maritime Provinces of New Brunswick, Nova Scotia, and Prince Edward Island.

empty areas with recreational attraction to American coastal cities, so are the Atlantic Provinces attractive vacationlands which bring in a seasonal income; but this scenery competes for the American market with similar landscapes in New England.

In the past the ports of Halifax and Saint John were the usual winter gateways for the railways to interior Canada when the St. Lawrence was frozen; but the use of ice-breakers in the gulf and estuary of the St. Lawrence now permits ships to penetrate as far inland as Quebec City and sometimes to Montreal. As in Appalachia, there are some economic growth centers, but they are inadequate to bring the Atlantic Provinces up to the national level. More industrial development is needed if the cities are to absorb the outflowing rural population; but the region is peripheral to the main Canadian markets, and its local market of a half million households with an estimated income of about $3 billion is too small and scattered. Preliminary discussions of a possible political union of the three Maritime Provinces have taken place, in order to reduce the duplication of government expenditures and to enable the region to speak with a common voice on economic matters.

Nova Scotia

The most populous of the Atlantic Provinces has much of its settlement dispersed around or near the coast. The first settlers were Acadian French, many of whom were later transported to Louisiana and elsewhere by the British. Many Scottish Highlanders found the mediocre soils and chilly climate of Nova Scotia not inferior to those of their homelands. As in New England, many of the subsistence farms cleared on the rocky hills and thin soils of interior Nova Scotia were abandoned when better lands were opened for settlement in central and western Canada. Most of the province is still covered with forest, and new clearing for agriculture seldom occurs. Farms are small and are dispersed mostly along the main roads. The largest areas of prosperous agriculture are in the apple-growing Annapolis Valley and the livestock region of Chignecto Isthmus near New Brunswick. After the Annapolis Valley apple growers lost their export market during World War II, they turned to apple processing for the eastern Canadian market and diversified their farms. Poultry, dairy products, and livestock for the nearby Halifax market are now significant agricultural products there.

The geography of coastal settlement is changing as a result of the centralizing of fish processing and the modernization of fishing vessels. New freezing or filleting plants turn out a higher-quality fish product; workers are moving to the larger towns where these factories are located and abandoning the small fishing villages. The picturesque old schooners and small fishing boats of the villages are being replaced by modern trawlers and draggers which operate out of the larger settlements and go farther from shore. This centralization of the fishing population is similar to the movement of farm workers to the cities elsewhere in Anglo-America. These trends are well advanced in Nova Scotia, are beginning in Newfoundland, but are lagging in east coast New Brunswick. Much of the Atlantic Coast fish catch is obtained offshore in international waters as far east as the Sable Island Banks; the scallop catch, for example, comes from Brown's Bank off New England and is landed at Digby. Lobsters, the most valuable of the ocean products, are trapped in the Bay of Fundy or along Northumberland Strait.

Each of the provinces of Canada tends to be dominated by one large city, and Halifax is that prime industrial, commercial, and service city of Nova Scotia. Halifax and its across-the-harbor suburb of Dartmouth have the usual wide variety of consumer-goods manufacturing found in most Anglo-American cities (Figure 19-4). Some of their industries take advantage of the spacious port and are based on imported products such as petroleum, textiles, auto assembly, sugar, and cacao. As the largest city and capital of Nova Scotia, Halifax attracts numerous professional and service activities which cannot be supplied elsewhere in smaller towns. It is also the commercial center of Nova Scotia, having many head offices of firms operating throughout the Atlantic Provinces.

The urban cluster of Sydney–New Waterford–Glace Bay on Cape Breton Island (85,000 population in 1966) does not have the manufacturing diversity of Halifax. The

FIGURE 19-4 Note that these Canadian graphs use data for all Canada, not for the United States, as the baseline. Canadian census data are comparable with U.S. census categories although the categories are in a different order; to make comparison easier, the United States order has been followed. As on United States graphs, D indicates that the data cannot be disclosed without revealing confidential information—in such cases the length of bars has been estimated. Should the Cape Breton Island steel industry become unprofitable, for example, the primary metal bar would show a decided negative deviation.

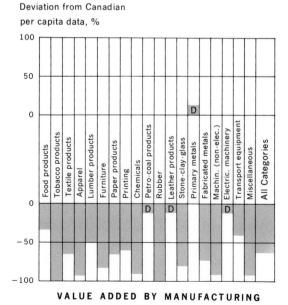

VALUE ADDED BY MANUFACTURING
Nova Scotia = 3.9% Canadian Pop.

HALIFAX HARBOR, looking to the north. The railway and harbor and warehouse facilities occupy the foreground section of Halifax. The new residential areas of Dartmouth lie across the harbor. The two cities are functionally tied together by the large new bridge. The inner harbor, called Bedford Basin, is off the picture to the left.
(Nova Scotia Information Service photo.)

major industry, iron and steel, with its associated coal mining, was in economic difficulties in the 1960s. Coal mining, as elsewhere in the Appalachians, is a declining industry. It has been aided by federal government subsidies and, if the recommendation that these be removed is followed, this industry will suffer further declines. The steel industry is poorly located with relation to the main Canadian markets, despite having access to nearby raw materials, and the company owners wish to close the large plant. The displacement of so many workers therefore becomes a political problem. On a smaller scale, the problems—and perhaps some of the solutions—of American Appalachia, apply to the coal mining and marginal agriculture of Cape Breton Island and

other parts of Nova Scotia. A diversification of industry has already occurred in many places in Nova Scotia, and, in general, the economic development of this province is well above that of the other Atlantic Provinces.

New Brunswick

This rectangular province has a hilly, forested interior and a broad eastern coastal plain. On a smaller scale, this coastal plain adjoining the central hills is the Canadian equivalent to the Atlantic Coastal Plain and the Appalachian Hills. Most settlement in New Brunswick is peripheral, along the eastern and southern coasts, but towns and farms also spread along the St. John Valley in the western section. New Brunswick has one distinctive cultural distribution pattern not found in the other Atlantic Provinces—this is the dominance of French Canadians in the northern and eastern parts of the province. As part of a general outflow of French Canadians from southern Quebec, these settlers migrated into the farmlands of northern New Brunswick; they also constitute much of the labor in the forestry and fishing industries.

Before 1940 the people lived mainly in rural areas; agriculture was not particularly prosperous, but the land produced sufficient food for local needs. As in the rest of Anglo-America, this population is now moving into the towns and cities for industrial, commercial, and service employment; uneconomic farms are gradually being abandoned. Farmers in New Brunswick have some of the same problems as those in Nova Scotia. Except in the St. John Valley and the uplands of the northwest, soils are not particularly fertile, are heavily leached, or are stony. Many farms, too small to be economic units, have a surplus labor supply; local markets are not large. Frequently wholesalers in the Maritime cities import food from central Canada's well-organized agriculture, even though the crop might be grown within the local region. Most of the commercial farmers carry on dairying in the lower St. John Valley and near Moncton, or operate large potato farms in the northwestern plateau. The part-time or subsistence farmers along the East Coast obtain additional income by working in the logging camps in winter or by fishing in summer.

Forests cover 80 percent of the province, and forestry is the most important primary industry. In the previous century lumbering was the major occupation in many East Coast towns, but in the present century the pulp and paper industry is the main forest utilization. Some of the pulp and paper mills are located at river mouths on the northeast coast, from whence the manufactured products can be exported directly into ocean vessels. The rivers tap the interior forests where there is little land transport, and they are used to transport pulp logs in spring and summer. The paper mills in southwestern New Brunswick make greater use of roads and trucks to assemble their logs; they also use railways to export the newsprint to eastern United States.

Mining was unimportant in New Brunswick until the early 1960s. The discovery of lead, zinc, and copper near Bathurst brought a little diversity to the backward economy of the northeast coast. This area of subsistence farms and poorly equipped fisheries received federal government assistance through ARDA (Agriculture Rehabilitation and Development Act), which is attempting to raise the level of incomes in several poor rural sections of Canada. It is believed that the "rural poverty" can be reduced by moving the surplus population to certain Maritime towns where industries such as new smelters are receiving government encouragement to locate or expand.

Saint John, the largest urban center in New Brunswick, is not as large as metropolitan Halifax, but many of its industries are similar. Some of Saint John's manufactures are based on imported raw materials; other industries such as food processing and the pulp and paper mill obtain their supplies from the St. John River hinterland. The harbor used to be an important winter outlet for Canadian grain and certain manufactured products from central Canada, but this function is decreasing as St. Lawrence winter navigation increases.

Moncton, the only other city of size (46,000 in 1966), is growing rapidly as it takes greater advantage of its central position in the Atlantic Provinces region and its location on transport routes which converge on the Isthmus of Chignecto connecting New Brunswick and Nova Scotia. Moncton has several transportation functions and activities and is a supply and distribution center for the areas between the immediate hinterlands of Halifax and Saint John.

Most Canadian provincial capitals are the largest cities of the province, but one of the exceptions is Fredericton. The capital of New Brunswick is a quiet, pleasant city which is the supply-service center for the central St. John Valley; its major occupations are related to government services and the provincial university.

Prince Edward Island

This small island (about the area of the state of Delaware) is known as "the Garden Province," not only because of its size but because its land is used mainly for agricultural purposes. There is no mining on the island, virtually no forest cutting except for fuel from farm woodlots, and the little fishing is mainly for lobsters close to the coast. Perhaps owing to past physical separation and a higher level of agricultural prosperity, the "Islanders" have a pride and culture which sets them off as a distinctive group within the Atlantic Provinces. The slightly rolling landscape is a picture of

green during the summer—pasture and grain are the major land uses—with splashes of red from road cuts in the distinctive reddish soils. The major sources of farm income are livestock products, including dairy products, and potatoes. Much of the food is exported from the island; the livestock products go partly to food-deficient Newfoundland, and the excellent seed potatoes are sent to southern United States and the Caribbean countries.

The population of Prince Edward Island has changed very little throughout the present century. The land is fully occupied under present agricultural practices, and the only city and capital, Charlottetown, remains small. The surplus farm population has moved to other parts of Canada. Communication and transport to the mainland of Canada are maintained by ferries which break the ice of Northumberland Strait during the winter. From time to time proposals for building a causeway across the strait are put forward—some observers note with malice that such discussions have preceded federal elections!

Newfoundland (Figure 19-6)

This newest province, which includes the Labrador section on the mainland, was a self-governing dominion in the British Commonwealth until its people voted to join with Canada in 1949. Throughout its history of settlement by British people, the population distribution has been dominantly coastal, and before 1940 comprised mainly fishermen. As in other parts of Anglo-America, the dynamic nature of geography can be illustrated by the changing geographical patterns of peoples and economy in Newfoundland.

Newfoundland island has been used by fishermen since the sixteenth century. Eng-

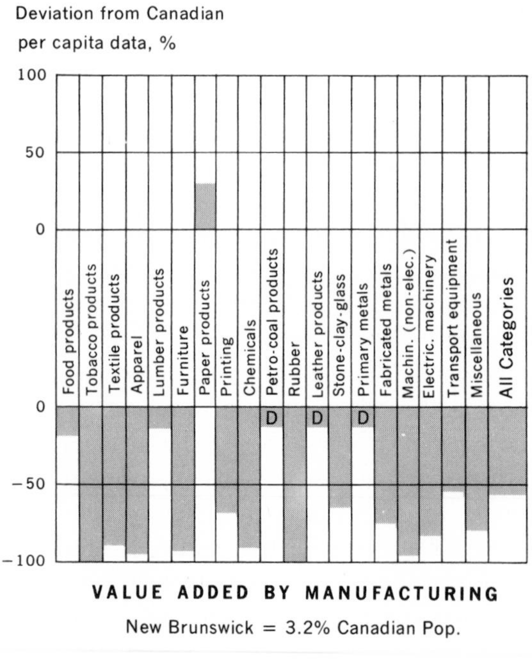

Deviation from Canadian
per capita data, %

VALUE ADDED BY MANUFACTURING
New Brunswick = 3.2% Canadian Pop.

FIGURE 19-5   The Maritime Provinces are not outstanding as a manufacturing region, as this and Figure 19-4 indicate. What are the significant differences between the graphs for Nova Scotia and New Brunswick?

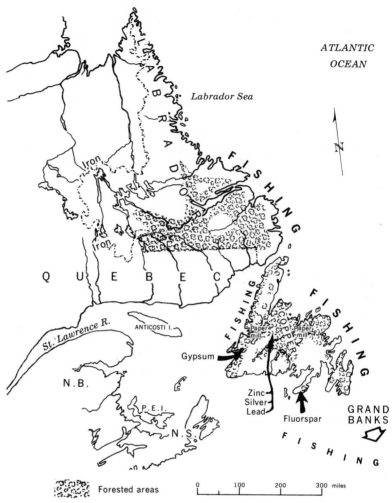

FIGURE 19-6 *The natural resources of Newfoundland are dispersed in relatively small sections of the island and on mainland Labrador. The amount of land used for agriculture is too small to show on a map of this scale.* (After Summers.)

lish fishermen first used the sheltered bays of the east and northeast coasts as summer bases for drying codfish caught on the off-shore banks; gradually more and more people began to winter there, establishing small and dispersed villages. St. John's, one of the harbors closest to England, grew as an administrative town and a supply and collecting center for the "outpost" villages. French fishermen had rights to the south and west coasts of Newfoundland, and these shores were never occupied with the same densities as the east and northeast coasts.

Newfoundland was not an attractive land for agricultural settlers (Figure 19-7). The eastern coasts are hilly, rocky, and cool.

Level land is limited in area; soils are thin or lacking on the low hills, headlands, and islands; the cool Labrador current along-shore keeps summer temperatures low and promotes offshore fogs. The unattractive physical environment of the land offered little to European settlers of the nineteenth century; the few people who came to the island obtained a scanty living from the resources of the sea.

After 1920 diversification character-ized the economy, accelerating after 1950.

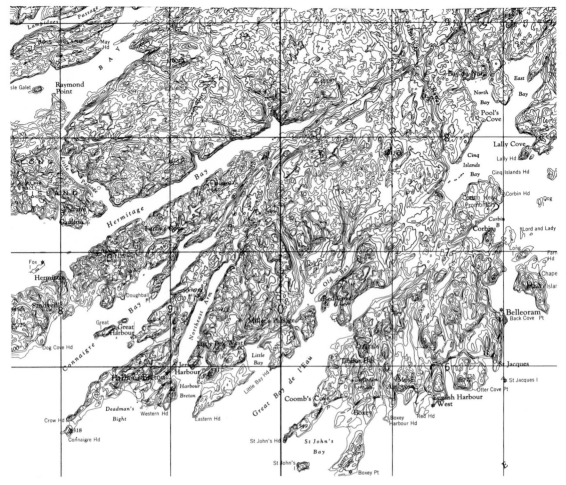

FIGURE 19-7   *The low, rugged hills of the south coast of Newfoundland are mapped by the contour lines on part of a topographic map. Settlements are small and isolated except by sea; there are only a few local roads. On the military grid shown, each square is 10,000 meters (32,808 feet) on each side. The highest elevation on the map area is 1,235 feet. The nearest town, Grand Bank, is 30 miles to the south, across Fortune Bay.* (Belleoram quadrangle, 1962.)

For example, the unused coniferous trees of the northern and western interior were suitable for pulpwood, and the longest of the rapid-strewn rivers could produce hydroelectric power. The use of these resources resulted in pulp and paper mills at Corner Brook, on the west coast, and at Grand Falls, on the Exploits River near the northeast coast. They provided alternate sources of income and another export product which soon equaled fish exports in value. Mining developed at the turn of the century when an iron ore mine was opened on Bell Island in Conception Bay. For more than 60 years, until its closure in 1966, this mine supplied iron ore to the steel mills at Sydney, Nova Scotia. Other ore bodies were discovered, particularly copper and asbestos on the northeast coast, opening new possibilities for employment. This mining population is coastal, as are the fishing settlements.

Changes are also occurring in the fishing industry. Before 1940 fish products were of low-quality, mainly dried or salted cod, obtained along the northeast or east coasts. Small groups fished close to shore from small boats, or they stretched nets off the many headlands or islands. Only about 25 percent of the Newfoundland fish catch came from the international waters above the Grand Banks some distance offshore to the southeast. After about 1950 more fish freezing and filleting plants were built to produce a higher-quality product. The government is encouraging fishermen to move from the many small villages which lack social services and urban amenities to the larger towns where they can keep the fish-processing plants supplied; government loans are permitting fishermen to buy modern trawlers and draggers and to fish offshore in international waters. As a result, in the 1960s about 50 percent of the Newfoundland catch was obtained from offshore banks. By 1961 fishermen constituted only 10 percent of Newfoundland's working population and numbered about 10,000 persons. Thus the geographical patterns of the fishing industry were much different in the 1960s from what they were early in the century.

On a smaller scale, similar changes have occurred in Labrador. Before 1940 most of the scanty population lived in small fishing villages along the south coast, and about 1,000 Eskimo depended on sea resources, mainly seals, along the north coast. During World War II a large airport was built at Goose Bay, in relatively fog-free interior southern Labrador, as a base for trans-Atlantic flights. During the 1950s Goose Bay was the largest settlement in Labrador as a result of the servicing at this airport. Further technological changes, however, resulting in greater use of long-range aircraft made it unnecessary to stop often at Goose Bay where there was little local traffic or freight. Goose Bay's site is unchanged, but its position in modern transportation changed twice within two decades. In the 1960s another new pattern of settlement in western Labrador was the result of the discovery of large reserves of medium-

quality iron ore. Modern technology and blast-furnace demands permit these ores to be concentrated into iron pellets for export; therefore the mining towns of Labrador City and Wabush near the Quebec border became the largest settlements in Labrador.

St. John's, the capital, has always been the largest city in Newfoundland. Whereas the other towns noted in preceding paragraphs are mainly one-industry centers, St. John's has a greater variety of manufacturing, plus commercial, service, and government functions. Part of its harbor facilities were rebuilt in the 1960s, thus improving its transportation functions; much of the deep-sea fishing fleet uses St. John's as a base. Although the city is growing in population—its 100,000 people in 1966 was about 20 percent of the population of Newfoundland—it does not dominate the population distribution pattern of the island as much as it did in 1901 when 70 percent of the population lived in St. John's. Although still the primate city of Newfoundland, the declining percentage illustrates the diversity of other occupations and resource centers in other parts of the province.

QUEBEC

In culture and language, the population of Quebec differs from the rest of Canada. Settled by the French in the sixteenth century, Quebec had about 60,000 settlers along the St. Lawrence in New France when it was conquered by the British in 1763. With very little further immigration from France the French-speaking population increased to more than 5 million persons in 1961. This expanding core of French Canadians had fully occupied the lowlands along the St. Lawrence River; established Canada's largest city, Montreal; moved into the farmlands of the rolling Appalachians to the southeast; and pushed on into northern New England and northern New Brunswick. Smaller colonies of French-speaking settlers migrated into pockets of level land within the Canadian Shield to the north, and formed dispersed groups of linguistic minorities across western Canada.

This dual cultural origin gives variety to Canadian society but also poses political problems for Canadian parliamentary leaders who must give consideration to the rights of this large minority group. More than 80 percent of the people of Quebec are of French Canadian origins and of Roman Catholic religion. About 60 percent of the population stated in the census that French is their primary mother tongue; in the rural areas of the Appalachians or Canadian Shield many cannot speak English. The largest groups of English-speaking people in Quebec province are in Montreal, and many of these persons occupy important positions in the upper levels of management and business. One of the resentments in Quebec is the apparent better advancement available in business for those of Anglo-Saxon background; those of nationalistic sentiment in Quebec object because most French Canadians need to speak English to advance economically in Canada, whereas English-speaking Canadians show no overwhelming desire to use the French language to communicate with the largest cultural minority. For two centuries French Canadians have been able to preserve much of their culture, language, laws, and religion within their Quebec core; their vocal nationalistic expressions in the 1960s are partially a defensive reaction to the increasing penetration of English-speaking influences from surrounding Canada and the United States. French Canadians remain a geographical entity occupying particular areas in Canada, but their cultural homogeneity is not as strong as it was in the previous century.

The population and economic core of Quebec is in the St. Lawrence Lowland (Figure 19-8). Much of this flatland was formed from marine deposits laid down at the end of the Glacial Age when the area was under an inland extension of the brackish Gulf of St. Lawrence, called the Champlain Sea. The core is a triangular area extending from Quebec City to Ottawa on the north to about Lake Champlain on the United States border to the south. The region is dominated by Canada's largest city, Montreal, on its island site near the center of the lowland core. Strips of settlement extend northward into river valleys of the Canadian Shield, and settlement is relatively compact on the small agricultural lowlands in the Lake St. John–Saguenay Valley to the northeast and, to the northwest, in the Clay Belt south of James Bay. North of these regions most of the province is unoccupied.

Montreal Metropolitan Area

Montreal and Toronto are rivals for Canadian commerical and industrial leadership. Each metropolis has more than 2 million persons, about one-tenth of Canadian population, and each has a high proportion of Canadian finance, commerce, industry, and service activities. Montreal was traditionally Canada's leading seaport—its collection and distribution port functions being comparable to those of New York to the American hinterland. Two factors affecting Montreal's geographical position are changing: Whereas the port used to be closed by ice for three months of the winter, greater use of icebreakers in the river and in the Gulf of St. Lawrence now permits more winter accessibility; an opposite influence was the opening of the St. Lawrence Seaway west of Montreal—the city is no longer the inland head of navigation for ships of medium draft. The fact that Montreal's commercial and industrial interests did not oppose the building of the seaway—as did such groups in East Coast American ports—indicates that the port functions of Montreal are not as important as those other activities which

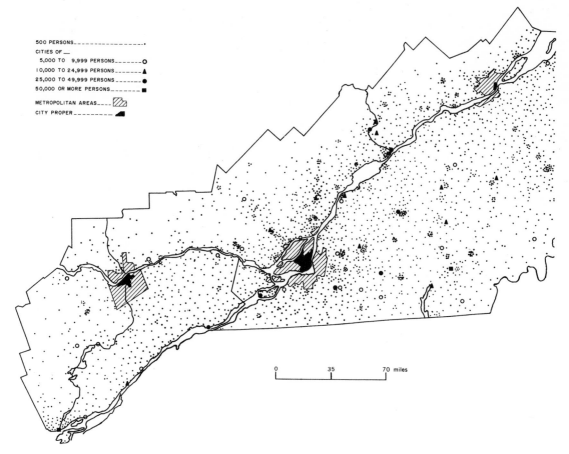

0   35   70 miles

FIGURE 19-8 Population distribution on the St. Lawrence Lowland, 1961. The population of the three metropolitan areas shown is about 60 percent of that of the province of Quebec. Rural settlement is fairly evenly spread over the level lowland. Study the geometry of the distribution of small towns in southeastern Quebec. (After a map by Dominion Bureau of Statistics.)

are strengthened by improvements in transportation.

Montreal is Canada's leading industrial city. The annual value of its manufactures, for example, exceeds that of the total of the three western provinces of British Columbia, Alberta, and Saskatchewan. Not only do the city's industries have the large local market for consumer goods such as food products and household equipment, but also the advantages of large-scale production permit Montreal to send its manufactures to its consuming hinterlands in the Prairie Provinces and the Maritime Provinces. Some Montreal manufactures are based on imported raw materials such as petroleum, sugar, textiles; other industries such as flour mills, meat packing, and metallurgical plants are the result of the

excellent railway connections to Canadian natural resources. Products such as transportation equipment and a variety of machinery and chemicals relate to Canada's national economy. In 1966, employment in a wide variety of manufacturing plants represented about half the employed persons of the city.

Partly as a result of its early start, but also related to its central position in eastern Canada, Montreal is a leading financial and commercial city. Many of Canada's large firms have their head offices in Montreal.

THE CITY CENTER OF MONTREAL, looking northwest from part of the harbor in the foreground to the forested slopes of Mount Royal in the right-center background. The low buildings of the old city, near the docks and railways, are used for warehouses and small factories. The new high-rise skyline of commercial buildings of the CBD is left of center. The residential area of Montreal West is in the upper left corner of the picture. (Photo by Ville de Montréal.)

About 16 percent of Montreal's employment is engaged in trade, and nearly 8 percent in finance, insurance, and related commercial activities. Montreal's other tertiary occupations are similar to those of other large Anglo-American cities: for example, transportation and communication, 12 percent; and services, 9 percent.

Montreal's first industrial area grew up along the St. Lawrence River, on the south and east side of Montreal Island, and inland along the Lachine Canal across the southern part of the island (Figure 19-9). The terminals of Canada's two transcontinental railways were established east of the canal entrance. The main commercial core spread north of this industrial area to the base of an old volcanic plug, Mount Royal, which rose about 600 feet above the lowland. A first-class residential area was established on the view slopes of Mount Royal, and it has maintained separate political status as the enclave city of Westmount. Postwar suburban Montreal expanded outward, like other Anglo-American cities: The dairy and vegetable farms of Montreal Island have nearly disappeared under the waves of modern ranch-style houses; new industrial zones stretch outward along the railways and highways; large suburban shopping centers are dispersed through the suburbs, serving the housewives who are too far away from the downtown stores. Although parts of downtown Montreal and some old sections of the city have a "foreign" appearance which gives "character" to Montreal, the new suburbs look much the same as the suburban sprawl of most Anglo-American cities.

Montreal dominates the economy of the

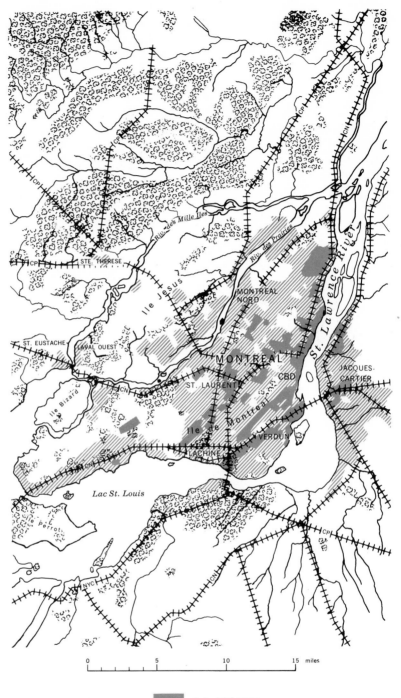

FIGURE 19-9 *Land use in the Montreal area. The areas without symbols are mainly agricultural. The main industrial zones are along the harbor and the railways. Most of Montreal Island is occupied by residences, but there are still farmlands in the western section. Suburban growth to the south and east sides of the St. Lawrence River is beginning. North of the city, much of the land is still in forest, despite its favorable location near the large urban market.*

Industrial areas

Residential and commercial areas

Forested areas

Railways

RURAL SETTLEMENT along the south shore of the estuary of the St. Lawrence. The farmhouses are close together along the road and near to the large church; the narrow fields are at right-angles to the road. In the distance, the marine terrace above the river has been fully cleared for long-lot farms, but the poor sandy soils of former beachlines remain in the forest. (Photo by Quebec Department of Tourism.)

Quebec Lowland; there are no other large cities nearby. Some of the small cities of the surrounding Montreal Plain manufacture yarn or textiles, and send their products to the clothing factories in Montreal. The immediate hinterland of Montreal is an excellent dairy region in which most of the forest has been removed by two centuries of farming. These farms near Montreal are not the picturesque "habitant" farms described in the nineteenth century, but are modern, well-equipped dairy farms which supply fresh milk to the large urban population.

The distinctive long, narrow farms—the result of the old French Canadian land subdivision system—are still obvious features in the rural landscape. The old farmhouses are close together along the rivers and roads, and each narrow farm stretches several hundred yards at right angles to the transport line. Small villages, each dominated by a large Catholic church, are spaced at fairly regular intervals along these roads, often at crossroads junctions. This type of linear rural settlement is common on the St. Lawrence Lowland between Montreal and Quebec City, but is less characteristic of the sections close to the United States border which were settled by United Empire Loyalists who had a different land division system.

This latter region of original English-speaking settlement, known as the Eastern Townships, has a different landscape appearance because of its squarish farms and also because of more forest mixed with pasture on the linear hills of the Appalachians. Within the present century most of the English-speaking settlers have moved from rural southeastern Quebec, being replaced by French-speaking people from the surplus farm population of the lowland core. The Eastern Townships have many features similar to the New England rural areas south and east of them—some of the small towns have pulp and paper mills or textile mills like small New England towns. Thus Sherbrooke, main supply-distribution center for the Eastern Townships, has factories processing farm products as well as a textile industry.

Quebec Metropolitan Area

Quebec City, the provincial capital, is the only large urban area in the eastern part of the St. Lawrence Lowland. Quebec, Fredericton, and Victoria are the only provincial capitals that are not the largest cities of their provinces. There are many parallels between Quebec and Victoria, British Columbia, as capitals and cultural centers in their historical competition with their counterpart larger industrial cities of Montreal and Vancouver. Although Quebec is closer to the Atlantic, many ships bypass it to travel further inland to the larger urban markets and transport facilities at Montreal. The old city of Quebec, with its picturesque narrow streets and crowned by the ancient stone walls of the Citadel rising over the rock cliffs above the St. Lawrence River, is a well-known tourist attraction. Although having about one-quarter the population of Montreal, Quebec is the second largest city in the Atlantic Gateways region; its metropolitan urban area ranked as the seventh most populous city in Canada in 1966. As a large city, Quebec has a variety of small

industries, local businesses, and the usual range of residential housing that is found in nearly all Anglo-American cities. Manufacturing employment—three-eighths of its workers—is relatively less significant than in Montreal. More people are engaged in government and in service occupations. Unlike Montreal, there are very few wholly English-speaking persons in Quebec City; most business is carried on in French.

The chief industrial section of Quebec is along the banks of the St. Charles River, north of the Citadel and old commercial core. These factories produce clothing, boots and shoes, chemicals, pulp and paper for the national market, and the usual range of food and consumer goods for the local population. Grain elevators are a dominant feature of Quebec's harbor. Quebec, like the other large cities discussed in the Gateways region, is an eastern Canadian port. Some of its industrial and commercial functions depend on imports and exports, others on its geographical position related to the resources of its hinterland. The activities of these port cities demonstrate the importance of foreign trade in the economy of eastern Canada.

The Shield

Many of the primary raw materials used in the industries of southern Quebec come from the Shield region. Much of the resource development takes place close to the southern Shield edge, with decreasing intensity of use to the east and north. The Shield is a land of forests, minerals, and waterpower. Vast areas of coniferous forest cover the southern part of the Quebec Shield. Spruce, fir, pine, and larch form solid stands, occasionally interspersed with poplar or alder; the continuous green cover is broken by lakes, rivers, swamps, or muskeg. Part of the forest is being converted into newsprint which is exported by ship or rail to northeastern United States. Paper mills were built in the late nineteenth century on the lowland on the rivers flowing southward into the St. Lawrence. As suitable trees became scarce on the lowland, logging moved northward along the river valleys into the spruce-fir forests of the Shield. The same Shield rivers used to float logs, and for the washing of the pulp in the mills, also produced hydroelectric power to operate the machinery. Early in this century new pulp and paper mills were erected within the forest region, the largest group being in the Lake St. John–Saguenay Valley with other clusters at Trois Rivières and along the St. Maurice Valley.

Before 1940 the Quebec Shield had not revealed its mineral wealth to the same extent as had the Shield in Ontario. Most of the prewar mines in west central Quebec, producing gold or copper in a zone between Noranda-Rouyn and Val d'Or, were an eastward extension of a major mining region in northeastern Ontario. After 1950 the mining frontier pushed outward to the northeast. Copper and other base metals were discovered at Chibougamau and Matagami; new northern railroads brought their ores to smelters at Noranda or Montreal.

The iron ore in the Shield on the Quebec-Labrador boundary had been known since the beginning of the century but was then too isolated to be developed profitably. Its geographical position in Anglo-America changed, however, with the approaching depletion of high-quality hematite ore in the Lake Superior region, and with the opening of the St. Lawrence Seaway. It became economical to transport the good-quality Labrador-Ungava iron ore to blast furnaces in the Lake Erie region. Port facilities were built at Sept Iles on the Gulf of St. Lawrence, a 360-mile railway constructed by 1954 across the rocky, lake-dotted Shield, and miners were housed and supplied in the new, planned town of Schefferville, on the Quebec side of the Newfoundland (Labrador)–Quebec boundary. This boundary was ill defined because it was decreed in Eng-

land in 1926 by boundary commissioners who had never seen the area; it is the "drainage divide" in a region of deranged drainage where lakes may drain in several directions. The boundary is politically not recognized by maps of the government of Quebec.

Another large iron deposit was discovered at Gagnon, Quebec, and a similar pattern of resource development resulted in new harbor facilities at Port Cartier and another new railway to the mining town. The towns represented by these new place names on the map of Canada have little resemblance to the boom towns on the mining frontier in the last century. People will no longer move into the wilderness without the urban facilities and conveniences of southern Canadian cities. The new resource-oriented towns are planned and well organized; their curving residential streets and gaily painted houses are supplied by modern supermarkets and recreation facilities. All are served by air transport, as well as railways, so that the attractions of big city life are only a few hours away.

The hydroelectric power of the Shield rivers not only supplies local industries such as pulp and paper mills, mines, aluminum smelters, and urban housing; it is also exported to the cities and industries of southern Quebec. As the technology of power generation and transmission improved, southern Quebec was able to bring its power from farther and farther away in the Shield. Early in the twentieth century several falls of the St. Maurice River were dammed, and the turbines in the power plants supplied part of the electric power needs of Montreal. By the 1920s the power of the Saguenay River could be transmitted to Quebec City. In the 1950s some of the tributaries of the Saguenay River were harnessed; the 4 million horsepower generated from several plants was more electric power than was produced by any other Canadian river system. In the late 1950s another 2 million horsepower was obtained farther east from the Bersimis River; this power was transmitted into the grid which serves southern Quebec. In the 1960s the Manicouagan-Outardes rivers were dammed and by the early 1970s will be producing more than 6 million horsepower for expanding Quebec industries. And still farther beyond in Labrador lies the enormous power potential of Churchill (formerly Grand) Falls on the Churchill (formerly Hamilton) River.

The geography of resource development in the Canadian Shield shows outward-moving concentric patterns from the core area along the St. Lawrence. Mines and northern railroads are penetrating farther north into the mineral-rich Shield; pulp and paper companies are making more intensive use of the southern Shield forests and are pushing logging roads into areas where there is no other settlement. The geographical patterns of settlement are changing in the Canadian Shield of Quebec.

The Economy of Quebec

About 80 percent of the people living in the occupied southern part of Quebec live in urban centers having more than 1,000 persons. More than one-third of the provincial population lives in one large city, Montreal. On the agricultural lands of the St. Lawrence Lowland, as in the rest of rural Anglo-America, farms are becoming larger, and farming population is declining rapidly. The occupation groups in Quebec province reflect this increasingly urban-industrial society (Table 19-3). These occupation figures are obviously greatly influenced by the kinds of employment followed by people in the two large cities of Montreal and Quebec.

The traditional view of Quebec as an agricultural economy refers to large *areas* of southern Quebec, but not to many people. Manufacturing, service, and trade occupations are important. Manufacturing no longer depends mainly on local raw materials; in 1962 those manufactures based largely on local food and natural resources accounted for only 32 percent of manufacturing employment (Figure 19-10). Because it is one of the gateways to Canada, Quebec processes imported raw materials such as petroleum, bauxite, cotton, and wool; it also converts the products of its hinterland such as wheat, meat, and ores. Quebec manufac-

TABLE 19-3   Distribution of Labor Force: Quebec, 1931 and 1961 (percent of total)

Industry	*1931*	*1961*
Agriculture	22.1%	7.5%
Forestry	1.7	2.4
Fishing	0.6	0.2
Mining	0.8	1.5
Subtotal	25.2	11.6
Manufacturing	22.4	25.2
Construction	7.8	7.7
Transport and Communication	6.7	7.1
Trade	9.8	12.9
Finance	2.6	3.6
Services (including government)	19.8	25.0
Others or Not Stated	5.7	6.9
Total	100.0	100.0

SOURCE: Census data in George W. Wilson et al., *Canada: An Appraisal of Its Needs and Resources,* Twentieth Century Fund, New York, 1965, p. 148.

turing values are, however, only half those of adjoining Ontario, the industrial heartland of Canada. Despite the industrial expansion of the two decades 1945 to 1965, Quebec manufacturing is not growing as fast as in the industrial base of Ontario.

The potential of urban and industrial southern Quebec is great. North of it lies abundant raw-material wealth in minerals, forests, and waterpower; within the region there is a skilled and hardworking industrial population. The Quebec Lowland lies on an international waterway, leading not only to the heartland of Canada, but to the productive industrial and agricultural regions of the American midwest. Quebec should be able to share the advantages experienced by Eastern seaboard states, and also those of the inland heartlands.

CONCLUSIONS

Canada, handicapped by its northerly climate and large areas of barren land, and somewhat overshadowed economically by its neighbor, the United States, is nevertheless a major world power. Canada is comparable in economic wealth to most Western European countries; its gross national product approaches that of the United Kingdom, and its people are among the best educated in the world. Developed more slowly than its southern neighbor, and by fewer people, Canada tends to be overwhelmed by expanding American industry seeking both its raw materials and its markets. Although friendly rivalry and occasional arguments between the two Anglo-American nations seem inevitable, there is no doubt that in political, economic, or military crises the two peoples and their governments will cooperate.

Canada, like the United States, has many unsolved economic problems. Both countries have rural areas where standards of living are lower than the national average; both countries have cities which are becoming overcrowded and have unattractive sections for urban workers. Each country has regional problems which must be considered from a local viewpoint as well as in terms of national policies.

The Atlantic Provinces of Canada, so dependent on forest products, fish, a few minerals, and a few agricultural specialties, are rich by world standards but are below

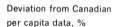

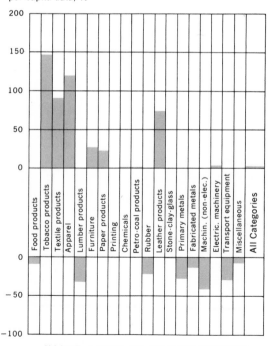

VALUE ADDED BY MANUFACTURING

Quebec = 28.9% Canadian Pop.

FIGURE 19-10 Two-thirds of the value added by manufacturing in the province is produced in Montreal and Quebec City; many of the industries are related to the ports and use raw materials transported to the cities either from within Canada or imported. (Refer to Figure 19-9.) Quebec has every category of industry; even those categories with a considerable negative deviation may represent sizable industries. For example, the value of forest products of about $200 million (value added about $100 million annually) is large, but is not sufficient to give Quebec an above average share per capita of Canadian production.

Anglo-American expectations. They are cut off from the industrial and population heartlands of Canada whereas their American counterpart, New England, is attached to the major manufacturing belt. Quebec believes that it suffers from being a linguistic and cultural minority in Anglo-America; yet its population core is well located astride one of the great gateways to the Anglo-American economy. A "quiet revolution" has changed the Quebec economy in recent decades in a way similar to the economic changes in the American South, and as in the South the new economy has brought social unrest and political uncertainty to some people.

SELECTED REFERENCES

Canada

CAMU, PIERRE, E. P. WEEKS, and Z. W. SAMETZ: *Economic Geography of Canada,* Macmillan, Toronto, 1964.

DOMINION BUREAU OF STATISTICS: *Canada Year Book* (annual), Queen's Printer, Ottawa.

———: *Canada. One Hundred: 1867–1967,* Queen's Printer, Ottawa, 1967.

EASTERBROOK, W. T., and H. G. J. AITKEN: *Canadian Economic History,* Macmillan, Toronto, 1956.

GENTILCORE, R. LOUIS (ed.): *Canada's Changing Geography,* Prentice-Hall of Canada, Scarborough, Ont., 1967. A selection of readings.

KRUEGER, RALPH R. (ed.): *Regional and Resource Planning in Canada,* Holt of Canada, Toronto, 1963, A selection of papers from Canada's "Resources for Tomorrow" Conference of 1961.

PLEVA, E. G. (ed.): *The Canadian Oxford School Atlas,* Oxford, Toronto, 1963.

PUTNAM, DONALD F. (ed.): *Canadian Regions,* Dent, Toronto, 1957.

WARKENTIN, JOHN (ed.): *Canada: A Geographical Interpretation,* Methuen, Toronto, 1968.

WATSON, J. WREFORD: "The Land of Canada," *Canadian Geographical Journal,* April, 1956, pp. 1–31. An excellent summary, with pictures, of the main physical geography patterns of Canada.

WILSON, GEORGE W., SCOTT GORDON, and JUDEK STANISLAW: *Canada: An Appraisal of Its Needs and Resources,* Twentieth Century Fund, New York, 1965; University of Toronto Press, Toronto, 1965.

Current geographical articles will be found in the periodicals: the *Canadian Geographer,* the *Canadian Geographical Journal,* and the *Geographical Bulletin.* Articles by geographers on Quebec (about two-thirds of them in French) appear in the *Cahiers* of Laval University and the *Revue* of the University of Montreal.

Maps of Canada and areas within Canada may be obtained from the Map Distribution Office, Department of Energy, Mines, and Resources, Ottawa. Index maps will be sent upon request.

Maps of land use of certain regions of Canada (all the Maritime Provinces except northern New Brunswick) may be purchased from the Geographical Branch, Department of Energy, Mines, and Resources, Ottawa.

See also the references at the end of chaps. 1–4.

The Atlantic Gateways

CANADA DEPARTMENT OF FORESTRY AND RURAL DEVELOPMENT: *ARDA Reports,* such as "Northeast New Brunswick," 1966, 39 pp., and "Development Plan for Lower St. Lawrence and Gaspé," Ottawa, 1967, 265 pp.

CLARK, ANDREW H.: *Three Centuries and the Island,* University of Toronto Press, Toronto, 1954.

CORNWALL, BROOKE: "A Land Use Reconnaissance of the Annapolis–Cornwallis Valley, N.S.," *Geographical Bulletin,* no. 9, pp. 22–51, 1957.

HARE, F. KENNETH: "New Light from Labrador: Ungava," *Annals A.A.G.,* vol. 54 (1964), pp. 459–476.

NOVA SCOTIA DEPARTMENT OF FINANCE AND ECONOMICS VOLUNTARY PLANNING BOARD: *First Plan for Economic Development to 1968,* Queen's Printer, Halifax, 1966.

QUEBEC DEPARTMENT OF INDUSTRY AND COMMERCE ECONOMIC RESEARCH BUREAU: *Atlas of Quebec Agriculture,* 47 maps, 1966.

RAYMOND, C. W., J. B. MCCLELLAN, and J. A. RAYBURN: *Land Utilization in Prince Edward Island,* Geographical Branch, Department of

Energy, Mines and Resources, memoir 8, Ottawa, 1963.

SUMMERS, WILLIAM F., and MARY E. SUMMERS: *Geography of Newfoundland,* Copp Clark Publishing, Toronto, 1965. A school textbook for Newfoundland children with interesting maps and photographs.

THOMSON, DON W.: *Men and Meridians: The History of Surveying and Mapping in Canada,* vol. I, *Prior to 1867,* Queen's Printer, Ottawa, 1966.

Various publications of the Atlantic Provinces Economic Council, University of New Brunswick, Fredericton, N.B.

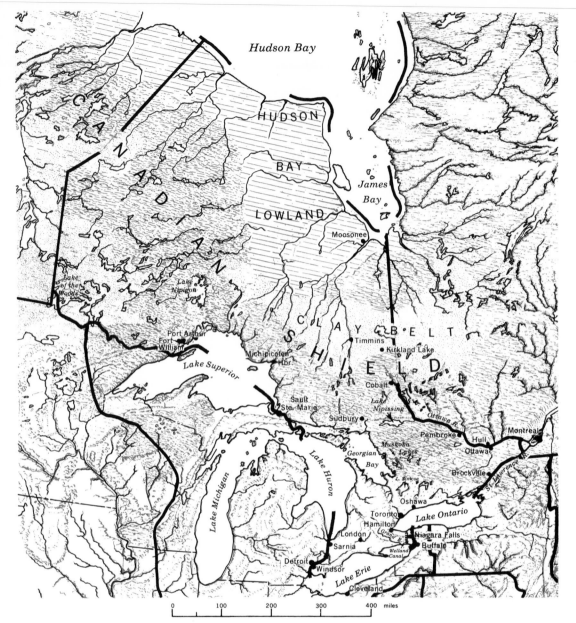

FIGURE 20-1 Landforms of Ontario. Ontario's central position lies between the southern Quebec Lowland to the east and the Canadian Interior Plains to the northwest. It adjoins the productive Great Lakes region of the United States to the south. The small extent of the densely occupied part of the southern Ontario Lowland between lakes Huron, Erie, and Ontario is apparent. (Base map by A. K. Lobeck. Reprinted with permission of The Geographical Press, Hammond, Inc.)

CHAPTER 20

HEARTLAND ONTARIO

ONTARIO

With more than one-third of the Canadian population, Ontario has a strategic position in the center of eastern Canada. The densely populated southern part of the province projects into the midst of the American Commercial-Manufacturing Core (Figure 20-1). Southern Ontario extends south to the 42d parallel, the latitude of northern California, and is almost surrounded by the climate-moderating Great

BASIC DATA:

AREA INCLUDES	Population Change, 1951-1960	1961 (thousands)	1966	Personal Income 1967 (billion Canadian dollars)
ONTARIO	35.6%	6,236	6,961	$17.8
METROPOLITAN AREAS				
Toronto	50.7%	1,824	2,159	$ 5.0
Ottawa	46.9	430	495	1.3
Hamilton	41.0	395	450	1.1
Windsor	18.2	193	211	0.5
London	40.6	181	207	0.5

Ontario, total land area: 412,000 square miles (including enclosed freshwater lakes).

CLIMATE Humid continental to subarctic; in the south moderated locally by the Great Lakes.

	Temperature (°F) Jan.	July	Annual Precipitation (inches) Rainfall Equivalent	Snow
Toronto	25	71	31	55
Windsor	25	73	33	36
Port Arthur	8	63	32	93
Kapuskasing	−1	63	28	96

VEGETATION Mixed forest in the southern third; boreal or coniferous forest (spruce-fir) northward, stunted both by long winters and thin soil cover.

SOIL Gray-brown podzolic soil changing northward to shallow, rocky podzols with many marshy and bare areas.

MINERALS A great variety of metallic ores in the Canadian Shield section: nickel, gold, iron, uranium, lead, zinc, cobalt, silver, platinum; nonmetallics in the Lowlands section: limestone, gypsum, salt; lacking in mineral fuels except for some natural gas.

Lakes. The region has the best combination of environmental conditions for agriculture in Canada; in addition, the productive forests and the metallic ores of the Canadian Shield are adjacent to the north. Ontario's manufacturing industries, which produce half the annual value of Canadian manufactures, were well supplied by electric power from centrally located Niagara Falls before 1940. Additional power for its postwar industrial expansion came from power dams on Canadian Shield rivers to the north (as occurred in Quebec also), and in addition from thermal power supplied by imported American coal and petroleum and natural gas from western Canada. Ontario leads Canada in many productive categories: in value of crops sold, manufacturing, trade, financial services, and mining; it accounts for two-fifths of all Canadian income. Its economic core, extending from Niagara Falls around the western end of Lake Ontario to Toronto and Oshawa, has been called Canada's *Golden Horseshoe.*

Settlement

The area which is now Ontario was explored by the French who followed the river routes of the Ottawa and St. Lawrence west of Montreal. A few fur-trading posts were established but little agricultural settlement resulted except opposite Detroit. The French Canadian core in Quebec did not have time to expand westward before the British conquest of 1763; in contrast to the well-populated Quebec Lowland, southern Ontario was virtually unoccupied. The first British settlements were by Loyalists (called Tories by the Americans), some of whom settled along the Niagara River in 1780 while others founded Kingston in 1783. The Niagara Peninsula was accessible through upper New York State; in addition, Indian relations with these settlers were more favorable on the Canadian side of the boundary. In Ontario, people of British origins now outnumber the French nearly six to one; other continental European groups combined outnumber the French nearly three to one.

Southern Ontario was occupied by agricultural settlers in the early nineteenth century in much the same way that the Ohio Valley was settled about that same time. The heavy stands of deciduous forest were cut down slowly by primitive clearing methods; sometimes the trees were burned to obtain a "cash crop," potash, from the ashes. British immigrants poured into the sparsely occupied region; eastward along the St. Lawrence River the land was occupied by the French Canadians, and to the north the rough, rocky hills of the Canadian

Shield repelled settlers looking for farmland. By 1851 Ontario had surpassed Quebec in population. Shallow canals bypassed the rapids in the St. Lawrence River west of Montreal, and the Welland Canal provided a water route around Niagara Falls. River and lake traffic and its resultant trade came to some southern Ontario cities; but railways were more important than water traffic. By 1881 most of the farmland of southern Ontario had been occupied and much of the original forest was removed. The squarish field patterns contrasted with the long, narrow fields of southern Quebec, but most of their crops were similar. Small service and supply towns grew up along the transport lines in the same manner as in the Midwest states south of the Great Lakes. Toronto, the provincial capital and a lake port, became the largest city. Its growth was related to its central position as a focus of railways leading westward into the United States and northward into the Canadian Shield.

The development of the natural resources of the Shield stimulated the growth of cities in the Ontario Lowland and helped to funnel capital and business into Toronto. By about 1870 the lumbering frontier had moved into the southern Canadian Shield in the upper Ottawa River Valley and east of Georgian Bay. Within about 20 or 30 years most of the good white pine had been cut, and the lumber industry declined in importance. The mining frontier penetrated into the Shield in the 1880s with the discovery of nickel-copper at Sudbury, and the opening in 1903–1905 of rich silver mines at Cobalt. These resources were transported southward and broadened the industrial base of some cities of the lowlands. Until World War I, however, most of southern Ontario remained dominantly rural in settlement and agricultural in occupation. Manufacturing developed during the war to supply the armies in Europe and then expanded rapidly during the 1920s for local

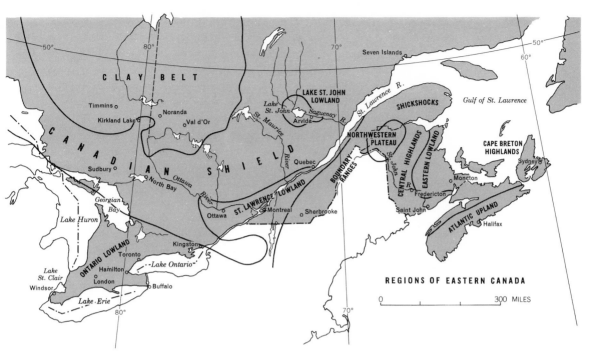

FIGURE 20-2 Much of the population of eastern Canada is in two lowlands, each of which has a sparsely populated area to the north (see Figures 19-8 and 20-3). (Otis W. Freeman and John W. Morris, WORLD GEOGRAPHY, McGraw-Hill, New York, 1965, p. 143).

consumption. A tariff barrier was erected to protect new Canadian industries, and therefore many American companies located branch plants in Ontario to supply the growing Canadian market; these Ontario plants could also export to British Commonwealth countries as Canadian manufacturers.

Industrial Development

As in the American manufacturing belt south of the Great Lakes, Ontario industrial expansion was most rapid during and after World War II. Almost the complete range of manufactured products that are made in the cities of the American Midwest are also produced in the Ontario industrial cities. The factories look the same, the brand names are similar, and many of the company names are familiar to Americans. If one compares the manufactures of Ontario and Ohio, for example, one can note the similarities but also some differences. Five industrial types are relatively (per capita) better developed in Ontario than in Ohio:

textiles, clothing apparel, food products, chemicals, and paper; the first three are consumer-goods industries. Four other industries, for example, are better developed per capita in Ohio: primary metals, machinery, electrical apparatus, transport equipment; these are more complicated industries in which a large market is required. (See Figure 20-3.)

As in the adjoining parts of United States, the rise of industrialization in Ontario paralleled the growth of large cities and resulted in a relative decline in agricultural activities. By 1961 about 80 percent of the population of Ontario was urban, and a somewhat larger percent of the labor force was engaged in city-based employment. Manufacturing and construction activity accounted for 50 percent of provincial employment; and about 40 percent were engaged in trade, financial, professional, and government oc-

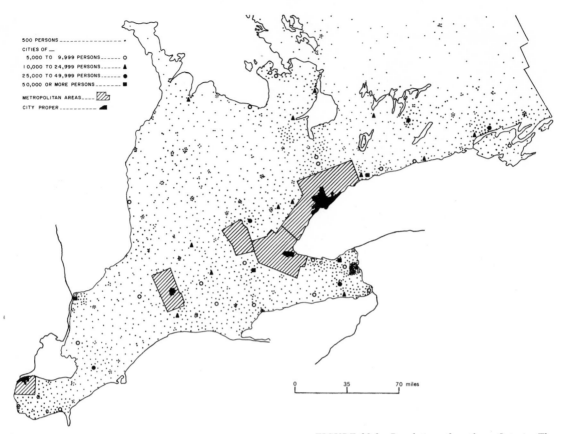

FIGURE 20-3   Population of southern Ontario. The high urban densities and industrialization of the metropolitan areas around the western end of Lake Ontario form the "Golden Horseshoe." Rural population densities are higher north of Lake Erie than near Georgian Bay to the north. (After a map by Dominion Bureau of Statistics.)

cupations. Only 9 percent of employment was in primary industries such as agriculture and forestry. To the tourist driving across the good highways of southern Ontario, the landscape is a dominantly rural one, as it is in the Corn Belt of the United States, but most of the people and the productive wealth of the province are in the cities.

Although the northward movement of American industrial capital assisted economic development in southern Ontario, it has caused political uneasiness. By either purchasing Canadian companies or setting up subsidiaries, the number of American-controlled factories increased in southern Ontario, mainly in metropolitan Toronto. More than half of American branch-plant operations are in Toronto, reflecting not only the importance of that city in Ontario manufacturing but also its proximity and accessibility to Chicago, Cleveland, Buffalo,

and other large American cities. Another example, Windsor, Ontario, grew up as a small edition of industrial Detroit, across the half-mile-wide Detroit River. The Ford and Chrysler corporations located their Canadian companies in Windsor early in the present century, and many other Detroit firms placed their branch plants there. The free flow of technology, skills, inventions, and management across the international border has been of great benefit to Ontario's industrial production, but it leaves Canadians with a nagging uneasiness when some American-controlled firms make business decisions that are contrary to Canadian political and economic policies. The "domi-

IROQUOIS LOCK AND CONTROL DAM in the St. Lawrence Seaway, west of Cornwall, looking downstream. The lowland of Ontario, to the left, is more forested in this area than in southwestern Ontario. Medium-draft ocean-going ships may pass through the Iroquois lock in the left foreground. (Ontario Hydro.)

nation" of certain Canadian industries by American capital often enters internal Canadian political discussions.

The St. Lawrence Seaway

Some of the recent industrial and urban growth of sections of southern Ontario has been aided by the completion of the St. Lawrence Seaway in 1958. It is probable, however, that the seaway has a greater impact upon the trade and industries of several large American cities on the south side of the Great Lakes than upon Ontario cities. The latter have always been more dependent on railways (and lately on trucks and highways) for the movement of raw materials and manufactured products than on water transport. One can note, for ex-

ample, the contrast in ports and cities on Lake Erie; there are no large cities or ports on the Ontario side, whereas the south shore American cities have made great use of the Great Lakes. The deepening of the seaway along the St. Lawrence River meant that ocean-going ships could come directly to Toronto or Hamilton, but few foreign ships went beyond Lake Ontario to other Ontario ports; only a few grain ships penetrated into Lake Superior to Port Arthur–Fort William. It is not surprising that many Canadians favored raising the tolls on the Canadian-built Welland Canal, leading to Lake Erie, since most of the westward traffic was heading for American ports and benefiting mainly American trade and industries.

The removal of the many shallow and

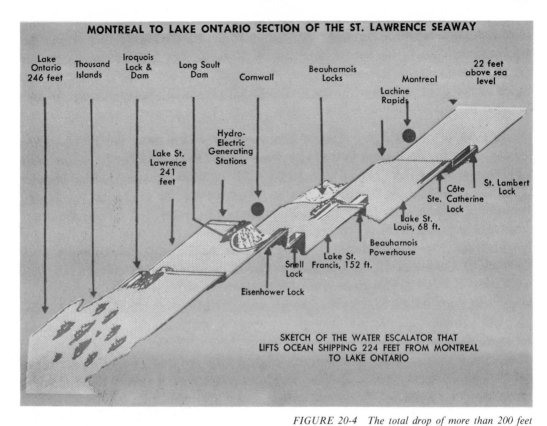

MONTREAL TO LAKE ONTARIO SECTION OF THE ST. LAWRENCE SEAWAY

SKETCH OF THE WATER ESCALATOR THAT
LIFTS OCEAN SHIPPING 224 FEET FROM MONTREAL
TO LAKE ONTARIO

FIGURE 20-4 The total drop of more than 200 feet is almost as much as at Niagara Falls. The electric power produced as a by-product of the seaway stimulated industries in both eastern Ontario and northern New York. The lower section of the seaway, northeast of Cornwall, is entirely in Canada. (Ontario Department of Economics and Development.)

short locks west of Montreal helped the Canadian grain trade in general, but hurt the Georgian Bay grain ports. Before 1958 much Canadian wheat and other grains were carried by long, narrow lake freighters from the twin cities of Port Arthur–Fort William to several Georgian Bay or Lake Huron ports for further transshipment by rail to Montreal for export. Now these lake vessels can continue downstream to Montreal without transshipment, and even beyond to new grain elevators closer to the Atlantic at Quebec City or Baie Comeau.

The opening of the seaway changed the geographical position of the Ungava-Labrador iron ores (Chapter 19). About half of this ore is carried upstream past Montreal, going mainly to Buffalo, Cleveland, and other Lake Erie ports. Some of the Labrador ore is delivered to Hamilton, Ontario, which has also benefited from the seaway in other ways. American coal is one of the products

carried downstream to Montreal in the St. Lawrence section of the seaway. This increased west-to-east movement of coal further hurt the Cape Breton coal industry which was attempting to sell to the Montreal market.

One of the by-products of the seaway has been the increased production of hydroelectric power from the dams across the St. Lawrence at Cornwall. It was, in fact, the agreement between Ontario and New York to build a power dam which finally forced the federal governments in Ottawa and Washington to agree on the construction of the seaway after about 40 years of discussion and lobbying. This electric power, shared by

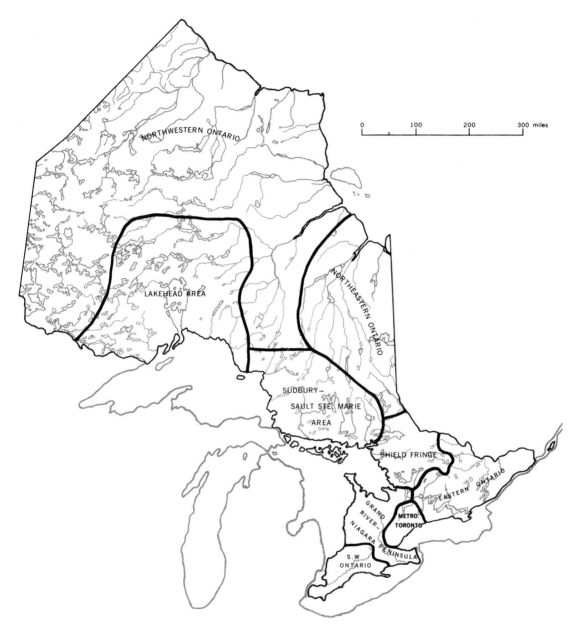

FIGURE 20-5   Regions of Ontario. Most of the population, including rural-agricultural and urban-industrial, live south of the Canadian Shield fringe. Northern Ontario has a large area but only a few major population clusters.

Ontario and New York, has assisted the lagging industrial development of eastern Ontario.

REGIONAL PATTERNS AND CHARACTERISTICS

Although Ontario occupies a central position in Canada it is its southern part that is the "heartland" of the country. Southern Ontario has most of the agriculture, indus-tries, and large cities; much of northern Ontario is relatively empty. The development of the north is related to primary resources and transportation. Southern Ontario is divided into two unequal parts by a southern extension of the Canadian

THE FEDERAL PARLIAMENT BUILDINGS in Canada's capital, Ottawa, above the steep bank of the Ottawa River. Pulp wood is being sorted into sizes for the pulp and paper mill on the opposite side of the river in Hull. (National Film Board of Canada photo by Malak.)

Shield, called the Frontenac Axis, which is crossed by the St. Lawrence River in the section known as the Thousand Islands. From about Brockville on the St. Lawrence River the subdued southern edge of the rocky Shield trends northward to about Renfrew and Pembroke on the Ottawa River (Figure 20-1). The eastern Ontario Lowland focuses on Montreal and Ottawa.

Eastern Ontario

Agriculture of the level plain of Eastern Ontario supplies milk to the urban population of Montreal and Ottawa. Although originally settled by British stock, mainly Irish, several of the counties along the lower Ottawa River now have 60 to 80 percent of their population recorded as of French Canadian origin. The rural landscape of Eastern Ontario, as illustrated by the rectangular field patterns and the styles of farmhouse architecture, is different from that of southern Quebec; but culturally and economically Eastern Ontario is part of the Montreal hinterland.

Ottawa, Canada's capital, is the largest city in the Ontario section of the Ottawa Valley. Like Washington, D.C., the Canadian capital has attracted a high proportion of professional and university-trained people. In the 1850–1870 period Ottawa was the center of the lumber industry in the Ottawa Valley, but now there are few industries in the city. Most of the population is employed by the federal government or is in commercial or service occupations providing for these civil servants. The city of Hull, across the Ottawa River in Quebec, is functionally part of the Ottawa urban region, and has some manufacturing. The beautiful driveways, parks, and gardens maintained by the federal government for the cities of Ottawa and Hull are well known to tourists.

Metropolitan Toronto

Toronto is steadily narrowing the gap between itself and Montreal in the contest to become Canada's leading city. In some financial and publishing functions it has already become the Canadian leader.[1] Although the annual values of manufacturing in metropolitan Toronto did not exceed those in Montreal in the mid-1960s, if one included the nearby industrial cities of Oshawa to the east, and the large city of Hamilton only 40 miles to the west, there is no doubt that the urban strip around the northwest side of Lake Ontario is the main industrial region of Canada.

The site of Toronto, along a natural harbor within a sandy hook, was known to the Indians as the "Toronto carrying place," the beginning of a portage route from Lake Ontario via Lake Simcoe to Georgian Bay. Toronto was chosen as the capital of Upper Canada (now Ontario) in 1793, partly because its site was thought to be a safe distance from the Americans at the Niagara River boundary. Local environmental factors, which are almost unnoticed by modern urban inhabitants, were important in the early growth of the city. The original settlement occupied a narrow sand and clay plain deposited near the shores of former glacial Lake Iroquois, which was larger than its successor, Lake Ontario. Two small rivers, the Don and the Humber, were the eastern and western boundaries to the early settlement. To the northward the sharp bluff of the former glacial lake beach line was a small topographic barrier which discouraged inland residential and street growth.

Much of Toronto's commercial and industrial growth can be attributed to its central position in southern Ontario; the city is well linked to its hinterland by a network of railways and roads. It is probable that about 30 percent of the Canadian market is within 100 miles of Toronto. The original industrial zone grew up adjoining the harbor and along the railways which paralleled the shore. Much of the cargo which arrives into Toronto's port is classified as general cargo. One of the heaviest import items is bituminous coal for the large thermal plants. There is much more inbound freight to Toronto than outbound, reminding one of the traditional importance of rail and roads in the distribution of Toronto's products.

The CBD core was established north of the railway lines and grew toward the parklike setting of the provincial parliament buildings and the university. As in other large Anglo-American cities, both industry and commerce have decentralized, and along with them residential sprawl has expanded outward, converting former farms into miles of suburban housing. Some of the new industrial zones in the outer part of the city are located on highways instead of railroads. The large suburban shopping plazas look like those anywhere in American cities and have the same broad parking lots and the same types of stores. The outward spread of suburban housing has increased the distance for commuting to the downtown financial and business core; this centrifugal movement has been partly balanced by the removal of old houses near the core and their replacement by high-rise apartments (Figure 20-6).

Toronto's early industries were mainly consumer-goods products for the local market. As transportation improved, raw materials were imported from farther away, some from the Canadian Shield. After the large iron and steel mill was established at nearby Hamilton, many steel products were manufactured in factories in Toronto. At present the metropolitan area produces virtually the complete range of manufactures found in most large Anglo-American cities, for ex-

[1]Donald Kerr, "Some Aspects of the Geography of Finance in Canada," *Canadian Geographer*, vol. 9 (1965), no. 4, pp. 175–192.

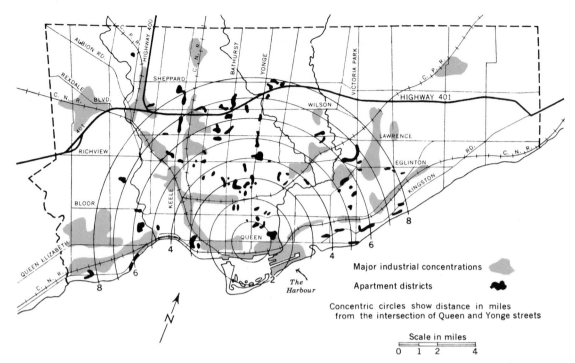

FIGURE 20-6   *Distribution of two important urban elements in metropolitan Toronto: The older industrial regions are near the harbor or along the rail lines built in the nineteenth century; new industrial regions are on the outer edges of the city and often on highways. High- and medium-rise apartments near the CBD have helped to counterbalance the outward areal spread of residential areas.* (From Kerr and Spelt, THE CHANGING FACE OF TORONTO, pp. 116, 131.)

ample, metal products, machine tools, agricultural implements, but also items such as clothing and books. Specialty production is located in some of the nearby cities, such as Oshawa (General Motors automobiles), Oakville (Ford Motor Company), and Port Credit with its oil refineries and chemical plants. But behind all the obvious industrial activity is the financial and business organization and manipulation which takes place in the high-rise office buildings. Many of the head offices of Canadian companies and American branch plants are in Toronto where other business connections and exchange are facilitated.

Will Toronto replace Montreal as Canada's leading city? The answer to this depends partly on one's definition of Toronto and on what one means by "leading." Already the concentration of urban and industrial activities around the western end of Lake Ontario—the Toronto-Hamilton region—has a greater number of people and value added by manufacturing than metropolitan Montreal. The rivalry and competition for growth between Montreal and Toronto can be compared to that between New York and Chicago—the seaport and the inland city. In Canada, however, these two major cities are only about 250 miles apart; their hinterlands overlap; whereas New York and Chicago can grow by duplicating functions as a result of their great separation. Part of the future growth of both Toronto and Chicago may be related to their use of the St. Lawrence Seaway and whether these cities become ports of world importance. Toronto's growth is also dependent upon future Canadian-American political and economic cooperation. Much of Toronto's industrial expansion was the result of inflows of American capital, and many of its markets are now in the United

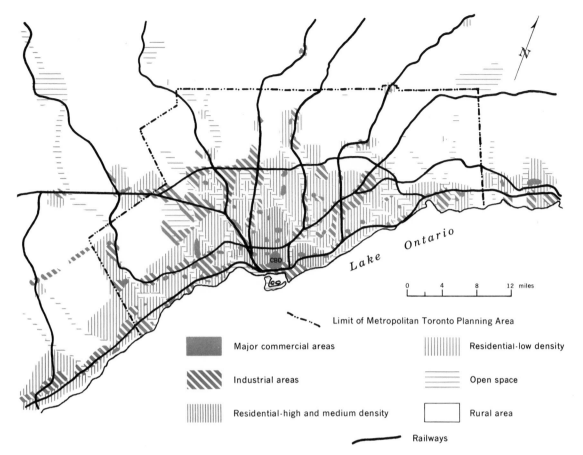

Limit of Metropolitan Toronto Planning Area

Major commercial areas

Residential-low density

Industrial areas

Open space

Residential-high and medium density

Rural area

Railways

FIGURE 20-7   Main functional zones of metropolitan Toronto: the CBD north of the railway and near the harbor was the original site of the city. Much of the suburban growth after 1945 consists of single-family homes resulting in low residential densities. Compare with Figure 20-6.

States. Toronto's commercial and financial place in the Canadian economy in competition with Montreal may also be influenced favorably by the subtleties of confidence which businessmen may feel about future "separatist" tendencies in the province of Quebec.

Grand River–Niagara Peninsula Region

This area west and southwest of Lake Ontario has urban characteristics similar to the Toronto region, except that the growing urban centers are still separated from one another by prosperous farmland. In a hierarchial arrangement of regions Hamilton could be considered either as a part of the metropolitan Toronto area or as the largest city on the edge of the Grand River–Niagara Peninsula area. Hamilton has distinctive industrial characteristics. Three-quarters of

its industrial employment is occupied in the manufacture of durable goods, particularly steel and its products, whereas less than half of Toronto's manufactures are in these durable categories. Hamilton has a more spacious harbor than Toronto, but much of the south side of the triangular harbor is already occupied by Canada's largest iron and steel plant. The areal expansion of Hamilton's urban functions was curtailed in the past by the 200- to 300-foot barrier of the Niagara Escarpment which rose sharply on the south and west sides of the city. When the engineering problems related to this topographic feature were solved, suburban housing and commercial strips spread across the plain above the older city.

The steel plant at Hamilton has neither iron ore nor coal nearby. The present company is the result of mergers of several smaller companies which operated early in the century, partly because of proximity of local limestone, but mainly because of the labor supply of Hamilton, supplies of scrap iron available, and good rail connections to nearby Ontario cities. Iron ore was imported by lake vessels all the way from company-owned mines in the Mesabi region of Lake Superior, and American coal moved across Lake Erie. In the 1950s, therefore, the apparent strange economic and political situation existed in which iron ore produced from mines in Minnesota was sent to a Canadian steel mill in Hamilton at the same time that iron ore mined at Steep Rock, in northwestern Ontario, was shipped to American steel plants on Lake Erie. In the

1960s the Hamilton steel plant has been obtaining more and more of its iron ore from the Labrador City–Wabush ore fields.

The narrow lowland strip extending east of Hamilton to the Niagara River and north of the steep Niagara Escarpment is one of the most intensive horticulture regions in Canada. These soils, laid down in the larger glacial lakes, produce most of Canada's grapes, and much of its peaches, pears, cherries, and plums. Much of the production of the small farms goes to the fresh fruit markets in Ontario during the summer, but processing such as in wineries and canneries is also important to the small towns. As the urban buildings of the "Golden Horseshoe" spread east of Hamilton, the conflicts in land use become more acute between urban uses and the valuable agricultural lands, particularly the "peach soils."

Niagara Falls lies at the eastern end of this urban and industrial development of the Niagara Peninsula, but the industrial zone actually extends farther eastward across the international boundary to Buffalo and Rochester. Niagara Falls, still a famous tourist attraction, has become a major industrial city. North of the city near the base of the Niagara Escarpment, Ontario's largest hydroelectric power plant can generate more than 2 million horsepower for the industries of south central Ontario. Several chemical and metallurgical plants were originally built near the falls because of the available electric power. When it became apparent that the hydroelectric power of the Niagara region could not supply the needs of southern Ontario manufacturing and cities, the Ontario government turned to thermal plants based on imported fuel, and began to harness the waterpower of the Shield rivers to the north.

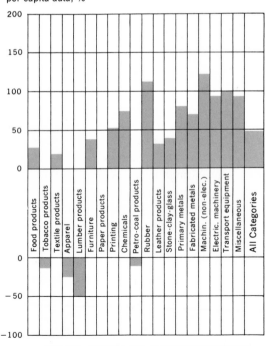

VALUE ADDED BY MANUFACTURING
Ontario = 34.2% Canadian Pop.

FIGURE 20-8   Compare this graph with that for Quebec. Account for the negative deviations in Canada's leading industrial province.

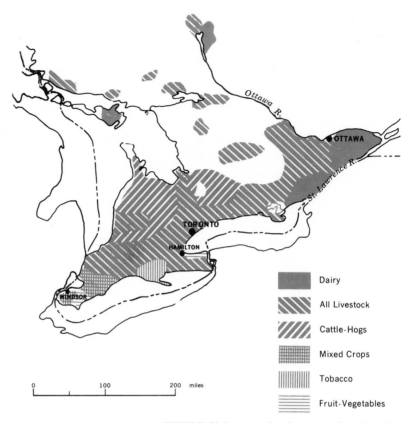

Dairy

All Livestock

Cattle-Hogs

Mixed Crops

Tobacco

Fruit-Vegetables

0   100   200   miles

FIGURE 20-9 Agricultural regions of southern Ontario. Most of the area produces pasture and feed crops for livestock. In some areas the chief source of agricultural income is from dairy products; dairying is also important in the livestock areas, but the farmers have other sources of agricultural income from the sale of a variety of livestock products. The fruit and vegetable areas and tobacco belt north of Lake Erie are specialty regions.

West of Hamilton a line of merging industrial cities occupies the Grand River Valley. Cities such as Brantford, Paris, Galt, Guelph, and Kitchener–Waterloo have many similarities in their industrial production although there is some local specialization related to particular companies. This industrial belt produces a wide range of metal products, textiles, clothing, rubber and leather goods. Although the urban areas are still separate political entities, they are connected by good highways, along which extend ribbon commercial developments. In turn, the Grand River cities are closely linked with the Hamilton–Toronto industrial zone. As the industrial and urban growth of these two regions merges together, a "Canadian Megalopolis" will have been created west of Lake Ontario. Forecasters expect that 5 million urban people will occupy the Lake Ontario–Grand River region by the mid-1970s. Having

noted the current problems of urban congestion in New York, Chicago, or Los Angeles, Canadians in this urban complex have an opportunity to plan so as to avoid the past mistakes made during the growth of large American cities.

Southwestern Ontario

Another line of large urban centers extends west of Hamilton and Brantford through London, Chatham, and Windsor. This "Ontario Corridor" is the main line of movement between Sarnia and Windsor on the west, and Toronto, Hamilton, and Niagara Falls on the east. It is an inland corridor, along which the industries of the cities were originally linked by railways and now are also served by trucks. The landscape of the southwestern peninsula differs from that around the western end of Lake Ontario mainly in the larger areas of farmland between the cities. The prosperous farm-houses, large cattle barns, and lush green summer pastures indicate that this is a major dairy region. A great deal of corn is grown on these farms, and some farmers in the southwest specialize in soybean produc-tion and early-maturing vegetables. An American visitor sees little in the rural landscape that he would not see in western Ohio or central Illinois.

Most of the manufactures of the south-western cities are similar to those of the Niagara–Grand River region. London, with a central position amid the most productive agricultural counties in Canada, has large food-processing industries as well as metal goods, textiles, and electrical goods. Chat-ham produces canned fruits and vegetables, and agricultural machinery. Sarnia has a large concentration of oil refineries and an allied petrochemical industry along its waterfront, south of its commercial core; the refineries are supplied by oil from the Prai-rie Provinces.

Windsor is Canada's most southerly large city and lies *south* of Detroit with which it is functionally closely connected. These two cities are an excellent example of economic and social interaction between urban units which are separated by an international boundary. In the 1930s Windsor assembled nearly all the Ford and Chrysler cars sold in Canada and called itself the "automobile capital of the British Commonwealth." Other American companies such as those producing pharmaceutical and chemicals located branch plants across the border in Windsor. Many Windsor residents carry border-crossing permits and work in De-troit; many Detroit businessmen are closer

to their offices in downtown Detroit if they live in suburban Windsor instead of in the urban fringes of Detroit. Many summer cottages along the Canadian shore of Lake St. Clair and the northwestern side of Lake Erie are owned by Americans; these week-end residents form long, bumper-to-bumper lines of cars through Windsor on Sunday nights as they inch toward the bottleneck crossings by a bridge and a tunnel, guarded by the "nuisance" of customs and immigra-tion inspection.

Northern Ontario

The Canadian Shield regions of northern Ontario contrast with the rolling lowlands of southern Ontario in forest and lake cover, landforms, agricultural land use, population density, and natural resources development. The line of demarcation is fairly obvious in the landscape; the contrasts in land use and forest cover can be seen easily by trav-elers flying north from Toronto (Figure 20-2). The functional links between the resources of the Ontario Shield and the urban centers on the lowland are similar to those in Quebec (Chapter 19).

The Shield fringe   East of Georgian Bay the southern fringes of the Shield had their first boom in 1880–1900 when lumbermen hacked into the forests and shipped the logs or lumber across the Great Lakes to help build the cities of the American Midwest. Farmers had moved into pockets of level land on the Shield edge before this time, but found that the soils were thin and rocky—a poor reward for many years of slowly clearing the forest to establish a farm. Farm abandonment was therefore charac-teristic of this region by the turn of the century. The forested area between Geor-gian Bay and the upper Ottawa River was a little-used part of Ontario until the mod-ern development of the tourist, camping, and recreation industry. The lakes and cool forests became havens for the crowded

THE CONTRASTING CBDs of Windsor, Ontario, in the foreground and Detroit, Michigan, northward across the Detroit River. In many ways these cities operate as a functional, international unit. The number and height of the commercial buildings of the downtown cores are proportionate to the contrasting sizes of the cities. (Photo by Lockwood Survey Corporation Limited, Canada.)

residents of the hot cities. Summer cottages became "a way of life" for many people in Toronto, and their numbers increased as roads improved. A variety of short-term accommodation extends across the southern Shield from the famous Muskoka Lakes near Georgian Bay, through Algonquin Provincial Park north of Peterborough, to the upper Ottawa Valley. This region is the recreational hinterland of Toronto, in the same way that the Laurentian Hills serve Montreal and the Catskill Mountains are used by New Yorkers.

North of the Lake Nipissing Trough—a historical, and modern, route between the upper Ottawa Valley and upper Great Lakes—the economy of northern Ontario is different. Most of the land is unoccupied; it is a region of forests, rocks, lakes, and rivers. People are mainly urban dwellers, living in towns and cities which are concerned with the extraction, processing, or transportation of the natural resources of

the Shield. The cities are scattered along the north shores of Georgian Bay and Lake Superior, along the three transcontinental railways which cross the Ontario Shield, and have a minor concentration in northeastern Ontario.

Northeastern Ontario and the Clay Belt This region has higher densities of occupation and a wider range of integrated resource use than other parts of northern Ontario. Agricultural settlers had penetrated into the Lake Timiskaming area of the upper Ottawa Valley by the 1880s, following the loggers and lumbermen. The catalyst, however, was the discovery of some of the world's richest silver mines at Cobalt in 1903–1905. From this mining town prospectors fanned outward over the Precambrian hills, and before 1914 Canada's largest gold mines had been discovered at Timmins–Porcupine and Kirkland Lake–Larder Lake. Railways were built to bring in sup-

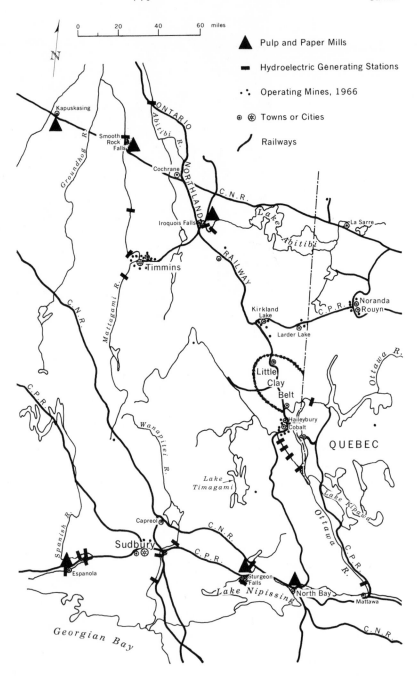

FIGURE 20-10 *Northeastern Ontario. An integrated, extractive economy is tied together by roads and railways. Pulp and paper mills are located in the spruce forests of the Great Clay Belt on northward-flowing rivers and in the mixed forests on rivers dropping southward out of the Shield to Georgian Bay. Mines, both large and small, cluster around Timmins, Kirkland Lake, Cobalt, and Sudbury. Hydroelectric plants are dispersed throughout the region. Much of the Little Clay Belt has been cleared for agriculture.*

plies; they made it possible later to harvest the forest and ship out pulp and newsprint by rail. The mines required electric power, and nearby Shield rivers were dammed for that purpose. The miners needed food, and therefore agricultural settlement expanded across the old glacial lake plain of the "Little Clay Belt" on the north side of Lake

Timiskaming. Roads were built to connect the growing towns. By 1940 this region had become a functional economic unit on the northern frontier of Ontario.

After World War I, in both Ontario and adjoining Quebec, agricultural settlers cleared small pockets of land along the northern Canadian National Railway across the northern Clay Belt. Large numbers occupied farms in the Clay Belt during the depression years of the 1930s when the provincial governments attempted to take people off the relief rolls in the cities and put them "back on the land." The misnaming of the region insofar as soils were concerned became apparent; many of the soils were sandy rather than clay, and they contained a great deal of peat. After 1950 agriculture declined rapidly in the Ontario Clay Belt. Marginal and subsistence farms were abandoned as farmers and their sons moved to better-paying jobs in Canadian cities. This abandonment and decline are not so characteristic in the Quebec section of the Clay Belt where low-income rural life around the parish church is accepted as a traditional way of life.

In Ontario the "north" is a resource frontier of urban peoples; it is no longer an agricultural frontier of rural settlers. Although the Clay Belt region as a whole has a variety of resource developments, most of the towns and cities are dependent on one particular product. Kapuskasing and Iroquois Falls, for example, are one-industry towns, dependent entirely on their pulp and paper mills. Timmins is the commercial and supply center for nearby gold, copper, and base metals mines; several of the gold mines at Kirkland Lake have closed, but iron ore pellets are now being produced nearby.

Northern Ontario has produced more than half of Canada's gold for much of the present century, but with the price of gold fixed at prewar levels, and production costs increasing steadily, many gold mines have been forced to close. Most of the gold mines still in operation are aided by federal government subsidies to prevent these one-industry towns from being abandoned. One has to know something of Canadian government policies and assistance arrangements to understand resource development and settlement in Canada's subarctic.

Sudbury-Sault Ste. Marie area When the Canadian Pacific transcontinental railway was being constructed west of North Bay in the 1880s, large deposits of copper-nickel ore were discovered by chance in a cut into the Precambrian rocks. By the turn of the century the city of Sudbury had arisen out of the rock and forest, its smelter processing the ores of several mines in the nearby elliptical geological basin; its growing commercial core was the largest between North Bay and Sault Ste. Marie. The ores were exported to the United States until World War I when a nickel refinery was built at Port Colborne near the electric power of Niagara Falls. The Sudbury mines became the world's largest source of nickel and platinum, and one of Canada's major copper producers. Sudbury has more than 25,000 industrial workers, the largest concentration in the Canadian Shield; its metropolitan population of 100,000 persons is equal to that of the twin cities of Port Arthur–Fort William. The modern stores of its CBD have little similarity to the rough commercial establishments of the last century.

West of Sudbury large deposits of uranium were discovered in the early 1950s. Because of the world shortage at that time the federal and provincial governments and private companies cooperated to build the planned city of Elliot Lake. With its gaily painted cottages, curving streets, and modern shopping centers, the city showed that life in a mining town need not be hard and rough. The mines nearby became one of the world's major sources of uranium. But the "boom and bust" of mining history

ELLIOT LAKE IN NORTHERN ONTARIO is typical of most of the new towns arising on Canada's northern "resources frontier." Its curving streets and neat houses are served by modern shopping centers. The city is surrounded by heavy coniferous forest. (Photo by Ontario Department of Mines.)

in Anglo-America was almost repeated here—in a much more beautiful setting. Within a decade the United States found its own sources of uranium, and the Elliot Lake producers lost much of this market. Only a few mines remained open in the mid-1960s, with curtailed production, and almost half the comfortable homes in the city were empty.

Farther west on the route to Lake Superior is the old city of Sault Ste. Marie; its site on the St. Mary River was occupied by a fur-trading post in the late eighteenth century. Three basic activities dominate the modern industrial life of the city. "The Soo" has many persons engaged in transportation activities—water traffic, railways, and the Trans-Canada Highway. The rapids in the St. Mary River long prevented water traffic on Lake Superior to the same extent as on the lower lakes. In the present century the locks and short canal around the rapids were gradually improved and deepened, culminating in the large McArthur Locks built during World War II. These were prepared to handle ocean vessels with 30 feet draft, but their full use had to wait until the St. Lawrence Seaway opened the bottle-neck in the lower lakes. The Trans-Canada Highway, the first paved road north of Lake Superior (1962), opened up new territory for tourists, and Sault Ste. Marie became the main center for tourist accommodation and outfitting for the Lake Superior area.

Industrial expansion began with one of the first pulp and paper mills within the Canadian Shield being built at the Soo at the end of the nineteenth century. Forest concessions from the Ontario government, careful woods management, and export to United States markets allowed the mill to prosper for more than 70 years. The major industry of the Soo is one of Canada's three major iron and steel mills. Iron ore is brought by rail from Wawa (Michipicoten) to the north, coal is imported by water from the United States, limestone comes from Lake Huron shores. Local hydroelectric power is available. Raw-material inputs were easily assembled at this site. The steel mill, better located than that at Hamilton with respect to raw materials, is handicap-ped by distance from the main Canadian market in southern Ontario.

The Lakehead area The chief settlements along the north shore of Lake Superior are small, modern pulp and paper towns at Marathon, Terrace Bay, and Nipigon. To the northward, Manitouwadge, for example, is a copper-mining town, and Hearst, on the northern branch of the Canadian National Railway, is a lumbering town. These small settlements emphasize the emptiness of the rest of the land north of Lake Superior. The only land transport line into the swampy, lake-covered Hudson and James Bay Low-land is a little-used railway in northeastern Ontario extending through Cochrane in the Clay Belt to the shallow harbor of Moosonee on James Bay. Large areas of

northwestern Ontario, north of the gold-mining town of Red Lake, are completely without people.

The Lakehead cities of Port Arthur–Fort William are the only truly urban concen-tration in northwestern Ontario. The large grain-storage elevators there are used in the transshipping of Prairie Province wheat and other grains from rail to water transport. A long ore-unloading pier permits Steep Rock iron ore to be loaded directly into lake freighters. The cities also have an industrial base; pulp and paper mills have manufac-tured newsprint for the United States mar-ket since the 1920s; a bus assembly plant produces city transport for western Canada. The cities also have well-developed com-mercial establishments since the area is the only service center of large size between Sudbury and Winnipeg, a distance of about 800 miles.

THE GREAT LAKES: HEARTLAND HIGHWAY OR INTERNATIONAL CESSPOOL?

The densely populated parts of Ontario as well as of Wisconsin, Illinois, Michigan, Ohio, and western New York are dependent on the Great Lakes for power, water supply, and transport. Less significant are the fish and recreational facilities. Increasing doubts have arisen within recent decades as to whether these resources are permanent. This is no trivial matter since within the Great Lakes drainage basin live one-seventh of the American population and one-third of the Canadian population; economically the cities in this basin are among the fastest-growing centers in Anglo-America. The Great Lakes are aging, both as the result of natural cause and human acts; the latter has greatly speeded up the natural aging of the lakes.[2]

[2] Charles F. Powers and Andrew Robertson, "The Aging Great Lakes," *Scientific American*, vol. 215 (1966), pp. 94–104; also Howard J. Pincus (ed.), *Great Lakes Basin*, American Association for the Advancement of Science, publication 71, Washington, 1962, especially pp. 269–300.

The pollution problem is not a forecast for 2000; it has already arrived in Lake Erie and southern Lake Michigan, and to a lesser degree, in western Lake Ontario. In these lakes the fishing industry has been almost destroyed; the use of bathing beaches stopped or restricted; and public water supply is often ill flavored, and safe only after chemical treatments. Sewage, chemicals, and muds are converting the waters into a poisonous soup, deposits from which will eventually choke the shallower sections of the lakes. In addition to germs and viruses, the lake waters contain high concentrations of inorganic nitrogen, ammonia, phosphates, and phenols. Harbors and the lower parts of tributary streams also have high contamination which affects the air of nearby shores.

Anthropologists report that Indian tribes, after occupying a village site for some years, left the environs so polluted by excreta that they moved elsewhere. With all our DDT, deodorants, and disinfectants, have modern Anglo-Americans done much better? The Great Lakes are a "Central Place" in Anglo-America with major concentrations of people, industry, and trade. Within the region are brought together most closely the businesses of the United States and Canada, as well as their wastes. Shall these Anglo-American neighbors keep this basin as a rich economic focus—the water highway through the heartland—or will it degenerate into an international cesspool?

CONCLUSION

Central location, one-third of Canada's population, and diverse natural resources have made Ontario the heartland of Canada. Its primary occupations based on natural resources directly give only modest employment: Forestry has about 20,000 employees, mining about 60,000; trapping, overshadowed by fur farming, provides part-time employment for only a scattered few in northern Ontario; hydroelectric plants employ few people once they are constructed. More important, these raw materials provide manufacturing employment in southern Ontario for a wide range of industries. Half the value of Canadian manufacturing is produced in Ontario, and these urban plants provide three-fourths of Canadian manufactured exports. In contrast, agricultural production, which makes southern Ontario the most valuable agricultural region of Canada, is mainly for the provincial market.

Ontario manufacturing is less diverse and smaller scale than in the United States, an obvious consequence of its smaller market. Yet Ontario industry is maturing, and with the population expected to increase rapidly, the local market will also grow. If more reciprocal trade arrangements are made with the United States, it will remain to be seen which Canadian industries will expand and prosper by serving the larger United States market, and which will wither and die if the protective tariff wall is lowered.

The main areas of settlement are well established. From Ottawa and Montreal to Toronto-Hamilton and on to Windsor-Sarnia is the Canadian Commercial-Manufacturing Core, beyond which intensive contiguous settlement seems unlikely in coming decades. No doubt new mineral discoveries, the northward expansion of the pulp industry, and increasing tourist and recreation use will add some thousands of people to northern Ontario, but most population growth will be within 100 miles of the Great Lakes and St. Lawrence Seaway.

SELECTED REFERENCES

DEAN, WILLIAM (ed.): *Atlas of Ontario*, Ontario Government, University of Toronto Press, Toronto, 1968.

KERR, DONALD, and JACOB SPELT: *The Changing Face of Toronto*, Geographical Branch, Department of Mines and Technical Surveys, memoir 11, The Queen's Printer, Ottawa, 1965.

KRUEGER, RALPH R. (ed.): *Regional and Resource Planning in Canada,* Holt of Canada, Toronto, 1963. Although this collection of papers deals with all of Canada, many of its articles refer specifically to Ontario.

LOWER, A. R. M., and H. A. INNIS: *Settlement and the Forest and Mining Frontier in Eastern Canada,* Macmillan, Toronto, 1936.

ONTARIO DEPARTMENT OF ECONOMICS AND DEVELOPMENT: *Ontario Economic Surveys,* Toronto. Statistical and Economic Surveys have been prepared for many of the economic regions into which the province has been divided. Each booklet is 100 to 200 pp., with numerous maps and tables.

ONTARIO DEPARTMENT OF ENERGY AND RESOURCES MANAGEMENT: A series of *Conservation Reports,* Toronto, 100 to 150 pp. each, have been published for most of the river-valley regions of southern Ontario. These reports deal with general land use, recreation, and forestry for each of the river valley authorities into which southern Ontario is divided for purposes of local government recommendations.

Ontario Geography, periodical published by Department of Geography, University of Western Ontario, London, Ont. Volume 1 started in 1967.

RAY, D. MICHAEL: *Market Potential and Economic Shadow: A Quantitative Analysis of Industrial Location in Southern Ontario,* University of Chicago Department of Geography Research Paper 101, Chicago, 1965.

REEDS, LLOYD C.: "Agricultural Regions of Southern Ontario: 1880 and 1951," *Economic Geography,* vol. 35 (1959), pp. 219–227.

WARKENTIN, JOHN (ed.): *Canada: A Geographical Appreciation,* Methuen, Toronto, 1968. Chapter 11 deals with the urban growth of southern Ontario, and Chap. 16 discusses the metropolitan centers of Canada.

For current information consult the annual reports of the various provincial government departments, such as Department of Lands and Forests, Department of Agriculture, or the *Bibliography for Regional Development,* published by Ontario Department of Economics and Development, 1965.

CHAPTER 21

THE CANADIAN WEST

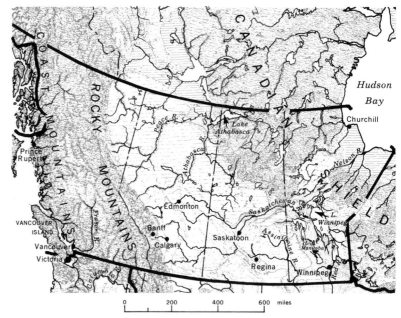

FIGURE 21-1 Landforms of the Canadian West. Compare with Figure 21-2. The Interior Plains narrow to the northward between the Canadian Shield and Cordillera. (Base map copyright by A. K. Lobeck. Reprinted with permission of The Geographical Press, Hammond, Inc.)

REGIONAL COMPARISONS

In terms of the physical environment, the American West is similar to the Canadian West in several ways (Figure 21-1). The political changes at the 49th parallel are minor: a different flag, a similar but different currency, a customs and immigration barrier. These are noticeable to the tourist who has the pleasure of being in a foreign land without any cultural discomfort. There are few differences in the landscape north or south of the border: The grassy plains with their dark soils continue northward, as do the forested mountains of the western Cordillera; the rectangular survey system, the railroads financed by land grants, the food in the restaurants, and the goods in the stores seem similar to those in the United States.

Closer examination shows several significant differences in the Canadian West:

1 *More northward:* The Canadian Plains are exposed more frequently to cold air masses from the north. Coolness makes the modest precipitation more effective, and as a result the forest has been able to establish itself across the northern and central Prairie Provinces. Northern latitude brings long summer days which, if combined with warm air masses, provide suitable growing conditions for grain.

2 *Less mountainous:* The mountain ranges of the Canadian Cordillera

BASIC DATA:

AREA INCLUDES	Land Area (thousand sq. mi.)	Population Change, 1951–1961	1961 (thousands)	1966	Personal Income 1967 (billion Canadian dollars)
CANADIAN WEST	1,040.0	29.5%	4,808	5,256	$12.2
Manitoba	211.8	18.7	922	963	2.2
Saskatchewan	220.2	11.2	925	956	2.3
Alberta	248.8	41.8	1,332	1,463	3.4
British Columbia	359.3	39.8	1,629	1,874	4.6
MAJOR METROPOLITAN AREAS					
Vancouver		50.7%	790	892	$2.0
Winnipeg		33.4	476	509	1.1
Edmonton		91.0	337	401	1.1
Calgary		96.1	279	330	1.0

CLIMATE   *Wide range, from a mild marine climate on the Pacific Coast to semi-arid continental climates in the southern Prairie Provinces and interior British Columbia. Great local variations in the mountains and valleys as a result of altitude and exposure.*

	Temperature (°F)		Precipitation (inches)	
	Jan.	July	Total Rain and Snow	Snow
Winnipeg, Man.	1	68	20	50
Saskatoon, Sask.	1	66	14	36
Medicine Hat, Alta.	14	70	14	42
Fort Nelson, B.C.	−7	62	16	67
Kamloops, B.C.	22	70	10	30
Vancouver, B.C.	38	64	57	25

VEGETATION   Western spruce, Douglas fir, hemlock, lodgepole pine on Pacific Coast and interior mountains; in Prairie Provinces shortgrass in southwest grading into medium grass and open deciduous forest; mixed forest and conifers to the north: spruce, fir, larch.

SOILS   Across the southern Prairie Provinces, lime-rich soils varying from brown soils to fertile chernozems; a wide variety of soils in mountainous British Columbia, but only certain valley soils have been mapped. Podzolic soils, often thin, across northern part of the area.

MINERALS   Petroleum, natural gas, sulfur, coal, potash in the plains region of the Prairie Provinces and northeastern British Columbia; in British Columbia and in the Canadian Shield part of the Prairie Provinces: lead, zinc, silver, gold, copper, iron ore, and molybdenum.

are higher on the average than the American ranges, but they are not as wide. The broad intermontane plateaus and elevated basins of the American western mountains are lacking or are relatively

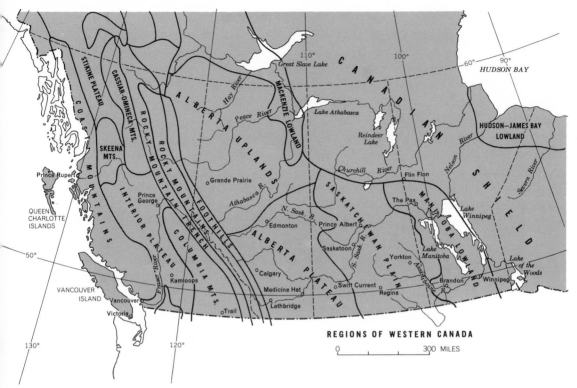

REGIONS OF WESTERN CANADA

0 _____|_____ 300 MILES

*FIGURE 21-2   Landform regions of western Canada.
Compare the widths of the Canadian regions with those
of the equivalent regions 100 miles south of the border.*
(Otis W. Freeman and John W. Morris, WORLD GEOGRAPHY,
McGraw-Hill, New York, 1965, p. 156.)

narrow in Canada. The mountain system
is about 400 miles wide across British
Columbia, in comparison with the 1,000
miles from Denver to the Pacific (Figure 21-2).

3 *More isolated:* The Canadian West is
farther from the Commercial-Industrial
Core of eastern Canada and the United
States than the American West and is
separated from it by 700 to 1,000 miles
of forested, rocky, and little-settled
Canadian Shield.

4 *Part of a less populated country:* Because
Canada has a population only one-tenth
that of the United States there is a smaller
local market for its staple products. Although Canadian wheat production, for
example, is about two-thirds that of the
United States, Canada consumes only
about one-quarter of its annual production, and the rest must be disposed of in
the world market. Similarly, although the
lumber cut in British Columbia is about

half as much as in Washington and Oregon, most of the British Columbia cut is
exported, whereas American production
stays within the country.

5 *Later economic development:* The Canadian West was occupied 20 or more years
later than the corresponding American
areas. The first transcontinental railway,
for example, crossed the Canadian Plains
17 years after the first rail line penetrated
across the American Cordillera. North
Dakota had its more rapid population
growth in the 1880s, whereas the waves
of agricultural settlement moved across
Manitoba and Saskatchewan in the early
1900s.

6 *Ethnic group settlement:* Early in the
twentieth century central Europeans and
French Canadians moved into the Cana-

dian West and settled in rather homogeneous ethnic groups. These cultural patterns are still present.

Settlement

The Canadian West was explored largely in the late eighteenth century by fur traders of the Hudson's Bay Company or the North West Company. Chains of forts (trading posts), portages, and canoe routes were established to connect either the Great Lakes or Hudson Bay with the Pacific and valleys in northwestern Canada (Figure 4-7). The fur traders maintained friendly relations with Indian tribes and established a two-way flow of furs and trade goods across the continent. The rivalry between the two companies ended when the Hudson's Bay Company absorbed the North West Company in 1821, nearly a half century before agricultural settlers began to arrive in significant numbers.

The Pacific coast was explored by Spanish and British ship captains in the late eighteenth century. In 1843 the Hudson's Bay Company moved its Pacific headquarters north from the Columbia River in Oregon Territory to Victoria on Vancouver Island in expectation of a northward extension of the United States boundary. The gold rush of 1858 to the Fraser River attracted many miners, particularly from California, and as a result the colonies of Vancouver Island and British Columbia were created to maintain British sovereignty. In 1870 the new Dominion of Canada purchased the enormous "trapping grounds" of the historic Hudson's Bay Company; they became the Northwest Territories, except for British Columbia and a tiny province of Manitoba created in that same year along the Red River Valley.

The western prairies were then opened to agricultural settlement. A survey system, almost the same as that of the township-range system of the United States, was established with two sections for the Hud-

son's Bay Company, and all odd-numbered sections for railway grants. Lands were also reserved for half-breeds (Métis) and for Indian reservations. Settlers poured into the empty plains after the Canadian Pacific Railway carved a route across the forests, rocks, and lakes of the Canadian Shield. The railway reached Winnipeg in 1881, and after a difficult route was built through little-known passes in the Cordillera, a western terminal was selected at Vancouver in 1887. Grain farming on the plains was further stimulated by the introduction of new varieties of spring wheat with a shorter growing period. Crops were difficult to market, however, because freight rates were high. In 1897 the Canadian government subsidized a second Canadian Pacific railway across the southern Rockies through Crow's Nest Pass in exchange for lower freight rates on all wheat and flour moving to the Lakehead cities on Lake Superior.

The first quarter of the twentieth century was the period of most rapid settlement. A third transcontinental rail line was built across the northern Prairies with its western terminal at Prince Rupert, close to Panhandle Alaska; it became part of the Canadian National Railways later. Branch railways formed a growing network across the southern plains; trains brought in immigrant settlers and took out their crops of wheat and other grains. Small service towns arose at railway junctions. Winnipeg grew as "the gateway to the West" and the main supply and distribution center. As more land was occupied, the new provinces of Saskatchewan and Alberta were created in 1905.

Penetration into the forested parts of the plains increased after 1920, but settlement was much slower compared with the rapid settling of the grassland plains. By 1940 the northern frontier of grain and livestock farming was fairly well established (Figure 21-3). This line extended northwest from the Interlake area of southern Manitoba, pass-

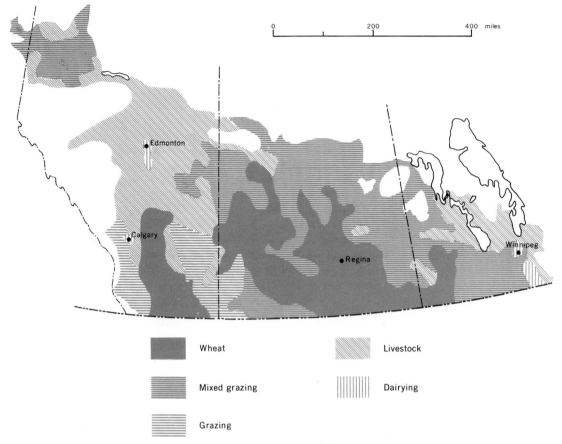

Wheat

Mixed grazing

Grazing

Livestock

Dairying

FIGURE 21-3 Agricultural regions, southern Prairie Provinces. Agricultural patterns have diversified in the past two decades. Most of the former grasslands now produce wheat and other grains and raise livestock, but the combinations of these crops and rural activities vary from region to region. The areas shown as "mixed grazing" grow mixed grains, including wheat, and place about equal emphasis on livestock. The small, but valuable, areas of irrigated crops in southern Alberta are not shown on the map. (Adapted by J. L. Robinson from the map of AGRICULTURAL REGIONS OF CANADA, Ottawa, 1961.)

ing just north of Prince Albert, Saskatchewan, and Edmonton, Alberta, to the Peace River area of northeastern British Columbia. After 1950 declining farm population and the consolidation of farm acreages into large, mechanized farm units became characteristic of the northern agricultural frontier, similar to changes in the rural economy in the American Midwest. The postwar discovery of new reserves of petroleum and natural gas, and later of potash, brought a Texas-type boom to the Prairie Provinces and diversified their economy.

Meanwhile in British Columbia settlers converged into urban centers in the southwestern corner of the province, in contrast to the rural settlement of the Interior Plains. Around Vancouver and along the shores of Georgia Strait, loggers cut slowly into the

coastal forest, and sawmills converted the large conifers into lumber for export. The period of great forestry expansion came after World War I when the Panama Canal permitted British Columbia lumber to be exported by ship to Europe and eastern United States. As transportation and logging technology improved, lumbering extended northward along the Coast, but the processing remained in the southwestern cities where there was reliable transport to foreign markets.

Before 1940 settlement remained sparse in interior British Columbia, and the northern half of the province was virtually unoccupied. A mining boom of 1890–1910 brought transport lines to mines and smelters in the Kootenay region of southeastern British Columbia; the expansion of irrigation in the Okanagan Valley in the 1920s resulted in the only strip of contiguous agricultural settlement in the southern interior. British Columbia was not an agricultural province. Its urban centers were concerned with forestry, fisheries, or mines, and the commercial control of these raw materials and their transport to foreign markets centered in Vancouver.

Income and Employment

The Western provinces have some individual characteristics in their economic development, yet in each the common emphasis is on industries using local raw materials (Figures 1-10 and 1-11). In the Prairie Provinces 25 percent of the labor force is engaged in agriculture, whereas in British Columbia only 4 percent is so employed. Service occupations are numerous in both subregions, accounting for 51 percent of the workers in the Prairie Provinces and 60 percent in British Columbia. Manufacturing employs a considerable proportion of non-service workers; in each of the Prairie Provinces the food and beverage industries employ the largest number of people, but in British Columbia wood industries are far ahead in employment. Mining occupations increased in Alberta after World War II as a result of its petroleum industry, and are becoming of greater importance in Saskatchewan and British Columbia.

THE PRAIRIE PROVINCES

Physical Regions

The landform regions of the Prairie Provinces consist of a number of south-northwest

trending bands, which are related to the underlying rock (Figures 21-1 and 21-2). Above the geological-landform regions the vegetation zones have a generally concentric pattern of semicircles. The driest area, and one with shortgrass vegetation, is along the United States border in southeastern Alberta and southwestern Saskatchewan. Around this area annual precipitation increases to the west, north, and east; as a result vegetation changes from shortgrass to tall prairie grass and merges into a "parkland" of deciduous trees and grass. Forest cover dominates on the foothills west of Calgary and on the plains west of Edmonton; the coniferous forest stretches for unbroken miles north of the North Saskatchewan River and across the Interlake area of southern Manitoba (Figure 19-2).

The provincial boundaries cut northward across the landform and vegetation regions.[1] Although Manitoba is considered as one of the "Prairie" provinces, most of its area is covered with forest rather than grass, and the rugged Candian Shield is the dominant landform in all except the southwest. Plains and grassland extend across southern Saskatchewan, but the central part of that province is a forested plain and the northern third is underlain by the old crystalline rocks of the Canadian Shield. Alberta is almost entirely a "plains" province, but its northern half is forested, and its southwestern boundary is along the high and majestic Rocky Mountains. Although the natural regions have influenced agricultural land-use patterns, the boundaries of the provincial regions are important in other resource development. In Canada the responsibility for resource development rests with the provinces rather than the federal government, but this power was not transferred to the Prairie Provinces until 1930.

---

[1] The boundary between Manitoba and Saskatchewan is not as straight as it appears on a small-scale map, having been adjusted to the township-range system with its correction lines every four rows of townships.

Rural and Urban Character

Large rectangular fields of wheat, other grains, pasture, and fallow make checkerboard patterns across the plains of the southern Prairie Provinces. Roads and railroads follow straight lines for many miles. The small towns are strung along the rail lines because one of their original commercial functions was to store the grain of the surrounding rural area until the railway carried it away. As road transport improved, grain could be carried farther to central places; many of the small villages no longer have this grain-collection function, and many branch railways are no longer economical. Although farm population is declining across the southern Prairie Provinces, the total population is increasing and cities are growing.

There is a hierarchy of cities, related to size and functions, on the Canadian Plains. The three largest cities have grown mainly because of their position rather than any particular advantages of their local sites. Winnipeg is central to all of Canada; nearly all east-west transport lines funnel through Winnipeg and the narrow zone between Lake Winnipeg and the international border. Edmonton is "the gateway to the North," serving the vast areas of the Mackenzie Valley and southern Yukon. Calgary is "the gateway to the Rockies," and is the primate city for people living nearby in a variety of environments ranging from grassland plains to scenic forested mountains. Somewhat smaller cities are Saskatoon, halfway between Winnipeg and Edmonton; and Regina, halfway between Winnipeg and Calgary. Other cities, not quite so large, service smaller local hinterlands between the above noted large cities. For example, Brandon lies between Winnipeg and Regina; Medicine Hat between Regina and Calgary; Red Deer is too close to both Calgary and Edmonton to have many urban functions of its own; Lloydminster and North Battleford vie for urban importance as the chief central place between Saskatoon and Edmonton.

The Canadian Shield

The northeastern part of the Prairie Provinces has a different landscape from that of the southern plains. Similar to the Shield sections of Ontario and Quebec, the western Shield has coniferous forests, irregular-shaped lakes, and rushing rivers. Across north central Manitoba, however, the low, knobby rock hills characteristic of the eastern Shield are not so dominant because of the mantle of lake and marine deposition of the Glacial Age. Despite these areas of relatively level land on the Manitoba Shield, there has been virtually no settlement because land in the plains to the south was more attractive to agricultural settlers.

Most settlements in the Shield of northern Manitoba and Saskatchewan depend on mines (Figure 21-4). Before 1940 the only major mines produced copper-zinc-gold near Flin Flon, on the southern boundary of the Shield geological region. A branch line from the Hudson Bay Railroad reached Flin Flon in 1930, permitting the smelted ore to be transported to Eastern markets. The post–World War II mining boom which opened up the eastern Canadian Shield also penetrated into the western Shield. Uranium deposits were brought into production on the north shore of Lake Athabasca in the late 1940s, and a new town of Uranium City was created to provide residences and commercial establishments for the nearby mines. Several of these mines closed when uranium deposits were discovered later at Elliot Lake, Ontario, closer to the United States market. Nickel was uncovered at Lynn Lake in the early 1950s and at Thompson in the 1960s, increasing Canada's world importance in the production of this metal. Similar to the areal patterns of mining in the eastern Shield at Schefferville and Chibougamau, for example, rail extensions were pushed north to Lynn Lake and

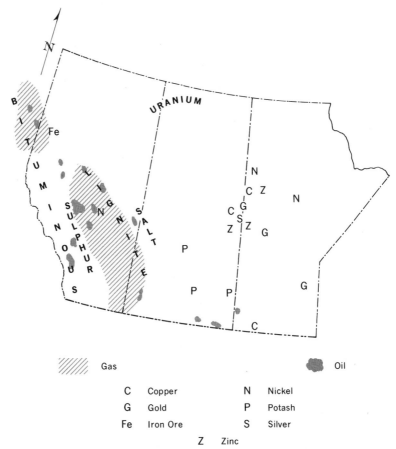

Gas

Oil

C	Copper	N	Nickel
G	Gold	P	Potash
Fe	Iron Ore	S	Silver
		Z	Zinc

FIGURE 21-4 Mineral resources, Prairie Provinces. Most of the metallic minerals are found in the old crystalline rocks of the Canadian Shield in the northeast; the younger, sedimentary rocks of the Interior Plains are sources of nonmetallic minerals. Most of Canada's petroleum, natural gas, potash, sulfur, and coal comes from this region.

Thompson. These northern towns are similar in appearance to the new mining towns elsewhere in the Shield: They have neat, well-built frame houses on curving streets; modern stores supply most of the usual consumer goods that can be purchased in southern Canadian cities; recreation facilities combat the feeling of isolation.

The Canadian Shield in general has enormous supplies of waterpower awaiting utilization, and the rivers of northern Manitoba are no exception. The Winnipeg River was dammed early in the present century where it drops out of the Shield, and it supplies electric power to the cities and industries of southern Manitoba. The Nelson River produces electric power for the towns and mines at Thompson. Expanded power facilities on the Nelson will produce

about one million horsepower which can be transported by long-distance lines to the markets of Winnipeg and adjoining United States.

The other natural resources are not so significant as those of the Ontario and Quebec Shield, and they are farther from markets in eastern Anglo-America. The coniferous trees are small and scrubby and are not a potential source of pulpwood in the foreseeable future; the forests of the adjoining northern plains are more likely to be used before those of the Shield. Fur

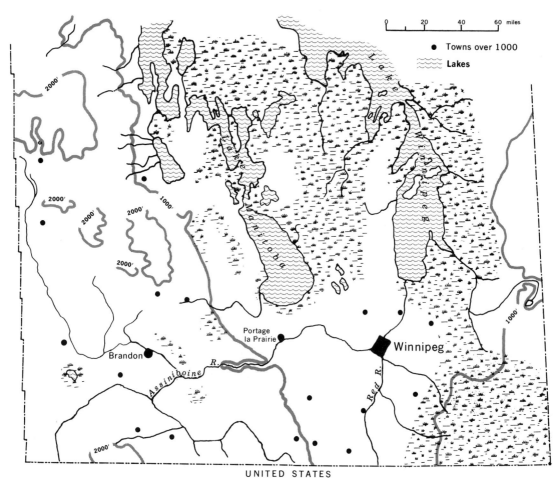

FIGURE 21-5   The southern Manitoba Lowland. This fertile lowland is bordered to the north and east by thinly populated forest areas, westward by a higher level of prairie (note the 2,000-foot contour), and southward by the international boundary. The original site of Winnipeg, in the center of the region, was at a river junction; now the city is a focus of rail and highway routes.

bearers still roam in these forests and provide a poor livelihood for a few thousand Indian trappers. The recreational attraction of the northern lakes and forests will increase, but the number of potential "consumers" of this scenic resource living south of the western Shield is not as great as those south of the eastern Shield.

The Manitoba Lowland

Southern Manitoba south and west of the Shield is a broad, flat lowland (Figure 21-5). Toward the end of the Glacial Age, this area (as well as slightly higher land east and west of it) was covered by large glacial Lake Agassiz which drained southward. As the front of the continental ice sheet melted northward, the huge lake was ultimately drained northward into Hudson Bay by the Nelson River. The present large lakes of southern Manitoba—Winnipeg, Manitoba, and Winnipegosis—are remnants of this former glacial lake. The fine-grained deposits laid down in the bottom of the old glacial lake are now the thick, fertile soils of the flat Red River Plain around Winnipeg. To the northward, in the section known as the Interlake area, the soils are thinner, contain more lime and have many stones.

Whereas the good soils of the southern

Lowland have supported prosperous grain and livestock farms—partly because of their favorable environmental characteristics but also because of proximity of the market and service facilities of Winnipeg—the poorer soils and forest environment of the Interlake area are marginal for agricultural settlement.[2] Much of this northern Lowland is unoccupied. Some pulpwood is cut, but it has to be transported several hundred miles by rail to the only southern Manitoba pulp and paper mill near the mouth of the Winnipeg River. If and when an external market for pulp or newsprint increases, the forest reserves of west central Manitoba could support another pulp mill, perhaps at The Pas, on the Saskatchewan River.

Small sections of the southern Lowland had farms long before the rest of the Canadian Plains was settled. In 1811 a small group of British settlers grew crops on the grasslands near Fort Garry, the Hudson's Bay Company fort and trading post at the junction of the Red and Assiniboine rivers, later to become Winnipeg. The farms barely survived, however, until shallow-draft steamers on the Red River gave later access to growing American settlements in the Dakotas and Minnesota.

Winnipeg

The population of Winnipeg increased as the western plains were occupied by farms. As the gateway to the West, Winnipeg became the main supply, distribution, and transport center for the expanding West. Its position of transport convergence was similar to that of Chicago, except that the latter city was part of an industrial and agri-

[2]The Interlake region is one of the ARDA pilot-study areas which was investigated by various specialists concerned with rural poverty.

cultural Midwest, whereas Winnipeg had the sparsely occupied Canadian Shield east of it.

As population increased on the Canadian Plains, the local market could be supplied by manufactures from Winnipeg (Figure 21-6). Although this industrial growth has continued and Winnipeg is still the largest city on the Canadian Plains, its rate of population growth has not been so fast as that of Edmonton and Calgary, its competing Western cities. About one-third of Winnipeg's workers are engaged in transportation, communications, and public utilities; another third are in manufacturing, trade, and financial occupations. Many of Winnipeg's manufactures are based on its agricultural hinterland: There are flour and feed mills, vegetable canneries, a sugar refinery (processing local sugar beets), and meat-packing plants. In the last-named industry some beef cattle from the western plains are brought to the feed grain of southern Manitoba for fattening before slaughtering, but other cattle are transported through Winnipeg to feeder lots in southern Ontario. The

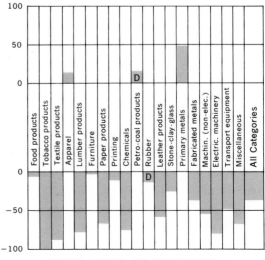

Deviation from Canadian per capita data, %

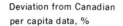

VALUE ADDED BY MANUFACTURING
Manitoba = 5.0% Canadian Pop.

FIGURE 21-6 Two-thirds of the value added by manufacturing is concentrated in metropolitan Winnipeg. Can you explain the deviations ranging from -10 to +50 percent for certain industries?

large stockyards in St. Boniface, a separate political entity within Greater Winnipeg, are therefore comparable in function to the stockyards in Chicago or Kansas City. With almost half a million persons in the urban area, Winnipeg is its own market for many consumer goods. For some products the cost of transporting them across the Canadian Shield from industrial southern Ontario gives Winnipeg a kind of "freight-protective" tariff for local industries.

Winnipeg has a wide mixture of ethnic groups, characteristic of the three Prairie Provinces. The sons and daughters of European immigrants have moved from prairie farms into the cities, and thus Winnipeg has ethnic diversity similar to the industrial cities of southern Ontario, such as Hamilton or Windsor. The largest group of French Canadians in the West live in St. Boniface, where they are trying to maintain their French language amid other ethnic groups who now accept English as their new mother tongue.

The city has rather effectively controlled the inevitable outward expansion of residential areas and the ribbonlike strips of commerce along the highways. As in most growing cities on the Canadian Plains, the boundary line between urban and rural activities is fairly sharp, with little of the intermixed structures of suburban sprawl. Winnipeg faces a number of natural hazards which are as difficult to control as are human beings: The spring flooding of the Red River cannot be contained by landform features on the flat plain, and therefore an expensive artificial channel was built around the city to divert floodwaters; although average snowfall is not great, much of it falls during occasional blizzards which disrupts city traffic.

The Saskatchewan Plain

A geological escarpment extends north-south across southwestern Manitoba, broken by the valley and old glacial delta deposits of the Assiniboine River. This 500-to 1,000-foot escarpment forms the eastern boundary of the Second Prairie Level, often called the Saskatchewan Plain. In west central Manitoba, the eroded, forested escarpment has been set aside as Riding Mountain National Park. Although these hills—and others north of them—are hardly "mountains" when viewed from the plain west of them, they were notable topographic features to the settlers of the flat Manitoba Lowland.

The plain which extends across southern Saskatchewan is about 2,000 feet above sea level; occasional flat-topped hills which are erosional remnants of harder rock rise a few hundred feet above it. Grassland is characteristic of the southwest, but north of the North Saskatchewan River the forest is dominant. Soils are brown in the southwest, dark brown on most of the southern Saskatchewan farms, and grade into black soils (chernozems) in an east-west belt through Prince Albert.

The Plains were occupied by Indian tribes who subsisted on the vast herds of buffalo which roamed the grasslands. The international border was of no significance to these herds or to the migratory Indians in the early nineteenth century. White man's occupation of the Canadian Plains was not characterized by Indian wars or by rancher-farmer feuds as in the American Plains. The minor skirmishes of the only "war," the Riel Rebellion of 1885, involved only a few thousand Indians and Métis, and deprived Canada of a "Wild West" myth—and the basis for a Hollywood-style movie and TV industry!

The orderly and methodical agricultural settlement of the Canadian Plains at the turn of the century was promoted and encouraged by the federal government which opened immigration offices in Britain and Europe, and it was greatly directed by the railway companies. Sometimes the railways, with their land grants, preceded settlement and then sold land to incoming immigrants; in other places settlers took up homesteads beyond the end of branch railways, and then the line was extended to them to carry out their wheat crops. About a half million people came to southern Saskatchewan in the period 1900–1914 and occupied most of the available suitable farmland.

The northward movement of the agricultural frontier was slower and more difficult. In the 1920s strips of settlement followed trails and crude roads into the forest north of the North Saskatchewan River. Land clearing was slow; it might require 20 years to clear a marginally economic farm unit of about 100 acres. A family could, however, obtain additional food from the fish of the lakes and game in the forest. Although precipitation on the northern frontier was more reliable than on the southern grasslands, the frost-free season was a little shorter. The northward agricultural migration reached its peak in the early 1930s when farmers had to leave the drought-stricken southern grasslands. (Although on a smaller scale, this exodus was similar to that out of the "dust bowl" of Oklahoma.) Many eked out a living on subsistence or livestock farms on the northern frontier. By about 1940 the northern extent of agricultural expansion had been reached. In the 1950s farm consolidation and farm abandonment resulted in a rapidly declining farm population within the forested area, similar to the decreasing farm population of the grassland region. Any further northern extent of agricultural settlement is doubtful: the forest environment is difficult for farming; the "pioneering spirit" has virtually disappeared; and new farmland is unnecessary when southern farms are producing a surplus.

Southern Saskatchewan is the major wheat-producing region of Canada. Farms are large, averaging a square mile (640 acres) in the south, and nearly all are larger than the original 160-acre homestead. As on the American Plains, more and more farms are being worked during the summer by a few men and many machines, and the families live in the growing towns and cities where better education and urban amenities are available. The farmer still has to contend with many hazards in the natural environment before he obtains a crop. Precipitation is barely adequate for wheat production across southern Saskatchewan, and probably many grain farms should have remained in grassland as cattle ranches. Annual precipitation averages about 10 to 15 inches, and about 60 percent falls during the four summer months. The actual amount that falls in any one year is below average more often than it is above (because the "wet" years may be very wet). Other natural problems include frost, hail, grasshoppers, and plant diseases. The results of these natural hazards are apparent in the total wheat production: Although wheat acreage varies little from year to year (about 22 to 25 million acres in the three Prairie Provinces), the annual wheat crop may range from about 400 million to 800 million bushels.

Because the population of the Prairie Provinces is small, most of the wheat crop is transported out of the region. The consumption of wheat products in eastern Canada is less than one-third of the average annual production; therefore Canada has to sell about 400 million to 600 million bushels of wheat in the world market each year. In the past, much of the wheat moved eastward by rail through Winnipeg to the Lakehead cities of Port Arthur–Fort William, and thence via the Great Lakes to Eastern ports. Small amounts moved northward along the Hudson Bay Railroad to the port of Churchill. The Great Lakes were closed by ice for three or four months of the year, and the Hudson Bay route was icebound for eight or nine months. Vancouver became a western grain port after the Panama Canal was opened in 1914. Southern Alberta grain

THE HEADFRAME, CIRCULAR STORAGE BINS, and other buildings of a potash mine near Esterhazy, Saskatchewan. Parkland vegetation and rectangular grain farms are in the background. (National Film Board of Canada photo.)

could be transported by rail to Vancouver and reach Europe by ship via Panama cheaper than being sent east through the Great Lakes; furthermore Vancouver could be used when the eastern water routes were frozen. As a result of the increasing market for wheat in the countries of the western Pacific, Vancouver is often the leading wheat-exporting port in Canada.

Although still known as the "wheat province" of Canada, Saskatchewan has a diversifying economy. The oil fields, better known in Alberta, cross the provincial border into western Saskatchewan, and the Williston Basin oil field of North Dakota extends into southeastern Saskatchewan. Enthusiasts who claim that there are now "more oil derricks than grain elevators" in Saskatchewan reflect the changing economy, although they may have counted neither phenomenon accurately! Further wealth from beneath the soil became available in the 1960s when mining technology found a way to obtain the deep and rich potash deposits. This potash production ranked second in Anglo-America to that of southeastern New Mexico, and brought new prosperity and new occupations to several small agricultural villages in central and eastern Saskatchewan.

The multipurpose dam across the South Saskatchewan River south of Saskatoon will bring further changes to that region. The impounded water can be led northward in irrigation aqueducts to improve crop yields south of Saskatoon; at a later date intensive vegetable farms similar to the irrigated areas of southern Alberta may develop. Turbines in the dam generate electric power to supplement the thermal power commonly used on the prairies. To the people of the dry prairies, however, one of the important "cultural" values will be the recreational use of the long, narrow lake which is slowly filling up behind the dam.

Manufacturing employment in Saskatchewan is increasing, but it is less than construction employment and has only one-eighth the number of people engaged in agriculture. However, as a larger percentage

A TYPICAL "MAIN STREET" of a small Prairie Province town. Stores have false fronts; the hotel and theater are the only "large" commercial buildings. The road is wide—dusty in summer and muddy after spring rains. This is High Prairie, Alberta. (Alberta government photo.)

of Saskatchewan's population concentrates into Regina, the number of manufacturing and service occupations will increase.

Regina The town was established in 1882 on a small creek in the midst of the flat plain as the capital of the (then) Northwest Territories. The Canadian Pacific Railway soon reached it en route to the West, and the city expanded its commercial and supply functions for the grain and cattle farms of southern Saskatchewan. When Regina became the capital of Saskatchewan after 1905, the various government occupations increased the city's population. Its growth was moderate, however, amid the dominant rural economy of the early part of the present century; there were only 35,000 people in the city in 1921. Postwar population growth has been related to industrial expansion: the traditional food-processing industries such as flour and feed mills and meat packing have been supplemented by oil refineries, a small steel mill (using scrap), and a cement plant. It is not likely, however, that Regina's industrial and commercial growth can equal that of Winnipeg or Calgary which produce a wider variety of consumer goods.

Saskatoon The urban growth of Saskatoon resembles that of Regina. The settlement grew up on both sides of a convenient crossing of the South Saskatchewan River. It is on the main line of the Canadian National Railway to Edmonton and the West Coast. Saskatoon supplies services to the surrounding rural population, and its industries are mainly related to food processing. Like Regina, Saskatoon's population doubled in the period 1951–1966, as both cities absorbed part of the decreasing farm population. Typical of the urban trends in other parts of Canada, the two largest cities of Saskatchewan had 26 percent of the provincial population in 1966, compared with 11 percent in 1931.

Alberta Plateau

Altitudes rise rather steadily to the west across the southern part of the Canadian Plains and are about 3,000 feet above sea level in southern Alberta. The low geological escarpment with a 200- to 300-foot gentle rise, marking the eastern boundary of the Third Prairie Level, is no more of a landform feature on the plains than are the steep, eroded banks of the entrenched rivers or the several flat-topped hills. In reality there are few differences in the landscape and landforms of southern Alberta compared with those of southern Saskatchewan.

North of the North Saskatchewan River the dominant forest cover creates an obviously different landscape from the southern grasslands. Northern Alberta also has more uplands, some of which have been eroded into hilly areas. As indicated by the direction of river flow, the land slopes

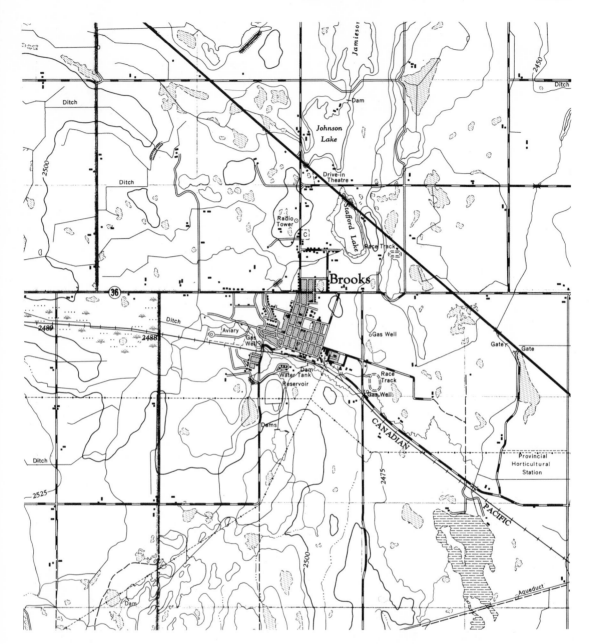

FIGURE 21-7   The small town of Brooks in southern Alberta resembles many American towns on the Plains. Its 3,400 people (1966) supply, service, or process the agriculture, which is largely irrigated, in the surrounding area. Because the land is divided into square-mile sections, the scale of the map can be readily determined. Like many American towns along the railways, the street grid is oriented to the railway instead of to the section lines. Since each rural house is shown on the map, the rural population per square mile can be calculated. (Reduced slightly from Brooks quadrangle, 1:50,000, 1960 ed.)

down to the northeast where the south end of the Mackenzie River Lowland is about the same altitude as the southern Manitoba Lowland.

In southern and central Alberta, the agricultural settlement and rectangular farm and field patterns are generally similar to those of southern Saskatchewan. Wheat and other grains such as oats, barley, or flax are the usual crops. On some farms they are

THE VARIETY OF LANDSCAPES in the foothills region of southwestern Alberta. The small town of Pincher Creek is in the foreground; strip farming with alternate strips of grain and fallow and widely dispersed farmhouses is in the center; the forested, low foothills lie at the base of the abrupt wall of the Rocky Mountains in the distance. (National Film Board of Canada photo by G. Hunter.)

grown for cash-crop sale, but on other farms the large livestock barns indicate that the grains are eaten on the farm and livestock products are sold (Figure 21-3).

The rural villages are also similar to those of southern Saskatchewan and are like those of the American Midwest (Figure 21-7). The commercial cores of these small towns often have a block or two of false-fronted stores, either parallel to the railway or at right angles to it. The grain elevator is always the highest building in the town, and the number of elevators appearing on the horizon as one approaches the town is often a good indication of the size of the commercial and residential areas of the town.

There are differences, however, in the rural landscapes of southern Alberta compared with the plains to the east. There are more cattle, and some sheep, ranches in the semi-arid lands of southern Alberta and in

the foothills near the Rocky Mountains. Some of these grasslands have been used for dry farming with narrow strips of wheat alternating with dark brown strips of fallow; other areas are in irrigated farms, looking from the air much like the irrigated lands northeast of Denver (Figure 15-5). These irrigated farms, which total about one million acres, produce sugar beets, alfalfa, vegetables, and wheat. The growing city of Lethbridge is the major supply and distribution center for the irrigation region.

Agriculture in Alberta extends north to the Peace River area, in latitude 55 to 56°N, the same latitude as Moscow in the Soviet Union. Northwest of Edmonton 150 miles of forest and muskeg separates the major farming region of central Alberta from the Peace River farms. Most of these lands were settled after World War I as the "last large area of available homestead land in Can-

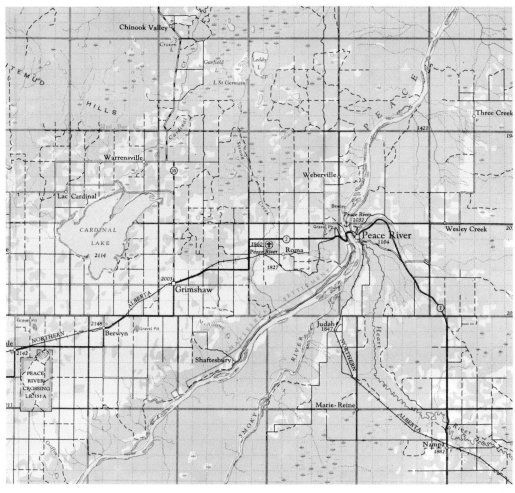

FIGURE 21-8 The Peace River region (56° N) is the northernmost area used for commercial agriculture in Canada. The gray area is forested; the cleared area is white. Note that most agricultural clearing is along the roads and railways and not in the river valleys. Since this map was published, a new railway has been completed, extending north of Roma to Great Slave Lake, connecting the Peace River region with the Northwest Territories. As in the United States, the land is divided into townships of 36 sections, each one mile square. What is the scale of this map in miles to an inch? (Reduced from Peace River, Alberta, quadrangle, 1:250,000, 1957 ed. Canadian topographic maps may be purchased from the Map Distribution Office, Department of Energy, Mines and Resources, Ottawa.)

ada." Their grain and livestock products were taken out to Edmonton by rail. Small service-supply towns, such as Grande Prairie in Alberta and Dawson Creek in British Columbia, arose to serve the rural areas. After 1950 accessibility improved when a second main road and a railway came into the region from Prince George in British Columbia. Vancouver and Edmonton now compete for the flow of products from the Peace River area.

Changing Economy The agriculture-oriented economy of Alberta changed after World War II. Small amounts of petroleum had been produced southwest of Calgary before 1940, but this supplied only a small propor-

tion of local needs. Several small natural gas fields were also exploited, supplying cheap heating to Medicine Hat and Edmonton, for example. The petroleum boom—a smaller replica of the Texas and Oklahoma discoveries early in the century—came to the Edmonton region after 1947. First the Leduc field was discovered south of the city, then the Redwater field to the northeast, and later the vast Pembina field west of Edmonton. Because petroleum reserves were greater than could be used in Alberta, the government authorized the building of pipelines to carry the petroleum—and later equally large amounts of natural gas—to urban markets in southern Ontario, the upper Midwest, and to both the Canadian and American Pacific Coast. At the same time petroleum refineries were built on the eastern edge of Edmonton and in other prairie cities, and the beginnings of a petrochemical industry were established at Edmonton.

In the 1960s new oil and gas fields were found to the northwest, both in Alberta (Swan Hills, for example) and as far north as Fort Nelson, on the Alaska Highway in northeastern British Columbia. In northeastern Alberta the bituminous, or tar, sands had been known for a long time. Depending upon the extraction method, the petroleum reserves have been estimated as 200 to 400 billion barrels—equal to the world's known reserves of "liquid" petroleum (i.e., excluding other tar sands or oil shales). Methods of separating the oil and sand were devised in the mid-1960s, and a pipeline from Fort McMurray brought the petroleum into the Alberta pipeline grid. Production from the Athabasca Tar Sands is given a quota by the provincial government so that other oil producers can continue to produce. Throughout Alberta new revenues from petroleum brought a new level of prosperity to many people ranging from farmers to businessmen. But whether the product is wheat, potash, or petroleum, the people of the Canadian Plains remember that their prosperity depends on the external world economy.

Alberta has other natural resources, such as coal and forests, which are not needed in Canada or the world at present. About half of Canada's bituminous coal reserves—an enormous 50 billion tons—underlies western Alberta, and another 25 billion tons is estimated to be in southern Saskatchewan. This coal is too far away, in terms of transport costs, to be used in the industries of southern Ontario, and locally it competes poorly with petroleum and natural gas. If coal is ever used as a chemical raw material instead of fuel, Alberta coal may have greater value. The coniferous forest of northern Alberta is a vast reserve of pulpwood; but only a few pulp mills operate there because the forest is poorly located in competition with the more accessible forest reserves of the eastern Canadian Shield or central British Columbia.

Edmonton and Calgary   These two rapidly growing cities are friendly rivals. Their urban growth rates are sometimes the highest in Canada, but this is partly a reflection of their small beginning figures. Edmonton, for example, increased in population from 80,000 in 1931 to 401,000 in 1966. The cities have many similarities in their origins, past functions, and present manufacturing types (Figure 21-9). A fur-trading post was built near the present site of Edmonton early in the nineteenth century, and this was its only function until a branch-line railway from Calgary reached it in 1891. Edmonton was chosen over Calgary as the capital of Alberta in 1905 partly because of its central location in the province. Before 1940 the growth of both cities was related mainly to the production of their agricultural hinterlands. Cattle from the Calgary ranching area and the Edmonton mixed farming area came to the stockyards of both cities, either to be transported eastward or to be slaughtered at local meat-packing plants. Calgary's origin as a "cowtown" is still commemorated in its publicized tourist attraction, the "Calgary Stampede."

After 1940 the wartime activity in Yukon

Territory and the postwar development of northern resources had their southern focus on Edmonton. Wholesalers, equipment suppliers, financial agencies, and transport companies all benefited from increased northern activities. The oil boom came after 1947. In addition to oil refineries Edmonton has access to other raw materials for the petrochemical industry, such as sulfur and salt. This raw-material base is therefore like that of the Gulf Coast of Texas; but the Edmonton region lacks a large local market, and it is far away from the chemical industries of southern Ontario and Quebec. Edmonton's other manufactures are consumer goods for the local market, as are found in most large cities. For example, the city has a small steel mill, fed on local scrap, which produces a variety of metal goods for the petroleum and agricultural implement industries.

Calgary's position may be compared with that of Denver, Colorado. Calgary is on the northwestern edge of a large irrigation district, and is the transportation gateway to tourist and recreation areas, such as Banff

National Park, in the Rocky Mountains. For many products and services Calgary's hinterland extends into the small towns of southeastern British Columbia. In both Edmonton and Calgary local planning authorities have been relatively successful in controlling and directing the areal expansion of their cities. Both cities are bisected by rivers and railroads and have had crossing problems to direct traffic flow from residential areas to working places. In their patterns of city growth the relatively recent expansion of the prairie cities has permitted them to benefit from the mistakes of older Eastern cities.

BRITISH COLUMBIA

Most of Canada's westernmost province is occupied by the mountainous Cordillera which extends the length of western North America. In terms of area, British Columbia is larger than California, Oregon, and Washington combined; it is a land of spectacular mountain scenery: deep, narrow valleys; broad, forested interior plateaus; and an indented, fjorded coast. In population it is the extreme example of the urbanization that characterizes the rest of Canada. Only 5 percent of the people of British Columbia live on farms; 50 percent are resident in the large urban concentration of Greater Vancouver, and 75 percent have homes in the southwestern corner of the province, near the shores of Georgia Strait or on the long delta of the Fraser River. The coastal concentration and urban characteristics are similar to those of the Pacific Coast states to the southward.

The interior of British Columbia was partly explored early in the nineteenth century and first settled from the east by

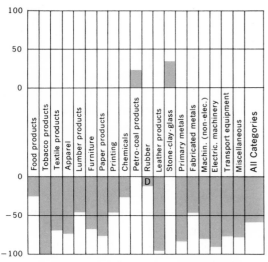

VALUE ADDED BY MANUFACTURING
Alberta = 7.6% Canadian Pop.

FIGURE 21-9 The negative deviation in food products does not reflect low food production but rather that greater manufacturing values are added elsewhere in Canada. Where?

fur traders who encouraged the interior Indians to trap for furs. Until 1858 the area which was to become British Columbia remained part of the vast fur empire of the Hudson's Bay Company which stretched west of Hudson Bay to the Pacific and Arctic Oceans. Then alluvial gold was discovered in the riverbed gravels of the Fraser River. Victoria controlled water access to the Fraser River and became the port of entry and supply center for the interior gold fields. Its function was therefore like that of San Francisco a decade earlier. By 1862 about 15,000 miners and associated service, commercial, and transport personnel were concentrated in or near Barkerville at the western foot of the Cariboo Mountains. Barkerville, now a restored Historic Site "ghost town," was then the largest British settlement west of the Great Lakes.

Within a few years the gold rush was over, settlements declined, and the interior of British Columbia had very little development for several decades. Lumbering was started on the southern coast, but the technology of the time had trouble with the large trees. Two sawmills began to clear the forest on the low shores of Burrard Inlet, the site of what was later to be Vancouver. By 1871 the colony of British Columbia was in poor financial condition and agreed to join the newly formed Dominion of Canada in return for a promise of a transcontinental railway to be built to the West Coast. The new province was to wait rather impatiently for 15 years before the Canadian Pacific Railway built its thin line of steel across the rocky Canadian Shield, over the grassy plains, and through the twisting valleys of the Cordillera. The city of Vancouver was born in 1887 as its western terminal. Within 24 years, in the census of 1911, Canada's new, and only, Western port had a population of 121,000.

The fundamental resource base of the West Coast economy was well established early in the present century. The port function of Vancouver remained rather minor early in the century because Pacific trade was not well developed. The tall coniferous trees of the Coast forest were gradually logged on the coastal lowlands and lower mountain slopes. The logs were towed to sawmills scattered around the shores of Georgia Strait, especially on the east coast of Vancouver Island, in Vancouver, and along the channels of the Fraser Delta. Fish canneries also began operations at the mouth of the Fraser River, and at other coastal rivers, where the salmon collected in late summer to start their migration to interior spawning grounds. Farms were cleared on the fertile alluvial soils of the Fraser Delta and to a lesser extent on the lowland of eastern Vancouver Island. Most population was clustered around Georgia Strait, in the southwestern corner, and only a few logging camps and fish canneries dotted the central and northern coast.

Greater Vancouver

Vancouver's urban growth was similar to that of Seattle and Los Angeles in that it was not proportionate to the moderate expansion of its hinterland resources. The city itself was its own best market. People flocked to the West Coast city for many of the same reasons that they moved across United States to Pacific Coast cities. To the young and adventurous it was a "far away" part of Canada where a new life could be started amid a magnificent physical setting; to the old the mildest winters in Canada and cool summers were desirable for retirement. To businessmen and industrialists the untapped resources of forest, fish, land, minerals, and power awaited their capital and technology. Most of these people settled in Vancouver and other adjoining cities.

An industrial belt spread along the railway which occupied the south shore of Burrard Inlet. In addition to the wharves for ocean vessels, the harbor industries include grain elevators, a sugar refinery, oil

SOME OF THE HARBOR FACILITIES at Vancouver, British Columbia. The vessel in the foreground is a passenger ship which calls at settlements north along the coast. Other cargo ships are loading lumber. The Canadian Pacific occupies the harbor strip, with the CBD behind it. Stanley Park, a large area of preserved forest adjoining the city center, is in the upper right of the photo. (Canadian National Railway photo.)

refineries, ship-repair facilities, chemical plants, and much warehousing. The saw-mills gradually gave up the valuable harbor land and moved outside of Vancouver, mainly along the Fraser River. The main commercial core of Vancouver grew up two blocks south of the rail terminal and harbor facilities (Figure 21-10). At first southward expansion of the city was curtailed by False Creek, a shallow inlet which could not be used by ocean vessels, but which was excel-lent for log booms going to sawmills. The eastern end of this inlet was filled in after World War I and became the terminal for the second transcontinental railway, now the Canadian National. The shallow valley used by the railway was later occupied by highways also and became the second in-dustrial zone of Greater Vancouver. Many of the assembly plants of large eastern

Canadian businesses, and local warehouses and consumer-good plants are located along this interior industrial zone which extends east into adjoining Burnaby. The third industrial belt is on the south side of the city, along the Fraser River, and is occupied mainly by sawmills and other wood-proc-essing plants.

Greater Vancouver's residential sections are cut up by coastal and river features. The residential cities of South Vancouver and Point Grey, on the south and west sides of Burrard peninsula, were greatly filled in during the 1920s, except for blocks of land kept by the Canadian Pacific Railway for later settlement. These "dormitory" cities were incorporated into the political limits of Vancouver in 1929. The separate towns of North and West Vancouver, on the north shore of Burrard Inlet, were connected by

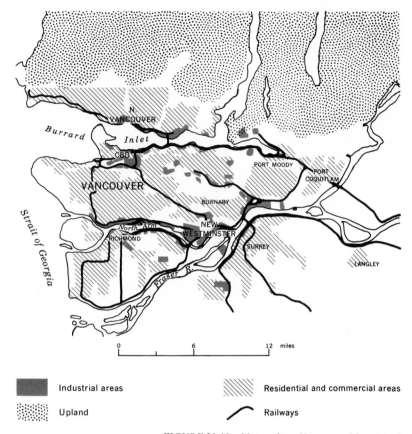

Industrial areas

Upland

Residential and commercial areas

Railways

FIGURE 21-10   Metropolitan Vancouver. The original site of the city was on the south side of Burrard Inlet, east of the protected, narrow entrance to the inner harbor. The present city has spread southward over the delta islands and lowlands of the Fraser River. To the northward the sharp peaks of the Coast Mountains form a scenic backdrop to the city setting.

ferry to the commercial core of downtown Vancouver until a bridge was built across the First Narrows entrance to the inner harbor in 1936. Residences then spread rapidly up the lower slopes of the North Shore mountains. This residential movement to the North Shore slopes accelerated after World War II when a second bridge crossed at the Inner, or Second, Narrows near the east end of the harbor. Postwar suburban expansion spread south of the North Arm of the Fraser River; prosperous dairy farms on the Fraser Delta were subdivided into residential plots. In the 1960s much of the western end of the Fraser Delta was converted into miles of middle-class housing and suburban shopping areas; there is very little agricultural land remaining between the city of Vancouver and the United States border.

New industry is locating outside of Vancouver itself (Figure 21-10), whereas the city is increasing its commercial, business, and service functions. The companies that operate the resource developments throughout the province have their head offices in Vancouver. Tall new office buildings in downtown Vancouver are similar to those in Toronto and Montreal. Few natural resources of British Columbia now come to Vancouver for processing, but the financial control of these industries is probably in Vancouver's CBD (Figure 21-11).

Victoria (Figure 18-6)

Although capital of the province and the main port of entry before 1890, Victoria was

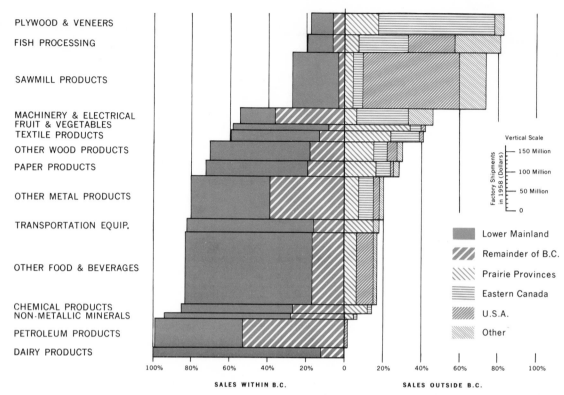

PLYWOOD & VENEERS
FISH PROCESSING
SAWMILL PRODUCTS
MACHINERY & ELECTRICAL
FRUIT & VEGETABLES
TEXTILE PRODUCTS
OTHER WOOD PRODUCTS
PAPER PRODUCTS
OTHER METAL PRODUCTS
TRANSPORTATION EQUIP.
OTHER FOOD & BEVERAGES
CHEMICAL PRODUCTS
NON-METALLIC MINERALS
PETROLEUM PRODUCTS
DAIRY PRODUCTS

Vertical Scale

Factory Shipments in 1958 (Dollars)
— 150 Million
— 100 Million
— 50 Million
— 0

Lower Mainland
Remainder of B.C.
Prairie Provinces
Eastern Canada
U.S.A.
Other

100% 80% 60% 40% 20% 0 20% 40% 60% 80% 100%

SALES WITHIN B.C.   SALES OUTSIDE B.C.

FIGURE 21-11   Types of manufacturing in the lower
mainland of British Columbia. Note that products sold
outside of British Columbia are mainly wood and fish
products; those sold within British Columbia are mainly
manufactured products for urban consumers or equipment and supplies for industrial processors. The United
States is the major market for British Columbia forest
products. (Adapted from a 1958 report of the Lower Mainland
Regional Planning Board.)

separated from the resource developments
of the mainland and lost its dominance to
the rail terminal of Vancouver. The city is
mainly an administrative center; adjoining
it is Canada's chief West Coast naval base.
Thus government occupations, both provincial and federal, are the chief nonmanu-
facturing employment. Local industries are
concerned with wood processing and ship
building. Victoria and the small towns north
of it on Vancouver Island are still popular
places for retirement because of their mild
climate. The city attempts to maintain some
sections of its urban landscape as "a little
bit of olde (sic) England," an attraction for
American tourists.

The Georgia Strait area of southwestern
British Columbia is an integrated, functional
region similar to urban complexes at the
southeastern end of Puget Sound or around
San Francisco Bay. Hourly ferry service
between Victoria and Vancouver, and between Vancouver and Nanaimo moves

people and products. Barges full of pulpwood chips from the Fraser River lumber
mills dot the strait as they move toward
pulp and paper mills. Dairy products and
vegetables from lower Fraser Valley farms
feed Victoria as well as the several cities of
Greater Vancouver. Ocean-going ships may
call at several of the ports around the strait
in assembling a mixed cargo. With three-
quarters of the population of British Columbia around its shores, the metropolitan
complex of the Georgia Strait region is
surpassed in Canada only by those of Montreal and Toronto.

The West Coast

The remainder of the Coast is sparsely occupied. It presents spectacular views to tourists on the coastal steamers—high mountains of 8,000 to 12,000 feet rising steeply above densely forested lower slopes to snowcapped peaks; an indented, fjorded, island-fringed coast of ever-changing landscapes. In winter, however, the rain comes down almost continuously and heavy clouds block out the mountain views. Most of the fish canneries along the central coast are now closed because modern fish-packing vessels carry the salmon, caught at river mouths, directly to large canneries at Prince Rupert or near Vancouver, where export transportation is available. Although logging camps dot the Coast, the huge logs are transported by modern self-dumping log barges and flat log booms to the processing plants around Georgia Strait. Mining revived on Vancouver Island and on the Queen Charlotte Islands in the 1950s. The small copper and iron deposits being worked have little direct effect upon British Columbia industry since the concentrates are shipped to Japan (Figure 21-12).

Two small cities, Prince Rupert and Kitimat, provide urban services for the northern coast near the Alaska Panhandle. Prince Rupert was created before World War I as a planned town; as the western terminal of the northern branch of the Canadian National Railway, it was expected to compete with Vancouver for the Pacific trade. Its growth did not materialize; the city did not have a developing resource hinterland, or the advantages of the established services of the Georgia Strait region. Although Prince Rupert was closer to Pacific ports of east Asia, most of British Columbia trade before 1940 was southward and via the Panama to the North Atlantic region. Prince Rupert has fish canneries and freezing plants and a cellulose factory, all of which process raw materials of the coastal environment. On the next large inlet to the southward, Kitimat is a modern planned city. In the early 1950s an imaginative power project dammed the Nechako River, a western tributary of the Fraser, backed up the water in a chain of lakes, and dropped it through a long tunnel under the Coast Mountains to a huge power plant carved into the rock base of the mountains. Fifty miles away an aluminum smelter was built, and near it arose the attractive residential city of Kitimat. All the bauxite and alumina is imported for processing at the site of cheap power.

Interior British Columbia

Resource developments in the interior accelerated after World War II, encouraged by improved road transport. Before 1940 interior settlement was in three separate pockets: the Kootenays, Okanagan Valley, and small centers on the Interior Plateau. The Kootenay region in the southeast had its mining boom in 1890–1910; many of the mines closed, but the large ore body at Kimberley, in the Rocky Mountain Trench, became Canada's major producer of lead-zinc-silver. The ore was smelted and refined some distance away at Trail, on the Columbia River near the border. As the only refinery in western Canada (and allied fertilizer plant), it processes the ores of southeastern British Columbia and also those from as far away as Keno Hill in the Yukon and Pine Point in the Northwest Territories.

Agricultural settlement is scanty in the narrow and dry valleys of the southern interior. British settlers started irrigation before 1914 on the narrow terraces of the northern Okanagan Valley. Apples did well, and the irrigated acreage spread southward in the interwar period. The linear region is now the leading apple-producing area of Canada, supplying the western Canadian market and having a surplus for export. The orchards also produce cherries, peaches, pears, plums, and Canada's only apricots. This irrigated orchard region competes with

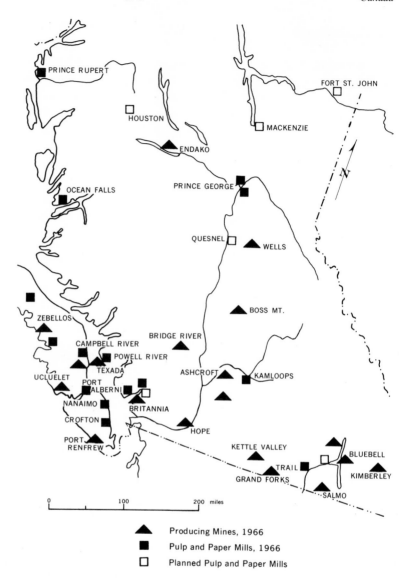

FIGURE 21-12 *Mines and pulp and paper mills in British Columbia. Mines are concentrated in three zones—in the southeast near the Trail smelter, near the few transport lines of the central interior, and along the coast for export (mainly) to Japan. All pulp and paper mills were coastal until 1962, and by 1966 the interior forests were being used for pulp (as well as lumber).*

that of the Niagara Peninsula of Ontario and is similar to the Wenatchee-Yakima fruit area nearby in interior Washington State.

The Interior Plateau of central British Columbia is well forested. Lumber was cut there before 1940, particularly around Prince George, for transport eastward by rail to the prairie cities. Because the valuable Douglas fir of the Coast Forest was in danger of depletion, and has been under government-regulated controlled cutting since World War II, lumbermen turned to the under-used interior forests. Exploitation was aided by the provincial railway, Pacific Great Eastern, extending from North Vancouver in the south through Prince George to the Peace River area. By the early 1960s the interior forests were supplying about half of the lumber cut in British Columbia;

it was transported eastward by rail mainly to urban markets in the American Midwest, or was brought to Vancouver for ocean transport to eastern United States or northwestern Europe.

The pulp and paper industry of British Columbia was entirely coastal before 1960. There it was integrated into the lumber industry; pulp mills often adjoined large lumber and plywood mills, using waste wood from the sawmills and smaller logs not suitable for plywood. The same type of integration began in the interior forestry industry in the 1960s, resulting in a more efficient use of resources. Pulp and paper mills at Kamloops, Quesnel, and Prince George, for example, have increased the value of forestry production from the Interior.

A great deal of water is unused in British Columbia. Before 1940 the major hydropower developments were on the short coastal rivers in the southwest to supply industries and other urban uses in Greater Vancouver, and on tributaries of the Columbia River in the southeast mainly for the large Trail smelter and refinery. The mighty Fraser River, an enormous source of power, remained untapped because of the provincial government decision not to interfere with the valuable salmon runs of the Fraser River Basin.

In the 1960s two new power projects were initiated in the Interior to meet the expected demands for electric power in British Columbia and the adjacent states. The Columbia River was already well harnessed for power production in the United States; but one-third of the river's volume comes from its headwaters in Canada. Flood-control dams in Canada were needed for more efficient use of the water going through the power plants downstream in the United States. After much political and financial negotiation, involving the federal governments of Canada and the United States, but also the provincial government

of British Columbia, the Columbia River Treaty was signed in 1964. Believing that the Columbia River power would not be sufficient for the future, the British Columbia government built another major power dam on the Peace River, where it tumbled northeastward out of the Rocky Mountains. Electric power should therefore be ample in British Columbia for any industrial expansion in the next decade.

Clear water is a valuable commodity, and the Canadian Cordilleran region has a surplus. Its use for electric power may face future competition from nuclear or thermal power, whereas its use for irrigation in the dry West, and for industrial and drinking needs in the Western cities will probably increase. Several imaginative—and extremely costly—plans have been proposed to direct the unused water of Yukon Territory, for example, through the interconnected valleys of British Columbia, such as the Rocky Mountain Trench, to expected markets in western United States. Such plans receive no encouragement from the Canadian or British Columbia governments, who say that they must first forecast and then protect the future water needs of their own citizens before export can be considered. In terms of national interests, it is more expedient politically to divert some of the Cordilleran water eastward to the semi-arid Prairie Provinces than to export it to competing croplands in the United States. For a country whose economy used to depend greatly on the export of its raw materials for processing elsewhere, a limitation on exports would be a change in Canadian economic policy.

CONCLUSIONS

There are contrasts in the Canadian West between the level lands and rural economy of the Interior Plains and the rugged, forested landscapes and urban centers of the Cordillera. In both subregions changes are occurring in the distribution of economic activities: Diversification is apparent on the Canadian Prairies; although wheat is still important, resource-oriented activities other than those related to grain are increasing, and cities are growing; although the cities of coastal southwestern British Columbia still dominate the Cordilleran economy, resource developments are increasing in the Interior. In both subregions the people and their occupations are maintained largely through the export of their surplus raw materials; wheat, other grains, petroleum, natural gas, and potash flow out of the prairies; lumber, plywood, pulp and paper, apples, fish, and several metallic ores are exported from the Cordillera.

With a total of almost 5.5 million people in an area of about 1 million square miles the West has a small and dispersed local market. Its manufactures are still small in volume and value, particularly when compared with those of Ontario, and are concerned mainly with partial processing of local natural resources. Fortunately, the region in total has a good variety, and large reserves, of natural resources, which should enable the continuation of this type of exploitive economy for future decades, providing the external world economy continues to demand these materials.

As in eastern Canada, only a small part of the four western provinces is effectively occupied. The northern sections of each province are almost empty. Similar to north central Quebec and northwestern Ontario, many thousands of square miles of northern Manitoba, northeastern Saskatchewan, and north central British Columbia have no land transport and virtually no resident people. Despite the increasing population of Anglo-America, and the world, it is doubtful whether these areas will ever be populated. Their value as agricultural land is not related so much to the hazards of the natural environment—and there are many—as to

the Anglo-American surplus of better land closer to markets. Their mineral and forest resources may be in demand elsewhere, but the small dots on the map representing urban people in these exploitive occupations will be minor concentrations amid the vast wilderness.

SELECTED REFERENCES

BRITISH COLUMBIA BUREAU OF ECONOMICS AND STATISTICS, DEPARTMENT OF INDUSTRIAL DEVELOPMENT: *British Columbia, Manual of Resources and Development.* 31 pp. Victoria, 1961.

British Columbia Geographical Series: An annual periodical, starting in 1960, of geographical articles about British Columbia. Published by Department of Geography, University of British Columbia, Vancouver, for the British Columbia Division, Canadian Association of Geographers. Volume 8 appeared in 1968.

Canadian Geographer: This should be the standard periodical reference for students wishing specific information on parts of Canada from a geographical viewpoint. For example, the issues between 1965 and 1967 had articles on western Canada such as: Irrigation in Alberta, Wood Processing in Vancouver, Retailing in Calgary, Glaciers in Alberta, Columbia River Treaty, Recreation in Saskatchewan.

CHAPMAN, JOHN D., and A. L. FARLEY (eds.): *Atlas of British Columbia Resources,* British Columbia Natural Resources Conference, Victoria, 1956.

MACKINTOSH, W. A., and W. L. G. JOERG (eds.): *Canadian Frontiers of Settlement,* in 9 vols.; note vol. 2, *History of Prairie Settlement and Dominion Lands Policy,* Macmillan, Toronto, 1938.

MCGOVERN, P. D.: "Industrial Development in the Vancouver Area," *Economic Geography,* vol. 37 (1961), pp. 189–206.

Proceedings of British Columbia Natural Resources Conferences. Annual volumes, starting in 1951, reporting on trends in resource developments; special inventory volumes were published in 1956 and 1964. Victoria, B.C.

ROBINSON, J. LEWIS: "The Northern Extension of the Pioneer Fringe of Agriculture on the Great Plains of Canada," *Proceedings of 8th General Assembly, International Geographical Union,* Washington, 1952, pp. 657–662.

Saskatchewan Economic Review: An annual statistical report of the Saskatchewan Economic Development Board, Regina.

WEIR, THOMAS R.: *Economic Atlas of Manitoba,* Manitoba Department of Industry and Commerce, Winnipeg, 1960.

————: *Rural Population Change: Interlake, 1941–1961,* Manitoba Department of Agriculture and Conservation, Winnipeg, 1964.

NOTE: Provincial atlases, similar to those available for British Columbia and Manitoba, are nearing completion for Alberta and Saskatchewan, being prepared under the direction of the departments of geography at the Universities of Alberta and Saskatchewan, respectively.

Information about current resources developments in each of the four western provinces may be obtained from the annual reports of the provincial government resources departments, such as Forests, Mines, Lands, Agriculture, Fisheries. Reports are published in the provincial capitals.

FIGURE 22-1 *Landforms of northern Canada and Greenland. Yukon Territory is part of the complex mountains of the Cordillera; the Mackenzie Valley, which contains most resource development in the Northwest Territories, is a narrow strip west of the Canadian Shield. Only the edges of Greenland are not covered by a large icecap.* (Base map copyright by A. K. Lobeck. Reprinted with permission of The Geographical Press, Hammond, Inc.)

CHAPTER 22

THE NORTHLANDS

PERCEPTION OF THE NORTH

The Northlands are sparsely settled. The small scale of their resource development, however, allows a study of locational and developmental principles which are more complex in the highly urbanized society in the remainder of Anglo-America. One is able to study the settlement processes as they are evolving now in the North. One reads in textbooks about the history of first settlement and economic development of most of Anglo-America, but one can read in current periodicals and newspapers about the exploration, settlement, and resource utilization of the Northlands. The northern quarter of Anglo-America differs from the rest of the continent in many ways. Its vast spaces are almost empty of population, and its natural resources either are scanty or cannot compete with similar resources located closer to markets. In the Northlands there seem to be few resources to attract large groups of people into a variety of occupations, and the problem of cold weather discourages many people.

The northern part of Anglo-America occupies a broad section of the world in latitude 60 to 65° (Figure 22-1). If Alaska (excluding the Aleutian Islands) and Greenland are included with the two Canadian territories, the region has an east-west longitude extent of at least 160°, more than one-third around the world. The total area of these three northern political units is 2.3 million square miles, equal to three times the size of Mexico or eight times the area of Texas. Distances are therefore great in the North; one has to adopt new scales of comparison differing from those used in the discussion of the small urban areas in previous chapters.

For about two centuries Anglo-Americans have been moving west across the continent; a number of phrases such as "go west, young man" or "westward the course of Empire" illustrate these themes in the settlement history of the United States. The same westward movement filled in the agricultural lands of western Canada in the first three decades of the present century. After World War II some Canadians have tried to create a northern image with slogans such as "Canada's destiny is in the North" and "Canada is a northern nation." Despite a definite increase in the number of people moving into the two northern territories—Yukon and Northwest[1] —and increasing resource utilization, the northern flow is but a trickle compared with the numbers that are concentrating into the cities across southern Canada, or compared with the major resource development in the "Near North" or "Middle Canada." The percentage increases sometimes quoted for the Canadian (and Alaskan) North are a reflection of their minor development before 1940. Yukon Territory, for example, increased in population from 5,000 in 1941 to 14,400 in 1966. This impressive percentage increase does indicate that something is happening in the North —but the total numerical increase of about 10,000 people in 25 years is less than the *annual* increase in population in any of the large Canadian cities.

[1] Northwest Territories is a misleading locational name since much of it is in northeastern Canada; the most northwestern part of Canada is occupied by Yukon Territory. A similar confusion occurred in the United States where the historical Northwest Territory is now occupied by the East North Central (Great Lakes) states. In Canada in 1869, the Northwest Territories was everything north and west of the small new provinces of Quebec and Ontario, except for British Columbia. In later years, the boundaries of Quebec and Ontario were extended north to Hudson Bay and Hudson Strait, and the four Western provinces were given political jurisdiction over the area to latitude 60° N. Yukon Territory was separated from the Northwest Territories in 1898.

"North" is, after all, a relative term to Canadians, most of whom live in a narrow strip across the southern part of their country. To the people of Quebec and Ontario the "North" is in the southern Canadian Shield, and the exciting resource expansion of the past 20 years has brought this southern Shield into the functioning economy of eastern Canada. Many of these new towns on the "northern frontier" of the eastern Shield are, in fact, in a latitude *south* of the cities of western Canada. To the four Western provinces their "northern" development is in the northern parts of their provincial area, and the phrase seldom refers to the Mackenzie River Valley or the valleys of Yukon Territory.

As congestion and decreasing natural resources become apparent in the densely occupied parts of Anglo-America (and elsewhere in the world), one has to assess the resource potential of these relatively empty northern lands. Does the Northland have a resource potential which will attract any significant exploitation and which will supply raw materials to the growing urban centers of the southern areas? Can the Northlands offer opportunities to modern pioneers comparable to those offered by the West during the last century?

An assessment of the Northlands should examine carefully the physical environment which differs radically from that of the rest of the continent. The adaptations and adjustments which man has made in settled Anglo-America have to be different in the North; the relationships between man and his natural environment are closer and more obvious than in the urban-dominated areas of the rest of Anglo-America.

The Northern Environment

In the total area of Yukon and Northwest Territories, 1,512,000 square miles, one could expect a variety of physical environments. Baffin Island, for example, is larger than California and as large as New Eng-

THE STEEP AND HIGH MOUNTAINS of the northern Cordillera look much the same in southeastern Yukon or in the Rocky Mountains. Slopes above about 5,000 feet altitude have no trees; some snow and ice fields remain throughout the summer. (Canadian National Railway photo.)

land plus New York, Pennsylvania, and Virginia. It is apparent that there are two Northlands—a northwest which has most of the white population and some resource potential, and the arctic areas of the northeast, the land of the Eskimo, with few natural resources.

Northern landforms are continuations of major features in the structure of the rest of Anglo-America. The Cordillera extends through Yukon Territory and arcs westward into Alaska; the Interior Plains narrow to the northward where they become the Mackenzie Valley; the Canadian Shield broadens northward to the Arctic Coast of mainland Canada—the ancient hard rocks of the Shield extend, in fact, to the northeastern islands such as Baffin and Ellesmere. The Arctic Islands, in themselves, have no topographic uniformity: the eastern islands are high and rugged, with long twisting fjords facing Davis Strait and Baffin Bay;

in contrast some of the central islands are flat, lake-covered plains which have only recently (in geological time) arisen from the sea after the removal of the weight of the continental icecap.

There are major contrasts in climate and vegetation between the northwest and northeast. Summers are relatively warm in the valleys of the northwest, giving the area a subarctic climate classification, in contrast to the cool summers of the northeast which has an arctic climate (Figure 22-2). Average July mean temperatures at the small settlements in west central Yukon and in the southern Mackenzie Valley are above 60°, and daily temperatures in July may sometimes rise into the 80s. As a result, coniferous forests have been able to grow during the warm summers in the northwest valleys, and some hardy crops can supply local food. Some writers have incorrectly attributed this summer warmth to the long duration of

CLIMATIC REGIONS

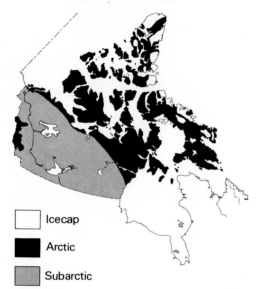

☐	Icecap
■	Arctic
▨	Subarctic

FIGURE 22-2 Climatic regions of the Northwest Territories. The subarctic areas in the western sections have warm summers, whereas the arctic areas remain cool throughout the summer. Both regions are very cold in winter.

NATURAL VEGETATION

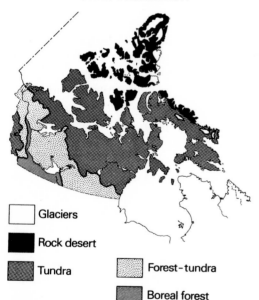

☐	Glaciers
■	Rock desert
▨	Tundra
▨	Forest-tundra
▨	Boreal forest

FIGURE 22-3 Natural vegetation of the Northwest Territories. Note the similarity to Figure 22-2. The tundra region coincides closely with the area of arctic climate. The northern sections of the arctic area have virtually no vegetation and are classed as rock desert. (Figures 22-2 and 22-3 from THE NORTHWEST TERRITORIES TODAY, Ottawa, 1965.)

daylight in these northern latitudes. Because the number of hours of daylight received in any one day is related directly to latitude (and the inclination of the earth's axis), one can note that equal hours of daylight in southern Baffin Island and southern Greenland do not give the same warmth as experienced in the same latitude of southern Yukon. One can reason therefore that hours of daylight are not necessarily equated to warmth of temperatures. There must be other factors involved, such as the temperatures of air masses.

In contrast to the northwest valleys, average July mean temperatures in the Arctic northeast are less than 50°. Trees do not grow there (Figure 22-3), and normal agriculture is not possible. Owing partly to the presence of cold water in the channels between the Arctic Islands and in Hudson Bay, summers are cool around the shores of Hudson Bay; the arctic climate extends far south along the east side of Hudson Bay, being 600 miles *south* of the Arctic Circle in Ungava Peninsula of northwestern Quebec. This southern extent of the arctic climate—and what this means in terms of scanty vegetation, negligible agricultural potential, and summer ice conditions—is in contrast to the narrow strip of arctic climate across the northern Soviet Union.

Permafrost is an additional environmental hazard, which is not experienced in southern Anglo-America. When the continental icecap covered northern Canada, the land and rock beneath it became permanently frozen to a depth of several hundred, perhaps several thousand, feet. Most of this icecap melted away 5,000 to 8,000 years ago, but a large remnant still occupies most of Greenland. During the summer, when temperatures are above 32° nearly everywhere in the North, the land thaws to a depth of a few inches or a few feet. If the surface consists of unconsolidated, fine materials, the land may become a soggy, spongy mass over which travel by foot or wheeled vehicles becomes almost impossible. Because underground drainage into the frozen material a few feet below is lacking during the summer, water collects at the surface forming innumerable irregular-shaped lakes, swamps, or muskeg. Overland travel is therefore much easier during the winter on a frozen surface. Permafrost, characteristic of the arctic areas, is found only in the northern sections of the subarctic region. The designing of suitable foundations for buildings erected in areas with permafrost is a construction problem in most parts of the Northlands, but these costly adaptations are not needed in the new towns on the "northern frontier" in the provinces.

Exploration and Settlement

The northern parts of Anglo-America may have been the first sections to be inhabited. It is probable that Asiatic peoples—the prehistoric ancestors of American Indians—migrated across Bering Strait to Alaska. Archeologists have yet to discover enough signs to prove the exact routes which these people followed—perhaps through the valleys of Yukon Territory or along the coast—to reach the central part of the continent. The Eskimo were likely a later wave of migrants, probably moving along the northern Alaskan coast in search of land game and sea mammals about 3,000 to 5,000 years ago. Eskimo had probably spread thinly across arctic Canada and reached western Greenland around A.D. 1,000—about the same time that the Norse were "discovering" North America for Europeans.

The exploration of the North holds a place of interest in Canadian history similar to the exploration of the West in American history. It was part of the futile search for a Northwest Passage, to get around Anglo-America which blocked the sea routes to east Asia. Slowly the map of the North was "unrolled." Europeans entered the eastern Arctic area from the North Atlantic dur-

ing the sixteenth and seventeenth centuries. These voyages during the brief summers charted many of the Arctic Islands and the shores of Hudson Bay; the sea captains reported on the unfavorable ice conditions and the barren landscapes. Most of the exploration along interior rivers took place early in the nineteenth century and was stimulated by the search for new fur-trapping areas. The Mackenzie Valley of the Northwest Territories was occupied in the early 1800s by a string of fur-trading posts along the river, at a time when Americans knew little about the country west of the Mississippi River. Fur traders did not penetrate into the Yukon valleys, however, until the middle of the nineteenth century. Because fur-bearing animals lived in the forests of the northwestern valleys and were scanty in the treeless northeast, the fur trade of the northwest was essentially the only resource utilization of the Northlands during the nineteenth century. The Arctic northeast had few settlements of Europeans until early in the twentieth century.

Minerals brought Europeans to the North in the present century. The story of the gold rush of 1898 to the Klondike area of Yukon Territory has been told many times—and over the decades facts and legends have become intermixed! Because many Americans took part in the Yukon gold rush, and Seattle and San Francisco were more important ports of departure than Victoria or Vancouver, many Americans believed that the Yukon was politically part of Alaska. The boom city of Dawson arose at the junction of the Yukon and Klondike rivers, and probably 20,000 to 30,000 people were in the area at the turn of the century. Within a few years, because the alluvial gold was no longer easy to recover by primitive hand methods, the Yukon lapsed into about 40 years of economic stagnation, and its population dropped below 5,000 persons.

Mining awakened the Mackenzie Valley

in the 1930s. Pitchblende—a source of valuable radium and later of uranium—was discovered on the eastern shores of Great Bear Lake, and gold was found on the northeast side of Great Slave Lake. Petroleum reserves, which had been known previously, were then brought into production to supply the new northern mines. These petroleum resources became of strategic importance during World War II when they were the only nearby source of petroleum products for military machines in Alaska. The building of an oil pipeline from Norman Wells, Northwest Territories, to a new oil refinery at Whitehorse, Yukon, plus the construction of a line of airfields across the northwest from Edmonton, Alberta, to Fairbanks, Alaska, and finally the engineering feat of carving the Alaska Highway through the little-known northwest brought this vast region into the expanding economy of Anglo-America.

World War II also brought Europeans into the Canadian Arctic in large numbers for the first time. Lines of airfields were constructed across the short polar route through northeastern Canada and Greenland; a network of weather stations dispersed through the Arctic Islands warned fliers of the movement of the large air masses which have their origins in northern Canada. Several of the airfields were abandoned after the war because the development of long-range aircraft made them unnecessary, but the need for more northern weather stations became critical with the expansion of North Atlantic commercial flying. The "cold war" of the 1950s brought a new type of military facility into the Northlands. In order to have a few hours of advance warning of possible air attack across the "top of the world," the United States received permission from the Canadian government to construct three lines of radar stations across Canada. The most northern of these, the DEW line (Distant Early Warning), is a series of stations along the Alaskan coast,

the Arctic mainland coast of Canada, and across Baffin Island, in about latitude 65°N.

These military-oriented activities had two notable effects: (1) They resulted in the first thorough accumulation of factual, descriptive information about the arctic environment which, in turn, made possible more careful planning of economic activity;[2] (2) the European population of the Arctic increased, although the total remained small. Before 1940 Europeans came from "outside" organizations; they were fur traders, missionaries, or policemen. After about 1950 government personnel became more numerous in hospitals, schools, and welfare offices; government research employees such as meteorologists and transport specialists also came north. Most of these Europeans stayed for only a few years and then were returned by their employers to southern positions.

The impact of this externally stimulated activity upon the native Eskimo was obvious. For centuries these few thousand people lived an almost primitive life of hunting (with some trapping after about 1920), in which the adjustments between man and his environment were very close, and changed with the seasons. Starvation was undoubtedly frequent when the caribou failed to appear or the seals were scarce. There were few other resources of the land or sea upon which the Eskimo could depend for a living. This close relationship of the Eskimo to his environment is described in most elementary school textbooks in the English-speaking world often as a happy example of a primitive economy. Although there were happy and peaceful moments for a people unconcerned with or unknowing of the problems of the rest of the world,

[2] J. Lewis Robinson, *An Introduction to the Canadian Arctic*, Geographical Branch, Department of Mines and Technical Surveys, Canadian Geography Information Series, no. 2, Ottawa, 1951, 118 pp.; and R. K. Odell (ed.), *Canada's New Northwest*, Department of Mines and Resources, Ottawa, 1947, 155 pp.

theirs was in reality a hard life. The fact that the 1 million square miles of arctic environment supported only about 9,000 Canadian Eskimo in 1940 suggests the scarcity of food and other resources which had prevented a population increase.

After 1940 the construction activity related to air bases, weather stations, and social facilities gave wider employment opportunities to the Eskimo. Although the external demand for their one fur-bearing animal, the white fox, declined, this was balanced by increased markets for Eskimo handicrafts such as carvings and paintings. These activities, mostly initiated by the white man from "outside," took place in particular places, and thus the Eskimo had to move to these centers of economic and government activity. Their migratory way of life is thus rapidly disappearing—the life of skin tents in summer and snowhouses in winter is being replaced by "urban" living in wooden houses, imported in precut form from the South. On a much smaller scale, the migration of "rural" people to urban places is taking place in the Canadian Arctic as it is in other parts of Anglo-America. And for the Eskimo, the problems of adjusting to a harsh natural environment (not unlike the adjustments which farming peoples made to their environments in the last century) are being replaced by new social problems.

TERRITORIAL ECONOMIES

Yukon Territory

Mining has been the major primary occupation of people in the Yukon throughout the present century, and transportation is the other main source of employment. As noted earlier, the alluvial gold of the Klondike River and its tributaries brought the Yukon into the Anglo-American economy at the turn of the century. A transportation system evolved which brought supplies and equipment to the miners and to the service and commercial establishments of Dawson. A narrow-gauge railway was built from Skagway through the mountain passes to Whitehorse where there were rapids in the Yukon River. North of Whitehorse, large flat-bottomed, paddle-wheeled river steamers carried freight and passengers downstream to Dawson, and later also to the lead-zinc-silver mine north of Mayo on the Stewart River. For about 40 years after 1900 the economy of the Yukon evolved about these three small towns and their water transportation links in the Yukon River Basin.

The wartime building of the Alaska Highway across southern Yukon opened up a new transport route in unoccupied area. At the junction of this new east-west route and the old north-south route was Whitehorse (Figure 22-4). In the 1940s this city had a population of about 15,000 persons involved in northern construction, and reminiscent of the boom in the Yukon 45 years before. But just as Dawson had declined in population after 1900, so did most of the people leave Whitehorse when the war was over. Whitehorse had a more strategic geographic position, however, than Dawson, being the junction of transport routes, and the southern gateway for people entering the Territory. The territorial capital was moved in the mid-1950s from Dawson to Whitehorse, which became the transportation, commercial, and service center of the Territory. Similar to the population distribution patterns in southern Canada, about 40 percent of the people of the Yukon live in Whitehorse and its suburbs. This example of Whitehorse suggests that "urban concentration," on a much smaller scale, is occurring in the North as in other parts of Anglo-America.

The economy that supports the urban growth of Whitehorse is aided little by natural resources except for minerals. Although thousands of acres in narrow strips in the river valleys could produce feed

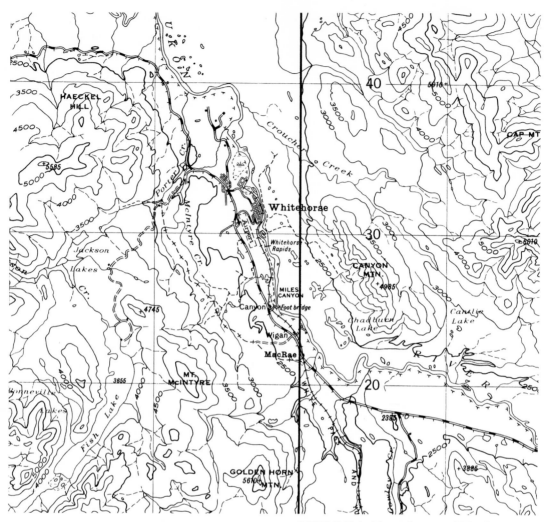

FIGURE 22-4   *The modern city of Whitehorse, population 5,000, is the largest settlement in the Canadian
Yukon. Located at the junction of the Yukon River,
Alaska Highway, and the railroad from coastal Alaska,
it is a crossroads town as well as the territorial capital.
Whitehorse has developed several suburbs since the
printing of this map. The areas shown on the map are
forested, but the treeline is encountered at about 4,000
feet.* (Scale of original map 1:250,000 or about four miles to
an inch. Whitehorse, Yukon, quadrangle, 1949 ed.)

grains or pasture, and more food was produced locally at the turn of the century than
in the 1960s, there is little present agricultural production. As a result of competition from imported food, the census of 1961
reported only four farms in the whole
Yukon Territory. Forests grow on the lower
slopes of the valleys in the Yukon Plateau,
and cordwood was used as fuel in the old
river steamers until about 1950, but only
a few small sawmills operate in the towns
for the local market. The scattered forest
resource in itself cannot compete with the
larger and better-located trees southward in
British Columbia. Fur resources supported
the few thousand Indians of the Yukon in
the quiet period of 1900 to 1940, but the
value of the fur catch in the Yukon is less
than 1 percent of the average annual value
of Canadian fur production—and the latter
in itself is a minor part of the Canadian
productive economy. Minerals are, therefore, the only Yukon resource that has

sufficient value to be in demand in the national or world economy.

The development of mineral resources is related to changes in transportation patterns and facilities. The Alaska Highway opened a new era for the Yukon economy. After about 1950 the Canadian government built new roads in the Yukon, feeding traffic toward Whitehorse and to the Alaska Highway leading to Edmonton. An all-season gravel road to the lead-zinc-silver mines at Keno Hill and on to Dawson caused first the decline and later the disappearance of the river steamers. The road was extended north of Dawson to the petroleum possibilities of the Eagle River plain in northern Yukon, and west of Dawson to the asbestos mine at Clinton Creek. This latter road continued westward into Alaska, making it possible for tourists to travel a dusty circular route over a gravel road through central Yukon and central Alaska. Although the alluvial gold of the Klondike was virtually depleted by 1966, it was possible that Dawson might be sustained by adding transportation and service functions for other regional mines. In southeastern Yukon, other base metal and tungsten mines were linked by new roads southward to the Alaska Highway. Because there are no smelters in the Territory or nearby, all concentrates are shipped out of the region. Just as the 1900 economy was functionally linked by water transport, so the 1960's mining development is functionally connected by roads. Thus the economy of the Yukon—so dependent on mineral production—is also dependent on external markets for its future development. Can its minerals compete with those more accessible to world markets? Should the government subsidize mineral development in order to maintain Northern settlement?

Mackenzie Valley, Northwest Territories

Although the economy of the western Northwest Territories is much like that of Yukon Territory, the physical character of the Mackenzie Valley is much different. The Yukon River and its tributaries cut down into the Yukon Plateau and flow in deep valleys with gentle upper slopes; the Mackenzie River is entrenched into the glacial deposits of a broad, flat plain and has steep gravel banks. Between the two main valleys of northwestern Canada lie about 300 miles of rugged, inaccessible mountains of the Mackenzie Mountain system. The political boundary between the Yukon and Northwest Territories follows the drainage divide in these mountain ranges; this boundary has not been demarcated on the earth's surface—a fact of little significance because few people have ever trapped or prospected in this uninhabited area. In climate, both the Yukon and Mackenzie valleys have warm summers where daytime temperatures may be in the 70s during July and August, and both have cold winters when temperatures drop to 30 to 60° below zero.

For about 130 years after exploration in the late eighteenth century, the fur trade, with its small trading posts along the Mackenzie River and its linking water transport using paddle-wheeled steamers, was the only resource-oriented activity. Mineral resources brought the Mackenzie Valley into closer touch with the Canadian economy, as in the Yukon, but not until the 1930s. Before 1940 pitchblende ore from Great Bear Lake was the world's major source of radium used in medical treatment, and after 1942 these same ores became a source of uranium for the world's first atom bombs. This mine closed in 1961 when its reserves were depleted. Gold has been produced at Yellowknife on Great Slave Lake since 1935, mainly because the largest mine there produced more ounces of gold per ton of ore than any other gold mine in Canada. Its ore quality thus balanced the high transport costs of supplies and equipment. After the pipeline to the Yukon was

YELLOWKNIFE, NORTHWEST TERRITORIES. *The main street and commercial core of the town is in the center foreground. The elementary school is in left foreground. The original townsite (1935–1947) was on the bare rocky peninsula in the center background jutting into Yellowknife Bay. The largest gold mine is off the picture about 2 miles to the left (west). The low, rocky hills of the Canadian Shield are in the distance to the north.* (Photo from Northwest Territories Tourist Office.)

abandoned in 1946, the oil field at Norman Wells supplied petroleum products to the few mines and other small settlements in the Mackenzie Valley; exploration proved that the field was a small one. The hopes that large oil fields like those of the Interior Plains of Alberta would also be found in the northern Mackenzie Lowland had not been fulfilled by the mid-1960s.

The mining economy of the Mackenzie Valley changed little during the period 1935 to 1960. Although there was talk in Canada about the "northern frontier," and some promotion to move northward—mainly from persons writing in comfort in the southern Canadian cities—there was little actual development (Figure 22-5). The European (non-native) population of the Mackenzie Valley increased from about

4,000 in 1941 to about 8,000 in 1961. The old, hard rocks of the Canadian Shield have not yet been fully prospected along the eastern edge of the Mackenzie Valley, and minerals may yet be found that can withstand the high costs of production in the North. The only new mine of the mid-1960s was that producing high-quality lead-zinc at Pine Point on the south side of Great Slave Lake. This mine brought the first railroad into the Northwest Territories in 1966 in order to transport the concentrates to distant Trail, British Columbia. It remains to be seen whether decreased costs as a result of a railroad will encourage the development of other mineral deposits near Great Slave Lake.

With one exception, fish, the other natural resource of the Mackenzie Valley,

DISTRIBUTION OF POPULATION BY COMMUNITIES OF 50 PERSONS AND OVER

BASED ON 1961 CENSUS

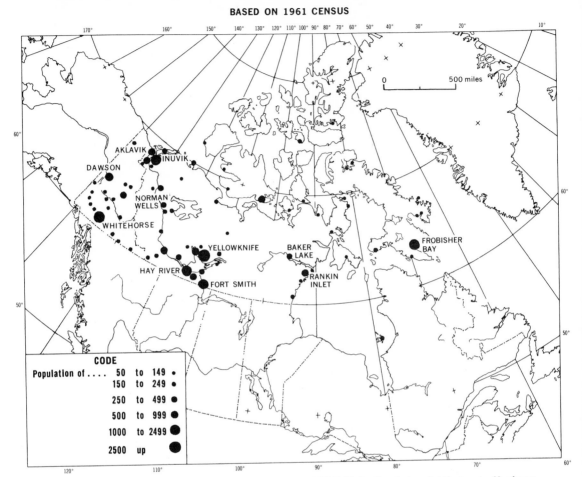

CODE

Population of	50	to	149	•
	150	to	249	•
	250	to	499	•
	500	to	999	●
	1000	to	2499	●
	2500	up		●

FIGURE 22-5 Population distribution in Northwest Territories. The largest settlements are in the Mackenzie Valley, particularly around Great Slave Lake. Nearly all Arctic settlements are coastal, and large areas of the interior are unoccupied for most of the year. Why was there a large settlement at Frobisher Bay in 1961?

are like the Yukon in their paucity. Fur resources are scarce and are harvested mainly by the scanty Indian population. Trees are small, but a little lumber is cut for local construction. The land and climate permit the growing of hardy grain crops and vegetables, but the local demand is minor. The additional Mackenzie Valley resource not present in the Yukon is the fish of Great Slave Lake. The cold and clear water of this large lake yields high-quality lake trout and whitefish which are transported by refrigerated trucks or railway from Hay River to markets in the American Midwest.

The transportation system of the Mackenzie Valley has not changed so completely as that of the Yukon. A road network has not yet evolved. The first road into the Northwest Territories, built in the late 1940s, was the Mackenzie Highway from the Peace River area of Alberta to Hay River on Great Slave Lake. It was extended around the west and north sides of the lake, reaching Yellowknife about 1960, and decreased the cost of importing food and supplies to this largest town in the Territories. Otherwise, the small settlements along the Mackenzie River, and the new,

AN ESKIMO TRAVELING by dogsled, pulled by husky dogs in a fan formation in which each dog pulls by his own leash. The sled carries personal clothing and boxes of food. The picture is taken on the snow-covered sea ice off the northeast coast of Baffin Island. (National Film Board of Canada photo by D. Wilkinson.)

planned town of Inuvik on the east side of the Mackenzie Delta, are serviced by aircraft or by small diesel tugs pushing shallow-draft barges.

Yellowknife, the service-supply center for a few gold mines, has about the same population as Whitehorse. In 1967 its functions were expanded when it was chosen as the first capital of the Northwest Territories. One can speculate concerning the wisdom of the choice in terms of the experience of the history and geography of the Yukon. Gold-mining cities do not live forever, as Dawson demonstrates. Yellowknife's geographical position on the edge of the economic development of the southern Mackenzie Valley is similar to Dawson's, off the main stream of east-west movement across southern Yukon. One can wonder whether the geography of the Mackenzie Valley should have suggested an administrative capital somewhere near the transportation center of Hay River at the southern entrance to the Territory, similar to the position of Whitehorse in the Yukon?

The Arctic Mainland and Arctic Islands

The northeastern and northern parts of the Northwest Territories do not have the resource potential or even the small-scale economic development of the northwest. The northern tree line, which can be used to mark the boundary between the arctic and subarctic climates, is also a cultural line; Indians live south of this line and Eskimo north of it.

The treeless, arctic land of the Eskimo has few natural resources—either for the local population or for the external market. Normal agriculture is not possible, as much due to lack of soils as to the cool summer climate. Fish are virtually lacking in the enormous water areas of Hudson Bay, but a few thousand arctic char are exported as a "luxury crop" from a few Arctic rivers. The introduction of guns resulted in the rapid depletion of the caribou on the mainland, and these animals were never plentiful on the Arctic Islands. Similarly, walrus, almost exterminated in the eastern Arctic, are now legally protected. The extensive killing of seals in the international waters of the northwest Atlantic can be expected to affect this important food resource of the Canadian Eskimo. It now seems obvious that the scanty game resources on the land or sea of the Arctic cannot support a large native population.

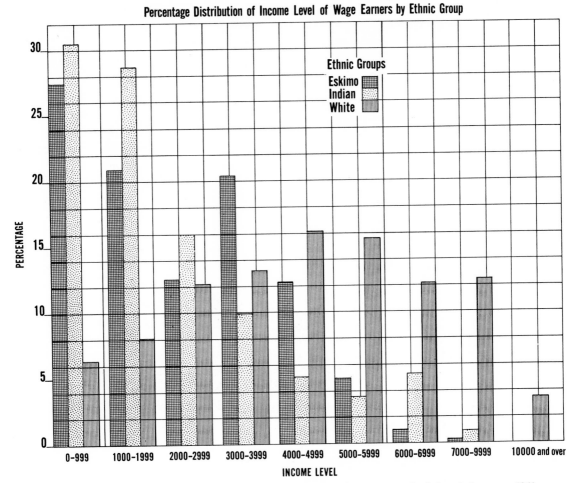

FIGURE 22-6   Income levels by ethnic groups, 1961. About 80 percent of the Eskimo earned less than $4,000, and about 75 percent of Indians earned less than $3,000 in that year. In contrast, about 60 percent of the white population received more than $4,000 in wages. (Figures 22-5, 22-6, 22-7 from THE NORTHWEST TERRITORIES TODAY, Ottawa, 1965.)

As in the northwest, therefore, mineral resources are the hope for the future economic development of the Arctic. The ancient Precambrian rocks, mineralized in the southern Canadian Shield, extend northward through Baffin Island. Scattered mineralization has been reported, the richest find being a large iron deposit inland on northern Baffin Island. The short ice-free season of about three months poses an environmental problem which creates high costs of production in comparison with iron ore fields elsewhere. The Canadian Shield west of Hudson Bay has not been thoroughly prospected, but areas of volcanic rocks, similar to those of the mineralized southern Shield, have been mapped by federal geologists. At Rankin Inlet on western Hudson Bay a nickel mine operated for a few years, using some Eskimo labor, suggesting a new occupation for the Eskimo who were moving into settlements. The depletion of the mine, however, ended this economic and social experiment. The younger sedimentary rocks of the northwestern Arctic Islands may contain petroleum. Seepages have been reported by explorers; a few drill holes revealed new geological information but no oil.

Percentage Distribution of Indian Income by Source Northwest Territories, 1964

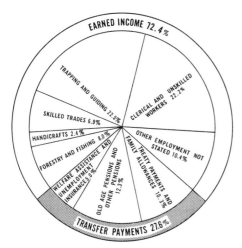

EARNED INCOME 72.4%

TRAPPING AND GUIDING 22.3%

SKILLED TRADES 6.9%

HANDICRAFTS 2.4%

FORESTRY AND FISHING 8.0%

CLERICAL AND UNSKILLED WORKERS 22.2%

OTHER EMPLOYMENT NOT STATED 10.4%

TREATY PAYMENTS AND FAMILY ALLOWANCES 10.3%

OLD AGE PENSIONS AND OTHER PENSIONS 12.3%

WELFARE ASSISTANCE AND UNEMPLOYMENT INSURANCE 5.0%

TRANSFER PAYMENTS 27.6%

FIGURE 22-7   Indian income in Northwest Territories, 1964. The 5,300 Indians in the Northwest Territories (including women and children who were not wage earners) obtained their livelihood in a variety of ways. The traditional occupations of trapping and guiding accounted for only 22 percent of their earned income. The figure of another 22 percent of income obtained from clerical and unskilled work indicates the degree of their integration into the Canadian work force.

For 10 to 11 months of the year the northern Arctic Islands, joined together by ice, can be considered as one large "land" mass. Travel from island to island by dog team or modern tracked vehicles is therefore possible in winter. But the open season is a very short one for less expensive water transport which may be used to supply weather stations or to investigate mineral possibilities. Although modern technology can employ under-ice submarines, powerful icebreakers, and even enclosed giant domes for workers, the problems of ice and cold are just as real to modern northern pioneers or adventurers as they were to the sea captains and explorers in their tiny ships of the nineteenth century.

GREENLAND

Since 1953 Greenland has been an integral part of Denmark; it formerly had been a Danish colony. Its military, commercial, and political relations with Anglo-America are so close, however, that it can be considered as part of this continent. Most of its nearly 40,000 inhabitants are descended from Eskimo who are believed to have migrated there from the Canadian Arctic in the eighth to tenth centuries. Danes, who were allowed to move freely to Greenland after 1951, number only about 1,000. Americans have permission from the Danish government to occupy the large air base and Arctic research station at Thule in northwestern Greenland.

Greenland was so named to attract settlers who might have been repelled had its name described it more accurately. The huge island with high mountains around its coasts is geologically similar to the Canadian Shield. Its interior is covered with an icecap estimated to be 6,000 to 10,000 feet thick, and occupying about nine-tenths of the island's area. The ice-free land, mainly a strip along the southwest, has tundra vegetation with predominantly North American plants.

Most Greenlanders live in the more favorable environment of the southwestern coast where Godthaab, the capital, and other small fishing villages are located. The southwest coast is often ice-free throughout the winter because of a warm ocean current from the North Atlantic; thus transport is possible most of the year in contrast to the short navigation season off Baffin Island on the opposite side of Davis Strait. Some of the villages at the heads of fjords have some level land and arable soil where it is possible to raise vegetables; sheep may be kept on the rough pasture. Fishing is the basic occupation; the only industry is the packing of seafood for export.

Like other Arctic areas, Greenland is highly subsidized; its deficit has increased in recent decades as Denmark has attempted to modernize the economy and government. Imports, largely from Denmark, are about double exports. The latter include cryolite and fish products, both shipped mainly to the United States. Lead, zinc, and coal mines have produced from time to time, but all mining is marginal. With a scattered and small population it seems unlikely that Greenlanders themselves can pay for the modern facilities the Danes wish them to have. In Greenland, as in the Canadian North and Alaska, the federal government puts more money into the North than it receives back in revenues or taxes. This investment may be for political or military reasons; to extend the "occupied" area of the country; or for humanitarian reasons to improve the social conditions of the native people.

CONCLUSIONS

The number of Northland people who are benefiting from the investment of Southern capital—which is mainly, but not entirely, governmental—is small. It is valid to ask whether the same investment in the settled areas of Canada or the United States would not benefit more people. Will it be more economical to recover more scrap metal from within our cities than to try to mine iron ore on northern Baffin Island? Even if we do find future need for the scanty resources of the Northlands, few people need live there to extract the raw materials to be consumed by Southern industries. It is probably less expensive—but neither just nor humane—to relocate all Canadian Eskimo into a few high-rise apartments on the edge of a city and support them on welfare payments than to pay the costs of government services and transportation for them in the Arctic. We know that we have social problems in our new urban world, but what is our social responsibility to the sparsely settled parts of the world?

Perhaps our future urban society will need these "empty" places. Just as the Appalachians will provide recreation for the Atlantic Megalopolis, and the desert and mountains will relieve the congestion pressures of California urbanites, and the lakes and forests of the Shield attract the people of Montreal or Toronto, so may the Northlands be the welcome change of environment for some urban residents of Canada and nearby United States. Area and space in themselves will become a resource to the future crowded residents of Anglo-American cities. A different environment—no matter how harsh or unattractive for permanent settlement—will provide an appealing change and a place to visit. If Ellesmere or Melville islands ever become crowded with visitors, then the geographical patterns of Anglo-America will be much different from what they are now!

SELECTED REFERENCES

Atlas of the Northwest Territories, Canada, prepared for the Advisory Commission on Government, vols. 1 and 2, Ottawa, 1966.

DEPARTMENT OF NORTHERN AFFAIRS AND NATIONAL RESOURCES: *This Is the Arctic,* Ottawa, 1958, 54 pp. A popular-style booklet meant to answer general questions about the Arctic.

———: *Northwest Territories: People and Industries,* Ottawa. This publication is revised frequently to present current information.

———: Northern Co-ordination and Research Centre and Industrial Division, Northern Administration Branch. These government departments have published a number of regional economic surveys, and resource-use studies of certain arctic areas.

Geographical Branch, Department of Energy, Mines and Resources, Ottawa, has published a number of geographical memoirs on particular arctic areas, such as: *Mackenzie Delta, Southampton Island, Bathurst Inlet, Queen Elizabeth Islands.*

MACDONALD, R. ST. J. (ed.): *The Arctic Frontier,* University of Toronto Press, Toronto, 1966.

METEOROLOGICAL BRANCH, AIR SERVICES, DEPARTMENT OF TRANSPORT: *The Climate of the Canadian Arctic,* Toronto, reprinted from the *Canada Year Book: 1967.*

PHILLIPS, R. A. J.: *Canada's North,* Macmillan, Toronto, 1967. An excellent summary of past and current developments in the Yukon and Northwest Territories.

Many articles on northern Canada have been published in the *Canadian Geographical Journal,* Ottawa, and *The Beaver Magazine,* Hudson's Bay House, Winnipeg. A wide range of scientific reports are published in *Arctic,* issued by the Arctic Institute of North America, Montreal. A number of physical geography studies have appeared in the *Geographical Bulletin.*

PART VI
CONCLUSIONS

ANGLO-AMERICANS have become a city people; three-quarters of them occupy the minute urban portion of their home-lands. They have tested the lands of their continent and have found only one-quarter of its 8 million square miles suitable for intensive settlement, and much of this portion is being exploited by fewer men and more machines. Using the resources of the countryside with hard work and intelli-gence, they have built an affluent society which is increasingly dependent on urban skills. Their well-settled lands include carefully tilled fields, opulent suburbs, towering business centers, and thoughtfully designed industrial parks; and in contrast, smog-submerged cities, slums, noisy indus-tries, congested traffic arteries, polluted rivers, eroded hillsides, and decadent towns. Thus the speedily transformed Anglo-American landscapes record human mis-takes along with striking human successes. The problem of attaining adequate material production has been almost solved; less successful has been the just distribution of life, liberty, and happiness throughout all levels of society. Within coming decades, our leaders should be able to use planning skills and productive machinery to redesign the Anglo-American environments and their economies to provide homelands suited for satisfying living.

CONTOUR FARMING and well-planned use of the rural terrain produce beautiful rural landscapes such as in this area in southern Wisconsin. (USDA photograph.)

CHAPTER 23

THE FUTURE OF ANGLO-AMERICA

Manufacturing areas

FIGURE 23-1 Major industrial concentrations of Anglo-America. This highly generalized map cannot portray the details of Anglo-American manufacturing. Many industries are "footloose" and can locate in almost any town with passable labor near markets. The map emphasizes, therefore, the specialties with more specific locating factors. However, broad industrial categories conceal significant differences: Thus "transport equipment" in Michigan is largely automobiles; in California aircraft and some automobiles; and in Texas both aircraft and automobiles. The 800-mile gap in the High West, omitted on the map to permit use of a larger scale, accounts for only 1 percent of Anglo-American value added by manufacturing, and most of this is concentrated in a half-dozen cities, the most productive being Denver.

The Indians and the Eskimo, in several millenniums, did little to develop the great natural wealth of Anglo-America. In sharp contrast, in less than four centuries, European settlers and their descendants created an economy which rivals and, in some respects, surpasses that of their homelands. Furs, lumber, cheap farmlands, gold, iron, coal, and petroleum contributed to this economic growth, but these resources would have been valueless without the spark provided by daring, hardworking, and ingenious men.

No doubt bounteous resources provided capital for economic expansion! No doubt the success of the first pioneers attracted still other energetic men! European culture was stimulated in this almost virgin continent and took on new vigor, producing cultural mutations which proved useful in the new land. The New World also took on with amazing speed the innovations of the European commercial and

BASIC DATA:

REGION	Land Area (thousand sq. mi.)	Population[1] Change, 1950–1960	1960 (millions)	1967	Personal Income 1967 (billions)
UNITED STATES	3,549	18.5%	178.2	200.0	$616.0
New England	64	12.5	9.9	10.7	35.9
New York Gateway	48	16.6	19.4	22.7	84.4
Delaware-Chesapeake Gateways	44	13.2	15.9	17.9	58.7
The Ohio Basin	152	9.4	18.3	20.1	53.6
Great Lakes Region	145	21.1	25.4	27.8	96.5
Midwest	534	10.5	17.7	17.8	54.4
Southern Uplands	148	5.2	13.5	14.6	33.8
Southeastern Plain	127	29.2	9.7	11.3	28.4
Gulf South	212	17.1	12.3	14.1	31.7
Southwest	533	15.8	11.3	12.5	32.9
High West	601	21.1	4.3	5.0	13.9
Southern California	65	59.6	9.7	12.8	45.3
San Francisco Focus	115	33.4	6.8	7.9	29.1
Pacific Northwest and Alaska	739	20.0	4.9	5.5	17.5
CANADA	3,560	30.2%	18.2	20.0	$45.0[2]
Atlantic Gateways	717	25.6	7.1	7.8	14.9
Ontario	344	35.6	6.2	7.0	17.8
Canadian West	1,040	29.5	4.8	5.3	12.2
Northland	1,458	48.5	0.038	0.043	0.064
GREENLAND	840	No data	0.035	0.039	0.025

[1] Canadian population data are based on census data for 1951, 1961, and 1966. All personal income data are estimates. United States populations for 1967 are estimates based on 200 million total reached Nov. 20. Columns do not add to totals because of rounding.
[2] Canadian dollars.

industrial revolutions. Indeed the close ties with Western Europe remained; how different Anglo-American life might have been if different decisions and innovations had been made overseas!

The greatest areal expansion of occupied Anglo-America took place during the urbanization of Western Europe; Anglo-American urbanization followed shortly. Urban activities, always important, began to dominate the Anglo-American economy at the end of the last century and now provide most of its current income. In most of Anglo-America, the countryside no longer dominates the city; rural values depend on their abilities to serve city people. Rural foodstuffs and raw materials remain significant, but their distribution plays a continuously decreasing part in explaining Anglo-American population geography. In fact, even the present settlement patterns are closely related to resource exploitation largely because immobile capital investments, human inertia, and vested interests have made it socially impracticable to relocate settlements to fit a new set of economic conditions. Although Anglo-American industries were often founded in relation to resources, the pattern of industrialization is tending to coincide with patterns of urban settlement (see endpaper maps). It is no longer possible to think of our economy as a simple exchange between rural resources and urban industries and services; rather the great majority of our Anglo-American commerce is among the various urbanized areas. The map of SMSAs (Figure 4-1) is a map of major American markets; Canadian markets are equally concentrated in metropolitan areas.

The Basic Data show the uneven distributions of population, population growth, and personal income. The use of dollars of personal income, of millions of people, of population growth rates is not intended to imply that huge populations growing rapidly in numbers and incomes represent utopia; rather they are concise quantitative statements of what we have in Anglo-America. Certainly these accumulations of wealth and numbers have not maximized human satisfaction in Anglo-America. The clamor for economic and social justice, the squalor of many of our settlements, and the increasing man-induced ugliness of many of our landscapes seem to call for a further changing occupance of our lands.

Our metropolitan areas, often developed haphazardly, are centers of economic power, but they hardly represent an ideal occupance of the land. Consequently demands for urban renewal are widespread; laissez-faire is giving way to the concept of the planner—not an altogether new concept; for the colonial street plan of Philadelphia, the rectangular township-range survey, and the land grants to railroads present clear examples of past planning. Hopefully with our broader view of the

history and geography of settlement, social scientists and engineers can work more effectively to plan the geography of the future. No doubt many of the plans developed (and the forecasts on which they were based) will prove ill conceived, but it seems probable that the outcome will turn out better than planless chaos. Perhaps if we can visualize, with a considerable allowance for probable error, the way ahead in this increasingly crowded Anglo-America, more livable geographic settings may be designed. What will be the geography of Anglo-America in the year 2000 when some of the present generation of students will be leaders in an economy based on over 300 million Americans and over 30 million Canadians, each with a much higher spending power than is available today?

ANGLO-AMERICA IN 2000

If we may judge by recent decades, Anglo-Americans will be not only more numerous but also healthier, better educated, and wealthier. They may also be differently distributed, for new economic situations may give rise to new adjustments to the land. Most routine jobs will be automated; consequently manufacturing activities will join agriculture and the extractive industries in requiring decreasing proportions of the labor force. The necessities of life will require a smaller proportion of the greatly increased family incomes; expansion (other than that necessitated by an increased population) will be largely in the service industries: educational, professional, governmental, and especially, recreational—all metropolitan occupations. On the other hand, the surplus time and energies of some will be used for wider participation in sports and the arts—activities which may flourish in more rural settings. With the advances of science and industrial engineering, adequate goods should be available for all; the problem will be the wise distribution and use of what is available.

Within Anglo-America a more affluent population may choose either to live in a pleasant environment or to reconstruct its environment to fit its desires. No longer will most livelihoods be tied to a Corn Belt, a Cotton Belt, a coalfield, or a waterpower site; the necessary exploitation of such resource-tied activities may even be largely automated with the necessary work being handled from a distance by electronic controls or by visiting labor task forces. The bulk of all services will be performed where people want to live—perhaps the treks to California, British Columbia, the Southwest, and Florida are but the beginning of a greater migration to milder climes. Other possible solutions are the complete enclosure of cities liable to severe weather, or perhaps techniques to prevent unpleasant weather where men have chosen to congregate.

The increased ability of men to travel and communicate by telephone and television may make many metropolitan activities possible in more suburban settings. Hitherto the lack of connectivity has led people to communicate through a central place hierarchy; the individual who needed complicated services visited the metropolis, or if his requirements were more highly specialized, the primate city in the nation or in the world. By 2000 most of these services may be available in smaller cities by telephone and television. Already there is a tendency for more complete services to develop on the peripheries of metropolitan areas, thus avoiding the congestion and obsolescence of the central city's CBD. With increased real incomes and more leisure to patronize recreational facilities, people in cities of 50,000 to 100,000 may be able to enjoy locally the recreational and professional services now available only in metropolises the size of New York, Montreal, Chicago, and Los Angeles.

ENOUGH RESOURCES? ENOUGH LAND?

Conservation

Within this century perceptive students have become aware that our supplies of many essential materials might become exhausted. The United States imports essential raw materials from Canada and more distant points; even "material-rich" Canada imports coal, bauxite, and tin. The exhaustion of a specific raw-material resource may create ghost towns, change the competitive position of raw-material-oriented industries, and create dangerous shortages in critical materials in times of war. Often the resource-shortage problems created are local rather than national; many national shortages have been solved with surprising speed by using substitutes and by eliminating extravagant or nonessential uses. Within the present century a severe shortage in Anglo-American raw materials (Table 23-1) seems likely only in two resources; ironically these are the two that have been long considered "free goods": fresh air and pure water.

The supply of adequate pure air and water and most nonfuels is largely a matter of good environmental housekeeping. With minute exceptions (as in nuclear explosions and electrolysis), man does not destroy air, water, metals and most nonmetallic minerals; rather he dissipates them, mixing each element with others so that they are so diluted that their purification or other recovery becomes uneconomical. Thus gold and other minerals may be recovered from ocean water, but only a few of these are now worth recovering (such as along the Texas Gulf Coast: sodium chloride, magnesium, bromine, and, increasingly, distilled water). With the impending shortage of high-grade sources of minerals and wood, and with improved technologies, almost all scrap may be reclaimed economically instead of only the best. This would add to the beauty and health of the community as well as to its raw-material resources. Thus sewage could be processed and separated into pure water and fertilizer, as is done in Milwaukee; waste paper could be converted into wood pulp; automobile graveyards could be emptied for scrap metal; and smokestacks could have their smoke filtered to recover sulfur, nitrates, and carbon.

Land Shortage?

General estimates for Anglo-American land use about 1960 are given in Table 19-1. More detailed estimates for United States land use, 1900 to 2000, appear in Table 23-2. Similar Canadian projections are not available, but the land shortage there is con-

TABLE 23-1   Adequacy of Major Anglo-American Resources, 1965 and 2000

	Situation in 1960s		2000
Raw Material	*United States*	*Canada*	*Forecast for Both*
Land	Adequate	Adequate	Adequate if conserved
Fresh Air	Locally scarce	Adequate	Adequate if conserved
Water	Locally scarce	Adequate	Adequate if conserved
Grain	Net export	High export	Adequate
Meat and Fish	Net import	Small export	Adequate
Leather and Skins	Balanced	Small export	Adequate
Wool	Net import	Net import	Synthetics may replace wool
Cotton	High export	High import	Adequate
Wood and Wood Pulp	High import	High export	Adequate if conservation enforced
Iron	Scrap, local and imported ores	High export	Adequate if scrap used
Manganese	Mainly imported	Import	Import needed
Nickel	Imported from Canada	High export	Adequate
Chromium	High import	Import	Import needed
Tungsten	Import and local ores	Import	Import needed
Copper	Net import	Net export	Adequate if scrap used
Bauxite	Import	Import	High import needed
Lead and Zinc	Net import	Export	Adequate if scrap used
Tin	High import	High import	High import and scrap
Sulfur	Net export	Export	Adequate
Potash	Net import	Growing export	Adequate
Coal	Net export	Net import	Adequate
Petroleum	Net import	Net export	Adequate
Uranium	Adequate	Net export	Adequate
Waterpower	Inadequate	Adequate	Other power needed
Synthetics	Balanced	Balanced	Dependent on petrochemicals, power, etc.

NOTE: Estimates on the adequacy of resources depend on assumptions as to population growth, substitution of materials, discovery of new deposits, technology, and competition of resources from overseas.

SOURCES: Evaluations are based on the publications of Resources for the Future, Inc.; *Minerals Yearbooks: Canada Year Book; Statistical Abstract of the United States;* George W. Wilson et al., *Canada: An Appraisal of Its Needs and Resources;* etc.

sidered to be less critical than in the United States. Even American land shortages seem to be the result of land misuse and excessive demands for particular kinds of land rather than symptoms of an absolute shortage.

After the full settlement of an area, changes in land use involve relatively small proportions of the total land area.[1] Increases or decreases in the intensity of particular land uses are likely to be more important than changes in area. Urban use of land is growing; yet urban land represents at most 1 percent of all Anglo-American land and seems unlikely to increase to beyond 2 percent within this century. Agricultural land represents about 30 percent of all land in the United States, but this includes much poor farmland, grazing lands, and uncultivated areas included in farms; farmland generally is transferred to urban use when needed because of the much greater pro-

[1]The following sections owe much to Marion Clawson et al., *Land for the Future*, published for Resources for the Future, Inc., Johns Hopkins, Baltimore, 1960.

duction of wealth per acre obtainable from urban activities. A decrease of possibly 10 percent in agricultural acreage may occur by 2000, some of this land becoming urban and other land (largely submarginal agriculturally) being converted into recreational or forest use.

Urban growth and associated land uses such as transportation and recreation are not expected to overwhelm rural land uses in Anglo-America. Within specific regions, different predictions can be made which are summarized below.

The Atlantic Megalopolis

From Portland to Norfolk and extending inland up the river valleys will develop a giant megalopolis devoted almost entirely to commercial and political services and the more complex types of manufacturing (Figure 23-1). Basic problems will be adequate unpolluted water supplies, the opening up of congested and obsolescent areas in the old cities, and the provision of parks and

TABLE 23-2 Land Use in the United States, 1900, 1930, 1950 with Projections for 1980 and 2000 (in millions of acres)

				Projections	
Land Use	*1900*	*1930*	*1950*	*1980*	*2000*
Cities of 2,500 or More	6	12	17	30	41
Public Recreation Areas	5	15	46	72	95
Agriculture	449	531	523	503	503
Forestry	525	495	484	475	455
Grazing (rangelands)	808	735	700	700	680
Transportation	17	24	25	28	30
Reservoirs, etc.	—	3	10	15	20
Primarily for Wildlife	—	1	14	18	20
Other (mining, deserts, swamps, barren mountain tops, etc.)	94	88	85	63	60
Total	1,904[1]	1,904[1]	1,904[1]	1,904[1]	1,904[1]

NOTE:　Estimates as to future needs for land and resources depend on assumptions as to future population growth, substitution of materials, technology, and competition of resources from overseas. Discovery of undiscovered mineral deposits is another variable.

SOURCE:　Marion Clawson et al., *Land for the Future*, published for Resources for the Future, Inc., Johns Hopkins, Baltimore, 1960, p. 442.

[1] Does not include Alaska or Hawaii.

THE CITY SWALLOWS UP even the best farmland as is illustrated by two photos of Santa Clara County, California. The picture to the left was taken in January, 1950 near San Jose; the picture to the right was taken in June, 1956. (USDA photographs.)

playgrounds within the cities, and of vacation areas outside the thickly settled areas. Increasingly, functions now performed in the central cities will be relegated to suburban satellites. Agricultural land use will decline while the remaining farmland will be used more intensively for garden and specialized crops. Forests will be expanded but primarily for recreation rather than for lumber. Local fuels and raw materials will be even more negligible than they are today; ports will handle increasing amounts of bulky commodities in addition to general cargo. The political structure will require simplification with a single megalopolitan government to deal with water supply, pollution, routes, and public transport.

The Atlantic Gateways of Canada

The problems of this region will be similar to those of the preceding area. A triangular megalopolitan area forming between Ottawa, Montreal, and Quebec will perform functions comparable to those of the Atlantic Megalopolis on a smaller scale. It will have several advantages: less crowding than in the Atlantic Megalopolis, available raw materials by land and sea, and industrial sites along navigable waterways. The rigors of the winter may be controlled by roofing over urban areas and by devising techniques to keep the St. Lawrence open all year. With adequate lands for recreation close to urban populations, this will make a pleasant homeland for a vigorous people.

The Great Lakes States and Ontario

It seems likely that the international boundary will not prevent further integration into a regional economy. Many of the problems to be solved (water pollution, navigation, power systems, tourism, marketing) involve both sides of the border; a customs union (following on the heels of the automobile-exchange agreement) seems in line with the international trade arrangements developing in other continents. The Great Lakes provide an ideal core for a megalopolitan area which may stretch from at least Milwaukee and Chicago to Buffalo and Toronto with a penumbra of inland towns oriented to specialized industries. A related outlying development will occur in the Ohio Valley. No doubt the best farmland will continue in agricultural use, but much submarginal (and fertile land near metropolitan cities) will be converted to industrial, commercial, residential, and recreational use. The main resource of this area aside from its skilled people is an adequate supply of water—adequate if it can be properly controlled and purified.

The Plains States and the Prairie Provinces

In these vast regions, farming has been a way of life as well as a business. To the immigrant from Europe, a farm meant security and status. Now with many of the farms offering underemployment two-thirds of the year, the old quarter-section or half-section farms seem anachronisms. Farming is becoming big business with the farm units of the future probably measurable in square miles instead of acres. Most of the farm work can be automated, or at least mechanized; and most, if not all, work can be accomplished by skilled labor residing most of the year in cities. A continued outflow of population from most rural parts of this interior plain seems inevitable; the growth of cities as rural service stations and manufacturers of specialized goods seems equally likely. For those who like the continental climate, this land offers good livelihoods; out-migration from the rural and small-town areas suggests that many are attracted to milder climes.

Appalachia and the South

Appalachia has three assets: scenic beauty, water, and a pleasant climate. Its minerals have not been included because by the year

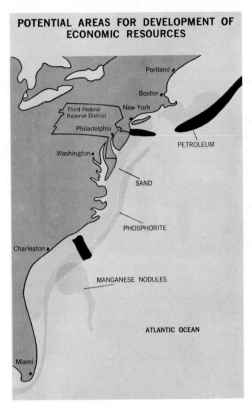

FIGURE 23-2   *Potential offshore areas for the development of economic resources. The exploitation of resources on the continental shelf has barely started, and the ocean depths are almost unexplored. Many of these potential resources are submarginal with present technologies but may be developed when land-based resources become scarce.* (Philadelphia Federal Reserve Bank and Woods Hole Oceanographic Institution.)

2000 they will be exhausted, obsolete, or mined by a very small labor force for the benefit of surrounding areas. But Appalachia does offer recreational areas to citizens of densely populated nearby areas, north and south. The South also offers great promise for the future: Its mild climate with a long growing season and its available potential urban sites would seem to provide ideal settings for medium-sized urban developments. The hot, long summers seem a handicap to many, but with adequate trees, broad porches, air-conditioned buildings, fresh foods from nearby areas, the South may prove ideal for the suburban type of life already developed in

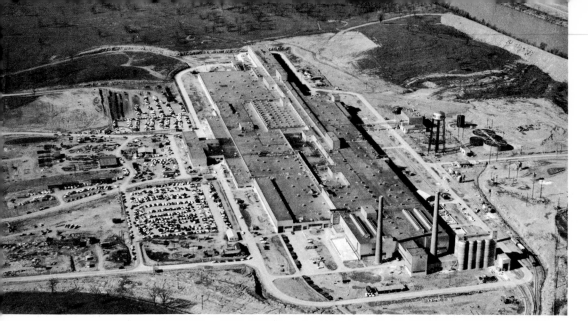

WITH ADEQUATE PUBLIC OR PRIVATE TRANSPORTATION there is no reason why factories need crowd into the cities. Most modern factories are attractive, and many actually add to the beauty of the landscape. The Ford Motor Company glass plant shown here is near Nashville, Tennessee. (Bill Goodman, *Nashville Banner* staff.)

southern and central Florida. The future distribution of Negroes and whites within both urban and rural areas, including not only areal distribution but also distribution in relation to income, occupational, and social opportunity, pose cultural problems for the South as well as for many Northern SMSAs.

The Southwest

Air conditioning has also been a blessing to the Southwest, an area in which diverse

FIGURE 23-3   As pure water becomes more scarce, the water resources of the South may become significant. The map shows the water-storage facilities constructed or to be constructed on the lower Arkansas River.

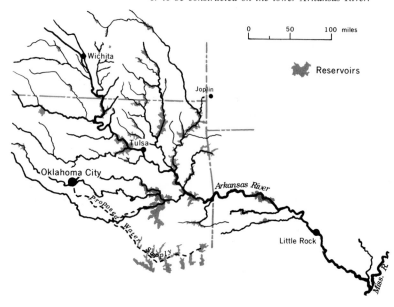

This Is Anaconda–1967

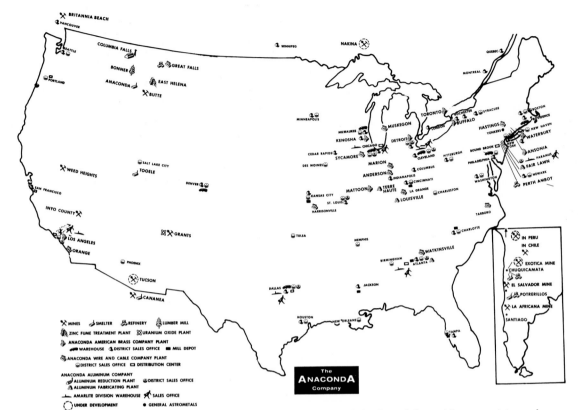

FIGURE 23-4 One of the world's great mining and metal-processing corporations started as the Anaconda Mining Company in western Montana. Today most of its income is based on the processing of metals rather than on the mining of ores. The headquarters of the company is in New York; its plants are in most of the major Anglo-American manufacturing centers and in South America. (The Anaconda Company.)

ethnic groups have still retained much individuality. Petroleum, natural gas, and copper have yielded much capital for other developments in these sunny lands. The main problem is to obtain enough water; the potentialities of desalinization and long-distance water piping, both powered by the atom, seem more practical each year.

The High West

The High West resembles the Southwest but lacks its scorching summers. Blessed with much mineral wealth, the High West does not seem to have benefited as much as the Southwest from its natural wealth. If people wish to dwell in beautiful settings, the High West has these in abundance. Its tourist industry, highly seasonal, has been only modest because of its remoteness from the large urban areas, a remoteness being over-

come by air routes and expressways. Water supply remains a continuing problem.

The Canadian extension of the High West is cooler and moister. An elaborate and expensive proposal, called NAWAPA (North American Water and Power Alliance), suggests tapping headwaters of Canadian western streams (including the Mackenzie), pumping them south along the Rocky Mountain Trench and on into the Great Basin. It seems unlikely (at least for the near future) that Canada will sell or divert any of this surplus water to interests promoting this scheme.

FIGURE 23-5   The production of metallic aluminum requires cheap power; until recent decades, hydroelectric power was commonly used. Newer plants are turning to natural gas, coal, and even nuclear power. Note that the cartographer found it possible to save space by omitting parts of the interior West. (Federal Reserve Bank of San Francisco.)

California

The local predictions for California population growth seem overwhelming. If correct, most of the good land and water now used for agriculture will be needed for people. The result will be a huge local market for their own products. As in the High West, water is a major problem but desalinizable Pacific water is adjacent. Because of the concentrated numbers of people, automobiles, and factories, the pollution of air and water are increasingly critical problems.

The Pacific Northwest

This region has four major natural resources: lumber, hydroelectric power, fish, and freedom from climatic extremes; British Columbia and southern Alaska have mineral resources in addition. Major problems of these areas include lack of industrial diversification. Although this is an attractive area for residence, Oregon and Washington have grown only at approximately the national rate (much more slowly than California and Florida); much of this growth is concentrated around a Puget Sound core for a potential megalopolis, possibly to extend from Vancouver to Portland. Percentage growth in British Columbia and Alaska has been more rapid, partially because their starting populations prior to recent growth were small. For the entire area the growing availability of oil and gas and hydroelectric power from the interior is promising for the future.

The Northlands

The population and productive bases are so low in the Northlands that a few thousand immigrants or the opening of a new mine may result in percentage increases that are as great as they are misleading. There is no good reason why this huge area with equally huge problems should ever support even a half million people. If new resources are discovered, they can be exploited by advanced equipment and relatively few people. Almost any other part of Anglo-America could be made habitable for considerable numbers with much less effort.

WORLD RELATIONSHIPS

The amazing productivity of the Anglo-American economies[2] has produced a high level of living for most of its citizens, permitting its governments to grant or loan huge sums to their poorer world neighbors; yet the world's economic problems are far from solved. Indeed even in Anglo-America, the poor and underprivileged are still with us. With all the tremendous Anglo-America overseas help, starvation and malnutrition, disease, political and social unrest, and inadequate housing, clothing, and education remain widespread overseas, and not unknown in Anglo-America. The "cold" wars between the communist and noncommunist powers, between the former colonial powers and the anticolonialists, between segregationists and integrationists, use up enough potential capital to solve most of the world's economic problems; yet the major problem remains to get men to cooperate in solving one another's problems.

United States foreign trade (imports and exports) represents about 7.5 percent of the total personal income, Canadian foreign trade about 30 percent of the income; foreign trade is therefore four times as important to Canadians as to Americans. Trade

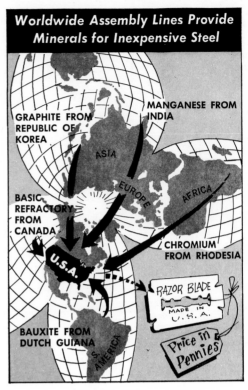

FIGURE 23-6   *Although Anglo-America is large and rich in raw materials, it imports many essential materials from overseas.* (American Iron and Steel Institute.)

between the two Anglo-American neighbors bulks large, but trade with the United States is more than half of all Canadian trade, whereas trade with Canada is less than one-fifth of United States foreign trade. Thus, even between two neighbors so alike in ways of life and goals, difference in size interposes a fear that the smaller nation will be dominated by the larger. Indeed the Canadian point of view seems destined to be ambivalent; the northern country wants American tourists, American investment, and American trade; yet fears American business and political dominance, and the less attractive aspects of American "material culture" (the boundary does not keep out American radio and television programs). So important is Canada to the United States for raw materials, markets, and Arctic defense that Washington must consider

---

[2] Anglo-American development has not been unique. The rise of Western Europe made possible much Anglo-American progress. Equally amazing have been the later economic developments in, for example, Japan, Eastern Europe, Australia, South Africa, and parts of Latin America. Even the accomplishments of some of the poorer countries, such as India, have been praiseworthy, considering the handicaps under which their leaders have operated.

THERE IS NO REASON WHY men need stay indoors when the weather is fine. Pittsburgh's civic auditorium has a retractable dome which can be closed in 2½ minutes. The building is in an extensive urban-renewal project in downtown Pittsburgh. (Robert E. Dick Studios from Chamber of Commerce of Pittsburgh.)

northern Canada as the boundary of its sphere of influence. So important is the United States to Canada that the latter cannot push away the American embrace while constantly complaining about it. Canada is a major world power today with its high rank obscured mainly by the shadow of the United States.

Yet both Canada and the United States have a common problem, perhaps appropriately called the "rich nation's burden." To avoid international tensions, the rich Anglo-Americans must help to raise the level of the poverty-stricken half of the world. But help in the form of gifts leads to accusations of political interference; if private investments are substituted, their investors are "imperialists" whose factories, mines, and plantations "deserve" to be expropriated! If they do neither, they are "heartless!" The fact that the underdeveloped countries are largely nonwhite is a coincidence which adds a racial tangent to economic problems severe and complex enough without it.

CONCLUSIONS

The following developments seem likely in Anglo-America in coming decades:

1 Urban and suburban living will become almost universal in Anglo-America. Much of the population will be organized into megalopolitan clusters including an American-Canadian Commercial-Manufacturing Core extending eastward from Minneapolis–Kansas City to Quebec (city), Boston, and Norfolk. An equally congested megalopolis will occupy the Pacific counties of California from San Francisco southward. A smaller megalopolis may develop in the Willamette–Puget Sound–Vancouver area. Well-set-

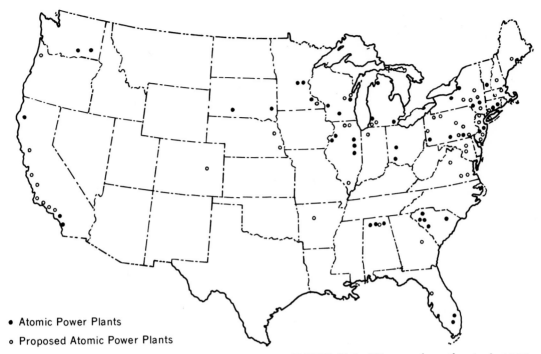

- • Atomic Power Plants
- ○ Proposed Atomic Power Plants

FIGURE 23-7 This map shows the atomic power plants that are in operation or to be completed shortly. Nuclear power will help to cut down air pollution; it also reduces greatly the transportation of such fuels as coal and petroleum. (Atomic Industrial Forum and Federal Reserve Bank of Philadelphia.)

tled areas with many cities and small metropolises will occupy southern United States from Richmond to central Florida and westward to Phoenix and Tucson.

2 Concentrations of skills and markets will replace fuels and raw materials as major bases for industrial location.

3 Improved transportation and communication will break down much of the friction of space, thus permitting most people to live and work away from unpleasant settings.

4 With the increasing control of the environment, the progress of particular sections of Anglo-America will depend increasingly on the quality of their inhabitants. If a potential homeland attracts energetic people, this in itself will create markets and industries.

5 In much of Anglo-America at least, the problem of the production of wealth has been solved. Within the present century, many of the luxuries of the rich have become the necessities of the poor. Forecasts for coming decades envisage a tre-

mendous increase in average purchasing power per capita so that by the year 2000 two to three times the present consumption of goods and services seems likely, at least in progressive areas, for the average Anglo-American. Indeed this is an affluent society! But as John Kenneth Galbraith[3] concludes:

To have failed to solve the problem of producing goods would have been to continue man in his oldest and most grievous misfortune. But to fail to see that we have solved it and to fail to proceed to the next task, would be fully as tragic.

The next task is to ensure that this high production brings a satisfying and rewarding way of life. Our efficient

[3] *The Affluent Society,* Houghton Mifflin, Boston, 1958, p. 356.

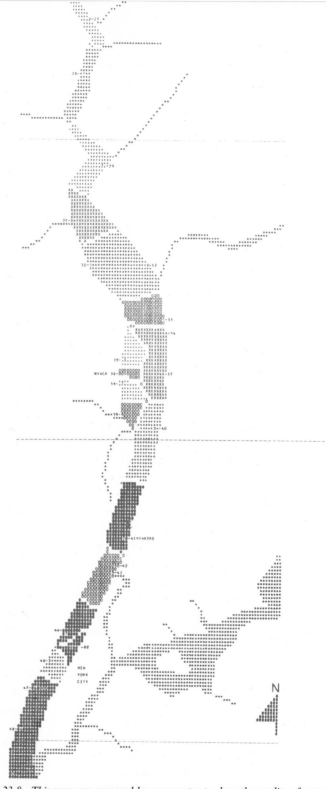

FIGURE 23-8 This map was prepared by a computer to show the quality of water around and north of New York. In the future it will be possible to make maps directly from punch cards with census data without the use of a cartographer. (From *Context*, no. 1, February, 1968, courtesy of the Laboratory for Computer Graphics, Harvard University.)

economic machinery seems to have also produced directly and indirectly a world of multiplying problems ranging from air pollution and war to social and political corruption. Life, liberty, and the pursuit of happiness remain as goals almost as difficult to achieve as they were in 1776. If productivity has been achieved, certainly the problem of distribution has not.

6 The pioneer and the advancing frontier characterized Anglo-America until the present century; even today, on a small scale, pioneers are seeking new land with new resources. But new resources have taken a second place to new techniques in stimulating Anglo-American economic growth. The advance in the laboratory has overshadowed advances into new lands. A quarter of a century ago, nuclear power became feasible; today electricity can be produced more cheaply from the atom than from fossil fuels. Thus, although many have worried about the exhaustion of fossil fuels, they may become obsolete long before they are exhausted.

In the light of rapid technological changes, such as those resulting from nuclear power, automation, and computers, forecasts are rash for even the coming decades. Three trends, however, seem apparent: First, the rate of change in the human use of the Anglo-American landscapes will be speeded by multiplying scientific discoveries and technological innovations; second, with increasing production, more capital will be available for replacing obsolescent structures (urban renewal, etc.); third, service activities, especially those connected with education, the arts, and recreation, will expand most rapidly. These changes, it is hoped, will redesign Anglo-America for living instead of for merely "making a living."

SELECTED REFERENCES

All the publications of Resources for the Future, Inc. (published by the Johns Hopkins Press, Baltimore) are pertinent and to be recommended. Especially relevant are:

CLAWSON, MARION, R. BURNELL HELD, and CHARLES H. STODDARD: *Land for the Future,* 1960.

LANDSBERG, HANS H., LEONARD L. FISCHMAN, and JOSEPH L. FISHER: *Resources in America's Future,* 1963. An abstract of this book is also available as a John Hopkins paperback: Hans H. Landsberg, *Natural Resources for U.S. Growth,* 1964.

LOWENTHAL, DAVID: "The American Scene," *Geographical Review,* vol. 58 (1968), pp. 61–88.

U.S. DEPARTMENT OF THE INTERIOR: *Conservation Yearbook* (annual since 1965), Washington.

WILSON, GEORGE W., SCOTT GORDON, and JUDEK STANISLAW: *Canada: An Appraisal of Its Needs and Resources,* Twentieth Century Fund, New York, 1965; University of Toronto Press, Toronto, 1965.

INDEX

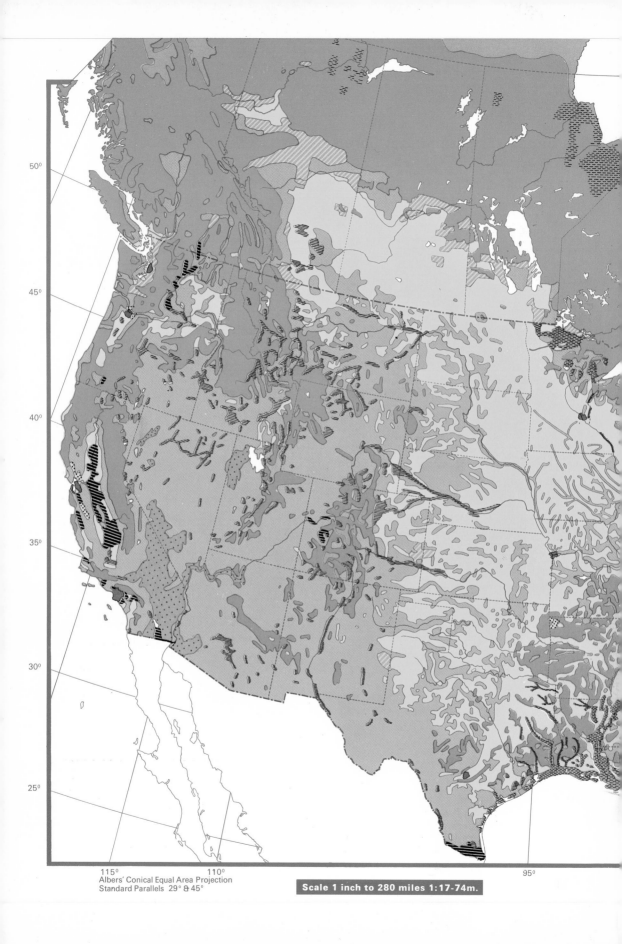

50°

45°

40°

35°

30°

25°

115°   110°   95°
Albers' Conical Equal Area Projection
Standard Parallels 29° & 45°

Scale 1 inch to 280 miles 1:17-74m.